Civil Engineering and Urban Research collects papers resulting from the conference on Civil, Architecture and Urban Engineering (ICCAUE 2022), Xining, China, 24–26 June 2022. The primary goal is to promote research and developmental activities in civil engineering, architecture and urban research. Moreover, it aims to promote scientific information interchange between scholars from the top universities, business associations, research centers and high-tech enterprises working all around the world.

The conference conducts in-depth exchanges and discussions on relevant topics such as civil engineering and architecture, aiming to provide an academic and technical communication platform for scholars and engineers engaged in scientific research and engineering practice in the field of urban engineering, civil engineering and architecture design. By sharing the research status of scientific research achievements and cutting-edge technologies, it helps scholars and engineers all over the world comprehend the academic development trend and broaden research ideas. So as to strengthen international academic research, academic topics exchange and discussion, and promote the industrialization cooperation of academic achievements.

PROCEEDINGS OF THE 4TH INTERNATIONAL CONFERENCE ON CIVIL ARCHITECTURE AND URBAN ENGINEERING (ICCAUE 2022), XINING, CHINA, 24–26 JUNE 2022

Civil Engineering and Urban Research
Volume 1

Edited by

Hazem Samih Mohamed
School of Civil Engineering and Geomatics, Southwest Petroleum University, China

Jinfang Hou
Tianjin Port Engineering Institute Co., Ltd. of CCCC First Harbor Engineering Co., Ltd., China

CRC Press is an imprint of the
Taylor & Francis Group, an **informa** business

A BALKEMA BOOK

First published 2023
by CRC Press/Balkema
4 Park Square, Milton Park, Abingdon, Oxon, OX14 4RN
e-mail: enquiries@taylorandfrancis.com
www.routledge.com – www.taylorandfrancis.com

CRC Press/Balkema is an imprint of the Taylor & Francis Group, an informa business

© 2023 selection and editorial matter, Hazem Samih Mohamed and Jinfang Hou; individual chapters, the contributors

The right of Hazem Samih Mohamed and Jinfang Hou to be identified as the authors of the editorial material, and of the authors for their individual chapters, has been asserted in accordance with sections 77 and 78 of the Copyright, Designs and Patents Act 1988.

All rights reserved. No part of this book may be reprinted or reproduced or utilised in any form or by any electronic, mechanical, or other means, now known or hereafter invented, including photocopying and recording, or in any information storage or retrieval system, without permission in writing from the publishers.

Although all care is taken to ensure integrity and the quality of this publication and the information herein, no responsibility is assumed by the publishers nor the author for any damage to the property or persons as a result of operation or use of this publication and/or the information contained herein.

SET
ISBN: 978-1-032-44484-0 (hbk)
ISBN: 978-1-032-44485-7 (pbk)

Volume 1
ISBN: 978-1-032-36838-2 (hbk)
ISBN: 978-1-032-36840-5 (pbk)
ISBN: 978-1-003-33406-4 (ebk)

DOI: 10.1201/9781003334064

Volume 2
ISBN: 978-1-032-44487-1 (hbk)
ISBN: 978-1-032-44489-5 (pbk)
ISBN: 978-1-003-37241-7 (ebk)

DOI: 10.1201/9781003372417

Typeset in Times New Roman
by MPS Limited, Chennai, India

Civil Engineering and Urban Research – Mohamed & Hou (Eds)
© 2023 the Editors, ISBN 978-1-032-36838-2

Table of contents

Preface — xi
Committee members — xiii

VOLUME 1

Research on civil geological structure and hydraulic engineering construction

Dynamic response of long-span bridge under the oblique incidence of seismic waves — 3
Wei Yan

Analysis and discussion on design points of sea discharge sewage pipeline project — 11
Lanfang Zhang & Dongyin Guan

Morphological response under waves of a typical double-sandbar artificial beach system — 20
Shan Li, Mingxiao Xie, Guangjia Ding, Chi Zhang & Zhenhua Gu

Numerical simulation study on the stability of four-story slope under rainfall infiltration conditions — 28
Yifei Zhang & Junrui Chai

Ship-bridge collision analysis of the Wuhan Yangtze River Bridge based on finite element method — 38
Shiheng Jin

Advances in water system connectivity from 1990 to 2021 — 47
Lingzhen Zhang, Yongfei Fu, Lu Liu, Yuqing Feng & Qi Wang

Study on the effect of anchor cable locking force on deep displacement in pile-anchor retaining system of ultra-deep foundation pit — 53
Chuan-yao Gu, Ya-xin Zhang & Jin-hui Han

A simulation method for complex boundary and coupling conditions in structural analysis — 60
Tao Huang, Meng-ge Wang & Zheng-wei Liang

Seismic responses of underground subway station located in gently inclined liquefiable ground — 70
Yu Qiu & Xiwen Zhang

Study on double diffusion phenomenon near Changjiang Estuary and its influence on coastal engineering — 76
Baisu Zhu & Chen Li

Numerical simulation study on the stability of abandoned soil field of Songkte Bridge — 82
He Jian, Zhao Li & Ren Qiang

Application study on defect analysis and treatment of existing frame structure buildings — 90
Si Daolin, Qu Dalin & Wang Huiling

Analysis of the stratum deformation law and influence zone for double-line
tunnels in water-rich sand layer 95
Jiaying Zhang

Analysis and study of the seismic response of large chassis connected to
high-rise structures 104
Wang Zeyun & Tang Xianzhe

Structural and seismic analysis of conjoined buildings 110
Ranran Zhang

Numerical simulation study on the influence of lattice anchor rod on rock
slope stability 116
Yunpeng Xie

Analysis of the influence of foundation pit excavation on adjacent metro section 123
Haiyan Ju, Xingxing Liu, Chen Yang, Yan Liu, Meng Hu, Mingfu Fu & Xiaoyong Fang

Numerical analysis on settlement of high fill subgrade of high-speed railway 130
Xiaolei Liu

Numerical simulation of interface slip of steel-concrete composite beam 139
*Shirap Tenzin, Nima Ciren, Yuandan Duoji, Jiacheng Zhao, Guangming Wang,
Li Zhu & Haolin Guo*

Numerical analysis of the impact of deep foundation pit excavation induced
ground and pipeline responses 145
Ren Qiang & Wei Kuang Min

Seepage pressure prediction model of concrete dam based on EEMD-GRU 152
Haishan Qiao, Zhi Zhang, Zhigang Wu, Zhenghua Wen & Shengfei Zhang

Deep-water rubble mound breakwater construction in the open Mediterranean
Sea under adverse conditions: Main breakwater extension of Hadarom Port,
Ashdod, Israel 160
Ran Tao, Rui-yi Huang, Xian-dao Feng & Yue-ji Huo

Finite element analysis of pile-soil-structure dynamic interaction on layered soil site 168
Ziqiong Yang & Wenhao Qi

Seismic vulnerability analysis of reinforced concrete frame structures built in
different times 179
Lixin Shang, LingXin Zhang & JiaLu Ma

Study on the influence of subway foundation pit excavation sequences
on the deformation of retaining structure 189
Song Xu, Changjie Xu, Lihong Tong, Haibin Ding & Zhilong Wu

Analysis of full support structures of bifurcation tunnel based on finite
element method 196
Yu Peng, Li Ruiqing, Yao Xiaomin, Nian Fuxi & Zhang Bing

Study on strain of non-integrity prestressed concrete pipe pile in loess area 205
Wei Liu, Guangli Sun, Jianyang Fu & Meng Hu

Study on the thermal temperature field of hydration of prefabricated box
girders at an early age and its effects 212
Li Yan, Gu Chuanyao & Wang Youzhi

Crack detection of T700 composite specimen based on the natural frequency 221
Hao Yang, Yu'e Yang & Cheng Liu

Analysis of seismic damage phenomena and causes of frame structures with external verandah 229
Zeren Tang, Jianing Gu, Di Liu & Zijian Liu

Large underground cavern excavation scheme design and surrounding rock stability influence 236
Tian He, Hao Ding, Zhenhua Peng, Renjing Zhu, Xinghong Jiang & Liang Cheng

Building protection restoration technology and construction transformation technology

Analysis of reverse modeling techniques for BIM application in different construction projects 249
Yu Zhang, Dehai Zhang, Daguang Han, Long Chen, Kaixin Hu, Di Tao, Mingshuo Gao & Ming Chen

Information acquisition method of steel bridge manufacturing process oriented to intelligent construction 255
Jizhuang Hui, Yafei Wang, Chao Li, Xiaodong Yang & Jinlong Zhang

The evolution roadmap of building carbon emissions based on scenario analysis method 263
Hongkai Wang, Dong Mao & Hanyu Rao

Application of BIM technology in the process of construction under the development of internet of things 269
Bingran Chen

Research on shield separate launching technology in limited space 274
Yang Lei

Moderate resolution imaging spectroradiometer (MODIS)-based internal wave detection in the East China Sea 280
Baisu Zhu & Chen Li

Application study of digital twin seawall based on GIS-BIM 286
Yi Hou, Kaiyun Jiang, Yadong Yu, Hengyan Huo & Andong Wang

Study on the protection strategy of Dong traditional dwellings from the perspective of rural revitalization 295
Haifeng Chu, Dianqi Fang & Xiaoling Zhang

Load transfer mechanism during building rectification using jacked pile 302
Hao Chen, Kai Li, Changjie He, Jitao Bai, Weiqiang Pan & Dongfan Shang

Protection and repair technology of ancient building walls based on big data 311
Sha Tao

Exploring the design of public space renovation in old city communities in the post-epidemic era 318
Ning Xian & Yuqing Zhao

Research on risk assessment and control of BIM application in prefabricated medical building projects 326
Lili Jiao

Quasi-static seismic tests and damage evaluation of high-strength reinforced concrete columns *Huang-bin Lin & Qi-fang Zeng*	332
Research on renovation design of modern office space *Chi Sun & Long Cheng*	342
Research on the influencing factors of residential satisfaction in the renovation of old communities *Xueting Huang & Guanghua Li*	349
Application of concrete pouring construction technology in construction engineering construction *Nan Zhao*	356
Numerical simulation of corrosion of steel liner based on meso-structure of containment *Zhimin Li, Shenggang Chen, Kun Liu & Xianda Feng*	363
Research on the repair measures of the destabilized embankment of blasting and squeezing *Xiao Jianbo, Huang Weihong & Fang Yuhang*	370
Application of incremental launching technology in prestressed concrete box girder construction *Xue Fan, Wu Rui, Lu Tao & Yang Tianliang*	377
Application and guiding value of BIM technology in road engineering design *Lingmei Zhang*	384
Development and testing of remote monitoring system for roadbed construction quality *Zhongke Tian, Lu Yang & Bin Li*	394
Application research of BIM technology in outdoor engineering of a data center project *Hang Zou, Zhanqiang Liu, Jianchao Wang & Lin Xue*	400
Risk assessment of tunnels using 3S technology: A case study of the Atal Tunnel *Yu Bian, Hao Chen, YongPeng Yang, Meng Li, Ya Guo, Ling Chen, Xin He & Hao Tang*	406
Study of external FRP-angle combination reinforcement node method *Chen Qianqian & Xu Ruiqing*	415
Jacking construction technology of No.3 landscape bridge around Ma'an Island Road *Xu Qi, Wen Dingxu & Yang Jun*	423
Analysis of influence effect of widening subgrade fill width on deformation *Zhiqiang Wang, Junjie Fan, Shijie Cui & Wenbin Xiao*	432
Home interior decoration design strategy based on AR technology *Li Jianjing*	438
Application analysis of BIM technology in electromechanical design *Yang Xinghua*	445
Research on elderly-friendly indoor renovation for rural houses in Northeast China *Jingdong Liu & Jingwei Chang*	452

Preferential study on environmental protection for highway slopes in rainy
areas of South China based on the amount of water-based polyurethane 460
Enlian Xie

Study on diagonal brace resistance to lateral loads in frame structure building 471
Keding Wang

Study on the optimal proportion of ecological protection substrate for
highway slopes in rainy areas of South China 481
Enlian Xie, Xuejun Ma & Bin Xue

Research progress of asphalt soot detection technology and odor removal
technology 493
Hongchao Zhang & Lianghao Sun

Research on construction safety evaluation of prefabricated medical building
based on cloud model 503
Aiping Song & Fanghong Tao

Evolution characteristics of displacement and crack of rock mass under the
shallowly buried explosion loading 510
Qindong Lin, Chun Feng, Wenjun Jiao, Yundan Gan, Yulei Zhang & Jianfei Yuan

Research on underwater nondestructive testing technology of hydraulic culvert
based on ROV 516
Chao Zhang, Mangqiang Li, Kai Zhang & Xin Yang

Research on the application technology of the integrated scaffolding and
formwork system with steel platform alternately supported by steel columns and
tubular frames for high-rise structure 523
Ma Wei & Wu Lianding

Research on ventilation support parameters in high altitude tunnel construction 532
Mingzhu Zhang & Guoquan Xu

Analysis of vibration reduction effect of vibration reduction hole parameters in
tunnel blasting construction 537
Baofu Duan, Zhaowen Yu, Chunwu Zhang & Zongjun Sun

Simplified analysis of breach outflow hydrograph of Embankment Dam break 545
Jiayi Lin, Yao Xu, Ronglu Wang, Fang Xiao & Xiulin Li

Theoretical investigation on the crack initiation mechanism of brittle rock
specimen with a 3D internal open-type flaw 554
Yusong Zhao, Qi Qi & Congcong Chen

A method of reinforcing stringer with silver ingot tenon 562
Yucheng Li, Xiaofang Li, Qiang Sun & Shouyi Bu

Study on influencing factors of tunnel ventilation 566
Mingzhu Zhang & Guoquan Xu

Research on the reinforcement measures of the existing wind turbine foundation 574
Guohua Li, Hanke Sheng, Lifen Li & Wenming Wang

Study on deterioration law of concrete in corrosive environment 581
Yujie Jiang, Guanglun Jiang, Kunlin Wang, Lei Yu, Xiuqiang Song & Xiaoyu Yang

Author index 587

Preface

The 2022 4th International Conference on Civil Architecture and Urban Engineering (ICCAUE 2022) was successfully held online through Zoom on June 24, 2022. Due to COVID-19 and the pandemic-related nationwide lockdowns and other coordinated restrictive measures, the organizers decided to hold a conference in a virtual format with the organization of access for all participants to the presented reports with comprehensive discussion for ensuring the event at a high scientific level.

The conference is an international conference for the presentation of technological advances and research results in the fields of civil architecture and urban engineering. The conference brings together leading researchers, engineers and scientists in the domain of interest from around the world. We warmly welcome previous and prospected authors submit your new research papers to ICCAUE 2022, and share the valuable experiences with the scientist and scholars around the world.

The safety and well-being of all conference participants is our priority. The COVID-19 is unpredictable, so conference postponement met uncertainty, while many scholars and researchers want to attend this long-waited conference and have academic exchanges with their peers. But I want to note that there are no barriers to science, and we continue to work on our research areas remotely, using modern technical means. Under this situation, the conference model was divided into three sessions, including oral presentations, keynote speeches, and online Q&A discussion. In the first part, some scholars, whose submissions were selected as the excellent papers, were given about 5–10 minutes to perform their oral presentations one by one. Then in the second part, keynote speakers were each allocated 30–45 minutes to hold their speeches.

More than 300 participants attended the meeting. We were greatly honored to have invited two professors as our Conference Chair. There were over 20 experts and scholars in the area of Civil Architecture and Urban Engineering representing different famous universities and institutes around the globe to form Conference Committees.

In the keynote presentation part, we invited three professors as our keynote speakers. The first keynote speakers, Assoc.Prof. Hazem Samih Mohamed, Egypt, Southwest Petroleum University was invited to present his talk *Rehabilitation of corroded offshore tubular joints with Carbon Fibre Reinforcement Polymers (CFRP) laminates*. Professorial Senior Engineer, Assistant Manager, Jinfang Hou, China, Tianjin Port Engineering Institute Co., Ltd. of CCCC First Harbor Engineering Co., Ltd. She was our second keynote speakers and presented a talk: *Research and application of self-propelled immersed tube transportation and installation integrated ship and complete construction technology*. Prof. Daxin Tian, Beihang University, China, our finale keynote speaker. He presented a talk: *Secure and Reliable Edge Computing for Cooperative Vehicle Infrastructure System (CVIS)*.

We are glad to share with you that we received lots of submissions from the conference and we selected a bunch of high-quality papers and compiled them into the proceedings after rigorously reviewed them. These papers feature following topics but are not limited to: Civil Engineering, Architecture, Urban Engineering, Urban traffic management. All the papers have been through rigorous review and process to meet the requirements of international publication standard.

We are really grateful to the International/National advisory committee, keynote speakers, session chairs, organizing committee members, student volunteers and administrative assistance of the management section of University, including accounts section, digital media and publication house. Also, we are thankful to all the authors for contributing a large number of papers in the conference, because of which the conference became a story of success. It was the quality of their presentations and their passion to communicate with the other participants that really make this conference series a great success.

The Committee of ICCAUE 2022

Committee members

Conference Chair
Professorial Senior Engineer Aimin Liu, *Tianjin Port Engineering Institute Co., Ltd. of CCCC First Harbor Engineering Co., Ltd., China*
Associate Professor Hazem Samih Mohamed, *Southwest Petroleum University, Egypt*

Academic Committee Chair
Senior Engineer Guangsi Chen, *Tianjin University, China*

Academic Committee Members
Prof. Xu Zhang, *Henan University of Technology, China*
Prof. Yuhang Wang, *Chongqing University, China*
Prof. Shuitao Gu, *Chongqing University, China*
Prof. Li Ma, *Southwest University of Science and Technology, China*
Prof. Lei Wang, *Changsha University of Science & Technology, China*
Assoc. Prof. Dr. Yang Wang, *Guangzhou Institute of Geography, China*
Assoc. Prof. Norzailawati Hj Mohd Noor, *International Islamic University of Malaysia, Malaysia*
Assoc. Prof. Meng Liu, *Shanghai Estuarine and Coastal Research Center, China*
Assoc. Prof. Chao Liu, *State Key Laboratory of Hydraulics and Mountain River Engineering, Sichuan University, China*
Assoc. Prof. He Zhang, *School of Architecture, Tian Jin University, China*
A. Prof. Norhisham Bakhary, *School of Civil Engineering, Universiti Teknologi Malaysia, Malaysia*
Dr. Zhongzheng Lyu, *Dalian University of Technology, China*

Organizing Committee Chair
Senior Engineer Bin Li, *Tianjin Port Engineering Institute Co., Ltd. of CCCC First Harbor Engineering Co., Ltd., China*

Organizing Committee Members
Professorial Senior Engineer Jinfang Hou, *Tianjin Port Engineering Institute Co., Ltd. of CCCC First Harbor Engineering Co., Ltd., China*
Assisstant Professor Ali Rahman, *School of Civil Engineering, Southwest Jiaotong University, China*
Dr. Binbin Xu, Geotechnical Engineering Department, *Tianjin Port Engineering Institute Co., Ltd. of CCCC First Harbor Engineering Co., Ltd., China*
Dr. Jingshuang Li, Geotechnical Engineering Department, *Tianjin Port Engineering Institute Co., Ltd. of CCCC First Harbor Engineering Co., Ltd., China*
Dr. Jianbao Fu, *Tianjin Port Engineering Institute Co., Ltd. of CCCC First Harbor Engineering Co., Ltd., China*
Dr. Yiteng Xu, *Tianjin Port Engineering Institute Co., Ltd. of CCCC First Harbor Engineering Co., Ltd., China*

Vice-Chief Engineer Zhifa Yu, *Tianjin Port Engineering Institute Co., Ltd. of CCCC First Harbor Engineering Co., Ltd., China*
Engineer Changyi Yu, *Tianjin Port Engineering Institute Co., Ltd. of CCCC First Harbor Engineering Co., Ltd., China*

Publication Chair
Senior Engineer Bin Li, *Tianjin Port Engineering Institute Co., Ltd. of CCCC First Harbor Engineering Co., Ltd., China*

Research on civil geological structure and hydraulic engineering construction

Dynamic response of long-span bridge under the oblique incidence of seismic waves

Wei Yan*

Xiamen University Tan Kah Kee College, Xiamen, China

ABSTRACT: The non-uniform effect of the spatial variation of ground motion on long-span bridges cannot be ignored, and the oblique incidence is the main factor causing this spatial variation. Based on the viscoelastic artificial boundary and the input method of obliquely incident ground motion, a long-span bridge structure-pile-soil integral model was established by ANSYS, and the seismic response of the long-span bridge under the oblique incidence of seismic waves was analyzed. The research shows that whether P wave or SV wave, the internal force of the bridge pier under the oblique incidence of seismic waves is significantly different from that of vertical incidence. The influence of oblique incidence seismic input on the internal force of long-span bridges cannot be ignored. In the seismic analysis of bridges, the influence of the oblique incident input of seismic waves should be considered.

1 INTRODUCTION

Bridges are the pivotal projects of the transportation system and are internationally known as lifeline projects for earthquake and disaster relief. With the rapid development of the economy and the rapid expansion of the urban population, people's dependence on the transportation network will be higher and higher. Once the bridge is seriously damaged by the earthquake, the direct and indirect economic losses that may be caused will become larger and larger (Jiang 2008). Seismic waves are incidents at a certain angle near the source site, rather than vertically incidents. It is reasonable to use the vertical incidence of seismic waves for local sites of far-field seismic waves. When the structure is close to the epicenter, it is more reasonable and practical to consider the oblique incidence of seismic waves (Du 2007).

The Eurocodes first consider the spatial variability of ground motion (Eurocode 8 1995), and Chinese bridge seismic rules also make relevant provisions for the problem of non-uniform excitation of ground motion (Zhu 2020). When the span of a large-span structure is in the same order of magnitude as the wavelength of seismic waves, the temporal and spatial variability of ground motion input should also be considered. Wang Chenyu (2021) concluded that the seismic wave incident angle had an important influence on the seismic response of the vehicle-bridge coupling system in the study of the seismic response of the vehicle-bridge system in the valley terrain under the oblique incidence of P waves. However, there are few studies on long-span bridges under the oblique incidence of seismic waves, especially in 3D models. In this paper, a long-span continuous rigid frame 3D solid model is established to study the influence of oblique incident seismic waves on long-span bridges.

---

*Corresponding Author: 254068205@qq.com

2 OBLIQUE INCIDENCE SEISMIC WAVE INPUT METHOD

2.1 Equivalent artificial boundary

In the seismic wave analysis of a local site, it is necessary to cut out a finite-sized calculation area from an infinite medium. In this paper, the uniform viscoelastic artificial boundary proposed in reference (Gu 2007) is adopted. On the boundary of the established finite element model, extend a layer of the same type of element, then fix the outermost boundary of the finite element model, and finally define the equivalent shear modulus, equivalent elastic modulus, and equivalent damping of the boundary element, to achieve a consistent viscoelastic artificial boundary.

Equivalent shear moduli and elastic moduli of artificial boundary elements in the 3D finite element model are expressed as:

$$\begin{cases} \tilde{G} = hK_{BT} = 2\alpha_T h \dfrac{G}{R} \\ \tilde{E} = 2\dfrac{(1+\tilde{v})(1-2\tilde{v})}{(1-\tilde{v})} hK_{BN} = 2\alpha_N h \dfrac{G}{R} \cdot \dfrac{(1+\tilde{v})(1-2\tilde{v})}{(1-\tilde{v})} \end{cases} \quad (1)$$

Damping of artificial boundary elements in the 3D finite element model is expressed as:

$$\tilde{\eta} = \dfrac{\rho R}{3G}\left(2\dfrac{c_s}{\alpha_T} + \dfrac{c_p}{\alpha_N}\right) \quad (2)$$

where
c_s—velocity of S wave;
c_p—velocity of P wave;
P—mass density of medium;
G—media shear modulus;
R—the distance from the wave source to the artificial boundary;
α_T and α_N—artificial boundary parameters in the reference (Gu 2007).

2.2 Equivalent force calculation under the oblique incidence of seismic waves

In this paper, the one-dimensional algorithm proposed in (Wang 2007) and the lumped-mass motion equation of artificial boundary nodes is used to transform the seismic wave problem into the wave source problem. The oblique incident ground motion field is converted into the equivalent load applied to the artificial boundary node by using MATLAB, and the effective input of the wave is realized.

3 FINITE ELEMENT CALCULATION MODEL

The project background of this paper is a prestressed concrete girder bridge, as shown in Figure 1 below, the main bridge is a continuous rigid frame bridge with a total length of 560 meters, the span arrangement is 100 m + 180 m + 180 m + 100 m, and the main beam is a section box girder. The finite element model was established using the finite element program ANSYS, as shown in Figure 2. From west to east are piers from No. 1 to No. 5. The main beam, pier, pile, and cap are made of Beam 188, and the foundation soil is simulated with Solid 45 solid element. MASS21 is used for the facility and the second-phase dead load, and BEAM4 is used for the rigid arm. The left boundary, right boundary, and bottom boundary of the foundation soil are set as uniform viscoelastic artificial boundaries. The upper boundary of the foundation soil is the free boundary of the surface.

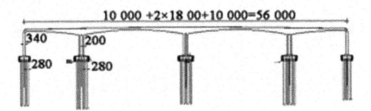

Figure 1. Layout of the bridge.

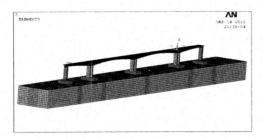

Figure 2. Bridge-pile-soil interaction model.

Due to the limited space, only the dynamic characteristics of the first eight-order formation of the calculation model are given in Table 1, and the first eight-order vibration shape diagrams of the calculation model are shown in Figures 3–10.

Table 1. Dynamic characteristics of the calculation model.

Order	Frequency (Hz)	Mode shape characteristics
1	0.35619	The first-order longitudinal drift of the main beam
2	0.71726	First-order antisymmetric transverse bending of the main beam
3	0.73761	First-order positive symmetrical transverse bending of the main beam
4	0.83761	First-order antisymmetric vertical bending of the main beam
5	1.0158	First-order positive symmetrical vertical bending of the main beam
6	1.0250	Second-order positive symmetrical transverse bending of the main beam
7	1.0768	Second-order antisymmetric transverse bending of the main beam
8	1.2319	5# side pier longitudinal vibration

Figure 3. First order.   Figure 4. Second order.   Figure 5. Third order.   Figure 6. Fourth order.

It can be seen from Table 1 that the frequencies of each order are very dense, and there is no frequency jump phenomenon, which is also the embodiment of the dynamic characteristics of the continuous rigid frame bridge. The mode shape coupling phenomenon between the main beam

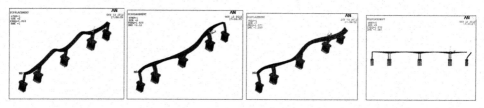

Figure 7. Fifth order.   Figure 8. Sixth order.   Figure 9. Seventh order.   Figure 10. Eighth order.

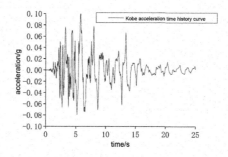

Figure 11. Acceleration curve of the seismic wave in the Kobe earthquake.

and the pier is obvious. The measured first-order frequency is 0.362, which is consistent with the calculated value of the model, and the model is accurate and reliable.

4 SEISMIC WAVES INPUT

To study the seismic response of the bridge, the actual seismic wave record from the Kobe earthquake with the acceleration peak value adjusted to 0.1 g is selected, and the acceleration time history is shown in Figure 11.

5 RESULTS AND DISCUSSION

To intuitively express the amplitude ratio between the oblique incidence and the vertical incidence of the bridge pier response, the non-uniform seismic influence coefficient (η) is defined, as shown in Equation (3).

$$\eta = \frac{\max |F| - max |F_0|}{\max |F_0|} \tag{3}$$

where
F_0—the internal force of the bridge pier at vertical incidence;
F—the internal force of the bridge pier at oblique incidence.

5.1 P wave

Table 2 shows the non-uniform seismic internal force influence coefficient of No. 3 pier under the oblique incidence of the P wave. After analysis, we obtain several conclusions. (1) The shear force is 2.6 times higher than the vertical incidence when the seismic wave is obliquely incident at 15°, and the shear force is 4.9 times higher than the vertical incidence when the seismic wave is obliquely incident at 30° (2) The axial force of the pier bottom is 51.3% higher than that of the vertical incidence when the seismic wave is obliquely incident at 15°, and the axial force of the pier bottom is 1.09 times higher than that of the vertical incidence when the seismic wave is obliquely incident at 30° (3) The longitudinal bending moment of the pier bottom is 2.5 times higher than that of the vertical incidence when the seismic wave is obliquely incident at 15°, and the longitudinal bending moment of the pier bottom is 4.7 times higher than that of the vertical incidence when the seismic wave is obliquely incident at 30° (4) The influence of different oblique incidence angles on the transverse bending moment response of the No. 3 pier bottom is very small.

Table 2. Influence coefficient of non-uniform seismic internal force of pier No. 3 under oblique incidence.

Type of internal force	0° (kN)	15° (kN)	30° (kN)	$\eta_{15°}$	$\eta_{30°}$
Shear force	124.526	449.348	739.374	260.8%	493.7%
Axial force	5372.88	8129.84	11280.7	51.3%	109.9%
The longitudinal bending moment of the pier bottom	2559.9	8967	14709.6	250.3%	474.6%
Transverse bending moment of the pier bottom	34459	34461	34657.5	0.006%	0.57%

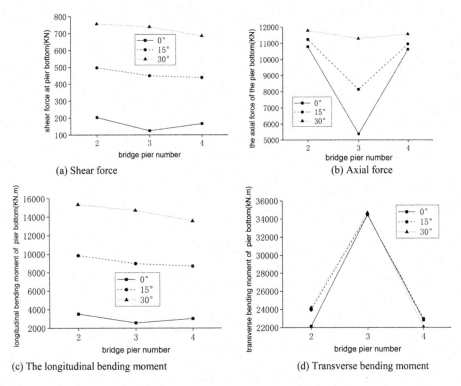

(a) Shear force

(b) Axial force

(c) The longitudinal bending moment

(d) Transverse bending moment

Figure 12. Amplitude of internal force at pier bottom when seismic waves are incident at different oblique incidence angles.

Figure 12 shows the amplitude of the internal force at the pier bottom at different oblique incidence angles of the P wave. The amplitude of the internal force at the pier bottom at vertical incidence is symmetrical about the vertical centerline of the structure. It can be seen from Figure 12(a) that the shear force of the same pier number increases with the increase of the incident angle, and the increase of each pier with the incident angle is almost the same. From Figure 12(b), it can be concluded that the axial force of piers No. 2 and No. 4 increases less with the incident angle, while pier No. 3 increases greatly. Figure 12(c) shows that when the seismic wave is vertically incident, the longitudinal bending moment amplitude of piers No. 2 and No. 4 is greater than that of No. 3; the longitudinal bending moment of piers with the same pier number increases with the increase of the incident angle, and the increase of each pier with the incident angle is almost the same. Figure 12(d) shows that the transverse bending moment of pier No. 3 is greater than that of No. 2 and No. 4 when the seismic wave is incident vertically or obliquely; despite the increase in angle, there is little change in the transverse bending moment at the bottom of each pier.

From the above analysis, it can be concluded that when the P wave is incident, the shear force, the longitudinal bending moment, and the axial force increase with the increase of the oblique incidence angle. The oblique incidence has little effect on the lateral moment response of the pier bottom.

5.2 SV wave

Table 3 shows the non-uniform seismic internal force influence coefficient of pier No. 3 under the oblique incidence of the P wave. It can be seen that (1) when the seismic wave is obliquely incident at 15°, the pier bottom shear force is reduced by 11.1% compared with the vertical incidence, and when the seismic wave is obliquely incident at 30°, the pier bottom shear force is reduced by 36.3% compared with the vertical incidence; that (2)the axial force of the pier bottom is 10.9% higher than that of the vertical incidence when the seismic wave is obliquely incident at 15°, and the axial force of the pier bottom is 50.1% higher than that of the vertical incidence when the seismic wave is obliquely incident at 30°; that (3) when the seismic wave is obliquely incident at 15°, the bending moment of the longitudinal bridge at the pier bottom is reduced by 9.6% compared with the vertical incidence, and when the seismic wave is obliquely incident at 30°, the bending moment of the longitudinal bridge at the pier bottom is reduced by 31.6% compared with the vertical incidence; and that (4) when the seismic wave is obliquely incident at 15°, the bending moment in the transverse bridge direction is reduced by 21.4% compared with the vertical incidence, and when the seismic wave is obliquely incident at 30°, the bending moment in the transverse bridge direction is reduced by 37.5% compared with the vertical incidence.

Table 3. Influence coefficient of non-uniform seismic internal force of pier No. 3 under oblique incidence.

Type of internal force	0° (kN)	15° (kN)	30° (kN)	$\eta_{15°}$	$\eta_{30°}$
Shear force	1122.22	997.847	715.26	−11.1%	−36.3%
Axial force	3090.03	3428.13	4639.1	10.9%	50.1%
The longitudinal bending moment of the pier bottom	21956.8	19838.1	15018.3	−9.6%	−31.6%
Transverse bending moment of the pier bottom	12029	9455.56	7518.23	−21.4%	−37.5%

Figure 13 shows the amplitude of the internal force at the pier bottom at different oblique incidence angles of the SV wave. Figure 13 shows that the amplitude of the internal force at the pier bottom at vertical incidence is symmetrical about the vertical centerline of the structure. Figure 13(a) shows that the shear force at the bottom of the pier with the same pier number decreases with the increase of the oblique incident angle. Figure 13(b) shows that the axial force at the bottom of the same pier number increases with the increase of the oblique incident angle, and the increasing degree of the axial force at the bottom of each pier number is quite different. Figure 13(c) shows that the longitudinal bending moment of the pier bottom with the same pier number decreases with the increase of the oblique incident angle. Figure 13(d) shows that the transverse bending moment at the bottom of the pier with the same pier number decreases with the increase of the oblique incident angle.

It can be concluded from the above analysis. When the SV wave is incident, the shear force at the pier bottom, the longitudinal bending moment of the pier bottom, and the transverse bending moment of the pier bottom decrease with the increase of the oblique incidence angle. The amplitude of the internal force at the bottom of the pier is symmetrical about the vertical centerline of the

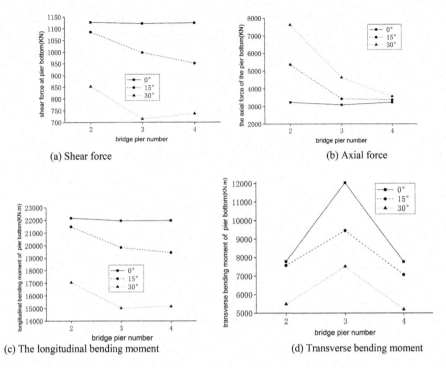

Figure 13. Amplitude of internal force at pier bottom when seismic waves are incident at different oblique incidence angles.

structure when the incident is vertical. When the seismic wave is incident obliquely, the symmetry of the force on the bridge structure no longer exists. The axial force of the pier bottom increases by 50% at the oblique incidence compared with the vertical incidence. The effect of oblique-incidence seismic input on the axial force of continuous rigid-frame bridges cannot be ignored.

6 CONCLUSIONS

By establishing an overall model of long-span bridge-pile-soil dynamic interaction, and considering the spatial propagation characteristics caused by oblique incidence, we can obtain the following conclusions.

(1) Under the action of the P wave, the shear force, the longitudinal bending moment, and the axial force all increase with the increase of the incident angle. Compared with the vertical incidence, the shear force, the longitudinal bending moment, and the axial force increase by 493.7%, 474.6%, and 109.9% respectively.
(2) Under the action of the SV wave, the shear force, the longitudinal bending moment, and the transverse bending moment decrease with the increase of the incident angle, while the axial force increases. Compared with the vertical incidence, the shear force, the longitudinal bending moment, and the transverse bending moment decrease by 36.3%, 31.6%, and 37.5%, respectively, and the axial force increases by 50.1%. The influence of oblique incident seismic input on the internal force of long-span bridges cannot be ignored, and the influence of oblique incident seismic input should be considered in the seismic analysis of bridges.

This paper only discusses the influence law of the seismic response of the long-span continuous rigid-frame bridge structure. Different bridge structure forms, span arrangements, stiffness, and support methods should be analyzed, and more general conclusions should be drawn. Considering that the dynamic response analysis of bridge structures is limited to the elastic range, the nonlinear dynamic response research of large-span bridges under the action of non-uniform ground motion can be further carried out.

ACKNOWLEDGMENT

This work was supported by the Education and Research Project for Young and Middle-Aged Teachers in Fujian Province—*Seismic Performance of Curved Girder Bridges Considering the Oblique Incidence of Seismic Waves* (Grant No. JAT191088).

REFERENCES

Du Xiuli & Chen Wei (2007). Preliminary study of time-domain seismic response for underground structures to obliquely incident seismic waves [J]. *Technology for Earthquake Disaster Prevention* 2 (3): 290–296.
Eurocode 8 (1995), Structures in seismic regions design, Part 2, bridges [S].draft. *Brussels European Committee for Standardizan-tion.*
Gu yin & Liu Jingbo. &. Du Yi xin (2007). 3D consistent viscous—spring artificial boundary and viscous—spring boundary element [J]. *Engineering Mechanics* 24 (12): 31–38.
Jiang Jingsong & Zhuang Weilin (2008). Investigation and analysis of seismic damage to Baihua Bridge in Wen chuan Earthquake [J]. *Bridge Construction* 6: 41–44.
Wang Chenyu & Qiao Hong (2021). Nonlinear aerostatic stability analysis for emergency bridge with cable-girder [J]. *Railway Engineering* 61 (7): 21–24.
Wang Yan (2007). *Research on numerical methods for nonuniform seismic wave fields and application in structural dynamic analysis* [D]. Beijing: Department of Civil Engineering, Tsinghua University.
Zhu Jun & Li XiaoJun (2020). Effects of a tunnel on site ground motion for 3D obliquely incident seismic waves [J]. *China Civil Engineering Journal* 53 (1): 318–324.

Analysis and discussion on design points of sea discharge sewage pipeline project

Lanfang Zhang*
Nanning University, Nanning, China

Dongyin Guan*
Guangxi Communications Design Group Co., Ltd., Guangxi, China

ABSTRACT: To implement the ecological civilization thought and the new development idea of promoting the high-quality development of the city, coastal cities have successively constructed or reconstructed sea discharge sewage discharge pipelines in recent years to discharge the urban sewage into the deep sea after it is treated and reaches the standard. Based on the reconstruction project of the sea discharge sewage pipeline in the Jingu Port Area of Qinzhou Port, this paper analyzes the route selection scheme in the engineering design process and the laying position scheme of the sea discharge pipeline at the east dike of the power plant according to the unique construction conditions of the project, and puts forward some matters needing attention in the design of the sea discharge pipelines crossing the existing projects: first, the EPC construction mode should be used as much as possible; second, a scheme selected should be conducive to the project construction on the premise of ensuring the safety of existing structures; third, the geophysical prospecting of the route should be properly carried out.

1 INTRODUCTION

In July 2015, the meeting of the Central Leading Group for Deepening Overall Reform deliberated and adopted the Plan on Supervision and Inspection of Environmental Protection (Trial), which specifies to establish of environmental protection supervision and inspection mechanism, and proposes to take place with prominent environmental problems and frequent major environmental incidents and ineffectively implementing environmental protection responsibilities as the supervision and inspection objects at the early stage to focus on implementing the decisions and arrangements of the Party's Central Committee, solving prominent environmental problems and fulfilling the responsibilities of environmental protection subjects. Under this background, the central environmental protection inspector arrived in Hebei in December 2015 and was stationed in Guangxi in 2016. According to the requirements of the central environmental protection supervisor, the marine supervisor, the municipal party committee, and the municipal government, Qinzhou City needed to complete the deep-sea discharge of the tailwater from Qinzhou Port Sembcorp Sewage Treatment Plant, PetroChina by the end of 2020. Due to historical reasons, the existing sewage outlet is located next to Guoxing Wharf in the Yingling operation area of Qinzhou Port. This was inconsistent with the plan, so the location of the sewage outlet shall be adjusted to the planned sewage discharge area. As the sea-discharge pipeline route needed to pass through the existing built area, it was necessary to compare and select the scheme in the design process to minimize the impact on the built area.

*Corresponding Authors: 22452302@qq.com and 646788936@qq.com

2 SUPPORTING WORKS

The planned sewage discharge area of the Jingu port area of Qinzhou Port was located at the Jingu River Estuary of Qinzhou Port (to the south of the coal wharf of SPIC Power Plant). Due to historical reasons, the existing sea discharge outlet of the sewage treatment plant in the Jingu port area of Qinzhou Port was located next to Guoxing Wharf in the Yingling operation area of Qinzhou Port, which was identified as a temporary discharge outlet by the national environmental protection inspector. According to the instruction of the inspector, the reconstruction should be completed before the end of 2020 to relocate the sewage discharge outlet to the planned sewage discharge area.

2.1 Project construction background

In May 2018, Qinzhou Port Environmental Protection Branch organized and entrusted a relevant qualified unit with preparing the Demonstration Report on the Setting of Guoxing Sea Discharge Sewage Outlet in Qinzhou Port of Qinzhou City, which analyzed and demonstrated the existing sewage outlet near Guoxing Wharf. According to the demonstration report, under the current planned full load, the discharge volume of 20,000 m^3/day at the sewage outlet near Guoxing Wharf (including 15,000 m^3/day of sewage from Sembcorp and 5,000 m^3/day from Guangxi Petrochemical) meets the current discharge requirements, and the impact to the environment is acceptable. However, according to the measures and suggestions proposed by the demonstration report, such as expanding the discharge volume in the future, since the Guoxing discharge outlet was on the shore, it was suggested to relocate the discharge outlet for deep-sea discharge. Therefore, according to the conclusion of the demonstration, the existing sewage outlet beside Guoxing Wharf could only meet the current discharge requirements. After the Huayi project is completed in the future, the subsequent sewage will also be discharged with the existing pipeline, and there will be an increase of about 10,000 to 20,000 m^3/day in sewage discharge, so the existing sewage outlets will not meet the discharge requirements after Huayi project is put into operation. Considering the development of the park, the sewage volume in the park will reach 192,500 m^3/day by 2030. Therefore, the design capacity of the sewage pipeline is 200,000 m^3/day.

2.2 Project construction location

The sewage discharge pipeline before reconstruction was from Sembcorp Sewage Treatment Plant to the west along Guoying Avenue, then to the south along the existing road, and discharged into the sea from the outlet at Guoxing Wharf. The land area of the pipeline from the existing sewage outlet to the planned sewage discharge area was built with roads, wharves, and plant areas. The impact on the existing structures and facilities should be fully considered when determining the route of the sea discharge pipeline.

3 OVERVIEW OF THE DESIGN OF SEA DISCHARGE SEWAGE PIPELINE

The sea discharge sewage pipeline is an important part of the sewage treatment project in coastal cities. To improve the sewage treatment capacity of coastal cities, protect marine resources and the environment, promote the sustainable development of the marine economy, and reduce sewage pollution to the sea, it is necessary to reasonably design the sea discharge sewage pipeline.

3.1 Analysis of design characteristics

The sea-discharge sewage pipeline project is the process of discharging municipal sewage into the sea. Therefore, the main structures involved include land-area discharge pipe, sea-area discharge pipe, surge shaft, and sewage outfall. According to the locations of structures, the project involves the design of both land area structures and water area structures. Therefore, the relevant specifications of land area projects and water area projects shall be followed in the design of the project (Guo 2018; Yang 2018).

In addition, since most sea-discharge sewage pipeline projects have been rectification projects in recent years, the relationship with the existing projects should be fully considered in the design to minimize the impact of the project construction on the existing projects and the convenience and economy of the project construction should also be considered.

3.2 *Key points of design*

According to the analysis of the characteristics of the project, this paper discussed the key design points of the Qinzhou Sea discharge sewage pipeline based on the route selection in the design process and the selection of the pipeline laying position at the east dike of the power plant.

4 COMPARISON AND SELECTION OF ROUTING SCHEMES

The construction of the Qinzhou sea-discharge sewage pipeline project comprises two parts: land area and sea area. The sea-area pipeline went down directly to the discharge point from the outlet of the Jingu River channel. The design of the route selection scheme was based on the *Request for Instructions on Determining the Route of the Sewage Discharge Pipeline in Guoxing Sewage Outlet of Qinzhou Port* (QGZJB [2019] No.78) submitted by the Housing and Urban-Rural Development Bureau of Qinzhou Port Economic and Technological Development Zone. The routing schemes were compared and selected based on the existing data.

4.1 *Route scheme I: Entering the sea at the south revetment of the 50,000-DWT wharf*

Connected with the tailwater outlet of SembCorp Sewage Treatment Plant, Qinzhou sea-discharge sewage pipeline is laid along the south side of Linhai Avenue to the northeast corner of SPIC Power Plant. The land area behind the 50,000-DWT wharf along the outer slope of the east dike of the power plant, and then under-crosses the south revetment (the south dike), from where a submarine pipeline will be constructed subsequently to the planned sewage discharge area (Li 2014, 2016). The total length of the sea discharge pipeline is about 3.4 km, with 1.78 km of land area section, including Linhai Avenue section, the land area section on the east side of SPIC power plant, and the section of pipe jacking under-crossing the south revetment, and 1.62 km of sea area section, including the sea area section on the east side and the sea-bottom section to the south of SPIC power plant, all adopting HDPE pipes, and partially adopting steel pipe to under-cross the revetment. Along the south side of Linhai Avenue, about 1 km tailwater discharge pipeline shared by PetroChina with SembCorp Sewage Treatment Plant will be changed from pipe gallery laying to buried laying.

4.2 *Route scheme II: Entering the sea from the north side of the 50,000-DWT wharf*

Compared with Route Scheme I, Scheme II considers entering the sea from the north side of the 50,000-DWT wharf. After turning to the south, the pipeline will be laid in parallel with the Jingu River channel to the tailwater discharge point. The North-South pipeline is about 140 m away from the front of the 50,000-DWT wharf in the east and 110 m away from the Jingu river channel in the west. The total length of the sea discharge pipeline is about 3.4 km, with 1.43 km of land area section and 2.21 km of sea area section, including the dike section and the sea area section to the east of SPIC power plant.

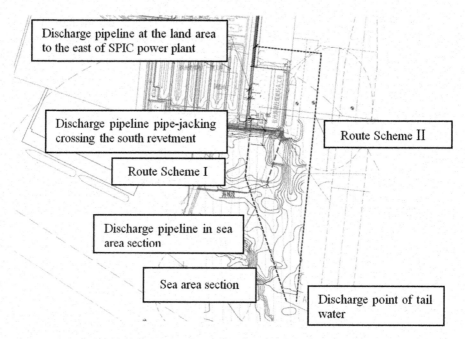

Figure 1. Route schemes for tailwater discharge pipeline.

4.3 *Comparison and selection of schemes*

The Route Scheme I has the advantages of simple routing, short path, and low investment. The route needs to enter the 50,000-DWT wharf area and goes into the water at a selected point behind the south revetment of the wharf. The belt conveyor pipeline and road from the wharf to the storage yard are located close to the south revetment. To prevent the impact on the operation of the wharf, the sewage pipeline in the south revetment area could not be excavated directly and bypass the surrounding facilities. A suitable location should be adopted as the pipe jacking works well to carry out pipe jacking operation underground. The pipeline will be jacked out of the land from the south revetment into the sea. The pipe jacking section is about 100 m. In this scheme, as the pipeline is deeply buried in the soil layer below the revetment, once the water is drained in the later stage, it is difficult to retain, and the leaked water will take away the backfill, resulting in the land settlement of the wharf and producing adverse effect to the stability of the revetment. According to the pipe jacking construction process, the plane length and width of the pipe jacking well should be 13 m, respectively. According to the riprap depth of the south revetment and the geology below, the well is about 13 m deep, belonging to a deep foundation pit, which needs a vertical water stop curtain and horizontal support and stability structure. The pipe jacking is surrounded by belt conveyor pipe gallery road and wharf auxiliary structures, so the support structure should ensure the safety of surrounding facilities and have strict deformation requirements. The construction scheme of the deep foundation pit shall be subject to special review. The pipe jacking construction of a deep foundation pit is characterized by a long construction period, high construction difficulty, and high construction risk. Once there is any problem, it will affect the wharf facilities and revetment.

To sum up, the disadvantage of this routing scheme is that the operation area behind the wharf is taken as the entry point, which is technically feasible, but if the pipeline leaks in the later stage, it will affect the land area and revetment of the wharf and will be difficult to maintain. Offshore pipeline construction requires complex construction technology, and the construction risk is high.

In Route Scheme II, the pipeline can be extended to the sea by directly and partially excavating the revetment of the east dike of the power plant along the slope. The construction risk is small, and it is easy to maintain. However, since the route passes through the planned wharf area and the turning water area of the built wharf area, the connection with the planned wharf structure shall be well designed to prevent any impact on the subsequent wharf construction. In addition, as the route passes through the turning water area in front of the built wharf, the operation of the built wharf will be affected during the construction of the project. For instance, if blasting is required for construction, it shall consider the impact on the structure of the built wharf, and an appropriate construction scheme shall be selected.

In the design of the project, after soliciting the opinions of all parties and comparison and selection, Route Scheme I was adopted.

4.4 *Design analysis of routes*

Since the project has been completed, according to the actual construction situation, there was not enough geological survey data during the pipe jacking construction in Route Scheme I since the construction was carried out on the built wharf. The pipe jacking scheme construction was changed to an open excavation revetment protection scheme due to various factors, which not only wasted the project investment but also increased the construction period. Besides, the design of the open excavation revetment protection scheme needed to be approved by the wharf owner and the management department of the power plant, which required lots of coordination and demonstration, and the scheme was adjusted several times. The whole process was time-consuming and costly to both parties.

When comparing and selecting routing schemes for similar projects, in addition to the technical feasibility of design, the construction feasibility also needs to be considered. When determining the design scheme, the construction party needs to participate in time and consider the construction scheme and construction period in detail to ensure the smooth implementation of the designed scheme.

5 COMPARISON AND SELECTION OF PIPELINE LAYING POSITIONS AT THE EAST DIKING OF POWER PLANT

According to the construction, the sewage discharged to the sea is about 200,000 m^3/day, and the design pipe diameter is 1.8 m. The DN1800 HDPE pipe with a ring stiffness equal to or greater than 8 kN/m^2 is adopted; the buried depth of the pipe top is 1.2 m, and the depth of the pipe bottom is 3.5 m. Simple support is adopted for the excavation, and the width is 4.0 m (Wu 2013). During the design of the project, the pipeline laying position at the east dike has a great impact on the construction scheme and progress of the project.

5.1 *Route scheme I for laying position of sea discharge pipeline at the east dike*

Considering the operable working surface of the construction and the current situation of the plant, the sea discharge pipeline at the east dike was laid directly by evacuating the lawn behind the dike and extended straightly to the sea working well near the south revetment of the coal wharf of the power plant. The lawn was restored after laying. This scheme has the advantages of low cost (the price per linear meter is 14,000 Yuan/m), convenient construction, fast construction speed, a high guarantee of construction safety, a long durability of pipes buried in the soil, easy maintenance during the operation period, and low maintenance cost, and the construction process will not affect the safety production of the power plant.

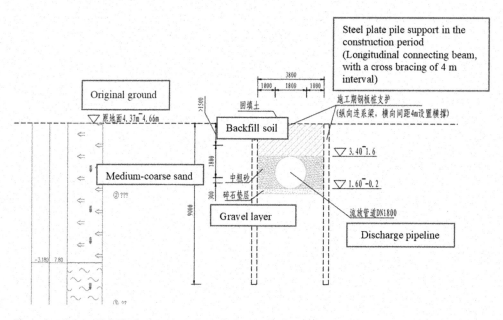

Figure 2. Scheme I for laying position of sea discharge pipeline at the east dike.

5.2 *Scheme II for the laying position of the sea discharge pipeline at the east dike*

According to the requirements of the built power plant, the construction of the project shall not occupy the land inside the east dike. The proposed Scheme II for the laying position of the sea discharge pipeline at the east dike is based on this design condition, as well as the as-built drawings of the power plant's eastern dike, warm water outlet, and rainwater inlet.

The east dike of the power plant uses sandbags as graded retaining dams to construct the dike in stages. The outer protection surface is stone revetment. The warm water outlet and rainwater inlet of the power plant are arranged 900 m along the east dike, with a large lateral scale. Construction conditions are as follows. The design high tide level is 4.16 m, the wave height H1% is equal to 2.65 m in the 50-year return period, the annual average high tide level is 1.8 m, the surface layer is a soft soil layer, and the bottom layer is rock surface.

A 910-meter pipe was laid on the mortar rubble revetment of the east dike of the power plant and passed through the warm drainage outlet of the power plant, the rainwater outlet, and the north revetment of the 50,000-DWT wharf.

The structural design of this Scheme shall comprehensively consider the stability of the pipeline during the construction period, the stability against wave impact during the service period, and the overall stability of the original dike after increasing the pipeline prism. The drainage pipe is laid on a shoulder with an elevation of 1.3 m and a width of 6 m. After the lower concrete base blocks are installed, the gravel layer will be paved and leveled. The upper pipe stabilizing block will be installed after the pipes are in place, and then the riprap slope protection will be constructed. The section is shown in Figure 3.

This scheme belongs to over-water construction and needs to cross the drainage structures of the power plant, so it is characterized by high construction difficulty, long construction period, and high costs (preliminary estimate: 40,000 Yuan/m). The outlet of the power plant is large, so structural measures are required under the wave deflector of the wave retaining wall. Partial of the concrete retaining wall and a 3.5-meter-depth dike need to be removed at the pipe connection of the north revetment. The above construction could only be carried out with the consent of the power plant.

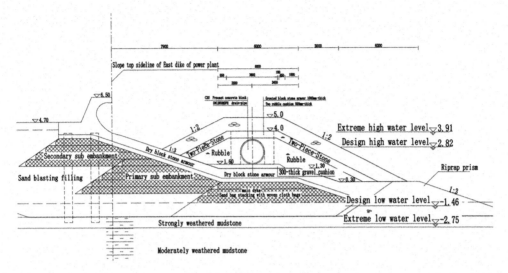

Figure 3. Scheme II of sea discharge pipeline laying position at the east dike.

Since the pipes are under alternate dry and wet environments and because of the sea wave, materials with strong anti-corrosion performance shall be selected. Although the concrete pipes have strong anti-corrosion ability, the pipes used in the project need to pass through the power plant structures, so deformable and bendable pipes shall be selected. The concrete pipe has many joints (4-m long per section), and when laid on the berm, the pipe joints are easy to be separated and leak affected by the waves and uneven settlement of the foundation bed. This does not meet the requirements of environmental protection requirements. Therefore, an HDPE pipe (ring stiffness is larger than or equals 8 kN/m^2) with the same material as that buried on the land area is selected. The pipe section is long, with good integrity, strong adaptability to terrain deformation, and is suitable for bypassing the structure section of the power plant, but its durability is poor in this environment. The anti-corrosion performance of GRP pipe is superior to that of HDPE pipe, and the pipe section is long, with good integrity. It can be used in the outer section of the embankment, but the unit price of the pipe is higher than that of the HDPE pipe. From the aspect of performance, steel pipes can also be used in the project, but special anti-corrosion measures are required in the existing environment, and the anti-corrosion cost is high. To sum up, FRP pipes are selected for this section. The maintenance of overwater structures during operation is not as convenient as that on land, and the maintenance cost is relatively high.

5.3 *Scheme comparison and selection*

According to the estimation, the project cost of Scheme I (laying pipes under the lawn at the land area of the east dike of the plant) is 12.75 million yuan, and the project cost of Scheme II is 36.8 million yuan. The project cost of Scheme II is 24.05 million yuan higher than that of Scheme I.

Scheme I of laying pipes under the lawn of the power plant has no impact on the overall landscape. There is no crossing at the north revetment, so demolition is avoided. The intersection of the drainage outlet pipes passes directly from above, and no other measures are required. Only the workload of the construction management behind the power plant is increased, and the management of pipeline construction equipment and personnel in the plant should be strengthened. In Scheme II of laying open pipes after entering the east dike, the fence needs to be set up behind the power plant during construction, so it has no impact on the rear area of the power plant. The impact on the rear of the power plant mainly comes from three intersection points: the crossing of the reinforcement measures above the drainage bell mouth, the crossing of the reinforcement above the rainwater bell mouth, and the crossing of demolished point of the north revetment.

5.4 *Discussion of design scheme*

Scheme II was selected as the design scheme when constructing the sea discharge pipeline structure at the east dike. It mainly considers the land requirements of the power plant. However, during the construction of the project, the selection of Scheme II greatly increased the construction period and difficulty. First, to avoid conflict with the structure of the drainage outlet and the rainwater inlet, the pile foundation scheme was adopted above the drainage outlet and the rainwater inlet in the design based on the opinions of all parties. Since the construction party was not determined during the design, there was no sufficient site for pile foundation construction due to failing to timely apply for sea use during the construction. Although coordination was conducted with the power plant during that period, the construction period was extended several times. Finally, after communicating with the power plant, the design was changed, and the pipeline was directly buried above the outlet structure and the rainwater inlet structure after evaluation.

The comparison and selection of pipeline laying position at the east dike of the power plant showed that the design process needs to be closely combined with the construction. Because different construction units will adopt different construction schemes and have different technical levels, the demand for the construction site will also be different. Since the land section of the sea discharge pipeline project needs to pass by the existing buildings, the construction site is very limited, so the construction unit needs to implement the design scheme on the limited site. Therefore, for such projects, the construction party needs to participate in the design process, which can save project investment and speed up the project progress. Further, if the proposed structure will not have a significant impact on the existing buildings, but is a feasible project that will require little investment and facilitate construction, it is important to coordinate with the owner to select a design scheme that will be most successful.

6 CONCLUSION

At present, the project has been completed. In addition to the construction land and progress caused by the route design scheme and the laying position scheme for the sea discharge pipeline of the east dike analyzed above, the main problems presented in the construction process also included the mismatch between the construction machinery mobilized and the site size in the land area. The following design points were discussed for such sewage sea discharge pipeline projects with more crosses with the existing buildings. First, the design and construction shall be closely coordinated, and the construction scheme shall be considered when determining the design scheme. It is suggested to adopt the EPC mode for project construction. Second, as such projects are constructed in the built-up area, and it is inevitable to cross with the existing civil engineering and pipeline works when selecting the scheme, it is necessary to consider the impact of the project construction on the existing projects and the feasibility of the project scheme, and the scheme that is most conducive to the implementation of the project and most economic shall be selected. If the owner of the existing projects proposes any opinions on the preferred scheme in the implementation process, the relevant parties shall fully communicate with each other to advance the project. Third, for underground works, it is necessary to carry out detailed geophysical prospecting on the project route to clarify the situations of underground pipelines and make reasonable avoidance in the design to reduce the crossing of temporary construction pipelines.

REFERENCES

Guo Pei Pei. Discussion on the design of tailwater discharge project of a sewage treatment plant in a development zone [J]. *Municipal Technology*. 2018,36(04):195–198+201.

Li Feng. Study on the selection and planning of phase II sewage mixing area of Yantai Taoziwan sewage treatment plant [J]. *Ludong University Journal* (Natural Science Edition). 2016,32(03):272–277+288.

Li Yi. *Deep sea discharge engineering design of Dajijia sewage treatment plant in Yantai Development Zone* [J]. Proceedings of the 42nd technical exchange of the national water supply and drainage technology information network. 2014-12-04:303–306.

Wu Wei. Study on the internal flow of marine sewage outfalls with PIV system[J]. *Journal of Experiments in Fluid Mechanics*. 2013,27(05):27–34.

Yang Bingfeng. Analysis of Sewage Discharge Engineering [J] *Railway Energy Saving & Environmental Protection & Occupational Safety and Health* 2018,8(01): 15–19.

Morphological response under waves of a typical double-sandbar artificial beach system

Shan Li
CCCC Tianjin Port Engineering Institute, Co., Ltd., Tianjin, China
CCCC First Harbor Engineering Co., Ltd., Tianjin, China
Key Laboratory of Coastal Engineering Hydrodynamic, CCCC, Tianjin, China

Mingxiao Xie*
Tianjin Research Institute for Water Transport Engineering, M. O. T., Tianjin, China

Guangjia Ding
CCCC Tianjin Port Engineering Institute, Co., Ltd., Tianjin, China
CCCC First Harbor Engineering Co., Ltd., Tianjin, China
Key Laboratory of Coastal Engineering Hydrodynamic, CCCC, Tianjin, China

Chi Zhang & Zhenhua Gu
State Key Laboratory of Hydrology-Water Resources and Hydraulic Engineering, Hohai University, Nanjing, China

ABSTRACT: A quasi-3D beach evolution numerical model was applied to investigate the influence of wave direction on the morphodynamics of a double-sandbar urban artificial beach system. Simulation results revealed that both wave direction and the outer bar bathymetry have a significant influence on the bar-coupling process, and the incident wave direction would greatly affect the evolution of the outer bar morphology. As the incident wave angle increases, if the outer bar was allowed to evolve, the interactions between the inner and outer bar would be significantly enhanced at first and then weakened. The interactions between the inner and outer bar continue to increase with increasing wave angles. It was found that the initially crescentic outer bar tends to evolve into longshore uniform patterns as the wave angle increases, and this was believed to be the main reason for the difference above.

1 INTRODUCTION

For building an ecological coastal environment and to facilitate the coastal tourism economy, in recent years the construction of artificial beaches (or beach nourishment) has become an important type of urban project. Amongst the existent artificial beach engineering, it is common to form a double-sandbar system to prevent sand loss. Sandbars in the coastal region are often characterized by three-dimensional and alongshore-uniform patterns. The typical three-dimensional pattern, commonly known as "crescentic" sandbars, is regarded as the alongshore spanning of horns and bays parallel to the shoreline. In general, under extreme weather, the observed sandbar shape is often alongshore uniform, while during lower energy conditions its geometry is often alongshore non-uniform which exhibits a striking crescentic pattern. Nearshore sandbars can prevent erosion of beaches as they strongly influence the wave energy dissipation through wave breaking during wave propagation onto the bars.

The double sandbar system, consisting of an outer bar and inner bar, is a common morphology unit for nearshore beaches, and the development of the inner bar may be influenced by the outer

---

*Corresponding Author: crabsaver@163.com

one. However, the interactions between these bars have not been studied until recently. A series of in-situ observations (Ruessink & Terwindt 2000) and numerical modeling (Masselink 2004) studies proved that the morphodynamic feedback under the impact of one bar on the other could be a key factor that governs the behavior of the integrated system. Having examined the 8-week data of a double sandbar system in Australia, Ruessink et al. (2007) found that the initial inner and outer bars were not essentially coupled. However, over time, those bars started to be coupled as the outer bar became more crescentic and moved onshore, showing that the geometry and position of the outer bar are important for the evolution of the inner bar. Ruessink et al. (2007) proposed that the two bars in the system occasionally show morphological coupling, especially when the three-dimensional outer bar patterns are well evolved. Castelle et al. (2007) found the alongshore variability in outer bar depth, and the alongshore variations in wave refraction and wave breaking across the outer bar are crucial to the coupling process. On the other hand, it was also indicated that the inner bar is likely to be coupled with the outer one with increasing variability in outer bar depth.

Furthermore, previous studies showed that except for the sandbar patterns, the incident wave condition, especially the wave angle is also important for the ultimate sandbar patterns and the morphological coupling between bars. Price et al. (2011) analyzed the evolution of bar patterns via imagery datasets for 9.3 years and concluded that the mean incident wave angle has important implications for bar morphology coupling. In addition, the longshore current will prevent the development of sandbar patterns and would make the bars from coupled to non-coupled. When the waves propagate to the bars with a large angle, the behavior of bars is likely to rely on their self-organization. Additionally, the wave direction also plays a crucial role in morphological coupling within a double-sandbar system, especially for the inner bar. As the wave incidence angle increases, the nearshore current changes from cell-like circulations to meandering longshore currents. Pre-existent results using numerical models have shown that with the increase of wave incidence angle, the wavelength of both bars increased, and the wavelength of the outer bar is even larger compared to the inner bar (Smit et al. 2008). However, at present, the mechanisms leading to different coupling processes of bars in a typical double sandbar system are still not well understood.

Despite observations and numerical modeling have proved that the outer bar geometry and incident wave angles can strongly affect the interactions between sandbars, the effect of wave angle on the bar coupling was rarely investigated, and the relationship between wave angle, outer bar geometry, and the interaction between bars still need to be established in more details. Due to the lack of measured data, previous research on the double sandbar system mainly relied on numerical simulations (Cheng & Wang, 2018; Dudkowska et al. 2020; Kim et al. 2017; Mulligan et al. 2019; Splinter et al. 2018). In this paper, a sophisticated numerical model was used to investigate the effect of wave angle on the interaction within a double-bar system.

2 METHOD

2.1 Model set-up

The numerical model used in this paper is the Nearshore Community Model (NearCoM), which is a state-of-the-art model coupled with a nearshore circulation model SHORECIRC, a wave model SWAN and a sediment transport module (Gu et al. 2016) have proved the present NearCoM model is suitable for simulating the nearshore hydrodynamics, sediment transport as well as the morphology evolution for a double-sandbar system. For more information about the model theory, readers may refer to the above papers, which are not listed here for brevity.

2.2 Wavelet analysis

The sandbar wavelength is a key indicator to present the characteristics of the sandbar shape. Therefore, to discuss the wavelengths of the sandbar system in more detail, the continuous wavelet transform (CWT) $W_n^z(s)$ was used. The CWT of a discrete sequence $z_n(n=0,...,N-1)$ with uniform spacing dz is defined as the convolution of z_n, with a scaled and normalized "mother" wavelet function ψ_0, see Equation 1.

$$W_n^z(s) = \left(\frac{dz}{s}\right)^{1/2} \sum_{n'=0}^{N-1} z_{n'} \psi_0^* \left\{\frac{(n'-n)dz}{s}\right\} \tag{1}$$

where dz is the uniform spacing in z_n, and * is the complex conjugate. When changing the alongshore scale s and translating along the alongshore coordinate n, we can get two-dimensional energy space (n, s) from the discrete sequence z_n. This can show us how the spatial modes vary in space. In addition, to know the potential inner-outer bar coupling, the wavelet-squared coherency indicator $R_n^2(s)$ is used, which is expressed by Equation 2, where S is the smoothing operator.

$$R_n^2(s) = \frac{|S\{s^{-1}W_n^{zy}(s)\}|^2}{S\{s^{-1}W_n^z(s)\}S\{s^{-1}W_n^y(s)\}'} \tag{2}$$

We select the sequences $Z_{\text{inner}}(n)$ and $Z_{\text{outer}}(n)$ to represent the morphology patterns of inner and outer bars, respectively. $R_n^2(s)$ is used to measure the coherency of the inner bar (denoted as $Z_{\text{inner}}(n)$) and outer bar (denoted as $Z_{\text{outer}}(n)$) in the alongshore direction. $R_n^2(s)$ of unity represents a linear relationship between the inner bar and outer bar at a specific scale and alongshore distance, while a value of 0 means there is no correlation. In this study, the Morlet wavelet was used as the mother wavelet ψ_0 as that in the paper of Ruessink et al. (2007) because it provides a good balance between space and frequency localization. The Morlet wavelet scale is almost the same as the corresponding Fourier wavelength $\lambda = 1.03\ s$. The term wavelength here refers to the Fourier wavelength λ equivalent to the wavelet scale s. The statistical significance of $W_n^z(s)$ and $R_n^2(s)$ was estimated against synthetic red noise series. The alongshore average values of $W_n^z(s)$ and $R_n^2(s)$ are denoted as $\overline{W^z}(s)$ and $\overline{R^2}(s)$.

2.3 Initial condition

Figure 1 illustrates the original bathymetry of a typical double-sandbar system of an artificial beach, in which the shape of the inner bar is alongshore uniform, and a crescentic-shape are used for the outer bar. The crescentic bar geometry is characterized by three parameters such as (1) the sandbar wavelength λ in the alongshore direction, (2) the horizontal horn-bay distance D_c, and (3) the vertical horn-bay amplitude D_v.

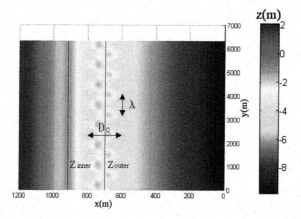

Figure 1. The initial double sandbar bathymetry. The out bar has a crescentic pattern with $\lambda = 840$ m, $D_c = 240$ m, and $D_v = 2.0$ m.

The width of the model area is 1200 m, and the mean sediment grain size D_{50} is selected as 0.1 mm, which represents a typical coastal sediment environment. The sediment porosity is used as 0.35. In the model, the grid spacings are 15 m and 35 m in cross-shore and longshore directions, respectively. In the simulation process, the wave parameters such as wave height, wave period, and wave direction are updated every 10 minutes. Note that the z-coordinate is corresponding to the Mean Sea Level (MSL), and an angle of 0° (in degree) means that the waves propagate onshore normally.

2.4 Computation settings

In this paper, we set two sets of cases to elaborate on the bar-coupling process. The first set is aimed to investigate the influence of the wave directly on the coupling of inner and outer bars. This set includes four cases. To make the wave dynamics large enough to re-suspend the bed sediments on the bars. In the first set, the wave height (H) and period (T) is constant, with $T = 6$ s and $H = 1.5$ m. By changing the incident wave angle, the new wave forcing with different wave directions is imposed on the initial bathymetry for a constant duration of 10 days.

The second set of cases is aimed to reflect the impact of the wave angle itself on the inner and outer bars coupling. Because in the first set the different outer bar morphological variability (caused by the different incident wave angles) can also influence the coupling process. Hence, to remove the influence of the difference in the outer bar morphology, in the second set the outer bar morphology is fixed, which means the outer bar morphology is always the same as that of the initial morphology during the whole computational duration. This set also includes four cases, amongst which the incident wave height and wave period ($H = 2.0$ m and $T = 6$ s) are fixed but with variable angles. According to simulated results, the influence of the different wave angles on bar-coupling would be effectively distinguished.

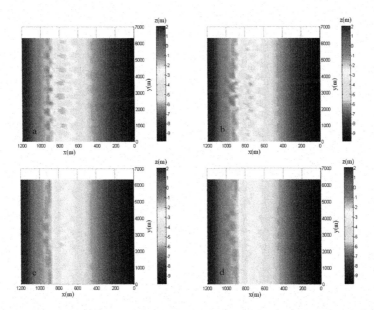

Figure 2. Modeled bar morphology after a 10-day simulation period ($T = 6$ s and $H = 1.5$ m), while the outer bar was allowed to evolve. a, b, c, and d corresponding to the incident wave angle θ of 0°, 10°, 20° and 30°, respectively.

3 RESULTS AND DISCUSSIONS

3.1 First set of computations

Figure 2 presents the modeled bathymetries after a 10-day simulation initiated from the original double-bar bathymetry, as shown in Figure 1. From Figure 2 it could be visualized that these 4 modeled bathymetries show remarkable differences in comparison with each other with different incident wave angles θ (0°, 10°, 20°, and 30°, respectively). As the incident wave angle increases, the crescentic patterns for both the inner and outer bars are not distinguished, and they tend to become alongshore uniform. When the incident wave angle is small, such as in Figure 2a and Figure 2b (the wave angle is 0° and 10°, respectively), obvious crescentic patterns can be found at the inner and outer bars, and the bays (horns) in the inner bar are always corresponding to the bays (horns) in the outer bar, that means the in-phase-coupling of bars is strong. In contrast, as the incident wave angle gets larger, such as in Figure 2c and Figure 2d (the wave angle is 20° and 30°, respectively), the inner and outer bars are almost alongshore uniform, then the inner and outer bar coupling is weak.

More details about the alongshore variability and the bar-coupling can be known through the wavelet analysis. Figure 3a and Figure 3b show the alongshore depth line Z_{inner} and Z_{outer} for the inner and outer bar morphology in Figure 2a, while in Figure 4a and Figure 4b we show the local wavelet spectrum and wavelet-squared coherency value for Z_{inner} and Z_{outer}, respectively. Figure 4a indicates that both Z_{inner} and Z_{outer} contain significant high intensity at $\lambda = 900$ m, where the wavelet-squared coherency value is around 0.90 in Figure 4b, then we can quantify the inner and outer bars coupling degree in Figure 2a as a value of 0.92. The details about the relation between wave angle and the degree of bar-coupling are demonstrated in Figure 5.

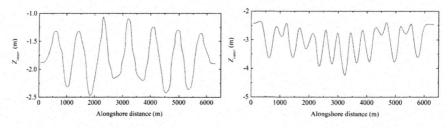

Figure 3. The alongshore depth line of bars in Figure 2a. (a) Alongshore depth line Z_{inner}. (b) Alongshore depth line Z_{outer}.

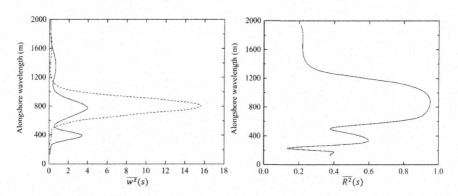

Figure 4. Wavelet analysis of bars. (a) Alongshore-averaged wavelet spectra $\overline{W^z}(s)$ (corresponding to Figure 3a for Z_{inner} and Figure 3b for Z_{outer}. (b) Alongshore-averaged wavelet-coherency squared $\overline{R^2}(s)$ between Z_{inner} and Z_{outer}.

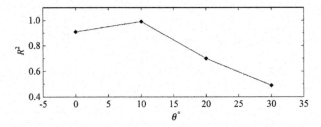

Figure 5. The relationship between the incident wave angle and the inner and outer bar coupling degree for the first set of computations. The horizontal coordinate means the incident wave angle, and the vertical coordinate means the wavelet-squared coherency value for the bars.

Following those analyses above, it can be found that the inner-outer bar coupling can be greatly affected by the incident wave angle θ. A significant increase in the coupling is observed as θ increases from 0° to 10°. Here, an interesting fact can be observed. At the process of the incident wave angle increasing from 0° to 30°, the coupling increases at first, but as θ continues to increase, the coupling decreases and keep at a relatively low level. The simulated relationship between θ and inner and outer bars coupling agrees with the study by Thiebot (2012).

3.2 Second set of computations

Pre-existent studies showed that the outer bar geometry can greatly affect the coupling effect. And the works above show that for the different incident wave angles, the resulting outer bar geometries are different too, and as the wave angles increase, the resulting outer bar geometries

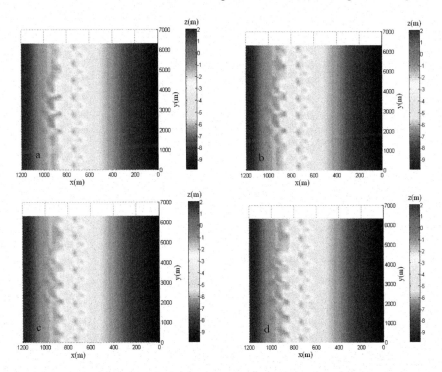

Figure 6. Final bar morphology after a 10-day simulation period ($H = 2.0$ m and $T = 6$ s) starting from the initial bathymetry shown in Figure 1, while the outer bar was fixed without deformation. a, b, c, and d corresponding to the incident wave angle of 0°, 10°, 20°, and 30°, respectively.

tend to become alongshore uniform. To remove the influence of the difference in the resulting outer bar geometries (caused by the different θ), and to further analyze the influence of wave angle itself on the bar-coupling. In this section, the morphology of the outer bar is set as fixed.

In this section, the incident wave angles are also selected as 0°, 10°, 20°, and 30°, respectively, and the incident wave height and wave period are always constant, with $H = 2$ m and $T = 6$ s. Figure 6 shows the four final bathymetries which result from 10-day wave forcing on the initial double sandbar bathymetry as shown in Figure 1. It could be visualized from Figure 6 that the inner bar alongshore morphology variability becomes larger as the incident wave angle θ increases. When θ is 0°, in Figure 6a, we notice that an obvious deformation of the inner bar can only be found at the alongshore coordinate between 2,000 m and 4,500 m. As the incident wave angle continues to increase, such as $\theta = 20°$ and 30°, the deformation of the inner bar becomes more obvious. Especially in Figure 6d, obvious crescentic shapes can be found almost along the whole inner bar. The above feature illustrates that under a large incident angle, the inner bar development is strongly relevant to the outer bar, proving a strong out-of-phase coupling between bars.

Additionally, Figure 6 also presents that as the incident wave angle θ becomes larger, the alongshore variability of the inner bar gets larger, too. This conclusion is different from that of the first set of computations above, in which the outer bar is not fixed. To shed lighter, the results of wavelet analysis are shown in Figure 7. For θ from 0°, 10°, 20° to 30°, the wavelet-squared coherency values for the bars are 0.65, 0.82, 0.83, and 0.9, respectively. If the outer bar is fixed without deformation, as θ increases, the alongshore morphological variability of the inner bar tends to develop from alongshore uniform to crescentic patterns, and the newly developed crescentic pattern for the inner bar is corresponding to that of the outer one, meaning the bar-coupling effect increases too. This conclusion is different from that in the first set of computations above.

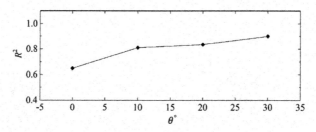

Figure 7. Relationship between the incident wave angle and the inner and outer bar coupling degree for the second set of computations. The horizontal coordinate means the incident wave angle, and the vertical coordinate means the wavelet-squared coherency value for the inner and outer bars.

4 CONCLUSIONS

In this paper, a quasi-3D beach evolution model NearCoM was applied to investigate the influence of wave incident angle on the morphodynamics under a double-sandbar system (inner and outer bars). Some key conclusions are listed as follows.

(1) If the outer bar is movable, when the incident wave angle θ increases, the inner-outer bar coupling effect increases at first, but as θ continues to increase, their coupling effect decreases and keeps at a relatively low level.
(2) On the contrary, if the outer bar is fixed without deformation, the sandbar coupling effect keeps increasing as θ increases. This conclusion shows that the coupling effect is significantly affected by the morphology of the outer bar, which agrees with that proposed in the literature.
(3) Model results show that both incident wave angle θ and the geometry of the outer bar greatly affect the inner-outer bar coupling. The increasing incident wave angle tends to enhance the coupling, while the decreasing morphology complexity of the outer bar tends to weaken the

coupling. If the wave angle increases from 0° to 10°, the increasing θ is the dominant factor. While the wave angle continues to increase from 20° to 30°, the coupling is affected by a competing process including both incident wave angle θ and the outer bar morphology.

The artificial beach is known as an important coastal urban project, and the double-sandbar system could effectively shelter the beach from erosion. Therefore, it is very important to comprehensively understand the morphodynamic response of the double-sandbar system under waves, especially their coupling mechanism. The above results could provide valuable experience to the designing of artificial beaches as well as the evaluation of sheltering effect.

ACKNOWLEDGEMENTS

This work was financially supported by the National Natural Science Foundation of China (Grant No. 52171260), and the Research Innovation Fund of Tianjin Research Institute for Water Transport Engineering (Grant No. TKS20200401).

REFERENCES

Bouharguane, A., Azerad, P., Bouchette, F., Marche, F., Mohammadi, B. 2010. Low complexity shape optimization & a posteriori high fidelity validation. *Discrete and Continuous Dynamical Systems, Series B*, 13, 759–772.

Castelle, B., Bonneton, P., Dupuis, H., Sénéchal, N. 2007. Double bar beach dynamics on the high-energy meso-macro tidal French Aquitanian Coast: a review. *Marine Geology*, 245 (1), 141–159.

Cheng, J. & P. Wang (2018). Dynamic equilibrium of sandbar position and height along a low wave energy micro-tidal coast. *Continental Shelf Research*, 165: 120–136.

Dudkowska, A., Boruń, B., Malicki, J., Schönhofer, J., Gic-Grusza, G. Rip currents in the non-tidal surf zone with sandbars: numerical analysis versus field measurements. *Oceanologia*, 2020, 62 (3): 291–308.

Gu, Z., Zhang, C., and Zheng, J (2016). Influences of wave forcing and morphological variability on the evolution of a double-sandbar system. *Journal of Engineering for the Maritime Environment*, 230 (3): 467–480.

Kim, D. H., Sanchez-Arcilla, A., Caceres, I (2017). Depth-integrated modelling on onshore and offshore sandbar migration: Revision of fall velocity. *Ocean Modelling*, 15: 21–31.

Masselink, G (2004). Formation and evolution of multiple intertidal bars on macrotidal beaches: application of a morphodynamic model. *Coastal Engineering*, 51 (8), 713–730.

Mulligan, R. P., Gomes, E. R., Miselis, J. L., McNinch, J. E (2019). Non-hydrostatic numerical modelling of nearshore wave transformation over shore-oblique sandbars. *Estuarine, Coastal and Shelf Science*, 5: 151–160.

Price, T. D., Rutten, J., Ruessink, B. G (2011). Coupled behaviour within a double sandbar system. *Journal of Coastal Research* SI64, 125–129.

Ruessink, B. G. & J. H. J. Terwindt (2000). The behaviour of nearshore bars on the time scale of years: a conceptual model. Marine Geology, 163 (1), 289–302.

Ruessink, B. G., Coco, G., Ranasinghe, R., Turner, I. L (2007). Coupled and noncoupled behavior of three-dimensional morphological patterns in a double sandbar system. Journal of Geophysical Research: *Oceans* (1978–2012), 112 (C7).

Smit, M. W. J., Reniers, A. J. H. M., Ruessink, B. G., Roelvink, J. A (2008). The morphological response of a nearshore double sandbar system to constant wave forcing. *Coastal Engineering*, 55 (10), 761–770.

Splinter, K. D., Gonzalez, M. V. G., Oltman-Shay, J., Ruttern, J., Holman, R (2018). Observations and modelling of shoreline and multiple sandbar behaviour on a high-energy meso-tidal beach. *Continental Shelf Research*, 159: 33–45.

Thiebot, J., Idier, D., Garnier, R., Falqués, A., Ruessink, B. G. 2012. The influence of wave direction on the morphological response of a double sandbar system. *Continental Shelf Research*, 32, 71–85.

Numerical simulation study on the stability of four-story slope under rainfall infiltration conditions

Yifei Zhang* & Junrui Chai*
State Key Laboratory Base of Eco-hydraulic in Northwest Arid Area, Xi'an University of Technology, Xi'an, China

ABSTRACT: The stability of unsaturated slopes under heavy rainfall is an important issue in hydraulic and geotechnical engineering. Based on unsaturated soil theory and considering the influence of the rainfall cycle and rainfall, this study analyzes the four-layer heterogeneous slope; explores the relevant laws of slope seepage, stress, and displacement fields; and evaluates the stability of the slope. Results show that the pore water pressure in the slope, the groundwater level, and the soil moisture content increase, and the effective stress, the shear strength, and the slope stability decrease with the rise in rainfall intensity. The safety factor of the slope will still decrease after the rainfall stops until the slope becomes unstable.

1 INTRODUCTION

The large-scale construction of railways and highways, water conservancy projects, and long-distance tunnel projects in recent years has resulted in a period of a high incidence of landslide disasters (Zeng 2017). The main external factors that cause landslides are precipitation, temperature, humidity, solar radiation, and wind. Any change in one of the abovementioned influencing factors will cause changes in soil moisture content and pore water pressure state inside the slope, which affects the stress state and stability of the slope; this condition ultimately results in slope instability and landslide accidents (Nicotera 2013). Rainfall is an important factor that induces landslide disasters. Among the influencing factors, rainfall is the most critical external affecting factor of landslide disasters (Yang 2017).

Given the influence of rainfall factors, scholars mainly analyze the stability of the slope through the relative changes in the seepage field in the slope, combined with the limit equilibrium method (Lei 2020; Shi 2016). The relationship between the internal seepage and stress fields in the rock and soil mass is ignored. In the actual seepage process, the change in pore water pressure will destroy the original equilibrium state of the rock and soil body, which causes the change in the skeleton stress of the rock and soil body; this condition will ultimately lead to the deformation of the rock and soil body. Meanwhile, the rock and soil bodies will be deformed. The deformation will affect the pressure and distribution of pore fluid. The interaction between the seepage and stress fields developing with time is called fluid-structure interaction (Wang 2020). The essence of slope stability is the coupling of seepage and stress fields (Sun 2012). At present, scholars mainly use the direct coupling method to calculate the double-field coupling. The direct coupling method can simultaneously combine the seepage field–stress field governing equations, and it can iteratively calculate the seepage and stress fields by the finite element algorithm. The results are relatively precise. Chai (2004) conducted a coupling analysis on the seepage and stress fields of a Xietan landslide in the Three Gorges Reservoir area, and the author concluded that the coupling effect slightly affects the seepage field but greatly affects the stress field. Chen (2020) established a

---

*Corresponding Authors: zhangyifei19980520@163.com and jrchai@xaut.edu.cn

rainfall-induced shallow landslide model and used the finite element analysis of fluid-solid coupling to simulate the entire progressive failure process of rainfall-induced landslide instability. Wang (2007) took the collapsing and sliding deposits as an engineering example; obtained the variation laws of the stress, displacement, and seepage fields of the slope; and discussed the deformation and instability mechanism of the landslide considering the coupling effect of the stress and seepage fields.

Based on previous studies, this work investigates the stability of four-layer heterogeneous slopes under heavy rain conditions. The relevant theory of unsaturated soil is also used to study the effects of rainfall cycles on the seepage field, stress field, displacement field, and stability of the slope.

2 THEORIES

2.1 Unsaturated seepage theory

For unsaturated soils, the permeability coefficient is not a fixed value, and the change can be generalized as a function of volumetric water content or matrix suction (Fredlund 2015). For the soil-water characteristic curve, that is, the function of matrix suction and volumetric water content, this paper uses the Van Genuchten model (Fredlund 2015) to fit the soil-water characteristic curve. Its control equation is as follows:

$$\theta_w = \theta_r + \frac{\theta_s - \theta_r}{\left[1 + \left(\frac{\psi}{a}\right)^n\right]^m} \quad (1)$$

where θ_w is the volumetric water content; θ_r is the residual water content; θ_s is the saturated volumetric water content; ψ is the negative pore water pressure; a, n, and m are the fitting parameters of the soil-water characteristic curve.

For the permeability coefficient of unsaturated soil, Van Genuchten proposed (Fredlund 2015) that the permeability coefficient is a function of matrix suction:

$$k_w = k_s \frac{\left[1 - (a\psi^{n-1})(1 + (a\psi^n)^{-m})\right]^2}{\left((1 + a\psi^n)^{\frac{m}{2}}\right)} \quad (2)$$

where k_s is the saturated permeability coefficient; a, n, and m are the fitting parameters of the soil-water characteristic curve, and $n = 1/(1-m)$; ψ is the required matrix suction range. This formula shows that the permeability coefficient function of the soil can be derived after the saturated permeability coefficient of the soil and the two fitted parameters are obtained.

2.2 Theory of shear strength of unsaturated soils

2.2.1 Fredlund's theories of shear strength

Fredlund (1978) proposed that two of the three stress state variables can be used to describe the shear strength formula of unsaturated soils.

$$\tau_f = c' + (\sigma - \mu_a)\tan(\varphi') + (\mu_a - \mu_w)\tan(\varphi^b) \quad (3)$$

where c' is the effective cohesion; φ' is the effective internal friction angle; $(\sigma - \mu_a)$ is the net normal stress; $(\mu_a - \mu_w)$ is the suction force of the matrix; φ^b is the suction force with the matrix $(\mu_a - \mu_w)$, which is related to the parameter representing the rate at which the shear strength increases with increasing matrix suction.

The abovementioned formula shows that the net normal stress and the matrix suction are two independent stress state variables, and the two cannot be added together.

3 NUMERICAL STUDIES

3.1 *Slope model and parameter selection*

The slope is located on the back hill of the town government of Luoyang Town, Guangxi (Lv 2020). Figure 1 shows the finite element calculation model of the slope. The finite element meshing adopts quadrilateral and triangular elements, with 466 nodes and 422 elements. Seven monitoring nodes are selected inside the slope and on the slope to better analyze the variation law of seepage and stress fields. The four rock and soil material parameters of the four-layer slope are shown in Table 1.

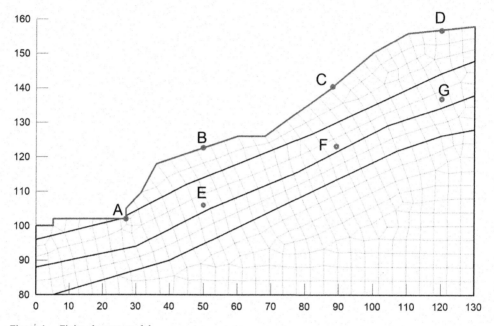

Figure 1. Finite element model.

Table 1. Physical parameters of rock mass in a four-layer numerical slope model.

Name	Volumetric weight (kN·m^{-3})	Cohesive forces (kPa)	The angle of internal friction (°)	Saturated water capacity (%)	Saturated hydraulic conductivity (m·s^{-1})	Poisson's ratio	Elastic modulus (MPa)
Residual layer	19	26	19.7	27.7	7.995*10^{-6}	0.31	23.5
Full regolith	19.11	18.7	16	27	6.08*10^{-5}	0.3	26
Strong regolith	19.5	24.2	21.4	25.2	2.28*10^{-5}	0.27	38.2
Middle regolith	26.7	180	33	5	1*10^{-6}	0.33	1000

According to the local rainfall conditions, the rainfall conditions in this study are set as follows: the total calculation time is 8 days, the first 6 days are the rainfall time, and the 6th to 8th days are the rain stop period; the maximum rainfall is 200 mm/d (simulating heavy rain conditions). The types of different rainfalls are shown in Figure 2.

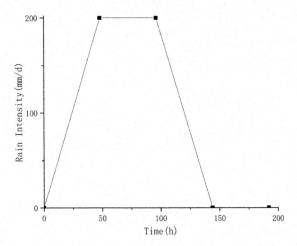

Figure 2. Rain type.

3.2 Seepage field analysis

Figure 3 shows the pore water pressure cloud map of days 0 to 8. As shown in the figure, the pore water pressure inside the entire slope increases, and the groundwater level continues to rise as time progresses. After the rain stops, part of the water in the soil will be discharged, and the pore water pressure will rise. On day 5, the water level is close to the level of the foot of the slope. The reason is that the foot of the slope receives not only rainfall but also rainwater collected by gravity on the upper four slopes. Moreover, the slope closest to the foot of the slope is steeper, which results in the

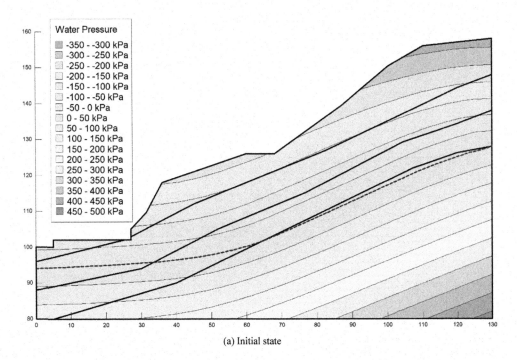

(a) Initial state

Figure 3. Contour map of pore water pressure distribution in different periods.

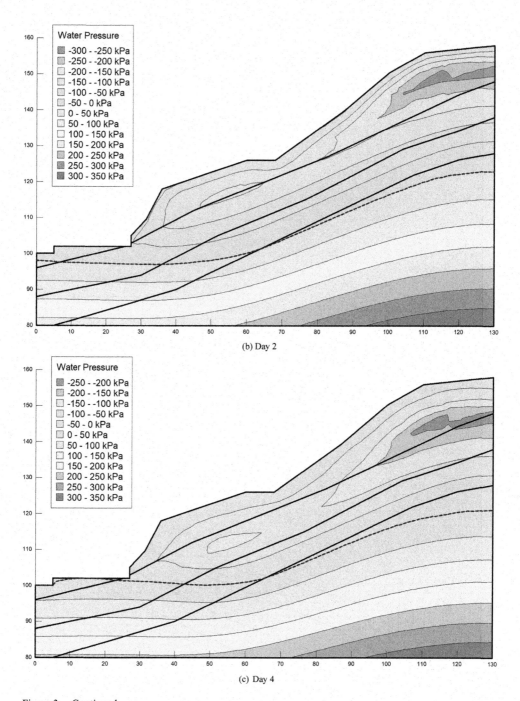

Figure 3. Continued.

high rise of groundwater level in this place. In the calculation, the water at the level of the toe of the slope will flow out in the form of runoff after the 5th day. The contours on the surface of the slope are dense, and the central area of the slope forms a closed area of pore water pressure contours that decreases with time and shifts to the right. The reason is that a certain hydraulic gradient

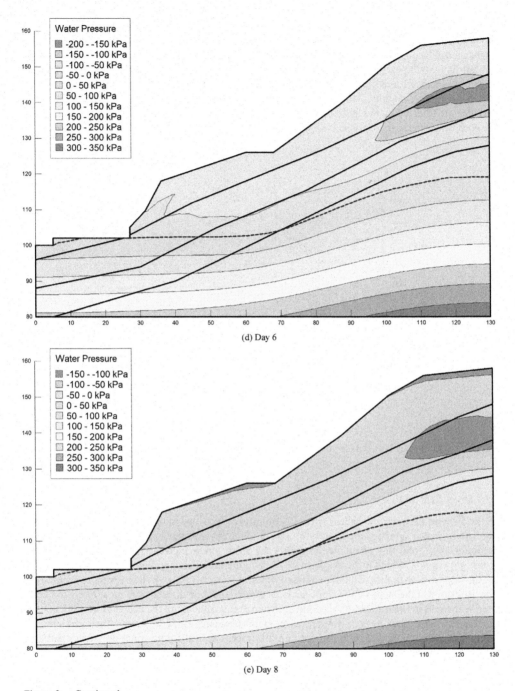

Figure 3. Continued.

exists between the layers of the finite element model, and the early rainfall increases suddenly. Furthermore, the shallow soil will soon reach saturation, while the deep soil has not been affected. With the increase in time and during rainfall, the wetting front moves down, the water stored in the shallow soil reaches the deep soil area, and a certain hysteresis occurs.

The pore water pressure of each monitoring node is shown in Figure 4. Point A is located at the level of the toe of the slope. Thus, its hole pressure is close to 0 on the 5th day and remains unchanged. The pore water pressure at points B, C, and D on the slope increases rapidly when the rainfall rises in the early stage, and it reaches a stable value. On the 2nd to 6th day, the rainfall remains unchanged, and the pore water pressure increases slowly. After the rainfall stops, the pore pressure decreases slightly. Points E, F, and G are located in the middle and lower part of the slope, and they are affected by the hydraulic gradient and elevation between different layers. As a result, the pore water pressure response is slow.

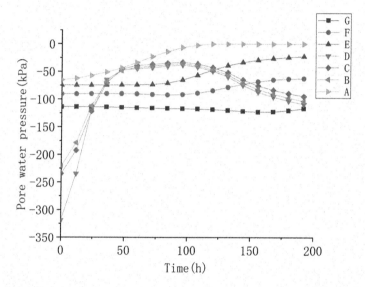

Figure 4. Relationship between the pore water pressure of each monitoring point and time.

3.3 Stress field analysis

Figure 5 shows the maximum shear stress distribution of the slope in the initial state and on the 8th day. The soil layer on the slope absorbs a large amount of rainwater with the continuous increase in rainfall time, and this phenomenon makes the shear stress increase rapidly. Point A has the fastest growth rate, which increases from 261 kPa in the initial state to 269 kPa on Day 2. Point D has the largest growth rate, which increases from 45 kPa to 116 kPa. A shear stress concentration zone is formed at the steps on the slope surface, where landslide disasters are most likely to occur. The shear stress in the middle of the slope does not change much, but the calculation results of the seepage field show that the pore water pressure at this place increases. Moreover, the shear strength decreases continuously during the whole rainfall process until the pore water pressure stabilizes, and it becomes steady after the rain stops.

Figure 6 shows the displacement of each monitoring point in the X and Y directions. The change in the seepage field leads to the change in pore water pressure, which reduces the shear strength of the stress field and the effective stress. This condition in turn induces the displacement of the slope in the X and Y directions. The figure shows that the horizontal displacement of point A is larger than the vertical displacement. The reason is that point A is located at the horizontal plane of the slope foot, which receives rainwater and rainwater collected by gravity on the right slope. The horizontal displacement increases gradually. After the rainfall stops, the excess water is discharged outward in the form of runoff, and the growth rate of the horizontal displacement slows down. The horizontal displacement of point C is the largest. The reason is that the slope of the slope is the

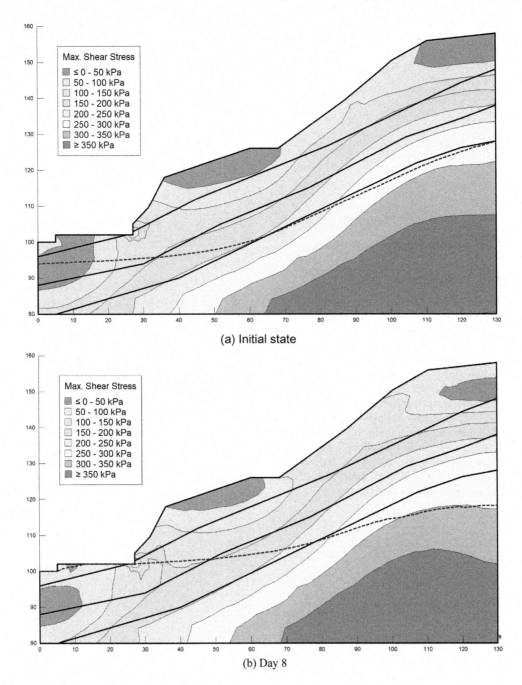

Figure 5. Contour map of maximum shear stress.

largest, no constraint is observed on both sides, and the displacement increases with the decrease in the effective stress. The vertical displacement of point D is the largest. Point D is located at the top surface of the slope body, where the slope is relatively gentle. After this part absorbs rainwater, it is displaced in the vertical direction.

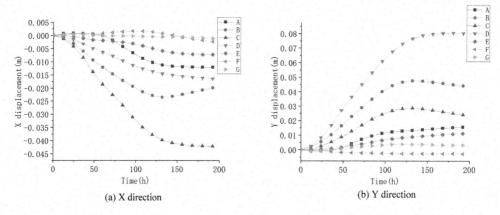

(a) X direction (b) Y direction

Figure 6. Displacement in X and Y directions.

3.4 *Stability analysis*

Figure 7 shows the variation law of the safety factor with time. From 0–48 h, the rainfall gradually increases, and the safety factor gradually decreases. At 48–96 h, the rainfall remains unchanged, and the decline rate of the safety factor slows down. At 96–144 h, the rainfall decreases, and the safety factor continues to decline. At 144–192 h, the rain stops, but the safety factor will continue to decrease until it decreases to 0.9624 and then increases again to 0.988. When the rainfall stops, the shallow soil gradually dehumidifies and the pore water pressure dissipates. An order of magnitude difference is observed in the permeability coefficient between the slope layers. Thus, the water dissipation response in the soil layer is slow. Subsequently, the pore water pressure of the deep soil body gradually dissipates, and the safety factor will rise to a certain extent. Under heavy rain conditions, a large amount of rainwater infiltrates, which causes the groundwater level to rise rapidly and the shear strength of the soil in the sliding zone to decrease. At the same time, the pore water pressure of the soil on the slope surface and the volumetric water content increase, which makes the saturation bulk density rise. Therefore, the sliding force of the entire slope increases, and the slope is in an unstable state.

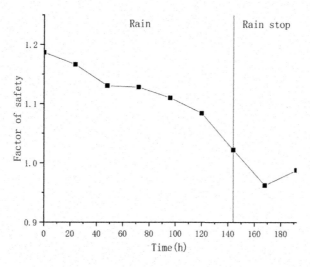

Figure 7. Relationship between slope safety factor and time.

4 CONCLUSIONS

The stability of the four-layer slope is studied in this work based on the seepage–stress coupling principle. The effects of the rainfall cycle and rainfall intensity on the seepage and stress fields of the slope are analyzed, and the conclusions are as follows:

1. The process of the destruction of slope stability by the rainfall process can be summarized as follows: 1) Rainfall makes the surface soil of the slope respond first, and the effective stress decreases rapidly, which in turn reduces the anti-sliding force and the slope stability. 2) With the continuous increase in rainfall time, the continuous collection of rainwater at the horizontal plane of the slope toe increases the horizontal displacement of the slope toe, which causes instability and failure. 3) The soil in the middle and rear of the slope is vertical at high places. The soil in these locations loses support because the leading edge has been destabilized and damaged. Furthermore, the saturated bulk density is reached due to the absorption of water, which results in a large sliding force; this condition ultimately causes the overall landslide disaster on the slope.
2. The safety factor of the slope decreases continuously when it encounters heavy rainfall. When the rain stops for a period, the surface layer of the slope responds quickly to rainfall, the deep soil responds slowly, and the upper rainwater is still infiltrating due to the hydraulic gradient in the permeability coefficient between the soil layers. As a result, the safety factor is still decreasing. Then, the pore water pressure in the slope gradually dissipates, and the slope safety factor gradually recovers. The slope is vulnerable to damage at this stage. Therefore, strengthening the monitoring of data of pore water pressure and water content in the slope is necessary when the rain stops for some time.

The research suggests that relevant indoor artificial rainfall models and soil centrifuge tests should be conducted. The test and numerical simulation results should also be combined to better verify the reliability of the numerical analysis. The influence of cracks on the seepage and stress fields of the slope should be explored as well based on stress coupling analysis.

REFERENCES

C. Junrui, L. Shouyi (2004) Couple analysis of seepage and stress fields in xietan landslide in three gorges region *Chinese Journal of Rock Mechanics and Engineering* **08**: 1280–1284.
C. X. (2020) Modelling rainfall-induced landslides from initiation of instability to post-failure *Computers and Geotechnics*, **129 (3)**.
Fredlund D G, Morgenstern N R and Widger R A. (1978) The shear strength of unsaturated soils *Canadian Geotechnical Journal* **15 (3)**: 313–321.
Fredlund D G. (2015) Unsaturated soil mechanics. Higher Education Press, BeiJing.
L. Wenkai, D. Hongyuan, C. Pan et al. (2020) Improved Green-Ampt infiltration model of soil slope considering inclination *HYDRO-SCIENCE and ENGINEERING* **184 (06)**: 104–110.
L. Yuhua. (2020) Study on the stability of unsaturated soil slope under rainfall conditions Guilin university of technology.
Nicotera S (2013) Unsaturated soil mechanics in rainfall-induced flow landslides *Eng Geol*.
S X, In L J, L J, et al. (2012) Coupling numerical analysis of seepage and stress fields after excavation of slope *Procedia Engineering* **28 (none)**: 336–340.
S. Zhenming, S. Danwei, P. Ming et al. (2016) Slope stability analysis by considering rainfall infiltration in multi-layered unsaturated soils. *Journal of Hydraulic Engineering* **47 (008)**: 977–985.
W. Bin, T. Huiming, Z. Jiebing, X. Wei and L. Jun (2007) Deformation and failure mechanisms of reservoir landslide considering fluid-solid coupling effect *Chinese Journal of Rock Mechanics and Engineering* **(S2)**: 4484–4489.
W. Li, W. Shimei, W. Lin, L. (2020) Research status and prospect of fluid-solid coupling of reservoir landslide *Water Resources and Power* **38 (01)**: 143–146+31.
Yang Z, Qiao J, Uchimura T, Wang L, Lei X and Huang D (2017) Unsaturated hydro-mechanical behaviour of rainfall-induced mass remobilization in post-earthquake landslides. *Eng Geol* **222**: 102–110.
Zeng L, Bian H B, Shi Z N, et al (2017) Forming condition of transient saturated zone and its distribution in residual slope under rainfall conditions *Journal of Central South University*. **24 (008)**: 1866–1880.

Ship-bridge collision analysis of the Wuhan Yangtze River Bridge based on finite element method

Shiheng Jin*
Department of Physics, University of California, Santa Barbara, CA, USA

ABSTRACT: Until the end of 2011, the Wuhan Yangtze River Bridge had undergone 76 times of ship-bridge collisions, and it is urged to explore the influence of collision accidents on the structural safety of the bridge. In this paper, finite element software ABAQUS is applied for numerical analysis of a typical Wuhan Yangtze River Bridge's ship-bridge collision case on June 6th, 2011. Through modal analysis of the benchmark model of the Wuhan Yangtze River Bridge and comparing the obtained first ten modes' fundamental frequencies with existing measured results, the parameters of the benchmark model are ameliorated, and its accuracy can be verified. The theoretical collision force is acquired by three standard ship-bridge collision formulas, applied as a body force, and exerted on the specific pier of the bridge. From the total deformation results under the above loads, it is concluded that the deformation caused by the collision force is trivial on both pier and the main bridge. On June 6th, 2011, the ship-bridge collision event had an insignificant effect on the structural safety of the Wuhan Yangtze River Bridge.

1 INTRODUCTION

As bridge collapse accidents occurred frequently around the world, bridge safety has become the focus of bridge design and maintenance (Peng et al. 2019; Zhou 2014). Wuhan Yangtze River Bridge (WYRB) is the first facility erected on the Yangtze River by the People's Republic of China. It had stood firmly for 65 years and is considered a representative construction that combined both technological and cultural significance (Xu et al. 2010). With meticulous construction technology and high-quality construction materials, WYRB still maintains structural stability and intact function after a long service time. Nevertheless, the structural safety of the WYRB still needs to be tested and guaranteed due to long-lasting negative factors such as natural aging of the structure, increasing vehicle load, and adverse environment. Among them, frequent ship collisions are the main challenge of WYRB. Restricted to the construction techniques in the 1950s, WYRB was designed to be supported by eight densely placed piers. The distribution of piers increased the possibility of ship-bridge collision, and from 1957 to 2011, WYRB had undergone such accidents for 76 times. The collision with the largest ship tonnage occurred on June 6, 2011, when an over 10,000-ton fleet crossed the Wuhan Yangtze River Bridge and collided head-on with the No. 7 bridge pier (Zhu 2012). Nevertheless, currently, the existing research on WYRB mainly focuses on the bridge health status and safety assessment system analysis, which is associated with the monitoring method design and information collection of WYRB, and targeted research on individual ship collision cases is omitted. Among that research, Du et al. (2015) designed a specific method of using sensors and other monitoring data acquisition systems to conduct long-term health monitoring of WYRB. Based on the system and obtained data from Du et al., Wang (2018) used the finite element model to analyze the behavior of the bridge under the influence of temperature

---

*Corresponding Author: shiheng@ucsb.edu

load and train load. Besides, on the aspect of ship-bridge collision, Zhou (2004) studied the effect of water level and impact angle on ship collision and proposed the selection and design of anticollision devices for the bridge. Generally, there is still a lack of targeted research on the impact of specific ship collision cases on bridge structure safety. Therefore, according to the current research situation, this paper will focus on the effect of the ship collision accident on June 6, 2011, on WYRB. The main contents of this paper include establishing the finite element benchmark model of the third bay of WYRB, and comparing and optimizing the mode frequencies obtained by modal analysis with the measured data in the literature (Wang 2018). And for the ship collision accident in June 2011, the standard formulas of ship collision force are used to calculate the theoretical impact forces, which will be exerted on bridge pier No. 7 as static effects to examine its influence on the bridge structure safety.

2 FINITE ELEMENT MODAL ANALYSIS

2.1 Engineering overview

The Wuhan Yangtze River Bridge (Figure 1) is located between Guishan Mountain and Snake Mountain in Wuhan, China. Construction of the bridge began in September 1955 and opened to traffic in October 1957. WYRB is 1,670.4 meters long and consists of the main bridge, approach bridge, and abutments. The main bridge is 1155.5 meters long, supported by eight piers, and divided into three bays. The main bridge is a double-deck steel truss bridge for highway and railway. The upper pavement is 18 meters wide, and there are 2.5 meters wide sidewalks on both sides. The lower level is a railway bridge with a width of 14 meters. The main girder of the bridge is a flat-string diamond truss, 16 meters high, 10 meters from the girder. Each truss hole is divided into eight large intersections (the interval between two adjacent points on the chord where the belly bar intersects), and each intersection has a length of 16 meters. Steel truss beam material is Q235 I-shape steel (Bai 2014; Xu et al. 2010; Zhou 2004).

Figure 1. The Wuhan Yangtze River Bridge.

The main bridge has eight piers and two abutments. The construction of the bridge pier adopted concrete-filled steer tubular columns. As pier No. 7 is placed on carbonaceous shale, a total of 116 tubular columns with a diameter of 0.55 meters are used as the foundation. The remaining piers are 1.55 m in diameter, and each pier consists of 30 or 35 tubular columns, which drill into the rock layer to a depth of 2 m to 7 m. The lowest height of the pier from the base to the pier cap is 47 meters, and the highest is 64 meters, with a clearance of 18 meters. Most of the eight piers adopt gravity solid plain concrete piers made of 15 MPa (C15) grade concrete. The designed bearing impact force is 1,500 kN longitudinally and 3,000 kN horizontally (Bai 2014; Zhu 2012).

2.2 Finite element model of the Wuhan Yangtze River Bridge

In this paper, finite element analysis software ABAQUS is applied to the modeling of WYRB. As the structure of the bridge's three bays is identical, the third bay contains pier No. 7 (struck by a barge in the accident on June 6th, 2011) is selected as the research object. To analyze the steel truss structure of the bridge, the upper and lower decks are simplified and treated as load without structural modeling. According to the *Technical Standard of Highway Engineering*, the automobile load of WYRB can be assumed as a uniform load of 10 kN/m without considering the dynamic action, which is exerted on the beams and upper chords as a linear load (Wang 2018).

The length of the third bay is 384 meters, and the width of each span is 128 meters. Its schematic diagram is shown in Figure 2. In the established model, the material of beam elements is Q235 steel, with a density of 7,850 kg/m^3, Young's modulus of 200 GPa, Poisson's ratio of 0.3 v, and yield stress of 235 MPa. The beam elements are assigned to the upper and lower chords, vertical and diagonal bars, highway and railway beams, and top and bottom lateral bracings. The bridge beam is 16 meters high, and each truss section is 16 meters apart (Bai 2014). The Mesh element type of truss structure is B31. The finite element model of the third bay truss structure of the main bridge is shown in Figure 3, and the overall model, boundary condition, and load condition are present in Figure 4.

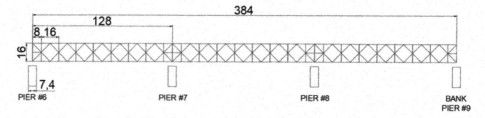

Figure 2. Schematic diagram of the third bay of WYRB.

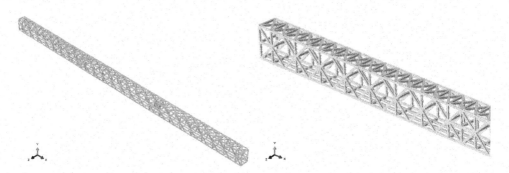

Figure 3. Finite element model of the truss structure. Overall truss structure (left) and details (right).

In this study, finite element models of bridge piers No. 6, 7, 8, and abutment No. 9 of WYRB are established according to actual geometric dimensions. Material properties of models reflect the real condition. The bridge pier is made of C15 concrete material (Zhu 2012), with a material density of 2,500 kg/m^3, Young's modulus of 22 GPa, Poisson's ratio of 0.16 v, and yield stress of 15 MPa. The beam units at the corresponding position of each pier and the main bridge are tied together. The mesh element type of piers parts is C3D8R. The finite element model and mesh division of the bridge pier is shown in Figure 5.

Figure 4. Overall model, boundary condition, and load condition.

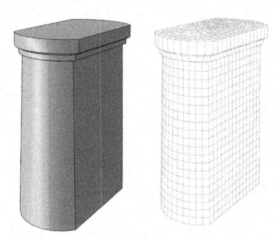

Figure 5. Finite element model and mesh division of bridge pier.

2.3 *Modal analysis*

The bridge's fundamental frequency obtained by finite element modal analysis is compared with the measured data. According to the monitoring data acquisition systems of WYRB designed by Du et al. (2015), the horizontal natural vibration frequency of the structure is generally within the range of 0.82 to 1.5 Hz, and the vertical natural vibration frequency from 1.5 to 2.3 Hz. Based on these actual measurements and more precise results, Wang (2018) made an advanced modal analysis through ANSYS and provided detailed first ten-mode fundamental frequency data of the third bay of WYRB, which has reference significance for the verification of the benchmark model's accuracy in this analysis. A more accurate finite element reference model is obtained by comparing the model's modal behavior with the theoretical results and finely adjusting the material parameters. The young's modulus of structural material is adjusted to calibrate the model until the fundamental frequency of the model is consistent with the measured data. After model calibration, the first ten orders of modal frequencies and modal shapes of the benchmark model are obtained. The frequencies and comparisons of the first ten modes are shown in Table 1 and Figure 6.

Table 1. Frequency data and contrast for the first ten modes.

Mode	Abaqus Mode Frequency (Hz)	Ansys Mode Frequency (Hz)
1	0.8235	0.9433
2	0.8593	0.9824
3	0.9284	1.1274
4	1.9001	1.7084
5	1.9301	1.8312
6	1.9903	1.9595
7	2.0334	2.2084
8	2.1896	2.2325
9	2.3322	2.5598
10	2.3900	2.6734

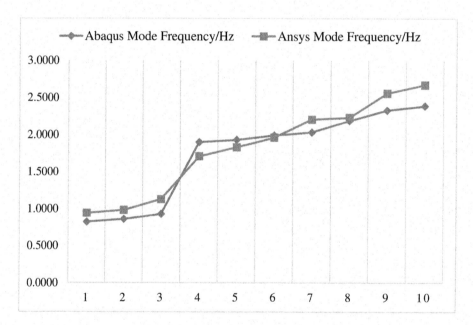

Figure 6. Frequency contrast diagram of the first ten modes.

As the numerical results are relatively close and the frequency performance shows almost the same pattern as the reference data, the first ten modes' frequency of the finite element model is consistent with Wang's data (2018). By analyzing the effective mass data from the Abaqus frequency analysis step field output, it is found that the first-order transverse fundamental frequency of the finite element model is 0.8235 Hz. The first vertical vibration frequency is 2.1896 Hz. The first ten modes' performance is shown in Table 2 and Figure 7. This data is consistent with the measured test report data of the bridge, that is, the transverse fundamental frequency is 0.82 to 1.5 Hz, and the vertical fundamental frequency is 1.5 to 2.3 Hz (Du et al., 2015). The above comparison shows that the adjusted finite element model can provide an approximate reference for further ship-bridge collision simulation experiments.

Table 2. Performance of the first ten modes.

Mode	Fundamental frequency (Hz)	Modal type
1	0.8235	Lateral
2	0.8593	Torsion
3	0.9284	Lateral bending
4	1.9001	Torsion
5	1.9301	Lateral bending
6	1.9903	Torsion
7	2.0334	Lateral bending
8	2.1896	Vertical bending + torsion
9	2.3322	Torsion
10	2.3900	Vertical bending + torsion

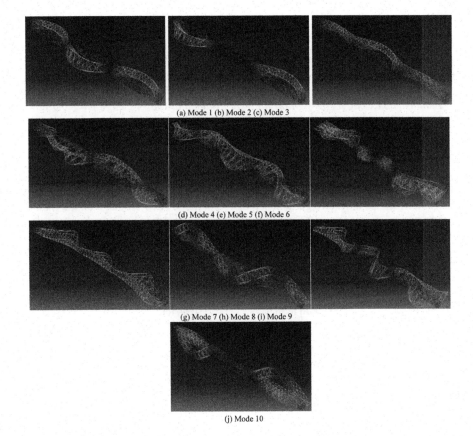

(a) Mode 1 (b) Mode 2 (c) Mode 3

(d) Mode 4 (e) Mode 5 (f) Mode 6

(g) Mode 7 (h) Mode 8 (i) Mode 9

(j) Mode 10

Figure 7. Performance diagram of the first ten modes.

3 FINITE ELEMENT SHIP-BRIDGE COLLISION TEST

3.1 *Ship-bridge collision force standard formulas*

(1) The standard formula of the American Association of State Highway and Transportation Officials (AASHTO 2012):

$$P = 0.98 \, (DWT)^{1/2} \, (V/8) \qquad (1)$$

where P is the magnitude of impact force (MN), DWT represents the deadweight tonnage of the ship (t), and V refers to the impact velocity of the ship (m/s).

(2) The European standard formula (ACWM 2017) is:

$$P = V(KM)^{1/2} \qquad (2)$$

where V is the velocity of the colliding body at the time of impact (m/s), and K is the equivalent stiffness of the collision body, that is, the stiffness of the ship. For inland ships, $K = 5$ MN/m, and for ocean-going ships, $K=15$ MN/m, where M represents the mass of the collision body (t).

(3) The standard formula of China's Fundamental Code for Design on Railway Bridges and Culverts (Beijing 2017) is:

$$P = \gamma V \sin\alpha \left(\frac{W}{C_1 + C_2}\right)^{1/2} \qquad (3)$$

where γ is the kinetic energy reduction coefficient $s/m^{1/2}$, with a magnitude of 0.3 in the frontal impact and 0.2 in oblique impact. α is the angle formed by the tangent line between the ship's approach direction and the impact point of the pier. V represents the impact velocity of the ship (m/s). W refers to the mass of the colliding ship (MN). C_1 is the elastic deformation coefficient of the ship, and C_2 is the elastic deformation coefficient of the pier body. According to *Fundamental Code for Design on Railway Bridge and Culvert*, $C_1 + C_2$ is 0.5 m/MN in normal conditions, and for piers with significant stiffness, $C_2 \approx 0$.

3.2 *Theoretical estimation of the ship-bridge collision force*

On June 6, 2011, the Yangtze River 62036, a fleet consisting of four barges and a powered tugboat, collided with the No. 7 pier of the Wuhan Yangtze River Bridge. Each barge weighed 3,500 tons, and the entire fleet had a deadweight tonnage of 13,500 tons. The first barge on the right of the fleet head-on collided with the pier. Then in the theoretical calculation by using the above standard formulas, the shipping weight applied is 3500 tons, and the shipping speed is 2 m/s, 3 m/s, and 4 m/s, respectively (Cao et al. 2021). The theoretical magnitudes of ship-bridge collision force are shown in Table 3.

Table 3. Theoretical collision force magnitude.

Ship velocity (m/s)	Standard formula	Peak force (MN)	Average (MN)
2	AASHTO	14.49	9.98
	European standard	10.45	
	China's standard	5.01	
3	AASHTO	21.74	14.98
	European standard	15.67	
	China's standard	7.52	
4	AASHTO	28.99	19.97
	European standard	20.90	
	China's standard	10.02	

3.3 *Numerical analysis and results*

The theoretical collision force of a 3,500-ton barge on WYRB pier 7 under three different velocities is calculated according to the above three ship-bridge collision force standard formulas. The average value of the theoretical peak force was applied to the lower unit of pier No. 7 as a physical force to study the overall effect of the static action on the pier and the third link of the main bridge. The results are shown in Table 4.

According to the results in Table 4, with the initial forward velocity of 2 m/s, the maximum deformation caused by the 3,500-ton barge to the front surface structure of the pier is 0.121 mm. From the cloud map, this impact mainly concentrates on the elements directly subjected to the body force load, which is approximately 2 meters above the water level. As the ship velocity increases from 2 m/s to 3 m/s, the maximum deformation of the central impact zone escalates from 0.121 mm to 0.182 mm. When the ship velocity increases to 4 m/s, the maximum deformation of the major impact zone is 0.242 mm. Furthermore, the cloud diagram shows that the deformation caused by the above collision decays violently in areas other than the central impact zone. The area of the affected region has no noticeable difference under the three initial conditions. Besides, the upper and rear parts of the pier and the truss structure of the main bridge remain unchanged. The order of magnitude of deformation described above has only a slight effect on the pier, so it can be concluded that the three sets of impacts have no significant impact on the bridge structure.

Table 4. Simulation results.

Ship velocity (m/s)	Average force (MN)	Stress nephogram	Maximum deformation (mm)
2	9.98	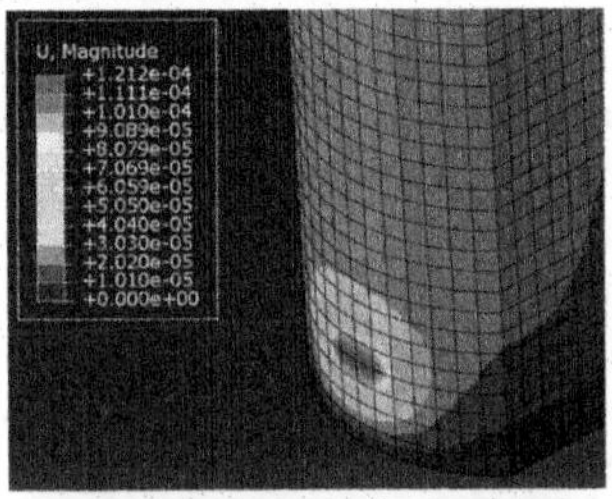	0.121
3	14.98	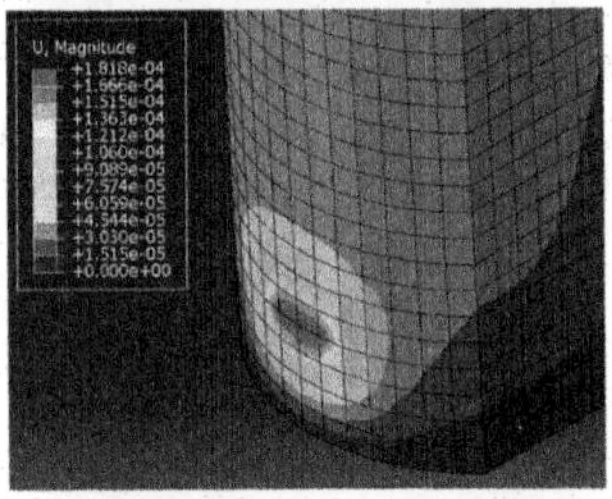	0.182
4	19.97	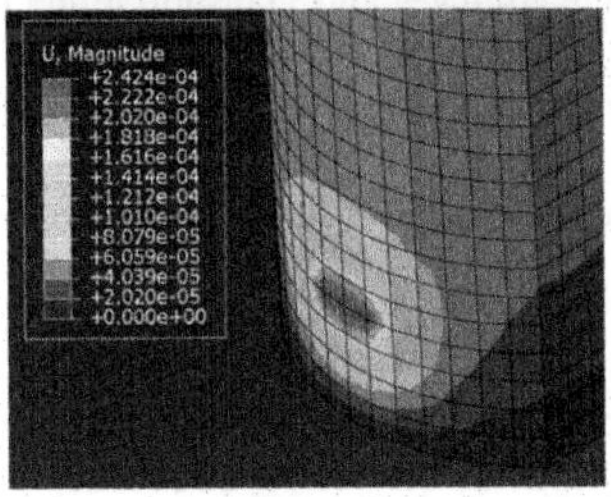	0.242

4 CONCLUSION AND LIMITATION

4.1 *Conclusions*

In this paper, a ship-bridge collision accident case to the third bay of the Wuhan Yangtze River Bridge is analyzed numerically by finite element software ABAQUS. Through modal analysis of the benchmark model, the first ten modes of WYRB's fundamental frequencies are extracted and compared with existing measured data. The first lateral fundamental frequency of the first bridge is 0.8235 Hz, and the first vertical fundamental frequency is 2.1896 Hz. Then the natural frequency of the finite element model is consistent with the measured natural frequency, and the finite element reference model is established correctly.

To examine the influence of the ship-bridge collision accident on June 6, 2011, three ship collision force standard formulas (AASHTO, European standard, China's standard) are used to calculate the theoretical collision force value of 3500-ton barge under velocities of 2, 3, and 4 m/s. The average impact force at each speed is exerted on the lower element (about 2 meters in height) of the bridge pier as a body force, and the magnitude of total deformation is obtained. At the above three ship speeds, the impact force has trivial effects on the front of the pier and almost no influence on the back and the main bridge. The finite element simulation results show that such a collision event is not enough to cause significant harm to the structural safety of the piers and main bridge of the Wuhan Yangtze River Bridge. The research results can provide a reference for the structural safety of the Wuhan Yangtze River Bridge.

4.2 *Limitations*

The modeling focuses on the truss structure of the bridges, and road and railway conditions are omitted. The pile foundation structure under the piers is not reflected in the model. And the environmental effects such as water flow exerted on the piers are not considered in this simulation. All the above elements will affect the accuracy of the benchmark model, which then results in a discrepancy in this numerical analysis.

Besides, ship-collision is represented as body-force load in this simulation, and the deformation behavior of the structure under the ship-bridge collision load only shows its general impact and can be considered as a reference, and the accurate damage model of concrete piers needs further analysis.

The Wuhan Yangtze River Bridge has encountered numeral ship-collision accidents, which might lead to cumulative damage or alteration to the bridge structure. Nevertheless, the simulation of this single event is based on the original condition of the bridge.

REFERENCES

A. C. W. M. Vrouwenvelder (2017). *Design for ship impact according to Eurocode* 1, Part 2.7. Routledge.
American Association of State Highway and Transportation Officials (2012). *AASHTO LRFD bridge design specifications customary U. S. units.*
Bai, L. (2014). *Wuhan Yangtze River Bridge construction from the STS perspective*. Guangxi University for Nationalities.
Beijing: National Railway Administration (2017). *Design code for railway bridges and culverts*. TB10002—2017.
Cao, M. et al. (2021). Finite element simulation of influencing factors of ship-bridge impact force. *J. Disaster Prev Manag.* 41 (3).
Du, Y. et al. (2015). Study on long-term health monitoring and safety assessment system of Wuhan Yangtze River Bridge. *J. China Railway Society* 37 (4) 101–110.
LovePik. Image of Wuhan Yangtze River Bridge https://id.lovepik.com/image-500645084/wuhan-dusk-yangtze-river-bridge.html.
Peng, W. et al. (2019). Review, analysis, and insights on recent typical bridge accidents. Chin. *J. Highway Transport* 32 132–144.
Wang, L. (2018). *Health status analysis and evaluation of Wuhan Yangtze River Bridge*. Shijiazhuang Tiedao University.
Xu, Y. & L. Huang (2010). Interpretation of Wuhan Yangtze River Bridge. *Huazhong Archit.* 28 166–169.
Zhou, X. (2004). *Study on Anti-collision of Pier of Wuhan Yangtze River Bridge*, Southwest Jiaotong University.
Zhu, H. (2012). Reflections on the 76 times collision accidents of Wuhan Yangtze River Bridge. *China Commun.* 2 422–427.

Advances in water system connectivity from 1990 to 2021

Lingzhen Zhang*
Shandong Survey and Design Institute of Water Conservancy, Jinan, China

Yongfei Fu*
School of Water Conservancy and Environment, University of Jinan, Jinan, China

Lu Liu*
Shandong Survey and Design Institute of Water Conservancy, Jinan, China

Yuqing Feng* & Qi Wang*
School of Water Conservancy and Environment, University of Jinan, Jinan, China

ABSTRACT: Water system connection is an extremely important content of water resources management and water conservancy construction. Much literature focused on different directions and research issues, lacking systematic bibliometric statistics. To analyze the current situation and trend of the research on the connection of rivers and lakes, the CiteSpace software was used to study the literature based on the data of WEB OF SCIENCE from 1990 to 2021. The results show that with the development of the economy and society, the connectivity of water systems is playing an increasingly important role, and the number of relevant research documents is increasing; the literature is concerned more with the ecological environment and water quality; the main journals include the *Science of the Total Environment*, *Hydrological Processes*, and *Water Resources Research*, the principal scientific research agencies include Chinese Academy of Sciences, United States Geological Survey, University of Aberdeen, and Griffith University.

1 INTRODUCTION

The river and lake system are not only a very important part of the ecosystem but also the carrier of water resources and the foundation of national development. In recent decades, numerous projects of river and lake system connection have been carried out around the world. Water system connectivity refers to repairing or constructing water flow connection channels to meet specific functional requirements to maintain relatively stable flowing water bodies and their interconnected material circulation conditions based on the existing river, lake, and reservoir water systems (Xia et al. 2012). Water system connectivity is related to the overall allocation of water resources, the health of rivers and lakes, and the resistance to flood and drought disasters, which is an important content of water resources security and management (Cui et al. 2018).

Many scholars and research institutions have gradually researched the connectivity of river systems. From the basic theoretical system of water system connectivity (Pringle 2003; Wang, et al. 2011; Zuo et al. 2012) to the implementation of water system connectivity (Dou, et al. 2020; Fu, et al. 2020; Gao, et al. 2018), many research achievements have been achieved. However, most research focuses on different directions and research issues, and there are few reviews and analyses involved, lacking systematic bibliometric statistics.

*Corresponding Authors: zhanglzsdsl@126.com, 1580018932@qq.com, 314674945@qq.com, 2219739353@qq.com and 1046944026@qq.com

In this paper, CiteSpace software and bibliometrics were used to conduct statistical processing of relevant literature data in the research field of river system connectivity from 1990 to 2021, and knowledge maps were drawn to discuss the research status and future development trend of river system connectivity, which can provide a reference for future related research in this field.

2 METHODS AND DATA SOURCES

CiteSpace is a visualization analysis software based on text mining developed by Professor Chaomei Chen of Drexel University in the United States, which can generate a three-dimensional visualization citation network (Chen et al. 2006). It makes use of the hot word analysis function to draw the knowledge map in the scientific field and visually display the information panorama of the research discipline. The knowledge map can reflect the research hotspot and development trend in a certain stage and has been widely applied in many disciplines (Lan et al. 2020; Wu et al. 2019; Zhang et al. 2021). In this paper, 1445 articles in the Web of Science (WoS) database from 1990 to 2021 were analyzed. Words such as "water linkage", "water systems connectivity", and "hydrological connectivity" appeared in the title, abstract and keywords of the WoS core collection were selected. The details relevant to the selection of publications were extracted and classified: the number of published papers, the authors, and the publishing institution.

3 RESULTS AND DISCUSSIONS

3.1 *Number of published papers*

The total number of papers published in the research field of river system connectivity from 1990 to 2021 can be divided into three stages: slow growth, fluctuating growth, and stable growth. Before 1993, the average annual number of articles published in this field was less than 10. From 1994 to 2008, the annual number of articles published in this field was 10-111, and the number of articles published increased. A great deal of research was published from 2009 to 2021, and the research entered a stage of steady growth. Over the past three years, the average annual number of articles published in this field has exceeded 300, which has attracted extensive attention from researchers.

3.2 *Journals of published papers*

The periodicals with many articles are *Science of the Total Environment*, *Hydrological Processes*, and *Water Resources Research* (see Table 1). The research fields (research directions) include

Table 1. Journals of published papers on water system connectivity from 1990 to 2021.

No	Number of published papers	Journals
1	167	*Science of the Total Environment*
2	151	*Hydrological Processes*
3	134	*Water Resources Research*
4	100	*Water*
5	59	*River Research and Applications*
6	53	*Ecohydrology*
7	45	*PLOS ONE*
8	43	*Aquatic Conservation Marine and Freshwater Ecosystems*
9	42	*Scientific Reports*
10	35	*Wetlands*

hydrology and water resources, environmental science, marine ecology, freshwater resources, ecological energy, geography, etc.

3.3 Keywords

The graph of the top 100 most-cited keywords in each time zone from 1990 to 2021 is shown in Figure 1. Among them, the biggest key node is "connectivity", followed by "hydrological connectivity". Other key nodes are "climate change", "water quality" and "water flow", "biodiversity", "ecosystem", "dynamics", "stream" and "transport".

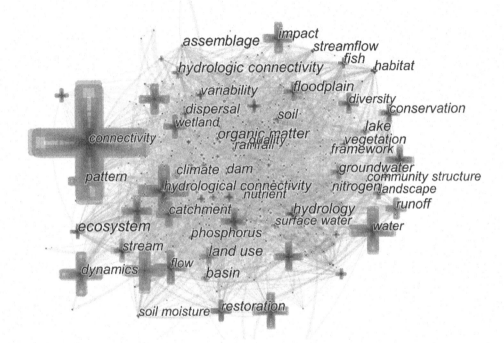

Figure 1. Network analysis of keywords in literature.

3.4 Authors

CiteSpace software was used to process WoS data, and the network atlas of co-cited authors was obtained as shown in Figure 2. Among them, Chris Soulsby published the most 17 articles, followed by Doerthe Tetzlaff (11) and Katarzyna Glinskalewczuk (10). From the perspective of the network map, the academic teams not only have close internal communication but also have close cooperation and communication among teams, first "small gathering" and then "large gathering". It is beneficial to the future development of the water system connectivity field.

3.5 Institutions

WoS data were processed to obtain the analysis network map of document publishing institutions in the connected field of the water system from 1990 to 2021 (see Figure 3), and the statistics of the top 10 institutions in the number of documents published (Table 2). From the perspective of

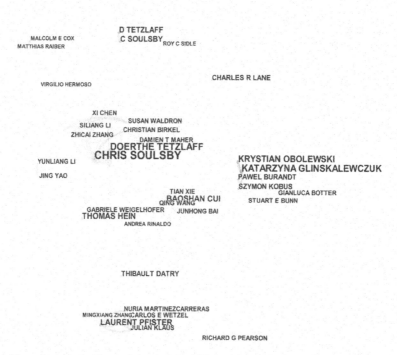

Figure 2. Network map of authors' group analysis of literature on water system connectivity from 1990 to 2021.

the number of articles published, *Chinese Acad Sci* has the highest frequency, with 107 articles published. It is the institution with the greatest number of publications in the field of hydraulic connectivity. The second and third place are US GEOL SURVEY (56), UNIV ABERDEEN (35), and GRIFFITH UNIV (35), respectively.

Figure 3. Network map of institutions of WoS published articles on water system connectivity from 1990 to 2021.

Table 2. The top ten institutions of WoS published articles from 1990 to 2021.

NO.	Number of published papers	Institutions
1	107	CHINESE ACAD SCI
2	56	US GEOL SURVEY
3	35	UNIV ABERDEEN
4	35	GRIFFITH UNIV
5	27	UNIV SASKATCHEWAN
6	24	BEIJING NORMAL UNIV
7	24	OREGON STATE UNIV
8	24	US EPA
9	20	TEXAS A&M UNIV
10	20	UNIV PADUA

4 CONCLUSION

With the promotion of science and technology, in the context of ensuring economic and social development, there is an increasing need to improve the management of river and lake water systems. The literature on water system connectivity was analyzed from the aspects of annual volume, regional publishing organization, keywords, author cooperation group, and publication source periodical. More attention needs to be paid to the following points in the future: strengthening multidisciplinary cooperation; enhancing water system connectivity in local areas; integrating water resources allocation, ecological environment, and economy. The results and analysis of different databases, topic keywords, and software are different, but the general rules are similar. We can choose more databases, keywords, and software for further research.

ACKNOWLEDGMENTS

This work was financially supported by the Young Scientists Fund of the Natural Science Foundation of Shandong Province (Grant No. ZR2019QEE006), and the Project Fund of the Water Research Institute of Shandong Province (Grant No. SDSKYZX202102).

REFERENCES

Chen, C. (2006) CiteSpace II: Detecting and visualizing emerging trends and transient patterns in scientific literature [J]. *Journal of the American Society for Information Science and Technology*, 57 (3): 359–377.

Cui, G., Chen, X., Xiang, L., et al. (2018) Evaluation of water environment improvement by interconnected river network in plain area [J]. *Journal of Hydraulic Engineering*, 48 (12): 1429–1437.

Dou, M., Shi, Y., Yu, L., et al. (2020) Optimization of connecting schemes for urban river networks based on graph theory: A case study of Xuchang section of Qingying River [J]. *Journal of Hydraulic Engineering*, 51 (06): 664–674.

Fu, Y., Chen, S., Zhao, J., et al. (2020) Practical experiences of building rural ecological water system in Hunan and Hubei provinces under the initiative of Yangtze River Protection [J]. *China Water Resources*, (11): 23–26.

Gao, Y., Tang, Y., Xiao, X., et al. (2018) Evaluation model of river network hydrologic connectivity based on improved graph theory and hydrological simulation [J]. *Water Resources Protection*, 34 (06): 33–37.

Lan, M., Lin, A., Jin, T., et al. (2020) Quantitative analysis of knowledge maps of natural resources accounting and assessment research in China based on CiteSpace [J]. *Resources Science*, 42 (04): 621–635.

Li, Z., Li, Y., Wang, Z., et al. (2011) Research on interconnected river system network: conceptual framework [J]. *Journal of Natural Resources*, 26 (3): 513–522.

Pringle, C. (2003) What is hydrologic connectivity and why is it ecologically important [J]. *Hydrological Processes*, 17: 2685–1689.

Wang, Z., Li, Z., Liu, C., et al. (2011) Discussion on water cycle mechanism of interconnected river system network [J]. *Journal of Natural Resources*, 26 (03): 523–529.

Wu, J., Wu, X., Zhang, J. (2019) Development trend and frontier of stormwater management (1980–2019): A bibliometric overview based on CiteSpace. *Water*, 11 (9), 1908.

Xia, J., Gao, Y., Zuo, Q. (2012) Characteristics of interconnected rivers system and its ecological effects on water environment [J]. *Progress in Geography*, 31 (01): 26–31.

Zhang, X., Feng, Y. (2021) Information service of "agriculture, rural areas and farmers" in grass-roots libraries based on CiteSpace [J]. *Agricultural Engineering*, 11 (02): 44–50.

Zuo, Q., Cui, G. (2012) Study on the theoretical system and framework of interconnected river system network [J]. *Water Resources and Power*, 30 (01): 1–5.

Study on the effect of anchor cable locking force on deep displacement in pile-anchor retaining system of ultra-deep foundation pit

Chuan-yao Gu*, Ya-xin Zhang* & Jin-hui Han*
Jinan University, Shandong Province, China

ABSTRACT: Through a concrete engineering example, the method of numerical analysis is used to simulate the change law of deep displacement of foundation pit under pile-anchor support system in the process of excavation, and compared with the measured results, the two-dimensional finite element numerical analysis can reflect the change law of deep displacement to a certain Further, by changing the locking force of anchor cable, the change law of deep displacement is analyzed, and the positive correlation law between deep displacement and locking force of anchor cable is obtained. The influence law expression of locking force of anchor cable on deep displacement is obtained.

1 INTRODUCTION

With the development of society, urban land resources are increasingly scarce, making deep foundation pit engineering widely studied by scholars in the industry (Bao 2014). However, deep foundation pit engineering has the characteristics of large excavation depth, high-risk factors, and complex and changeable construction factors, so it is particularly important to effectively control the deformation of the foundation pit, ensure the safety of buildings and public facilities around the foundation pit, and accurately estimate the deformation of soil and supporting structure caused by foundation pit excavation. As an indispensable and important part of deep foundation pit engineering, supporting structure has been further developed (Zhang 2014). At present, the pile anchor structure is the most used supporting structure.

However, with the continuous increase of the excavation depth, the pile-anchor support system may suffer from overall instability, kick failure, pile fracture failure, instability failure of the bolt-anchor system, and other failure forms, which have attracted the attention of many scholars at home and abroad (Bao 2010; Massoudi 2009). To further study whether the pile-anchor support system is safe and stable in deep foundation pit excavation, many scholars use the finite element numerical simulation method. Currently, the commonly used finite element analysis software includes ANSYS/LS-DYNA (Qiu 2011) and ABAQUS (Yi 2013).

In this paper, taking a deep foundation pit project in Jinan as the background, the field monitoring and numerical simulation methods are used to analyze the change law of deep displacement and the change law of anchor cable locking force in different excavation stages under pile drawing support structure. With the help of ABAQUS finite element software, the deformation form of soil in the excavation of the foundation pit in actual engineering is analyzed. The influence of anchor cable locking force on deep displacement is further analyzed based on practical engineering.

---

*Corresponding Authors: cea_gucy@ujn.edu.cn, lulufei0505@163.com and 572597332@qq.com

2 PROJECT OVERVIEW

The foundation pit project is located in Lixia District, Jinan City. The foundation pit excavation depth is 10.7–20.5 m, and the foundation pit support design scheme adopts the form of pile-anchor support; only the LM profile is studied and analyzed in this paper. The safety level of the foundation pit supporting structure is level 1, the excavation depth is 18.00 to 18.50 m, and the additional load on the foundation pit slope top is considered as a strip load of 20 kPa. The foundation pit adopts the form of pile-anchor support. The supporting pile and anchor cable parameters are shown in Tables 1 and 2 below, and the parameters of the soil layer are shown in Table 3 below.

Table 1. Calculation parameters of retaining pile.

Pile diameter (m)	Density (kg/m^3)	Modulus of elasticity (Pa)	Poisson's ratio
800	2,450	2.8 e8	0.3

Table 2. Calculation parameters of anchor cable.

Diameter (m)	Density (kg/m^3)	Modulus of elasticity (Pa)	Poisson's ratio	Expansion coefficient
18.9	7,850	2.00 e+11	0.3	1.20 e-05

Table 3. Design parameters of each anchor cable.

	Depth from pit top (m)	Length (m)	Incidence angle (°)	Locking value (kN)
The first anchor line	3.2	26	25	220
The second anchor line	5.7	20	25	220
The third anchor line	8.7	14	25	220
The fourth anchor line	11.7	12	25	220
The fifth anchor line	14.7	6	20	100

Table 4. Soil layer information.

Name of the soil	The average thickness (m)	The density of (KN/m^3)	cohesion (KN)	Angle of internal friction (°)	Young's modulus (kPa)	Poisson's ratio
Grain filling	6.2	1.85	15	15	20000	0.25
Miscellaneous fill	3.1	1.6	12	14	30000	0.32
Silty clay	4.7	1.86	41	20.8	60000	0.26
Moderately weathered limestone	8.7	2.7	100	40	200000	0.25

3 DATA ANALYSIS OF DEEP DISPLACEMENT DURING FOUNDATION PIT EXCAVATION

3.1 Model building process

To reduce the adverse effects caused by the model's boundary conditions, the corresponding parameters are selected according to the need for foundation pit engineering. Usually, the excavation depth is taken as the standard, and the width and height of the model are 3–5 times and 2–4 times the average, respectively. The two sides of the foundation pit are symmetrical to each other. One side of the foundation pit can be modeled and analyzed to reduce the workload. Based on the above theory, the width and height of the model are 60 m and 30 m, respectively. When dividing the finite region, each unit belongs to the plane strain element (CPE4R). In addition, the study was carried out through ABAQUS two-dimensional numerical simulation. The boundary conditions are as follows: the left part and the right part constrain horizontal movement, while the bottom part constrains horizontal and vertical movement.

The initial stress law of soil is obtained by analyzing the force of soil under its action before foundation pit excavation. When the operation no longer fluctuates, change the value of position movement and speed to zero. First, set up the bored pile, excavate the foundation pit, and add the supporting device to obtain the calculation result.

From the perspective of foundation pit excavation, the simulation calculation includes the following processes:

(1) Initial analysis process. The ground overload is set two meters away from the project to analyze the initial ground stress for subsequent foundation work.
(2) Set the cast-in-place pile. As its material type is concrete, it is set up and activated before foundation pit excavation. Both the left and right sides will contact the soil; therefore, it is set up as the pile-soil interface; it is composed of prestressed anchor cables.
(3) As the excavation of the foundation pit progresses, eliminate the contact surface between the excavation soil and the supporting pile when the hole reaches the specified depth.
(4) Once the excavation has been completed to the specified depth, activate the prestressed anchor cable, and apply the prestress.

After the simulation is completed, we can obtain the displacement cloud diagram (see Figure 1).

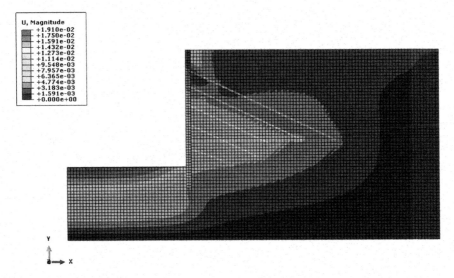

Figure 1. Displacement cloud map.

3.2 *Analysis of deep displacement monitoring value and simulation value*

The pit displacement data at each stage of excavation are summarized and sorted out, as shown in Figures 2 and 3 below. The positive and negative points of deep displacement are negative in the pit and positive in the direction of the pit exit. This regulation applies to this section and the following sections. After data collation, the deep displacement-depth variation curve is obtained.

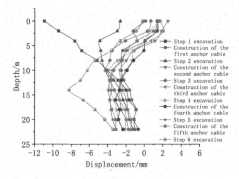
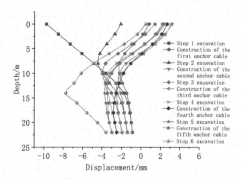

Figure 2. Change curves of measured values of deep displacement.

Figure 3. Variation curve of simulated values of deep displacement.

From the measured and simulated curves of deep displacement, the variation rule of deep displacement can be seen. After each step of excavation and before tensioning, the deep displacement of the foundation pit will deform into the pit. After each cable is tensioned and locked, the deep displacement of the foundation pit tends to deform outward. From the end of the first excavation, the deep displacement of the foundation pit presents a law from top to bottom: forward dip. After the first cable tensioning and locking, and in subsequent conditions, the deep displacement of the foundation pit displays a law of large displacement in the middle and small displacement at the top and bottom, similar to a crescent shape.

After each step of excavation, the maximum displacement of the deep foundation pit is mainly at the excavation site before tension locking. After each cable tension locking, the maximum displacement variation of the deep foundation pit is at the anchor cable locking location. The larger the distance from the locked position is, the smaller the change of deep displacement is. Different anchor cables have different influences on the deep displacement at different positions of the foundation pit. Anchor cables in the upper part of the foundation pit have a greater influence on deep displacement there than in the lower part of the foundation pit, and anchor cables in the lower part of the foundation pit have a greater influence on deep displacement there than in the upper part. The effect of anchor cable locking on deep displacement during foundation pit excavation is as follows: the greater the distance from the anchor cable, the less effect; otherwise, the greater effect.

The numerical simulation results of deep displacement agree with the measured values, and the deformation trend is consistent. It is shown that the results of finite element simulation are reliable, which provides technical support for the analysis of the active law of anchor cable locking force on deep displacement in the next section.

4 ANALYSES OF THE INFLUENCE OF ANCHOR CABLE LOCKING FORCE ON DEEP DISPLACEMENT

Based on the original design parameters of the foundation pit, the control variable method is adopted in this section to study the influence of anchor cable locking force on the deep displacement of the foundation pit by considering the change of locking force of each anchor cable, as shown in Figure 4 to 8.

It can be seen from the figure that with the increase of anchor cable locking force, the deep displacement of the foundation pit deforms outward. When the locking force of the first cable, second cable, third cable, fourth cable, and fifth cable is increased by 100 kN, the horizontal displacement of the pit top changes from 0.38 mm to 6.55 mm, 3.58 mm, 1.49 mm, 0.60 mm, and 0.28 mm from the outside the pit.

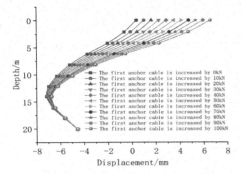
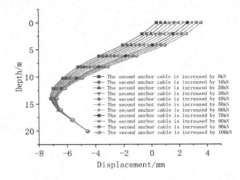

Figure 4. The graph of the deep displacement curve with the locking force of the first anchor cable increasing by 10–100 kN in section M.

Figure 5. The graph of the deep displacement curve with the locking force of the second anchor cable increasing by 10–100 kN in section M.

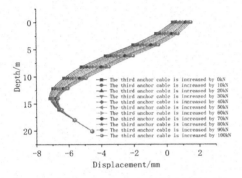
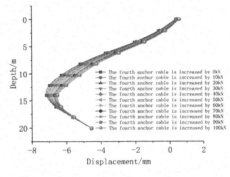

Figure 6. The graph of the deep displacement curve with the locking force of the third anchor cable increasing by 10–100 kN in section M.

Figure 7. The graph of the deep displacement curve with the locking force of the fourth anchor cable increasing by 10–100 kN in section M.

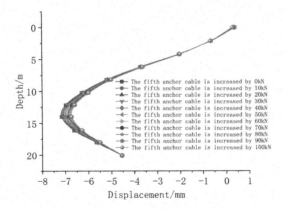

Figure 8. The graph of the deep displacement curve with the locking force of the fifth anchor cable increasing by 10–100 kN in section M.

According to the analysis of the data, if the first anchor cable, the second anchor cable, the third anchor cable, the fourth anchor cable, and the fifth anchor cable increase by 10 kN, the deep displacement at 0 m of foundation pit changes by 0.63 mm, 0.32 mm, 0.11 mm, 0.02 mm, and 0.01 mm, respectively. In combination with finite element analysis, the anchor cable locking force has the following rules, which can be expressed by the following formula.

$$Y_h = a_1 X_1 + a_2 X_2 + \cdots + a_n X_n + k \tag{1}$$

where Y_h is the deep displacement (mm); h is the depth; $a_1, a_2, \ldots, a_n$ represent 1 to n. The influence coefficient of deep displacement of n cable is described in mm/kN; $X_1, X_2, \ldots, X_n$ refers to the locking force of each cable (kN); k is a constant (mm). The values of coefficient a_n and constant k calculated by the finite element method with a pit depth of 0 m and below are shown in the following table.

Table 5. Influence coefficient of deep displacement and k value.

Depth (m)	a_1	a_2	a_3	a_4	a_5	k
0	0.062	0.032	0.011	0.002	0.001	23.06
2	0.054	0.032	0.014	0.004	0.000	23.53
4	0.044	0.031	0.016	0.006	0.001	23.49
6	0.033	0.027	0.017	0.008	0.001	22.54
8	0.022	0.021	0.017	0.010	0.002	20.81
10	0.014	0.014	0.014	0.011	0.003	18.25
12	0.008	0.009	0.009	0.010	0.004	15.30
14	0.005	0.005	0.005	0.007	0.004	12.40
16	0.002	0.002	0.002	0.003	0.004	9.00
18	0.001	0.001	0.001	0.001	0.002	6.74

When multi-channel anchor cable locking force values are changed simultaneously, the effect of anchor cable locking force on deep displacement is shown in Figure 9 below. Because the fifth anchor cable has little influence on the deep displacement of the foundation pit, this paper takes the first four anchor cables of the LM profile to change the locking force simultaneously to reflect the change of deep displacement. Figure 9 shows an increase of 20 kN for the first and second anchors, 10 kN for the other anchors, 30 kN for the first and second anchors, 10 kN for the other anchors, 40 kN for the first and second anchors, and 10 kN for the other anchors. And the change curve of 30 kN for the first three anchor cables and 10 kN for the other anchor cables.

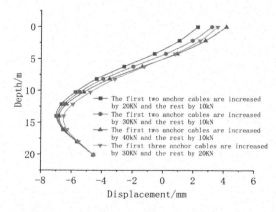

Figure 9. Influence curve of four anchor cables changing locking force on deep displacement at the same time.

5 CONCLUSIONS

This study focuses on specific deep foundation pit engineering. ABAQUS software in finite element software is used to perform a numerical simulation on actual engineering cases. The simulation results are compared with the monitoring results of the foundation pit, which verifies the reliability and effectiveness of numerical simulation results by using finite element software. Through this study, the following conclusions are drawn.

(1) After each step of excavation, the deep displacement of the foundation pit will deform inward before the tension lock. After each cable tension lock, the deep displacement of the foundation pit will deform outward. After the end of the first excavation, the deep displacement of the foundation pit presents a law from top to bottom: forward dip. In the conditions of the first cable tensioning and locking and the following conditions, the deep displacement of the foundation pit from top to bottom presents a law of large displacement in the middle and small displacement in the top and bottom, similar to the "crescent shape".

(2) The numerical simulation results of deep displacement are consistent with the measured results. The deformation trend is consistent, indicating that the results of finite element simulation analysis are reliable and provide technical support for analyzing the action law of anchor cable locking force on deep displacement.

(3) There is a positive correlation between deep displacement and anchor cable locking force. When multiple anchor cable locking force is changed at the same time, the influence of anchor cable locking force on deep displacement at a specific section of deep foundation pit under the pile-anchor retaining system (fixed soil parameters and surrounding environment) at a certain depth (fixed position) has the following rule, which can be used as the function $Y_h = a_1X_1 + a_2X_2 + \ldots + a_nX_n + k$. The influence coefficient a_n and constant k on the deep displacement at a certain depth of a specific section are constant values.

REFERENCES

Bao Chun-sheng, Wu Xiong-zhi, Bai Jin-jie. Experimental study on internal force of pile-anchor retaining structure [J]. *SUBGRADE ENGINEERING*, 2010, 000 (001): 94–96.

Bao Xiao-hua., Fu Yan-bin, Huang Hong-wei. Risk assessment and case study of deep foundation pit excavation [J]. *Chinese Journal of Geotechnical Engineering*, 2014, 36 (S1): 192–197.

Massoudi N. *Temperature Effect on Tieback Loads; proceedings of the International Foundation Congress and Equipment Expo* 2009, F, 2009 [C].

Qiu Wei-min, Liu Li-ming. The deep foundation pit deformation numerical simulation based on ANSYS is based on the deep foundation pit engineering in Yichang city [J]. *Journal of China Three Gorges University (Natural Sciences)*, 2011, 33 (01): 58–61.

Yi X D, Huang P, Wang Z C. Compared analysis of deformation monitoring with numerical simulation on pile-anchor supporting system of deep foundation pit in soil-rock dualistic area [J]. *Applied Mechanics and Materials*, 2013, 2545 (353–356):

Zhang Yu-cheng, Yang Guang-hua, Hu Hai-ying, et al. Combined application of multiple supporting types in design of oversized deep foundation pit [J]. *Chinese Journal of Geotechnical Engineering*, 2014, 36 (S2): 198–204.

A simulation method for complex boundary and coupling conditions in structural analysis

Tao Huang*, Meng-ge Wang* & Zheng-wei Liang*

School of Civil Engineering and Environment, Hubei University of Technology, Wuhan, China

ABSTRACT: The boundary conditions and coupling conditions have a great influence on the mechanical response of the structure, but the traditional analytical method, due to the shortcomings of the constructional displacement tolerance function, the solution scheme is often not applicable to a variety of complex boundary conditions, but only to solve the vibration characteristics of the structure under certain classical boundary conditions. On the other hand, in the commonly used finite element software, there is always a lack of unified modeling methods for complex boundary conditions and coupling conditions, which bring inconvenience to the numerical analysis. This paper takes a one-dimensional rod as an example to establish a unified analysis model of a one-dimensional rod under complex boundary conditions, and the method used is also applicable to derive a unified analysis model of a shell structure under complex boundary conditions, and this paper also gives details of the unified modeling method in the finite element software that can be applied to various types of structures under complex boundary conditions and coupling conditions, and finally verifies the correctness of the modeling method proposed in this paper through the examples of beams and shells.

1 INTRODUCTION

Boundary conditions and coupling conditions are important parameters affecting the structural response, and the solution of the vibration control equation depends largely on the boundary conditions and coupling conditions, and under certain conditions, the influence of structural boundary conditions and coupling conditions may be more sensitive than the structural parameters themselves (Dai et al. 2018; 2011; Gao et al. 2005), and an exhaustive understanding of their influence laws can provide a broader parameter design space.

However, the traditional analytical method has two shortcomings due to the defect of constructing displacement tolerance function, which makes it deficient in two aspects, one is that it can only be solved for some classical boundary conditions (simple support, solid support, etc.), and the other is that the solution scheme is not universal, and once the boundary conditions change, the displacement tolerance function must be modified to obtain a new solution, which makes these methods cumbersome in practical engineering applications (Shi 2018). However, in practical engineering, a variety of coupling conditions and boundary conditions are often encountered, and the traditional analytical methods are tricky to deal with these complex situations. Therefore, it is necessary to construct a set of unified analytic models for arbitrary boundary conditions and coupling conditions.

To solve this challenge, Li (2000; 2004) proposed a modified Fourier series method applied to the bending vibration of beams and rectangular plates under arbitrary support, and based on this, a

---

*Corresponding Authors: httcmwh@hbut.edu.cn, wangmengge1229@163.com and 46717433@qq.com

two-dimensional spectral geometry method (Jiang S L et al. 2013) was proposed for studying the vibration characteristics of the combined structures under different boundary conditions. Dai Lu (Dai et al. 2018) used a two-dimensional improved Fourier series to describe each displacement function of an elastic plate and cylindrical shell structures separately, and the complex boundary conditions were simulated by different combinations of elastic constraints. Shi Xianjie (Shi Xianjie et al. 2018) simulated various coupling effects between the structures by setting a three-dimensional elastic coupler with linear and rotational stiffnesses, and the vibration displacement tolerance functions of the cylindrical shell and annular plate were described uniformly as kind of improved triangular series in spectral form. Pang Fuzhen (Pang et al. 2020) and others studied the vibration characteristics of medium-thick laminated sector plates under complex boundary conditions found on the spring stiffness method. Li Haichaoet al. (2020) used Jocabi polynomials along the axial direction and Fourier series along the circumferential direction as displacement functions to analyze the free vibration characteristics of cylindrical shells under complex boundary conditions using the penalty parameter method.

On the other hand, in structural analysis calculations, there is equally the problem of how to simulate various complex boundary conditions and coupling conditions. In common finite element software (e.g., Ansys), traditional modeling methods can only deal with typical boundary conditions and coupling conditions, and there is no unified modeling method for arbitrary elastic constraints on the structure, which brings great inconvenience to the numerical analysis of the structure.

This paper uses the Rayleigh-Ritz method of the energy principle to establish a unified analytical model of a one-dimensional rod structure under complex boundary conditions, using a one-dimensional rod as an example, which can be adapted to various boundary conditions by simply adjusting the stiffness values of the support springs on the boundary, without the need to re-derive and implement new solution procedures. This paper also puts forward a simple and versatile modeling method for modeling elastic boundaries and elastic coupling using spring constraints in finite element software, which enables analytical calculations of structures with complex boundary conditions and coupling conditions.

2 THEORETICAL ANALYSIS

For classical boundary conditions: a certain generalized degree of freedom is either equal to zero (completely constrained) or completely free (unconstrained). In classical coupling conditions, the corresponding degrees of freedom at the coupling of two components are either equal or uncorrelated, but in engineering practice, there are often much more complex boundary conditions and coupling conditions than this.

For the complex boundary conditions and coupling conditions, the constraint spring and coupling spring can be simply used to establish a unified analysis model: at the boundary or coupling point, the corresponding linear or rotating spring is applied according to the generalized degree of freedom of the structure, and different elastic boundary conditions and coupling conditions can be obtained by changing the spring stiffness. For example, if the stiffness of the boundary constrained spring is set to infinity or zero, the fixed support and free boundary conditions can be simulated respectively; if the stiffness of the coupled linear spring is set to infinity, and the stiffness of the coupled rotating spring is set to zero, the hinge joint can be simulated.

The following is an example of a one-dimensional straight rod member to illustrate the principles of analytical calculations for structures with arbitrary elastic boundary conditions.

The elastic boundary constraint of the rod is shown in Figure 1, the rod is L in length, the coordinate x-axis is along the axis of the rod, the y-axis and z-axis are the neutral axes of the cross-section of the rod, and six groups of springs (three linear springs and three rotary springs) are arranged at the two boundaries of the rod to achieve all the elastic boundary conditions.

The four independent displacements of the rod are the linear displacements u, v, and w along the x, y, and z axes and the torsional angle φ of the cross-section. The displacement function of the

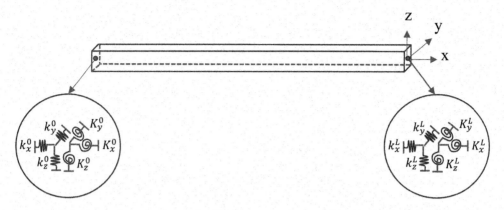

Figure 1. Geometric model and coordinate system for a one-dimensional rod supported by elastic boundaries.

rod can be expressed as an expansion of one of the series (e.g., a trigonometric series):

$$u(x) = \sum_{m=0}^{\infty} A_m \psi_m(x), v(x) = \sum_{m=0}^{\infty} B_m \psi_m(x)$$
$$w(x) = \sum_{m=0}^{\infty} C_m \psi_m(x), \varphi(x) = \sum_{m=0}^{\infty} D_m \psi_m(x)$$
(1)

where $\psi_m(x)$ denotes the items of the series, and A_m, B_m, C_m and D_m denote the unknown expansion coefficients of the series.

The relationship between the deformation and displacement of the rod is as follows:

$$\varepsilon_x = \frac{\partial u}{\partial x}, \theta_y = \frac{\partial w}{\partial x}, \theta_z = \frac{\partial v}{\partial x}$$
$$\kappa_x = \frac{\partial \varphi}{\partial x}, \kappa_y = \frac{\partial^2 w}{\partial x^2}, \kappa_z = \frac{\partial^2 v}{\partial x^2}$$
(2)

where ε_x denotes the axial strain, θ_y and θ_z denote the angle of rotation around the y-axis and z-axis, respectively, κ_x is the torsional rate around the x-axis, and κ_y and κ_z denote the deflection rate around the y-axis and z-axis, respectively.

The strain potential energy of the rod can be expressed as:

$$V_s = \frac{1}{2} \int_0^L \left[EA\varepsilon_x^2 + GJ\kappa_x^2 + EI_y\kappa_y^2 + EI_z\kappa_z^2 \right] dx$$
$$= \frac{1}{2} \int_0^L \left[EA\left(\frac{\partial u}{\partial x}\right)^2 + GJ\left(\frac{\partial \varphi}{\partial x}\right)^2 + EI_y\left(\frac{\partial^2 w}{\partial x^2}\right)^2 + EI_z\left(\frac{\partial^2 v}{\partial x^2}\right)^2 \right] dx$$
(3)

where E and G denote Young's modulus and shear modulus of the material, respectively, and A, J, I_y, and I_z denote the cross-sectional area of the rod, the torsional constant of the cross-section, the moment of inertia about the y-axis, and the moment of inertia about the z-axis, respectively.

The elastic potential energy stored in the restrained springs at both ends of the rod is.

$$V_b = \frac{1}{2}[k_x^0 u^2 + k_y^0 v^2 + k_z^0 w^2 + K_x^0 \varphi^2 + K_y^0 \theta_y^2 + K_z^0 \theta_z^2]_{x=0}$$

$$+ \frac{1}{2}[k_x^L u^2 + k_y^L v^2 + k_z^L w^2 + K_x^L \varphi^2 + K_y^L \theta_y^2 + K_z^L \theta_z^2]_{x=L}$$

$$= \frac{1}{2}\left[k_x^0 u^2 + k_y^0 v^2 + k_z^0 w^2 + K_x^0 \varphi^2 + K_y^0 \left(\frac{dw}{dx}\right)^2 + K_z^0 \left(\frac{dv}{dx}\right)^2\right]_{x=0} \quad (4)$$

$$+ \frac{1}{2}\left[k_x^L u^2 + k_y^L v^2 + k_z^L w^2 + K_x^L \varphi^2 + K_y^L \left(\frac{dw}{dx}\right)^2 + K_z^L \left(\frac{dv}{dx}\right)^2\right]_{x=L}$$

where k_x^0 and k_x^L, k_y^0 and k_y^L, k_z^0 and k_z^L denote the stiffness of the linear displacement-constrained spring in the x, y and z directions at both ends of the rod, respectively, and K_x^0 and K_x^L, K_y^0 and K_y^L, K_z^0 and K_z^L denote the stiffness of the rotational angular displacement-constrained spring in the x, y and z directions at both ends of the rod, respectively.

The total potential energy V of the rod is the sum of the structural strain potential energy and the elastic potential energy of the spring.

$$V = V_s + V_b \quad (5)$$

The total kinetic energy of the rod is

$$T = \frac{1}{2}\rho \int_0^L \left\{ A\left[\left(\frac{\partial u}{\partial t}\right)^2 + \left(\frac{\partial v}{\partial t}\right)^2 + \left(\frac{\partial w}{\partial t}\right)^2\right] + I_p\left(\frac{\partial \varphi}{\partial t}\right)^2 \right\} dx$$

$$= \frac{1}{2}\rho \omega^2 \int_0^L [A(u^2 + v^2 + w^2) + I_p \varphi^2] dx \quad (6)$$

where ρ denotes the density of the material, I_p denotes the polar moment of inertia of the crosssection, and $I_p = I_y + I_z$.

Taking z as an example of external load excitation, the work done by the external excitation force can be expressed as.

$$W_{ext} = \int_0^L f(x) w(x) dx \quad (7)$$

where $f(x)$ is the external load distribution function applied on the rod. For the point excitation force acting on the rod at the position x_e, the load distribution function can be expressed as.

$$f(x) = F\delta(x - x_e) \quad (8)$$

where $\delta(x - x_e)$ is the Dirac function and F is the magnitude of the point excitation force.

The Lagrange function of the rod structure can be expressed as.

$$L = V - T - W_{ext} \quad (9)$$

Combining Equations (1) to (9) so that the Lagrangian function takes extreme values for each unknown level expansion coefficient yields a series of linear equations written in matrix form as:

$$(\mathbf{K} - \omega^2 \mathbf{M})\mathbf{E} = \mathbf{F} \quad (10)$$

where **E** is the column vector containing all the unknown expansion coefficients, and **K** and **M** are the stiffness matrix and mass matrix of the rod structure. In the above equation, if $\mathbf{F} = 0$, the free vibration control equation of the rod is obtained.

when **K** and **M** of the rod are known, the dynamic equation of the structure can be expressed as follows:

$$\mathbf{M\ddot{E}} + \mathbf{C\dot{E}} + \mathbf{KE} = \mathbf{F} \tag{11}$$

If the damping matrix **C** is Rayleigh damping, then **C** can be described as a linear combination of the mass matrix **M** and the stiffness matrix **K**

$$\mathbf{C} = \alpha_0 \mathbf{M} + \beta_0 \mathbf{K} \tag{12}$$

where α_0 and β_0 are the frequency-independent Rayleigh damping coefficients.

In the case of statics problems, Equation (11) can be reduced to

$$\mathbf{KE} = \mathbf{F} \tag{13}$$

The above one-dimensional rod as an example to illustrate the structural calculation method under arbitrary elastic boundary conditions, the elastic boundary constraints of other structural forms, as well as the elastic coupling conditions between the structure can be similarly deduced, and will not be repeated here.

3 IMPLEMENTATION IN FINITE ELEMENT SOFTWARE

The finite element software usually used can only deal with classical boundary conditions directly, and this paper introduces a method for dealing with arbitrary elastic boundaries and arbitrary elastic coupling in finite element software, using the widely used Ansys as an example.

3.1 Modeling methods

The spring is simulated using the Combin14 unit available in Ansys. Depending on the degrees of freedom of the structure under analysis, the corresponding Combin14 unit is added at the boundary or coupling to the body structure, and the spring is made linear or rotational by setting the key option KEYOPT (3) for the Combin14 unit and assigning a value to the spring stiffness by setting a real constant.

The modeling of boundary-constrained springs and coupled springs is described below about the beam unit Beam188 in Ansys.

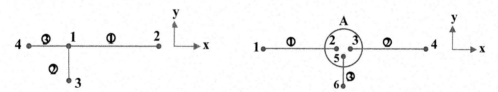

Figure 2. Boundary constraint spring modelling schematic.

Figure 3. Schematic diagram of structural coupling spring modelling.

Figure 2 is a schematic diagram of the modeling of the boundary constraint spring. Unit ① is a Beam188 beam unit, consisting of nodes 1 and 2. Assuming that a linear constraint spring in the y-direction (limiting the linear displacement of node 1 in the y-direction) and a rotational constraint spring in the x-direction (limiting the torsion angle of node 1) need to be set at node 1, create node 3 in the vicinity of node 1, along the y-direction, and node 4 along the x-direction, and form Combin14 unit ② from nodes 1 and 3, from nodes 1 and 4 to form Combin14 unit ③, the degrees of freedom of nodes 3 and 4 will be fully constrained, set the KEYOPT(3)=0 of the unit ② to make it a linear spring, set the KEYOPT(3)=1 of the unit ③ to make it a rotational spring, and set the stiffness of units ② and ③ respectively by the keyword r. The constrained springs in other directions of node 1 can be similarly set, this method of imposing both elastic boundary conditions.

Figure 3 is a schematic diagram for modeling a coupled spring. Beam 188 element ① (consisting of nodes 1 and 2) and Beam188 element ② (consisting of nodes 3 and 4) are coupled at node 2 and node 3 in the diagram are located at the same point. If the y-direction linear displacement degrees of nodes 2 and 3 need to be coupled, create another node which is numbered 5 at point A, and make node 6 along the y-direction. Combin14 element ③ is composed of nodes 5 and 6. Set KEYOPT (3) =0 of the element ③ to make it a linear spring and set its stiffness through the keyword R. All the degrees of freedom of node 6 should be constrained. The y-direction linear displacement degree of freedom of nodes 2, 3, and 5 need to be coupled using a constraint equation:

$$u_y^2 - u_y^3 = u_y^5.$$

The Ansys command is ce, 1, 0, 2, uy, 1, 3, uy, −1, 5, uy, and −1. The coupling of other degrees of freedom of nodes 2 and 3 can be established similarly.

3.2 Examples of beams

As shown in Figure 4. beam AB is 2m long. The vertical downward concentrated force acts on the midpoint of the beam, F = 10Kn. The beam section is a square with a side length of 0.03m. The material elastic modulus E = 2.1× 10^{11} Pa, Poisson's ratio μ = 0.3, and density ρ = 78 modeled[3].

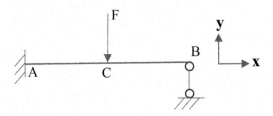

Figure 4. Diagram of the beam model.

Boundary A and B are modeled with elastic constraints. The stiffness of the linearly constrained spring in the x and y directions at A is denoted by k_x^A and k_y^A, respectively, and the stiffness of the rotationally constrained spring in the z direction is denoted by K_z^A. The stiffness of the constrained spring at B is denoted similarly.

The self-weight of the beam is not considered in the static analysis, and the calculation results are shown in Table 1 (linear spring stiffness unit N/m, rotating spring stiffness unit N·m/rad, force unit kN, couple unit kN·m).

Table 1. Results of static analysis.

Boundary condition	Stiffness value	Calculation results of ANSYS
A: fixed B: sliding hinge	$k_x^A = 10^{11}, k_y^A = 10^{11}, K_z^A = 10^{11}$ $k_y^B = 10^{11}$	A reaction force: $F_y = 6.8747, M_z = 3.7493$ B reaction force: $F_y = 3.1253$
A: fixed B: elastic	$k_x^A = 10^{11}, k_y^A = 10^{11}, K_z^A = 10^{11}$ $k_y^B = 10^3$	A reaction force: $F_y = 9.5051, M_z = 9.0101$ B reaction force: $F_y = 0.49493$
A: elastic B: sliding hinge	$k_x^A = 10^{11}, k_y^A = 10^3, K_z^A = 10^4$ $k_y^B = 10^{11}$	A reaction force: $F_y = 5.1363, M_z = 0.27258$ B reaction force: $F_y = 4.8637$

The calculation results in Table 1 are all in agreement with the theoretical solution, indicating that it is feasible to simulate complex boundary conditions by using constrained springs in the static analysis.

Under the boundary conditions of A fixed support and B sliding hinge support (see Table 1, line 2 for the value of spring stiffness), the modal analysis of the beam is carried out, and the calculated natural frequencies of the first 5 orders are shown in Table 2.

Table 2. Natural frequency of the beam (A fixed support, B sliding hinge support).

order	1	2	3	4	5
frequency (Hz)	27.542	89.115	185.50	316.26	372.10

The results are consistent with the results obtained by the classical boundary condition setting method in ANSYS, indicating that it is feasible to simulate complex boundary conditions by using constrained spring in dynamic analysis.

The first-order natural frequency of the beam is calculated by varying the value of the spring stiffness k_y^B under the boundary condition of A fixed support and B elastic support, and the results are shown in Table 3.

Table 3. Effect of boundary conditions on the natural frequency of beams.

Spring stiffness k_y^B	10	103	105	107	109	1011
The first-order natural frequency (Hz)	6.2910	6.8322	21.273	27.471	27.541	27.542

From the calculation results in Table 3, the boundary conditions greatly influence the dynamic performance of the beam, and the sensitive region for spring stiffness in this example is 103–105.

3.3 Examples of plate and shell coupling

The schematic and coordinate system of the elastic plate-cylinder shell coupling structure is shown in Figure 5 (Dai Lu 2013). The parameters are shown as follows, cylindrical shell: Radius R, length l_s, thickness h_s, elastic modulus E_s, Poisson's ratio μ_s, and density ρ_s; elastic plate: length l_f, thickness h_f, elastic modulus E_f, Poisson's ratio μ_f, and density ρ_f; φ indicates the position of the coupling angle between the elastic plate and the cylindrical shell.

Four types of spring constraints are applied on the ends $x = 0$ and $x = l_s$ of the cylindrical shell, i.e., axial, tangential, and radial linear springs, and radial rotary springs, as shown in Figure 5(a). Similarly, four types of spring constraints are also applied on the ends of the elastic plate $x = 0$ and $x = l_s$, as shown in Figure 5(b).

The coupling boundary is modeled as shown in Figure 5(c). The two long edges of the elastic plate, $y = 0$ and $y = b$, are connected to the cylindrical shell at the cylindrical shell circumferential angles $\theta = 2\pi - \varphi$ and $\theta = \varphi$, respectively. Four types of distributed coupling springs are set on the two coupling boundaries, and the subscript "c" indicates the coupling.

The geometrical parameters and material properties of the coupled elastic plate-cylindrical shell structure are now set as follows:

$$\phi = 115°, \quad R = 0.254\text{m}, \quad l_s = l_f = 1.27\text{m},$$

$$h_s = h_f = 0.00508\text{m}, \quad \mu_s = \mu_f = 0.3,$$

$$\rho_s = \rho_f = 7500\text{kg/m}^3, \quad E_s = E_f = 2 \times 10^{11}\text{Pa}.$$

In this example, shell 181 elements are used for the elastic plate and cylindrical shell, and combin14 element is used for spring.

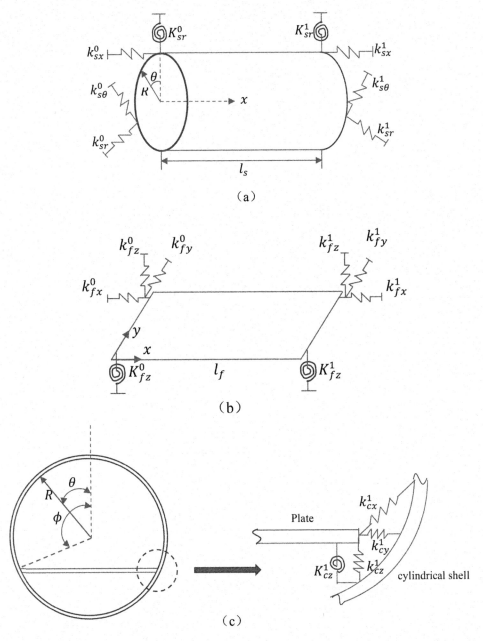

Figure 5. Modeling of the coupled elastic plate-cylindrical shell structure: (a) cylindrical shell boundary; (b) elastic plate boundary; (c) coupling boundary.

In order to verify the correctness of the method in this paper, under the conditions of simple support and rigid coupling at both ends (spring stiffness $k_{sx}^0, k_{sx}^1, K_{sr}^0, K_{sr}^1$ and $k_{fx}^0, k_{fx}^1, K_{fz}^0, K_{fz}^1$ equal to zero; the rest of the spring stiffness is infinite), The modal analysis of the coupled elastic plate-cylindrical shell structure was performed and the calculated results were compared with the Ansys conventional modeling method and literature calculation results, as shown in Table 4.

Table 4. Natural frequencies of the structure with simply supported and rigid coupling.

Modal form	This paper	Conventional method	Literature	Deviation (%)
1S	109.4	109.4	111.6	1.97
2S	242.4	242.4	242.2	0.08
3S	323.9	323.9	323.9	0
4S	396.4	396.4	394.5	0.48
1A	205.7	205.7	205.2	0.24
2A	265.2	265.2	264.9	0.11
3A	347.7	347.7	351.4	1.05
4A	441.9	441.9	441.6	0.07

From Table 4, the calculation results in this paper are consistent with those of the common modeling method, and the deviation between the calculation results and the literature results is very small, which shows that the dynamic properties of the structure can be analyzed accurately by simulating the boundary and coupling conditions using constraint and coupled springs.

For classical boundary and rigid coupling, ANSYS modeling can handle it, but for elastic boundary and elastic coupling, the ordinary way cannot handle it, using spring simulation is a better method.

It is assumed that the boundary conditions at both ends of the plate-shell coupling structure are still simply supported, and the value of elastic coupling stiffness is $k_{cx}^{0,1} = k_{cy}^{0,1} = k_{cz}^{0,1} = K_{cz}^{0,1} = 10^6$. The first 10-order natural frequencies of the structure are calculated and the results are shown in Table 5.

Table 5. Natural frequencies of structures with simply supported at both ends and elastic coupling.

Modal order	This paper	Literature	Deviation (%)
1	49.636	49.906	0.541
2	59.302	59.483	0.304
3	60.990	60.990	0
4	86.617	86.696	0.091
5	98.623	99.008	0.389
6	115.52	116.00	0.414
7	134.20	134.25	0.037
8	147.13	147.72	0.399
9	195.54	196.29	0.382
10	200.12	200.20	0.040

According to Table 5, the results calculated by the method of this paper are in good agreement with the results in the literature, indicating that the method is suitable for simulating complex elastic coupling of structures.

4 CONCLUSION

In the structural analysis, spring constraints are used to simulate complex boundary conditions and coupling conditions. A unified model for structural analysis under complex boundary conditions is established using a one-dimensional rod as an example, and a unified modeling method for simulating elastic boundaries and elastic coupling using springs in finite element software is given.

Calculation examples for beams and shells show that the method is theoretically correct and the calculation results are accurate. The simplicity and generality of the method make it a better method for modeling complex boundary conditions and coupling conditions, which can lay the foundation for subsequent in-depth studies on the effects of boundary conditions and coupling conditions on the mechanical properties of structures and the sensitivity analysis of constraint parameters.

REFERENCES

Dai Lu, Lin Yuan Sheng, Liu Yong, BAI Fan et al. (2018). Vibration analysis of coupled plate and shell structures with complex boundary conditions[J]. *Journal of Vibration and Shock*, 37(15): 270–276

Dai Lu, Yang Tiejun, Sun Yao, et al. (2011). Influence of boundary conditions on the active control of vibration and sound radiation for a circular cylindrical shell[J]. *Applied Mechanics and Materials*, 66/67/68(2): 1270–1277

Dai Lu. (2013). *Study on dynamic behavior and acoustic radiation for the coupling structure of cylindrical shells with complex boundary conditions*[D]. Harbin: Harbin Engineering University.

Gao Yue Fei. (2005). *Optimal design of the structural dynamic boundary conditions and implementation in engineering*[D]. Xi An: Northwestern Polytechnical University.

Jiang S L, Li Wen L, Yang T J. (2013). *A spectro-geometric method for the vibration analysis of built-up structures*[J]. NOISE-CON 2013, Denver, Colorado, 2013. Washington DC: The Institute of Noise Control Engineering of the USA:1–6.

LI Haichao, PANG Fuzhen, LI Yuhui, MIU Xuhong. (2020). Free vibration characteristics analysis of circular cylindrical shells under complex boundary conditions[J]. *Journal of Vibration Engineering*, 2020, 33(1): 56–63

Li W L. (2000). Free vibrations of beams with general boundary conditions[J]. *Journal of Sound and Vibration*. 237(4): 709–725.

Li W L. (2004). Vibration analysis of rectangular plates with general elastic boundary supports[J]. *Journal of Sound and Vibration*. 273(3): 619–635.

Pang Fuzhen, Huo Ruidong, Li Haichao, Ye Kaifu, Wang Xueren. (2020). Vibration characteristics analysis of moderately thick laminate sectors under complicated boundary conditions[J]. *Journal of Harbin Engineering University*, Doi: 10.1990/jheu.201901016.

Shi Xianjie, Li Chunli, Jiang Huabing. (2018). Analysis of vibration characteristics of coupled cylindrical shell-ring plate structures under complex boundary conditions[J]. *Journal of Vibration Engineering*, 2018, 31(1): 118–124

Seismic responses of underground subway station located in gently inclined liquefiable ground

Yu Qiu* & Xiwen Zhang*

School of Civil Engineering and Architecture, University of Jinan, Jinan, China

ABSTRACT: The dynamic response of subway stations to earthquakes is a hot research topic in the field of soil dynamics and geotechnical engineering. In this paper, the finite difference software FLAC3D was used to establish the numerical model of the soil-subway station structure in a gently inclined liquefaction site. And through the site liquefaction distribution and deformation characteristic, the influence of ground inclined angle to the underground station was studied. It is found that in the gently inclined liquefiable area, the underground station exhibited an inclined floating behavior with a larger horizontal displacement. The liquefiable soil presented an obvious lateral spreading, mainly due to the serious liquefaction of slop upper soil. By comparison to structural displacement, the inter-floor displacement angle was increased with the increase of the ground inclined angle.

1 INTRODUCTION

Many cities are built close to water sources, which can cause a high underground water table. Due to urban planning, the underground space structure will unavoidably pass through the soft soil and sandy soil layers. For example, Nanjing Subway Line 1 and Guangdong Subway Line 2 pass through the liquefiable soil layer. Under strong earthquakes, sand ground inevitably produces liquefaction, which is a serious reason for the destruction of underground structures in liquefied sites. The 1995 Kobe earthquake severely damaged many underground projects in Kobe city (Senzai 1997; Schiff 1998). The seismic resistance of underground structures has aroused great attention from scholars. In comparison with the aboveground structures, underground structures are more difficult to observe. Chen et al. (2012, 2007) carried out a shaking table test on subway station structure and analyzed the physical quantities such as acceleration, lateral earth wall pressure, stress, and strain. With the continuous progress of computer technology, various numerical modeling has been applied to seismic analysis of underground structures. Zhuang et al. (2012) used ABAQUS finite element software to analyze the earthquake damage mechanism of the large-bay subway station structure in the bad ground soil. Zhang et al. (2018) presented an innovative method combining Laplace transform and B-spline wavelet on an interval (BSWI) finite element method, which could not only decrease the element number but also increase the time integration interval. Du et al. (2016) also used ABAQUS to simulate the seismic response of Kobe subway station during the earthquake; a unified hardening constitutive model, which can reasonably reflect dilatancy, was used to simulate the mechanical behavior of the soil. However, due to the influence of geological structure, the surface of the coastal, river, and other zones containing liquefiable soil layer is often along with a 0° to 5° slope angle. Wang et al. (2018) based on ABAQUS finite element software, revealed the seismic response characteristics of subway underground station structure in the slightly inclined liquefied ground. Based on FE-FD coupled finite element method, Hu et al. (2015) conducted

---

*Corresponding Authors: qiuyu500510@163.com and cea_zhangxw@ujn.edu.cn

numerical analysis on an artificial island with an inclined liquefaction soil layer, and the analysis showed that the damage caused by sliding of the inclined sand layer in the liquefaction process was much greater than that caused by liquefaction of horizontal sand layer. The seismic response of subway stations is an important research topic, and most scholars' studies are focused on horizontal soil. However, the seismic response in the inclined soil is seldom considered in the current subway station analysis. Therefore, it is of great academic significance and engineering application value to study the influence of the gently inclined liquefaction site under the seismic response of the ground soil-subway station structure system and to discuss the displacement and deformation of the underground structure during the liquefaction process.

2 CALCULATION MODEL

2.1 Analytical method

FLAC3D provides two different plastic volumetric strain increment formulas, including the Finn model and the Byrne model. The essence of Finn's model is to add a rising mode of dynamic pore pressure based on the Mohr-Coulomb model and assume that the rising of dynamic pore pressure is related to the increment of plastic volume strain.

Martin (1975) proposed the Finn model to solve the volumetric strain and pore water pressure changes of soil under cyclic loading. The relation between the plastic volumetric strain increment and cumulative volumetric strain and shear strain is as follows:

$$\Delta \varepsilon_{vd} = C_1 (\gamma - C_2 \varepsilon_{vd}) + \frac{C_3 \varepsilon_{vd}^2}{\gamma + C_4 \varepsilon_{vd}} \quad (1)$$

where $C_i (i = 1, 2, 3, 4)$ is constant, γ is shear strain, ε_{vd} is volumetric strain, and $\Delta \varepsilon_{vd}$ is volumetric strain increment.

Byrne (1991) simplified the Finn model and obtained the Equation (2), which is as follows:

$$\frac{\Delta \varepsilon_{vd}}{\gamma} = C_1 exp \left(-C_2 \frac{\varepsilon_{vd}}{\gamma} \right) \quad (2)$$

where C_1 and C_2 are constants, and the empirical calculation formula is:

$$C_1 = 7600 \, (D_r)^{-2.5} \quad (3)$$

$$C_2 = \frac{0.4}{C_1} \quad (4)$$

where D_r is the relative compactness of soil mass.

2.2 Model establishment and parameters

The simplified model of soil and subway station is shown in Figure 1.

In the model, the surface inclination angle is 0°, 1°, 2°, and 3°, respectively, and the influence of gently inclined liquefied soil layer on subway station is studied. The soil-subway station structural grid model when the ground incline is 2° is shown in Figure 2. The elastic constitutive model is adopted for the two-story and two-span reinforced concrete structure of the station, and Mole-Coulomb is adopted for the plain fill and bedrock. The detailed parameters are shown in Table 1. The groundwater level is 2 meters below the surface, and the surface is the drainage boundary.

The original seismic wave is filtered and baseline corrected by the Seism Signal software. The processed seismic wave is shown in Figure 3.

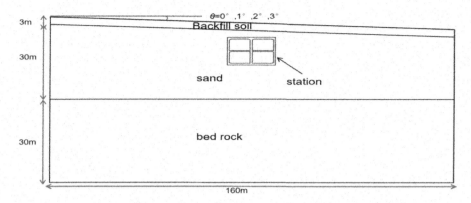

Figure 1. Schematic diagram of earth-subway station model.

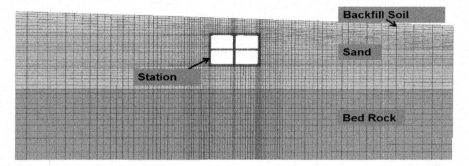

Figure 2. Soil-subway station structure grid model (incline 2°).

Table 1. The number of officially reported plague cases in the world.

Model	Shear modulus (MPa)	Bulk modulus (MPa)	Density (kg/m^3)	Friction angle (°)	Cohesion (kPa)
Backfill soil	3.3	10.0	1800.0	16	15
Sand	11.2	29.0	1800.0	30	0
Bedrock	31000.0	67000.0	2700.0	40	100
Station	14000.0	19000.0	2500.0	—	—

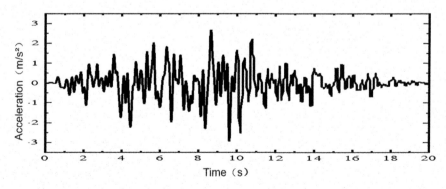

Figure 3. Input seismic wave.

3 LIQUEFACTION DISTRIBUTION OF SOIL AROUND THE STATION

Figure 4 shows the distribution of Epwpr of soils around subway stations at a 3° incline angle after the earthquake. When Epwpr ≤ 0, the soil does not liquefy, and when Epwpr = 1, the soil completely liquefies. When the liquefaction field is tilted, the liquefaction degree of soil on the left side is greater than the one on the right side, and the liquefaction degree around the station is heavier.

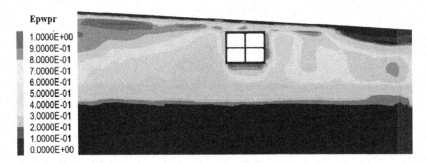

Figure 4. Liquefaction condition of soil ground (incline 3°).

4 SUBWAY STATION DEFORMATION ANALYSIS

4.1 *Vertical displacement of the subway station structure*

The displacement time-history curve of the middle part of the floor of the subway station is shown in Figure 5, from which it can be found that the station was in a floating state during the earthquake.

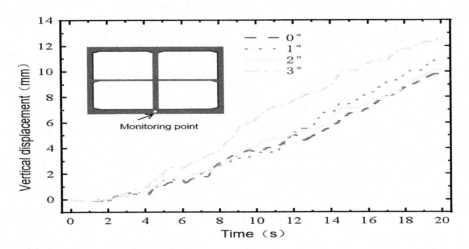

Figure 5. Vertical displacement time history curve (t = 20 s).

4.2 *Horizontal displacement of the subway station structure*

The time-history curve of the horizontal displacement of the midpoint of the station side wall is shown in Figure 6. The horizontal displacement gradually increases with the increase of the inclination angle, and the horizontal displacement difference between 0° and 3° is 30 mm.

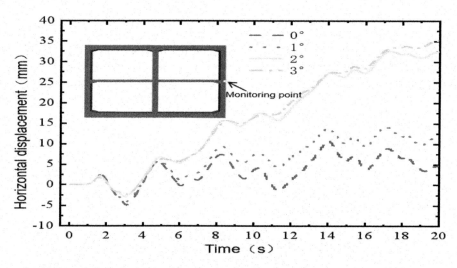

Figure 6. Horizontal displacement time history curve (t = 20 s).

4.3 *Maximum inter-story displacement angle of the subway station structure*

Table 2 shows the maximum horizontal relative displacement and the maximum inter-story displacement angle of the top and bottom of the upper and lower columns in the earthquake process. The inter-story displacement angle of the upper column is smaller than that of the lower column and increases with the increase of the ground inclination. According to the relevant provisions in Section 6 of the standard for seismic design of underground structures (GBT 51336-2018), the limit value of the elastic inter-story angular displacement of the ground-reinforced concrete frame structure is 1/550. In this paper, the structure of the station is in the elastic working state under the working condition of 0° to 2°, while the inter-story displacement angle of the structure exceeds the limit value of the specification under the working condition of 3°. Therefore, the seismic capacity of the station should be strengthened during the construction of the inclined site.

Table 2. Maximum horizontal relative displacement and maximum inter-story displacement angle of column top and bottom in the subway station.

Ground tilt angle	Hight	0° Δu	0° θ_e	1° Δu	1° θ_e	2° Δu	2° θ_e	3° Δu	3° θ_e
Upper column	5.75 m	2.92 mm	1/1968	3.98 mm	1/1445	7.82 mm	1/735	11.61 mm	1/495
Lower column	6.15 m	3.32 mm	1/1851	4.45 mm	1/1381	8.86 mm	1/693	12.98 mm	1/473

Note: ① Δu is the maximum horizontal relative displacement, and ② θ_e is the maximum inter-story displacement angle.

5 CONCLUSIONS

Through FLAC3D finite difference software, the dynamic analysis of subway stations in the liquefaction field with different inclination angles is carried out and the following conclusions are drawn.

(1) The station is in the sloping site, resulting in overall floating, and the floating amount gradually increases with the change of the inclination angle.
(2) The station in the sloping site has an obvious horizontal displacement after the earthquake, and the horizontal displacement reaches 40 mm.
(3) The maximum inter-story displacement angle increases with the increase of the inclination angle, and the maximum inter-story displacement angle of the lower column is larger than that of the upper column.

REFERENCES

Byrne, P. (1991). A cyclic shear-volume coupling and pore-pressure model for sand. C. Proceedings of the 2nd International Conference on Recent Advancesin Geotechnical E-arthquake Engineering and Soil Dynamics. *Rolla: University of Missouri*.

Chen, G.X.& Zhuang H.Y. (2007). A large-scale shaking table test for dynamic soil-subway tunnel interaction: Analysis of test results. *J. Journal of Earthquake Engineering and Engineering Vibration*. 27(1): 164–170.

Chen, G.X.& Zuo, X. (2012).Shaking table test on seismic failure characteristics of subway station structure at liquefiable ground. *J. Journal of Building Structure*.33(1): 128–137.

Du, X.L. (2016). Earthquake damage mechanism analysis of larger bay subway station by Kobe earthquake. *J. Journal of Disaster Prevention and Mitigation Engineering*,18(2): 165–171.

Hu, J.L.& Wang, G. (2015). Analyses of seismic liquefaction induced disaster in artificial island with sloping sand layer. *J. Dalian University of Technology*.55(05):504–510

Martin, G.R.& W. Finn & H.B. Seed. (1975). Fundamentals of liquefaction under cyclic loading[J]. *J.geotech.engrg.div*.101(5): p. 423–438

Senzai, (1997). A study of the damage of subway structures during the 1995 Hanshin-Awaji earthquake. *J. Cement & Concrete Composites*.

Wang, R. & Zhuang, H.Y. (2018). Seismic response of subway underground station buried in liquefiable soil foundation with the ground surface slight inclined. *J. Earthquake Engineering And Engineering Dyanmics*.38(0):130–140

Zhang, S.F.& Shen, W.& Zhang, X.W. (2018) Nondestructive ultrasonic testing in rod structure with a novel numerical Laplace based wavelet finite element method. *J. Lat. Am. j. solids struct*, 2018, 15(7).

Zhuang, H.Y. (2012). Seismic responses of surrounding site of subway station in liquefiable foundation. *J. Chinese Journal of Geotechnical Engineering*.34(01): 81–88.

Study on double diffusion phenomenon near Changjiang Estuary and its influence on coastal engineering

Baisu Zhu* & Chen Li*
CCCC Tianjin Port Engineering Institute Co., Ltd., Key Laboratory of Coastal Engineering Hydrodynamic, CCCC, Tianjin, China

ABSTRACT: Double diffusion is an important phenomenon in the ocean, which is induced by the thermohaline structure of the water column. Diffusive convection will occur when cold, fresh water overlies warm, salty water. Based on field observation in southern Changjiang Estuary, along the coast of Zhejiang, a double diffusion process was observed during spring. Our study is focused on calculating Turner (TU) angle values to describe double diffusion phenomena. During spring, the relatively cold and fresh Changjiang diluted water (CDW) covers the surface at our observation station, while the hot, salty Kuroshio water intrudes onshore from the bottom. The temperature and salinity both increase with depth. TU angles are mostly within the $-90°$ and $-45°$ intervals, which means diffusive convection is possible to occur. The Changjiang plume is the main reason to induce low temperature and low salinity of the surface layer in spring. Therefore, we believe that this region diffusion convection phenomenon occurs, and should be considered when coastal engineering and shipping are involved in this area.

1 INTRODUCTION

Oceanic mixing is a fundamental and important phenomenon in the ocean, which not only plays a decisive role in controlling the distribution of water mass properties but also has an important influence on nutrient flux and concentration of other chemical substances (Lozovatsky 2013; Matsuno 2006; Zhang 2014). As a very interesting phenomenon in the ocean, double diffusion mixing is different from turbulent mixing. It was caused by the diffusivity of salinity and temperature (Lie 1985; Shi 2007).

In fact, after the great use and development of modern ocean observation instruments in the 1960s, people discovered the "hot salt ladder" in ocean temperature and salt observation. This phenomenon has been proved to be caused by two basic double diffusion phenomena: diffusion convection and salt finger phenomenon, and plays an important role in enhancing the mixing across the isopycnic.

The double diffusion phenomenon can be divided into two types according to the variation of temperature and salinity with depth. When warm and salty water overlies cold and fresh water, temperature and salinity decrease with depth simultaneously. The water above the interface becomes denser and it will sink the upper layer. This phenomenon is called a salt finger. On the contrary, when cold, fresh water overlies warm, salty water, the temperature and salinity increase with depth. The phenomenon is manifested as diffusion convection. The double diffusion phenomenon is known to generate strong reverse flow and induce intense convection. The stability of marine structures and ships will be affected by double diffusion.

Based on the hydrologic observation data along the coast of Zhejiang, this study aims to explore the double diffusion phenomenon. This paper is organized as follows. The data and method are

---
*Corresponding Authors: zhubaisu@ccccltd.cn and lichen11@ccccltd.cn

presented in Section 2. Section 3 shows the hydrological characteristics and double diffusion phenomena in the southward Changjiang Estuary during spring. Conclusions are presented in Section 4.

2 DATA AND METHOD

Observations were carried out in April 2017. One transects includes 3 sampling stations, which are located on the coast of Zhejiang (Figure 2). We used the Conductivity-Temperature-Depth profiler (CTD, SBE25), sampling at 6 Hz, to measure the temperature and salinity. The photo of the field observation instrument is shown in Figure 1. The double-diffusive processes are mainly calculated Turner (TU) angle (Ruddick 1983) values to discuss.

Figure 1. Field observation of conductivity-temperature-depth profiler (CTD).

Turner (1973) suggested the use of the gradient ratio of thermohaline to measure the strength of the double diffusion phenomenon. The formula is as follows:

$$R\rho = \frac{\alpha \theta_z}{\beta S_z} \quad (1)$$

where α is the thermal expansion coefficient ($\alpha = -\rho \partial \rho / \partial \theta$), β is the haline contraction coefficient ($\alpha = -\rho \partial \rho / \partial S$), ρ is density, θ_z and S_z represent the vertical gradients of temperature and salinity, respectively. When $R\rho$ approaches 1, both the salt finger and diffusion convection intensity reach the maximum. To distinguish the two double diffusion processes more clearly, Ruddick (1983) introduced TU Angle, which is defined as: $TU = tan^{-1}(\alpha \frac{\partial \theta}{\partial z} - \beta \frac{\partial s}{\partial z}, \alpha \frac{\partial \theta}{\partial z} + \beta \frac{\partial s}{\partial z})$. The relation between $R\rho$ and TU Angle is:

$$R\rho = -\tan(TU + 45) \quad (2)$$

When TU is between $-90°$ and $-45°$ ($0<R\rho<1$), the water column is conducive to diffusive convection happened; for TU between $-45°$ and $45°$ ($-\infty<R\rho<0$), the water column is in a stable stratified; with TU between 45° and 90° ($1<R\rho<+\infty$), the water column is favorable to salt finger. Other TU values represent water column is in an unstable stratified.

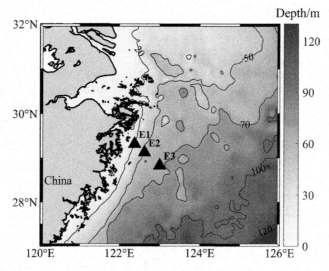

Figure 2. Bathymetry of the study area. Black triangles represent the transect stations obtained during the spring of 2017 and the station name is indicated nearby.

3 RESULTS AND DISCUSSION

The profiles of the temperature and salinity are shown in Figures 3 and 4. Hydrological distribution in our study area can be described approximately. During spring, the Changjiang diluted water (CDW) spread south along the coast. The CDW, which is characterized by low salinity, occupied the Jiangsu and Zhejiang coasts. The boundary of these coasts is identified by an isoline of 31 (Bai 2014; Quan 2013). The cold, fresh CDW occupies the surface layer in stations E1 and E2; while hot, salty TWC, and KC intrude onshore from the bottom near the shelf break region.

The surface layer water is relatively cold (T < 15°C) and fresh (S < 31) with the temperature and salinity all increasing from the surface to the bed. The highest temperature ($\sim$ 17°C) and salinity

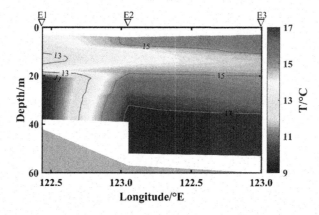

Figure 3. Vertical distribution of temperature in April 2017 at stations E1, E2, and E3. Gray solid lines represent temperature contours.

(> 34) occur at the bottom layer. The vertical variation of temperature and salinity can be generally separated into two layers: cold and fresh waters influenced by CDW in the surface layer; warm and salty waters in the bottom layer. The water is well mixed in the bottom layer and stratifies in the upper ~ 30 m.

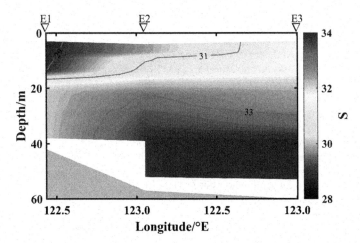

Figure 4. Vertical distribution of salinity in April 2017 at stations E1, E2, and E3. Gray solid lines represent salinity contours.

Take station E2 as an example, which as a typical station was chosen for analysis. We calculate TU angle values in station E2 and obtained the profiles of T, S, and Tu. The vertical distributions of temperature and salinity at E2 provide suitable environments for the occurrence of diffusive convection. At station E2 (Figure 5), which is nearest the Changjiang Estuary and the upper layer was covered by CDW (depth less than 18 m). Both the temperature and salinity increase with depth (from the sea surface to the bottom). Most of the TU angles of the whole profile are between the −90° and −45° intervals, which means diffusive convection is possible. From 5 m to the 10 m, the salinity increases while the temperature decreases, so the TU values between −45° and 45° indicate the water is generally stable (Figure 5c). Therefore, to avoid structural instability caused

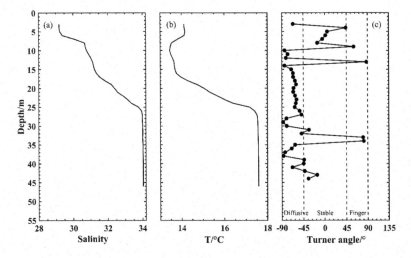

Figure 5. Vertical profiles of (a) salinity, (b) temperature, and (c) TU angle at station E2.

by strong convection, the occurrence of double diffusion phenomenon should be considered in regional ocean engineering.

4 CONCLUSIONS

Double diffusion is a universal phenomenon in the ocean, which is the most important mechanism affecting mixing across the isopycnic surface and the driving force of thermohaline circulation in the ocean. Due to its proximity to land, shelf area has a direct impact on human life. Therefore, the study of double diffusion in shelf area occupies an important and special position in the global ocean. However, due to many external factors, it is difficult for people to have a deep understanding of it. The ECS is the main area of maritime transportation, military activities, and fishery production in China. The study of double diffusion provides a sufficient theoretical basis for the technical application of these industries. Therefore, it is not only important in scientific research but also imperative to promote the development of China's maritime undertakings.

Based on the field observations in the south of the Changjiang Estuary, we studied the double diffusion process in the Changjiang plume. The diffusion convection phenomenon is mainly caused by the influence of the water masses and runoffs because it is consistent with the variations of temperature and salinity with depth on the surface. During spring, the CDW spreads southward, reaching our sampling stations. Affected by water masses, observation finds the relatively cold and fresh cover of the surface layer of coastal water. The hot, salty Kuroshio water intrudes onshore from the bottom. Temperature and salinity both increase from the surface to the bed. The calculated TU Angle shows that the strongest diffusion convection occurs in the whole water column, and the water column only has a stable stratification at 5 to 10 m. The low temperature and low salinity water of the Changjiang plume provide favorable conditions for the occurrence of diffusion convection. Therefore, we believe that this station is the main location where the diffusion convection phenomenon occurs during spring.

Through the field observation and analysis results, this paper has a more detailed description and formation mechanism analysis of the double diffusion phenomenon in the Changjiang river plume. Our study preliminarily determined the location and season of the diffusion convection in the Changjiang river plume provided an observation basis for the double diffusion phenomenon in other plumes and had reference value for the study of the dynamic mechanism. It provides dynamic characteristics for the implementation of coastal engineering. One important question remaining is to what extent ocean engineering is affected by a double diffusion process. Therefore, more numerical simulations or further comprehensive observations are needed to address this question in the future, which may provide further implications for understanding the construction of coastal engineering in the area.

REFERENCES

Bai, Y. He, X. Q. Pan, D. L. Chen, C. T. A. Kang, Y. Chen, X. Y. Cai, W. J. (2014). Summertime changjiang river plume variation during 1998–2010. *Journal of Geophysical Research: Oceans.* 119(9), 6238–6257.

Lie, H. J. (1985). Wintertime temperature-salinity characteristics in the Southeastern Hwanghae (Yellow Sea). *Journal of Oceanography.* 41, 291–298.

Lozovatsky, I. Liu, Z. Fernando, H. (2013). The TKE dissipation rate in the northern South China Sea. *Ocean Dynamics.* 63(11–12):1189–1201.

Matsuno, T. Lee, J. S. Shimizu, M. Kim, S. H. Pang, I. C. (2006). Measurements of the turbulent energy dissipation rate ε and an evaluation of the dispersion process of the Changjiang Diluted Water in the East China Sea. *Journal of Geophysical Research: Oceans*, 111(C11), C11S09.

Quan, Q. Mao, X. Y. Yang, X. D. Hu, Y. Y. Zhang, H. Y. Jiang, W. S. (2013). Seasonal variations of several main water masses in the southern Yellow Sea and East China Sea in 2011. *Journal of Ocean University of China.* 12(4), 524–536.

Ruddick, B. R. A. (1983). practical indicator of the stability of the water column to double-diffusive activity. *Deep-Sea Research*. 30, 1105–1107.
Shi, J. & Wei, H. (2007). Evidence of double diffusion in the East China Sea. *Journal of Marine Systems*. 67, 272–281.
Turner, J. S. (1963). *Buoyancy Effects in Fluids*. Cambridge Universit Press, Cambridge, UK, 367 pp.
Zhang, W. J. Zhu, S. X. Li, X. Q. Ruan, K. Guan, W. B. Peng, J. (2014). Impact of tide induced residual current and tidal mixing on the low salinity water lens in the northeast out of the Changjiang Estuary (in Chinese with English abstract). *Acta Oceanologica Sinica*. 36(3), 9–18.

Numerical simulation study on the stability of abandoned soil field of Songkte Bridge

He Jian*, Zhao Li* & Ren Qiang*
Guizhou Smart Water Conservancy Technology Co., Ltd., Guizhou, China

ABSTRACT: When the pier of the proposed bridge project is located in the area of the existing abandoned soil site, the stability of the abandoned soil site itself is crucial to the deformation and safety of the bridge structure. Based on the engineering examples and the engineering geological conditions of the abandoned site, the influence of the overall stability and its deformation on the pier structure of the proposed bridge is analyzed. Then two treatment schemes were proposed for the abandoned soil field. The control effect of each scheme on soil and bridge structure deformation of abandoned soil sites is studied in detail. This study can provide some guidance for engineering construction.

1 INTRODUCTION

The stability of the existing abandoned soil is very important to the deformation and safety of the proposed bridge engineering structure within its scope. This paper takes it as the research object and studies it with engineering examples. Songkan bridge is proposed to be built as a span bridge. Pile foundation and expanded foundation. Piers 10# ~ 12# of the proposed super large bridge are located in a high-speed construction abandoned soil site. The spatial position relationship between the bridge pier and the abandoned soil site is shown in Figure 1.

Figure 1. Space location of bridge pier and spoil yard.

In order to ensure the safety of the construction and operation of the proposed super large bridge, the influence of the stability and deformation of the abandoned soil field on the bridge pier should

---

*Corresponding Authors: 837870207@qq.com, rqing@139.com and zhaoli@gzzhsl.cn

be systematically analyzed, and targeted engineering treatment measures should be put forward. This paper first carries out a detailed investigation of the engineering geological conditions of the abandoned soil field area.

On this basis, the calculation model of spoil field stability is constructed, and the overall stability of the spoil field is analyzed. Then we put forward two kinds of projects for casting the field treatment scheme. Based on the finite element theory, We use Midas-GTS to process measures numerical simulation model (Li 2012; Wang 2013), comprehensively evaluate the treatment effect of each measure, and select the optimal scheme, so as to provide guidance for engineering construction.

2 BASIC CHARACTERISTICS OF ABANDONED SOIL SITE

The abandoned soil of a high-speed construction site is located in the range of 76 m to 160m. The abandoned soil site is about 240m long and 140 m wide, with a plane area of about 33,000 m2. The maximum filling depth is about 25m, the maximum filling height is 46m, and the filling volume is about 340,000 m^3.

Drilling reveals that its composition is clay, gravel, stone, and crushed stone, and the parent rock is muddy dolomite and dolomite, with a maximum thickness of about 25m. The lower original soil is residual slope clay, being plastic.

The lower original soil is residual slope clay, being plastic. According to the measured data of the topographic section on August 13, 2017, the pier 10~12# of Songkan Bridge is located on the abandoned soil field, and the abandoned soil is the newly accumulated plain filling soil. Due to the uneven distribution of abandoned soil thickness, the thickness of the front, and the thickness of the back, there is poor consolidation settlement, resulting in the formation of cracks in the rear of the abandoned soil field. In addition, the crack width will widen and deepen with the increase of settlement, which is conducive to rainfall infiltration, resulting in the overall reduction of the stability of the abandoned soil field. It is easy to collapse under the action of construction disturbance and rainstorms.

3 EVALUATION OF OVERALL STABILITY

3.1 Calculation model and method

In the natural state, the rear edge of the slope body is locally cracked. According to the field measured section data, the bridge axis direction (potential main sliding surface C-C′) is taken as the stability analysis and calculation section.

The geological model was constructed by Midas GTS, the strength subtraction was used as the calculation theory of the field stability (Chen 2005), and the stability and deformation status of the field were calculated and analyzed (Deng 2012; Wang 2020). The calculation model of the field is shown in Figure 2.

Figure 2. A numerical analysis and a computational model.

3.2 Mechanical parameters of the rock mass

The value of rock mass mechanical parameters are comprehensively determined according to geological engineering surveys, indoor and outdoor tests, engineering geological analogy, and inversion calculation and analysis, as shown in Table 1.

Table 1. Values of geotechnical physical parameters.

Rock soil	r (kN/m3)	C (kPa)	φ (°)	E (GPa)	μ
plain fill	19	31.8	10.9	0.02	0.35
undisturbed soil	18	19	12	0.05	0.33
intense weathering	24.5	200	35	10	0.30
Medium weathering	26.5	700	45	30	0.26

3.3 Calculation results

The stability calculation results in the natural state of the abandoned field are shown in Table 2, Figures 3 and 4.

Table 2. Values of geotechnical physical parameters.

Calculation condition	Computation method	Stability coefficient	Control standards
Normal working conditions	SRM	1.025	1.35
Rainstorm conditions	SRM	0.912	1.25

Figure 3. Calculation results of normal working conditions.

Figure 4. Calculation results of rainstorm working conditions.

According to the calculation results, the stability of the abandoned soil field does not meet the safety control standard of the slope. The abandoned soil field is in an unstable state in the natural state and an unstable state in the rainstorm condition. In addition, the dump is recently filled. According to the calculation of the settlement deformation in Figure. 5, the displacement deformation is about 42cm.

The horizontal displacement is about 40cm. If the deformation and stability of the dump are not controlled in time, it will have a huge impact on the construction of the bridge pile foundation and seriously threaten the safety of bridge construction.

Figure 5. Consolidation settlement deformation (total deformation).

4 NUMERICAL SIMULATION AND ANALYSIS OF 3 LOCAL TREATMENT MEASURES

According to the above calculation and analysis, the spoil site is unstable and likely to collapse under rainstorm conditions, and its consolidation and settlement deformation is large, so it is required to be treated for the spoil site to ensure the safe construction of the bridge engineering.

There are the following two engineering protection design schemes. Scheme 1: partial load reduction + antiskid pile; Scheme 2: partial load reduction + antiskid pile and anchor cable. And numerical simulation analysis is used to evaluate the effect of each scheme.

4.1 *Analysis of the result of cutting square and reducing the load*

After load reduction of the dump, finite element numerical analysis. See Figure 6 and soil deformation in Figure 7.

Numerical simulation shows that the overall stability coefficient of the spoil yard is 1.112, which does not meet the slope stability safety control standard (1.35); the soil consolidation settlement deformation decreases from 42cm to 15cm, and the horizontal deformation decreases from 40cm

Figure 6. Stability calculation results.

to about 10cm. Although the settlement deformation is largely controlled, the bridge construction requires further treatment measures for the spoil field.

Figure 7. Consolidation settlement deformation (horizontal).

4.2 *Analysis of treatment results*

The stability and deformation of the spoil yard do not meet the safety control requirements. After analysis and calculation of the potential main sliding surface of the spoil site, see the sliding thrust curve diagram, the antiskid pile is planned to be laid in A and B, and the antiskid pile is 23m. Among them, the type A antiskid pile is 22m long, and the type B antiskid pile is 30m long. Scheme 1: partial cutting load reduction + antiskid pile; 2: partial cutting load reduction + antiskid pile and anchor cable shall be used to treat the spoil site. Finite element numerical simulation is used to evaluate the governance effect of various schemes.

The stability and deformation of the spoil yard after load reduction, the A-skid pile, is 22m long and 30m long. Scheme 1: partial cutting load reduction + anti-sliding pile; 2: partial cutting load reduction + antiskid pile and anchor cable, and the control effect of the treatment scheme.

(1) Cutting side and load reduction + antiskid pile scheme

Figure 8 demonstrates the stability calculation results, and Figure 9 the soil deformation calculation results.

Figure 8. Scheme 1 stability calculation results.

After the engineering treatment of Scheme 1, the stability coefficient of the abandoned soil field is 2.23, which meets the safety control standard of the slope, and the deformation of the abandoned soil field has been controlled within a reasonable range. After the construction of the antiskid pile, the maximum horizontal displacement of the antiskid pile and the maximum horizontal displacement of the antiskid pile is 4.0cm, and that of the antiskid pile is 4.2cm. The deformation meets the deformation control requirements of the antiskid pile. After the construction of the bridge pile foundation, the maximum horizontal displacement curve of 10# and 11# pier shows

Figure 9. Scheme 1 deformation of soil consolidation (horizontal).

that the maximum horizontal displacement of 10# pier is 1.6mm, and the maximum horizontal displacement of 11# pier is 2.7mm, which meets the deformation control requirements of the special bridge (6mm). It shows that the load reduction + antiskid pile scheme is good. It should be noted that pier 12# is outside the range of the dump.

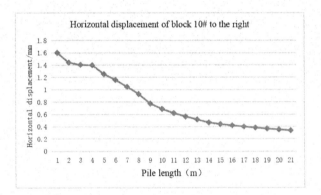

Figure 10. Horizontal displacement curve of pile foundation on pier 10 (Scheme 1).

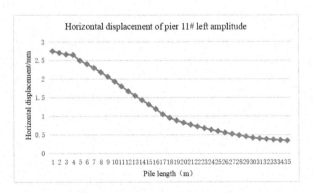

Figure 11. Horizontal displacement curve of pile foundation of pier # 11 (Scheme 1).

(2) Cutting square load reduction + anti-slide pile + anchor cable scheme

The project of cutting square load reduction + anti-slide pile + anchor cable is adopted for engineering treatment of the abandoned soil field. The anchor cable is prestressed (6 strands), the length of the anchorage section is 8m, and the applied prestress is 300KN. The numerical calculation model is shown in the figure, and the calculation results are shown in the figure.

Figure 12. Scheme 2 stability calculation results.

Figure 13. Scheme 2 Settlement deformation and deformation of soil consolidation.

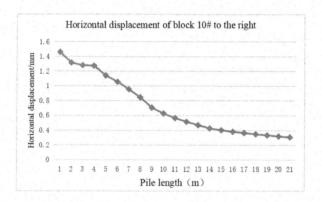

Figure 14. Horizontal displacement curve of 10 (Scheme 2).

After the engineering treatment of Scheme 2, the stability of the spoil field was further improved under the action of the prestressed anchor cable, reaching 2.45. For the abandoned soil and bridge pile foundation, after the treatment of Scheme 1, the maximum deformation of soil horizontal direction is 4.1mm, and the maximum horizontal displacement of the bridge pile foundation after construction is 2.7mm. After using Scheme 2, the maximum horizontal deformation of the soil is 4mm, and the maximum deformation of the bridge pile foundation is 2.4mm. The comparative analysis shows that the displacement deformation of abandoned soil sites and bridge pile foundation deformation is not obvious.

Considering the treatment effect of Scheme 1 and Scheme 2, on the premise of meeting the requirements of the dump stability and the bridge structure deformation control, Scheme 1 is better than Scheme 2.

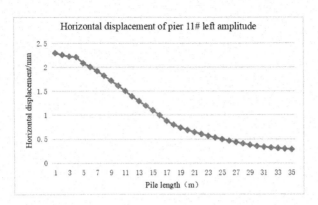

Figure 15. Horizontal displacement curve of pile foundation of pier # 11 (Scheme 2).

5 CONCLUSION

Through systematic analysis of the stability of abandoned soil and soil deformation on bridge pile foundation, the following conclusions:

(1) The abandoned soil site is unstable under a natural state, it is easy to collapse under rainstorm conditions, and the horizontal deformation of the soil site reaches 42cm after consolidation and settlement.
(2) After the load reduction of the part of the abandoned field, its stability increases, and the consolidation settlement deformation is controlled to a certain extent, but generally, it does not meet the safety control standards of the special bridge.
(3) After using Scheme 1 for the engineering treatment, the overall stability of the spoil yard is 2.23, which meets the slope safety control standards; The structure meets the requirement of deformation control.
(4) After using the cutting load reduction + antiskid pile + anchor cable, the stability of the spoil field is 2.45, the maximum horizontal deformation of the soil is 4mm, and the maximum deformation of the bridge pile foundation is 2.4mm. Compared with Scheme 1, the control effect of soil body displacement deformation and bridge pile foundation deformation is not obvious.

To compare the governance effect of Scheme 1 and Scheme 2, Scheme 1 is superior to Scheme 2 in terms of technology, economy, and security. This study can provide some guidance for similar engineering construction.

REFERENCES

Chen Zuyu, Wang Xiaogang, Yang Jian. *Stability analysis of rock slope – principle, method, and procedure* [M]. Beijing: China Water and Power Press, 2005.
Deng Shuang, Liang Zhengyong. Research on secondary excavation stability of highway cutting slope based on Midas/GTS [J]. *Highway engineering*, 2019, 44(06):266–270.
LI Zhi. *Application of Midas/GTS in geotechnical engineering* [M]. Beijing: China Architecture and Building Press, 2012.
Wang Haitao. *Numerical analysis and design of Midas/GTS geotechnical engineering* [M]. Dalian: Dalian University of Technology Press, 2013.
Wang Yangxing, Qiu Zhiyang. Analysis of slope stability in municipal or highway engineering construction based on midas and lizheng software [J]. *Value engineering*, 2020, 39(05): 213–215.

Application study on defect analysis and treatment of existing frame structure buildings

Si Daolin*, Qu Dalin* & Wang Huiling*
Jinan Engineering Polytechnic, Jinan, China

ABSTRACT: Through the engineering practice of the defect analysis and treatment analysis of existing frame structure buildings, this paper sorted out the common structural defects of existing frame structure buildings, expounded the treatment methods of various component defects, and provided a reference for the treatment of similar frame structure buildings.

1 INTRODUCTION

The teaching building of a college in Shandong is a reinforced concrete frame structure building, with one floor underground and six floors above the ground. The construction of the main frame structure was completed in 2015, and disputes between the construction parties led to the building being shelved for five years after the completion of the main body. Because the main structure of the building has been exposed for a long time, and there are many problems such as lax quality control in the construction process, the building has many structural defects. In order to continue the subsequent construction of the building, it is necessary to analyze the defects of the structural components of the building and put forward treatment suggestions.

According to the different structural systems of the frame structure, this paper analyzed the on-site defects and proposed the treatment methods of the building according to the column component, the beam-slab component, and the stair component, respectively.

2 ANALYSIS AND TREATMENT OF COLUMN COMPONENT DEFECTS

2.1 *Defect analysis*

During the on-site inspection, it was found that there were different degrees of poor concrete bonding and holes at the construction joints of the frame columns below the beam-column joints of the building, as shown in Figure 1. The concrete at the column root is loose and not dense, as shown in Figure 2.

The reason for this problem is that the concrete vibrates unevenly during the construction of the frame columns, and there is a vibration leakage phenomenon at the column root and construction joints.

2.2 *Defect treatment*

The replacement concrete reinforcement method should be adopted to deal with the defects for the poor combination of frame-column construction joints at beam-column joints and the components with loose and uncompacted concrete at the root of the columns. The replacement should be carried out under the condition that the component is completely unloaded, and the replaced components should be reliably supported before the replacement.

---

*Corresponding Authors: sdl198532@163.com, dalin82@126.com and gcxyjjc@126.com

Figure 1. Poor concrete bonding at the construction joints.

Figure 2. Unconsolidated concrete at the column root.

Under the unloading state, the defective concrete shall be chiseled clean. For the frame column with a poor combination of frame-column construction joints at beam-column joints, the extension to both sides of the construction joint shall not be less than 100mm when chiseling the hole. When chiseling the hole at the column root with non-dense concrete, the extension to the surrounding solid part shall not be less than 100mm, and the deepening from the hole depth to the solid part shall be more than 10mm. The hole edge should be chiseled into a 1:3 slope bell mouth.

When replacing, an interfacial agent is applied on the joint surface of the new and old concrete, and then the original defective concrete is replaced by high-strength micro-expansion non-vibrating grouting material with a strength grade no less than C45.

3 ANALYSIS AND TREATMENT OF BEAM-SLAB COMPONENT DEFECTS

3.1 *Defect analysis*

The defects of beam-slab members in this building are more prominent, which mainly include the defects of beam-slab reinforcement and beam-slab concrete.

3.1.1 *Reinforcement defect analysis*
Due to the inadequate control of the reinforcement protection layer thickness during construction, the minimum thickness of the concrete protective layer was not strictly followed. In addition, the main component was exposed for a long time, resulting in the exposure and corrosion of the reinforcement in the beam and plate and beam joints of each layer, as shown in Figure 3. There

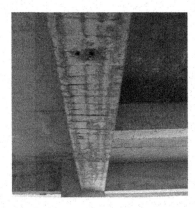 

Figure 3. Exposed reinforcement at beam bottom.

Figure 4. Exposed reinforcement in the skylight plate.

are many cracks along the reinforcement, exposed reinforcement, and corrosion in the skylight top cantilever plate, as shown in Figure 4.

The placement of the secondary beam longitudinal bars in the beam joint is unreasonable, and the placement position of the secondary beam longitudinal bars is too low, which results in the exposure of the secondary beam longitudinal bars, as shown in Figure 5. The reinforcement at the local beam joints is exposed, as shown in Figure 6.

Figure 5.   Exposed reinforcement of secondary beam.

Figure 6.   Exposed reinforcement of beam joint.

3.1.2 *Concrete defect analysis*

Due to the poor vibrating of the concrete during construction, inadequate post-maintenance, and the long-term exposed corrosion of the building, the concrete of the beam-slab members in the building has serious defects, such as concrete honeycombs, holes, and slag inclusions, as shown in Figure 7. There are different degrees of concrete shrinkage cracks in individual beam-slab members, as shown in Figure 8. The concrete of some roof slabs and roof beams has serious defects, such as cracks penetrating the floor slab.

Figure 7.   Concrete honeycombs.

Figure 8.   Concrete shrinkage cracks.

3.2 Defect treatment

3.2.1 Reinforcement defect treatment

For the beam-slab members with exposed, corroded, and rust-swollen steel bars, the loose concrete on the surface of the beam-slab members should be removed until the dense part, and the steel bars should be treated with rust-removing treatment and rust-inhibiting agent. Then the beam members shall be coated with 25mm thick polymer repair mortar, and the slab members shall be coated with 15mm thick polymer repair mortar.

In the case that the retained position of the longitudinal reinforcement of the secondary beam is too low, the beam should be supported first, the original beam should be unloaded, the exposed part of the longitudinal reinforcement should be cut off, and the concrete of the original beam should be removed. The newly added reinforcement should be planted in the main beam at one end, the other end should be welded with the longitudinal reinforcement of the original beam, and the single-sided weld is 10d. The removed part of the original beam should be repaired according to the original section size with high-strength micro-expansion non-vibrating grouting material, whose strength grade should not be less than C45. The new and old concrete joint surfaces should be painted with an interface agent.

For the exposed steel bars on the upper part of the beam at the top beam node, the exposed steel bars should be bent downward and welded with the newly added steel bars for reliable anchoring. The original beam concrete surface is chipped, coated with an interface agent, and repaired by high-strength micro-expansion non-vibrating grouting material whose strength grade should not be less than C45.

3.2.2 Concrete defect treatment

Different treatment measures shall be taken according to the width of the concrete shrinkage cracks of the beam-slab members in this project. Cracks with a width less than or equal to 0.2 mm should be sealed with a sealant, such as JH structural anchoring adhesive; for cracks greater than 0.2 mm, a special sealant or epoxy resin should be used for pressure grouting.

For the components with uncompacted concrete, such as honeycombs, holes, and slag inclusions, the loose concrete on the surface should be removed to the dense place, and then the steel bars should be rusted and painted with rust inhibitors. And the high-strength micro-expansion non-vibrating grouting material, whose strength grade should not be less than C45, should be repaired according to the original section size.

4 ANALYSIS AND TREATMENT OF STAIR COMPONENT DEFECTS

4.1 Defect analysis

There are many defects in the construction joints at the bottom of the ladder slabs in the building, such as loose concrete, poor bonding, exposed reinforcement, and corrosion, as shown in Figure 9. Some of the ladder slabs with small thickness have exposed steel bars at the supports, as shown in Figure 10.

4.2 Defect treatment

For the poor bonding of concrete and exposed reinforcement at the construction joint of the ladder slab, the poor bonding and loose concrete should be removed to the dense place, the steel bars should be de-rusted, the rust inhibitor should be painted, and then wiped polymer repair mortar to the bottom of the original plate flush. If the loss rate of the reinforcement section exceeds 5%, carbon fiber should be pasted on the bottom of the board for reinforcing treatment.

Given the small thickness of the ladder slab and the exposed reinforcement at the support of the ladder slab, the exposed reinforcement shall be de-rusted and coated with rust inhibitor, then the

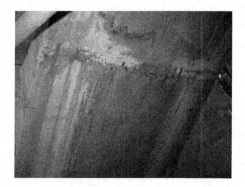

Figure 9. Exposed reinforcement at ladder slabs bottom.

Figure 10. Exposed reinforcement of ladder slab support.

polymer repair mortar shall be plastered on the top of the slab to repair the steps, and the carbon fiber shall be pasted on the bottom of the slab for reinforcing treatment.

5 CONCLUSION

There are a lot of defects in cast-in-place reinforced concrete buildings, such as cracks and exposed reinforcement, especially for buildings that have been idle for a long time due to performance disputes. The main reason for the defects of reinforced concrete buildings is that there are loopholes in the quality control during the construction process, especially the control of the thickness of the steel protective layer and the concrete vibration and maintenance is not in place.

Therefore, for new projects, we should strictly control the quality factors and implement refined quality management in the construction process to meet the functional and practical requirements of the building.

REFERENCES

Liu Xiaojun, Guo Lu, Liu Ming, Wang Qiling(2022). Discussion on relationship between temperature control of steam curing and cracks in double T-shaped plates of prestressed concrete. *J. Building Technology Development*. 49(04): 70–72.

Wang Min(2021). Reinforcement design of an existing building by column pulling. *J. Shanxi Architecture*. 47(07): 43–45. DOI:10.13719/j.cnki.1009-6825.2021.07.016.

Xie Guanpeng(2021). Method of shear wall in engineering working draws of precast concrete structures. *J. Journal of Taizhou Polytechnic College*. 21(02): 64–66.

Zhao Shanying(2021). Analysis of a case of reinforcement and repair of reinforced concrete frame-shear structure. *J. Building Structure*. 51(S1): 1666–1668.

Analysis of the stratum deformation law and influence zone for double-line tunnels in water-rich sand layer

Jiaying Zhang*
CCCC Tianjin Port Engineering Institute Co., Ltd., Tianjin, Tianjin, China
Key Laboratory of Port Geotechnical Engineering of Ministry of Communication, Tianjin, Tianjin, China
Key Laboratory of Geotechnical Engineering of Tianjin, Tianjin, Tianjin, China
CCCC First Harbor Engineering Company Ltd., Tianjin, China

ABSTRACT: The phase II of Harbin Metro Line 3 is in the rapid construction stage. According to the project plan, the section of Hesong Street station to Heshan Street station will change from an overlapping double-line to a parallel double-line. In this paper, based on the Harbin Metro Line 3 project, numerical models of overlapping and parallel double-line tunnels are established by Plaxis3D to simulate the construction process. According to the additional deformation of ground surface and tunnel hole, this paper analyzes the interaction influence degree of overlapping and parallel tunnels respectively and defines the strong, weak, and no influence zones of close construction. The numerical simulation result has been verified with the field monitoring data. The findings can be used to predict the influence degree of double-line tunnels and provide a reference for double-line tunnel settlement control in the water-rich sand layer of the Harbin area.

1 INTRODUCTION

Currently, subway construction in the Harbin region is rapidly developing. The subway tunnel construction will inevitably cause surrounding strata and ground surface deformation. And in serious situations, it will also lead to incline cracking of buildings and collapse of roads, which will threaten the stability of structures and tunnel construction safety. At the same time, due to the low cohesion, high porosity, and strong water permeability of sand, the tunnel excavation disturbance can easily lead to sudden collapse and excessive ground subsidence.

Because of the interaction between double-line tunnels, the ground deformation law of double-line tunnel excavation is quite different from that of single-line tunnel excavation. Theoretical analysis, numerical calculation, and field monitoring are used to study the adjacent tunnel construction problems. The theoretical solution can be obtained by the analytical method, which is convenient and requires less computation, but it is difficult to deal with the problems of inhomogeneous, nonlinear, and complex boundary conditions. The numerical simulation method is applicable and can overcome theoretical and empirical analysis shortcomings. Suchatvee Suwansawat and Herbert H. Einstein (2007) analyzed the monitoring data of the Bangkok metro project and believed that parallel and overlapping double-line tunnels could predict surface deformation by superimposing Gaussian curves. Hamid Chakeri, Rohola Hasanpour, Mehmet Ali Hindistan, and Bathtiyar Ünver (2011) established the parallel double-line tunnel 3D model for Tehran metro project and studied the influence of tunnel spacing, excavation sequence, and other factors on surface deformation and soil stress. Wei Gang and Pang Siyuan (2014) established the three-dimensional analytical solution of soil deformation based on the two-dimensional analytical solution of soil deformation caused by

---

*Corresponding Author: zhangjiaying2010@163.com

soil loss in double-line horizontal parallel tunnel construction, and the calculation showed that the predicted result was in good agreement with the measured result. Fan Yu, Su Yi, Yuan Yong, and Yao Xupeng (2020), relying on the double-line tunnels of Guangzhou Metro, researched the ground settlement law of tunnel excavation in the soft soil of limestone composite stratum and deduced the relative spacing coefficient of double-line tunnels based on the superposition principle. Qin Huihui (2012), based on the overlapping tunnels project of Beijing Metro Line 6, proposed the tunnel proximity influence zone by additional surface deformation, additional deformation around the tunnel hole, and stratum plastic zone. Zhou Zilian (2019) analyzed the soil properties of the Songhua River and the influence of different construction parameters on the sand mechanical state based on the Harbin Metro Line 2 project. Lu Xilin, Zhao Yucheng, Cai Jiantao, and Yao Xupeng (2020) studied the deformation characteristics of water-rich sandy stratum subsidence induced by support pressure and stratum loss change through 3D elastic-plastic finite element numerical simulation of tunnel excavation face. Furthermore, the influence of soil parameters changes and groundwater seepage are analyzed.

It can be seen that there have been some relevant research results on the stratum deformation law of double-line shield tunnels, but most of them are based on the soft clay geological condition. The definition of construction distance, interaction mechanism, and settlement deformation law of double-line tunnels in water-rich sand layers still need further research.

Based on the project between He Song Street station and He Shan Street station of Harbin Metro Line 3 Phase II, the deformation and evolution law of double-line tunnels are studied by numerical simulation and field monitoring, and the criterion of interaction influence zoning based on additional deformation of ground surface and tunnel hole is proposed. The research result can provide a reference for the deformation theory study of tunnels approaching construction in the water-rich sand area.

2 PROJECT PROFILE

The phase II of Metro Line 3 total length is about 32km, with 34 underground stations. The section starts from Hesong Street station and gradually changes from an overlapping double-line to a parallel double-line. The length of the left line is 834.179m, the right line is 824.638m, and the overlapping section is 538.9m. A schematic diagram of the tunnel project is shown in Figure 1.

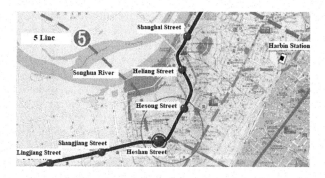

Figure 1. Plan of tunnel project between Hesong Street station and Heshan Street station.

The longitudinal section is a "V" shape, and the tunnel is deeply buried. The buried soil above the tunnel is about 11.5m $\sim$ 30m. The outer diameter of the tunnel is 6m, the inner diameter is 5.4m, the thickness of the assembled concrete lining section is 300mm, the ring width is 1.2m, and staggered assembly is adopted. The construction adopts an earth pressure balanced shield machine. The stratum which the tunnel mainly passes is the Songhua River floodplain geomorphic unit, and the ground elevation is about 118 $\sim$ 130m. The topographic fluctuation is large, the distribution of foundation soil is not uniform, and the property changes greatly. The stratum at tunnel excavation depth is mainly composed of sandy soil with strong permeability and silty clay with poor stability. Due to the good permeability of the medium sand layer, the soil is easy to be disturbed, and the strength is reduced during excavation. The sand flow phenomenon easily occurs under the water head difference, resulting in water gushing and sand gushing in the foundation pit. There are main traffic roads above the construction site, and heavy traffic and dense underground pipelines cause the construction risks. According to the survey report, the buried depth of the initial pore water level is 2.7~9.80m, the buried depth of static groundwater level is 2.30~8.90m, and the elevation is 112.96~117.82m (Dalian elevation system).

3 SHIELD CONSTRUCTION SIMULATION OF DOUBLE-LINE TUNNEL

Plaxis 3D is used for numerical calculation in this paper. Based on the engineering geological condition and construction method, HS hardened soil constitutive model is adopted for the soil, and the linear elastic model is adopted for the segment with 300mm thickness. The underground water level is set at -3m from the surface, the soil below the water level is saturated, and the pore water pressure remains unchanged. The soil layer is approximately simplified into four layers :(1) miscellaneous fill with the thickness of 3m (2) silt with the thickness of 7.5m (3) fine sand with the thickness of 4.5m (4) medium sand with the thickness of 65m. Although establishing the complete tunnel model can reflect the real condition of overlapping and parallel tunnels, the grid is too complicated, and the iterative calculation is difficult. Therefore the model is simplified as 44m linear tunnels. It is assumed that the position of one tunnel is unchanged, and the other takes a different net distance around it.

Table 1. Material parameters of each soil layer.

Parameter	Miscellaneous fill	Silt	Fine sand	Medium sand
Constitutive model	HS	HS	HS	HS
γ_{unsat}	18.5	18.4	19.3	20.6
γ_{sat}	19.5	19.4	20.3	21.6
$E_{50}(kN/m^2)$	3.0×10^4	6.0×10^4	9.0×10^4	6.0×10^4
$E_{oed}(kN/m^2)$	3.0×10^4	6.0×10^4	9.0×10^4	6.0×10^4
$E_{ur}(kN/m^2)$	9.0×10^4	1.8×10^5	2.7×10^5	1.8×10^5
m	0.50	0.50	0.5	0.50
φ	10	26.3	27.8	29.2

For overlapping vertical tunnels, the dimensions of model X, Y, and Z directions are 100m, 150m, and 80m, respectively. The buried depth above the upper tunnel is set as 15m, the vertical net distance L between the two tunnels is set as 3m, 6m, 9m, 12m, 18m, 24m, and 42m, and the outer tunnel diameter is set as 6m. The construction sequence is to excavate the lower tunnel first and then the upper tunnel. The shrinkage rate of tunnel excavation is set as 1%. A typical vertical overlapping tunnels model is shown in Figure 2.

For horizontal parallel tunnels, the dimensions of model X, Y, and Z directions are 150m, 150m, and 80m, respectively. The buried depth of both tunnels is set as 15m, the outer tunnel diameter is set as 6m, and the net distance between two tunnels is set as 3m, 6m, 9m, 12m, 18m, and 24m. The construction sequence is to excavate the right tunnel and then excavate the left one. The shrinkage rate of tunnel excavation is set as 1%. The typical horizontal parallel tunnel model is shown in Figure 3.

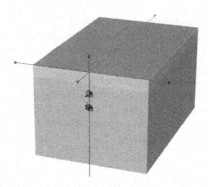

Figure 2. Typical vertical overlapping tunnels mode.

Figure 3. Typical horizontal parallel tunnels model.

4 NUMERICAL SIMULATION RESULT ANALYSIS OF VERTICAL OVERLAPPING TUNNEL

4.1 *Additional surface deformation*

Figure 4 shows the surface deformation curve when only the upper tunnel is excavated. It can be seen that the maximum surface settlement is 15.50mm.

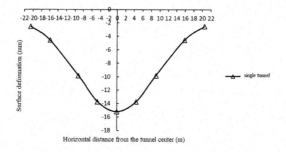

Figure 4. Surface deformation curve after the single tunnel excavation.

When the net distance between two tunnels is 0.5D, 1D, 1.5D, 2.0D, 3.0D, 4.0D and 7.0D, the maximum surface settlement is 23.38mm, 22.60mm, 22.36mm, 21.38mm, 20.47mm, 19.59mm and 18.12mm respectively. With the increase in distance between two tunnels, the vertical surface settlement gradually decreases, and the settlement groove width gradually increases, but the maximum settlement point is always located just above the center line of the two tunnels.

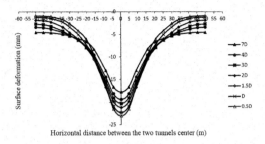

Figure 5. Surface deformation curves after tunnel excavation of different vertical distance.

It is difficult to judge the interaction influence of two tunnels only by final settlement after excavation. The interaction influence degree of two tunnels can be better studied by additional deformation of stratum surface and tunnel hole surrounding. In this paper, additional surface deformation is defined as the difference in the vertical surface settlement between the second and first tunnel excavation completion. Additionally, the surface settlement is recorded as a negative value. The additional deformation around the tunnel hole is defined as the difference between the horizontal or vertical deformation around the first tunnel hole when the second tunnel excavation is completed and the horizontal or vertical deformation around the first tunnel hole when the first tunnel excavation is completed. The unified rule is that the deformation of convergence to the hole is recorded as a negative value, and expansion is recorded as a positive value. This paper defines 6mm additional surface deformation as the critical value of the strong and weak influencing zone and 1mm surface deformation as the critical value of the weak and no influencing zone. 1mm additional deformation around the hole is taken as the critical value of the strong and weak influencing zone, and 0.5mm additional deformation around the hole is taken as the critical value of the weak and no influencing zone.

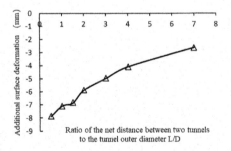

Figure 6. Additional surface deformation with different vertical distances of two tunnels.

It can be seen from Figure 6 that the adjacent construction increases the surface settlement. With the distance between two tunnels increasing, the surface deformation decreases rapidly at first and then becomes steady. When the distance between two tunnels is about 2D, the additional surface deformation value is less than the threshold value of 6mm; therefore, 2D is determined as the boundary point between the strong and weak influencing zone. When the distance between two tunnels is about 6D, the additional deformation is less than 3mm; therefore, 6D is determined as the boundary point between weak and no influencing zone. According to the criterion of additional surface deformation zoning, the strong influencing zone of overlapping vertical tunnels is $L \leq 2D$, the weak influencing zone is $2D < L \leq 6D$, and the no influence zone is $L > 6D$.

4.2 Additional deformation around the tunnel hole

It can be seen from Figure 7 that with the distance between two tunnels increasing, the horizontal convergence additional deformation and vertical settlement additional deformation change rapidly and gradually approach zero. Excavation of the upper tunnel causes the expansion in the vertical direction and convergence in the horizontal direction of the lower tunnel. The analysis shows that excavation of the upper tunnel has an unloading effect on the lower tunnel. When the distance between two tunnels is 1D, the additional deformation around the tunnel is less than the critical value of 1mm; therefore, 1D is determined as the boundary point of the weak influencing zone. When the distance between two tunnels is 3D, the additional deformation around the tunnel is less than the critical value of 0.5mm; therefore, 3D is determined as the boundary point of weak and no-affected influencing zone. According to the additional deformation zone criterion around the tunnel, the strong influence zone is L$\leq$D, and the weak influence zone is D < L$\leq$3D, and the no influence zone is L > 3D.

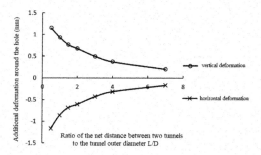

Figure 7. Additional deformation around the tunnel with different vertical distances between two tunnels.

5 NUMERICAL SIMULATION RESULT ANALYSIS OF HORIZONTAL PARALLEL TUNNEL

5.1 Additional surface deformation

It can be seen from Figure 8 that when the net distance between the two parallel tunnels is 0.5D, 1D, 1.5d, 2.0D, 3.0D, and 4.0D, the maximum surface settlement is 24.39mm, 22.58mm, 20.52mm, 18.66mm, 16.45mm and 15.79mm, respectively. With the distance between the two tunnels increasing, the vertical surface deformation curve changes from "V" to "U," and finally to a "W" shaped settlement groove, and the width of the settlement groove increases significantly. The maximum settlement point gradually approaches from the center of two tunnels to the side of the tunnel excavated first, and the maximum settlement value decreases gradually and approaches the maximum settlement value of the single tunnel excavated.

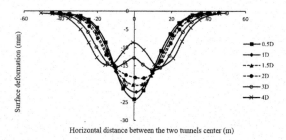

Figure 8. Surface deformation curves after tunnels excavation of different horizontal distance.

It can be seen from Figure 9 that when the distance between two tunnels is 1.5D, the additional surface deformation value is less than 6mm, and 1.5D can be determined as the boundary point between strong and weak influencing zone, and when the distance is 2D, the additional deformation is less than 3mm, and 2D can be determined as the boundary point between weak and no influence zone. According to the additional surface deformation zoning criterion, for horizontal parallel tunnels, the strong influence zone is L ≤ 1.5D, the weak influence zone is 1.5D < L ≤ 2D, and the no influence zone is L > 2D.

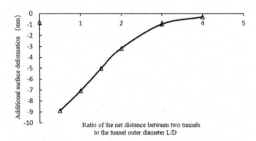

Figure 9. Additional surface deformation with different horizontal distances between two tunnels.

5.2 *Additional deformation around the tunnel hole*

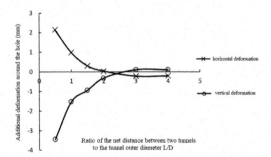

Figure 10. Additional deformation around the tunnel with different horizontal distances between two tunnels.

It can be seen clearly that with the increased distances between the two tunnels, the horizontal and vertical additional deformation change rapidly and then gradually approach zero. The excavation of the left tunnel makes the right tunnel converge in the vertical direction and expand out in the horizontal direction. When the net distance between two parallel tunnels is 3.0D and 4.0D, the deformation trend around the tunnel is opposite, but the overall additional deformation around the tunnel tends to be stable. When the distance between tunnels is 1.5D, the additional deformation around the tunnel is less than the critical value of 1mm, and 1.5D is determined as the boundary point of the weak influence zone. When the tunnel spacing is 2D, the additional deformation around the tunnel is less than the critical value of 0.5mm, and 2D is determined as the boundary point of a weak influence zone and no influence zone. According to the additional deformation zoning criterion around the tunnel, for horizontal parallel tunnels, the strong influence zone is L ≤ 1.5D, the weak influence zone is 1.5dD < L ≤ 2D, and the no influence zone is L > 2D.

6 FIELD MONITORING

The tunnel excavation from Hesong Street station to Heshan Street station has not been completed, so the monitoring result of another section of Harbin Metro Line 3 is used as a reference. The typical DBC1 monitoring section is selected for analysis.

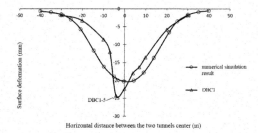

Figure 11. Settlement curve of the DBC1 section and the numerical calculation result.

It can be seen from Figure 11 that the final shape of the settlement trough of the field monitoring is the same as the numerical simulation result. However, the shape of the actual settlement trough is narrower than that of numerical simulation, and the position of the maximum settlement point is slight to the left line. The numerical simulation result shows that the maximum settlement is 20.52mm, and the actual monitoring data is 25.13mm, which is about 1.2 times the numerical simulation results.

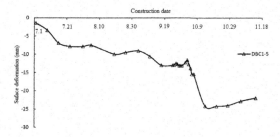

Figure 12. DBC1-5 surface settlement curve.

The monitoring point DBC1-5 with the largest deformation value is taken for analysis. It can be seen that the maximum settlement of DBC1-5 before excavation to the monitoring surface is 13.14mm, and the maximum settlement after left line crossing is 25.13mm. The surface settlement caused by earlier stage construction accounts for 52.29% of the total settlement. The surface settlement caused by the left line crossing accounts for 47.71% of the total settlement.

Due to the complexity of construction and soil conditions, there are some limitations to numerical simulation and model establishment. After the construction, the field monitoring data will be further analyzed, and the numerical model will be further revised and improved.

7 CONCLUSION AND SUGGESTION

Based on the tunnel project between Hesong Street station and Heshan Street Station of Harbin Metro Line 3, the PLAXIS3D model and simulation calculation is used to study the influence zones of overlapping and parallel shield tunnels construction in water-rich sand layer area, and the rationality and accuracy of the calculation result are verified by field monitoring.

1) According to the additional surface deformation zoning criterion, for the vertical overlapping shield tunnel, the strong influence zone is L ≤ 2D, the weak influence zone is 2D < L ≤ 6D, and the no influence zone is L > 6D. According to the additional deformation zoning criterion around the hole, the strong influence zone is L ≤ D, the weak influence zone is D < L ≤ 3D, and the no influence zone is L > 3D.
2) According to the additional surface deformation zoning criterion, for the horizontal parallel shield tunnel, the strong influence zone is L ≤ 1.5D, the weak influence zone is 1.5D < L ≤ 2D, and the no influence zone is L > 2D. According to the additional deformation zoning criterion around the hole, the strong influence zone is L ≤ 1.5D, the weak influence zone is D < L ≤ 2D, and the no influence zone is L > 2D.
3) By comparing and analyzing the deformation law obtained by monitoring data and numerical simulation, it is confirmed that the law obtained by numerical simulation is reasonable. However, further analysis based on the field situation is still needed, and the calculation model should be further modified and improved.

REFERENCES

Fan Yu, Su Yi, Yuan Yong and Yao Xupeng. (2020) Study on ground settlement law of double-line subway tunnel construction in composite stratum. *Chinese Journal of Underground Space and Engineering* 16(S2): 258–285.

Hamid Chakeri, Rohola Hasanpour, Mehmet Ali Hindistan and Bathtiyar Ünver (2011) Analysis of interaction between tunnels in soft ground by 3D numerical modeling. *Bulletin of Engineering Geology and Environment* 70(3): 439–448.

Lu Xilin, Zhao Yucheng, Cai Jiantao and Yao Xupeng. (2020) Numerical simulation of subsidence deformation of water-rich sand layer induced by shield tunnel construction disturbance. *Modern Tunneling Technology* 57(05): 108–113.

Qin Huihui. (2012) The adjacent influenced partition and deformation control technology of Overlapping tunnel with small radius curve. *Beijing Jiaotong University*, Beijing.

Suchatvee Suwansawat and Herbert H. Einstein, (2007) Describing Settlement Troughs over Twin Tunnels Using a Superposition Technique. *Journal of Geotechnical & Geoenvironmental Engineering* 133(4): 445–468.

Wei Gang and Pang Siyuan. (2014) Study of three-dimensional soil deformation caused by double-line parallel shield tunnel construction. *Rock and Soil Mechanics* 35(9): 2562–2568.

Zhou Zilian. (2019) Research on the mechanical effect of shield tunneling in the saturated sand layer of Songhua River. *Harbin Institute of Technology*, Harbin.

Analysis and study of the seismic response of large chassis connected to high-rise structures

Wang Zeyun* & Tang Xianzhe
Ande College, Xi'an University of Architecture and Technology, Xi'an, China

ABSTRACT: The seismic damage indicates that the corridor and the large chassis have a large influence on the seismic performance of the conjoined structure. In order to study the influence of the location of the connecting corridor and the number of storeys of the large chassis on the seismic performance of the structure, a finite element model of the connecting structure was established, and the seismic response of the connecting structure was studied using a frame core steel connecting corridor as a prototype. In this paper, PKPM software is used to establish three-dimensional modeling, and the vibration decomposition response spectrum method and dynamic time course method are applied to analyze the effects of different locations of the connecting corridor and the different number of floors of the large chassis on the force characteristics of the structure. The results show that the presence of the corridor has a certain influence on the displacement and shear force of the building, and the influence of the corridor is different when it is located at 1/2 height of the building, and the number of floors of the chassis is 2, which has the greatest influence on the structure. Only a small amount of kinetic energy is transferred to the connecting corridor, and most of the energy transferred to the structure is consumed through modal damping, so the relationship between the energy transferred to the connected building structure under earthquake action and the location of the connecting corridor is insignificant.

1 INTRODUCTION

In recent years, China's high-rise buildings have continued to develop in the direction of large-scale and multi-functional. Connected structures can increase the spatial connection between buildings and improve the use of building functions and are increasingly used in practical engineering.

There are many finite element research results on the dynamic response behavior of high-rise buildings under earthquakes, and the theoretical and practical development is more mature. Lu (Lu et al. 2013) et al. analyzed the efficiency and applicability of collapse mechanisms of high-rise buildings on 18- and 20-story structures. Rajmani and Guha (2015) studied the design criteria and response assessment of high-rise buildings of different shapes under wind and earthquake. The study was carried out in the following sections.

However, the dynamic response under earthquake action will become more complex for multi-tower conjoined structures. Lu (Lu et al. 2008) studied the seismic response of the Shanghai International Design Center by the shaking table test. Zhou Wenkai (Zhou 2016), on the other hand, used ETABS, SATWE, and other structural analysis software, combined with the reaction spectrum method and elastic time method to calculate the high-rise structure; through comparative analysis, the dynamic characteristics and seismic response of a joint high-rise structure were obtained. Liu Jingbo (Liu et al. 2004) further emphasized the in-plane elastic deformation of the plate during the model calculation and obtained a more accurate finite element space mass system model, and modal analysis and single mass acceleration response spectrum analysis were carried out. Xu Liwei (Xu

---
*Corresponding Author: zeyunwang@126.com

2005) further utilized hollow web reinforced concrete trusses instead of joint structure and analyzed that the hollow web reinforced concrete truss joint has better seismic performance. Shishun Zhang (2005) studied the dynamic response of high-rise buildings using the CQC method and concluded that the CQC method could better consider the flat-torsional coupling characteristics of buildings.

This paper continues the research and analysis of the dynamic response of high-rise conjoined structures under seismic action based on the existing research. The study uses PKPM software to establish a finite element model of a large chassis twin-tower conjoined structure with a steel truss structure, while the influence of the location of the conjoined corridor and the number of storeys of the large chassis are used as variables to analyze the dynamic response of the large chassis conjoined high-rise structure.

2 PROJECT OVERVIEW

This paper analyzes a large chassis continuous high-rise structure with 20 floors, no basement, and two floors of large chassis. The vertical direction of the structure consists of rectangular reinforced concrete columns with large cross-sectional dimensions and core shear walls. The shear wall on the bottom floor is 400mm thick and decreases to 200mm from the bottom to the top of the building, while the external frame column on the bottom floor is 1200mm×1200mm and decreases to 600 mm × 600 mm from the bottom to the top. The steel columns are 450 mm × 450 mm × 30 mm×30 mm, and the steel beams are 500 mm × 500 mm × 40 mm×40 mm. In addition, in order to study the impact of the large chassis on the seismic performance of the continuous structure, the model of the corridor on the 10th floor and the number of floors of the large chassis is four is named S5; the model of the corridor at the 10th floor and the number of floors of the large chassis are six is named S6; the concrete strength grade is C30, and the reinforcement is HRB400; the additional constant load on the floor is 2.5kN/m^2; the live load is 2kN/m^2, and the line load of the frame beam is 10kN/m; the seismic effect is based on 7 degrees (0.15g), site category II, seismic grouping group II. The connecting area is articulated with the two towers. The seismic grade is as follows: the shear wall and frame column are Grade 2, and the seismic grade of the shear wall and frame column connected with the continuous body and its upper and lower levels of the continuous body is increased to Grade 1.

3 MODEL BUILDING

The PKPM software was used to create conjoined structures with different heights of connecting corridors and conjoined structures with different levels of large chassis, as shown in Figure 1.

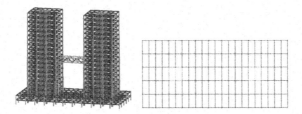

Figure 1. High-rise conjoined structure and its floor plan.

The importance factor of all structure members is taken as 1.00, and the reinforced concrete members are designed according to the ultimate strength method defined in the ACI code. The strength for concrete columns, walls, and beams is C30, while the yield stress f_y for the stressed reinforcement and hoop bars is taken as $f_y = 400$ MPa. Also, to meet the axial and bending stiffness requirements, the beams and floor slabs in the building are considered horizontal units, and the columns and shear walls are considered vertical units and are simulated using shell units. To save calculation time, the floor slab is set as a semi-rigid partition to simulate its actual stiffness characteristics. All floor slabs and shear walls in the structure are approximately divided into a mesh of 0.5m×0.5m, while the necessary constraints are given at the connections and supports of the model.

4 NUMERICAL RESULTS AND ANALYSIS

4.1 Period analysis

Table 1. Comparison table of the first three periods of different models.

Mode	Period/s	S1	S2	S3	S4	S5	S6
1	T1	1.833	1.828	1.838	1.856	1.8055	1.7868
2	T2	1.785	1.761	1.751	1.818	1.7052	1.7116
3	T3	1.776	1.707	1.732	1.738	1.6902	1.6762

As can be seen from the table, the first two orders of the structure are advective, and the third order is torsional. As the height of the gallery increases to 1/2 height, the period decreases, while the period increases from 1/2 height to the top floor of the conjoined structure. This indicates that the advective stiffness of the conjoined structure is greatest when the conjoined corridor is located at 1/2 height; as the number of storeys of the large floor increases, the self-oscillation period of the structure decreases, and the building stiffness increases.

4.2 Inter-storey displacement analysis

Inter-storey displacement is an important evaluation indicator for high-rise buildings under seismic action. It is also an important factor in the stability of tall buildings. The inter-storey displacements along the x- and y-direction of the continuous structure are shown in Figures 2 and 3, respectively.

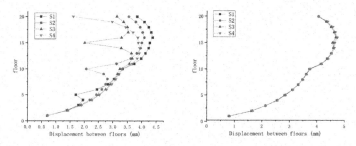

Figure 2. Comparative results of inter-storey displacements of the different heights of the corridor.

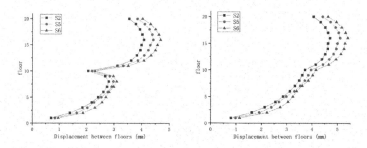

Figure 3. Comparison of inter-storey displacements of the different number of layers of large chassis.

As seen in Figures 2 and 3, the inter-storey displacement of the building always increases with height, both along the x-direction and the y-direction. It can be seen in Figure 2 that the trend of inter-storey displacements of the four options S1, S2, S3, and S4 are broadly similar. In the x-direction, the inter-storey displacements change abruptly when the corridor is in 1/4, 1/2, 3/4, and at the top of the building, and the inter-storey displacements at the floor where the corridor is located decrease as a result of the presence of the corridor increasing the stiffness of the floor. When the corridor is located at the top of the building, the structural inter-storey displacement is the smallest, and the reduction in inter-storey displacement is the most obvious. In the y-direction, the inter-storey displacements are similar for all four options, so it is clear that the position of the corridor in the weak axis has little effect on the inter-storey displacements. As shown in Figure 3, the inter-storey displacements in both directions increase slightly with the increase in the number of storeys of the large chassis, but the effect is less pronounced. It can be seen that changing the number of storeys of the large chassis only slightly affects the inter-storey displacements of the structure.

4.3 *Floor shear analysis*

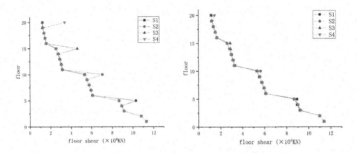

Figure 4. Comparative results of shear forces at different heights of corridor locations.

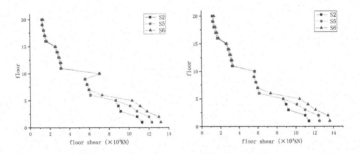

Figure 5. Comparative results of shear forces at different numbers of levels of large chassis.

Figure 4 presents the floor shear forces for different models of the corridor locations along the x and y directions. The following conclusions can be drawn: along the x-direction, the inter-storey shear of the storey where the gallery is located changes abruptly, probably due to the presence of the gallery increasing the stiffness of the structure and thus increasing the shear; along the y-direction, the inter-storey shear is similar for all four scenarios; thus, it can be seen that changing the position of the gallery does not significantly change the floor shear in the weak axis direction. Figure 5 gives the floor shear along the x and y directions for different numbers of storeys of the large chassis. It can be seen from the figure that below the 6th storey, an increase in the number of storeys of the large chassis causes the floor stiffness and the floor shear to increase; above the 6th storey, the floor shear is similar and decreases as the number of storeys increases.

4.4 Large-earthquake dynamic elastoplastic time analysis

A total of three groups of waves, namely natural wave 1, natural wave 2, and artificial wave, were selected for the dynamic elastoplastic analysis, and S2 was used as the model for the analysis. The maximum inter-storey displacement angle in the X-direction is 1/123, and the maximum inter-storey displacement angle in the Y-direction is 1/118, both of which meet the limit of $\leq 1/100$ for frame-core structures under rare earthquakes and meet the requirement of no collapse under large earthquakes.

Analysis of the plastic development of the structure shows that the structure behaves elastically during the initial period of the earthquake. The first plastic hinges then appear on the connecting beams on the core, with individual member performance levels of IO. More plastic hinges then appear on the peripheral frame beams, mostly at C; the connecting beams on the core undergo a large plastic rotation angle, reaching C. The plastic deformation of some of the peripheral frame beams increases, partially reaching D.

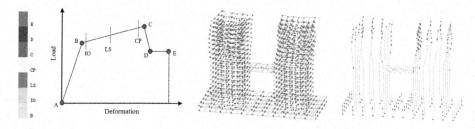

Figure 6. S2 model beam-column plastic hinge and its load-deformation curve.

Analysis of the performance of the elements shows that the vast majority of the frame columns are in a slightly damaged or lightly damaged condition, except for the individual outer frame columns of the two towers, which are moderately damaged. Key elements such as the connecting corridor remain in a resilient and undamaged condition. The core shear walls remain undamaged or slightly damaged at all levels, except for the first floor, where there is moderate and severe damage to individual wall elements.

4.5 Energy response

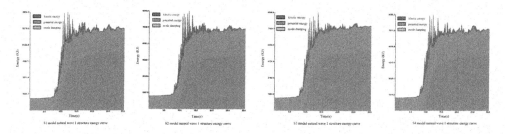

Figure 7. Energy response due to natural wave 1.

Using S1, S2, S3, and S4 as models, the time course curves of the energy response of the conjoined structure under the action of natural wave 1 are plotted, as shown in Figure 7. Figure 7 shows the energy transferred to the structure and the energy consumed by damping and inelastic deformation over time. The kinetic energy curve is jagged, with the peak kinetic energy approximately the same in all cases, and is not affected by the position of the linkage when it is not located at the 1/4 height position. However, when the corridor is at 1/4 height, the peak kinetic energy is slightly higher than in the other corridor positions. The kinetic energy curve also shows that only a small amount of kinetic energy is transferred to the corridor, and most of the energy transferred to the structure is consumed through modal damping. The relationship between the energy transferred to the connected structures by the earthquake and the location of the corridor is small.

5 CONCLUSION

This paper investigates the dynamic response of a high-rise building connected horizontally by a connecting corridor under seismic action. The effect of the location of the connecting corridor and the number of storeys of the large chassis on the dynamic response of the connected high-rise building is analyzed, and the following conclusions are drawn:

(1) Through the study of different models of connecting corridor locations, it is concluded that the lateral stiffness is greatest when the corridor is located at 1/2 the height of the floor. Therefore, in the design of a continuous structure, if it does not have a significant impact on the use of the building, we should position the corridor in the middle of the floor as far as possible to better meet the requirements of the overall structural index.
(2) With the increase in the number of storeys of the large chassis, the base shear of the conjoined structure gradually increases, but the increase in the number of storeys of the large chassis has little effect on the inter-storey displacement in both directions of the conjoined structure. Therefore, if the inter-storey displacement angle cannot meet the code requirements in the design of the conjoined structure, we should adopt a form of local strengthening to meet the code requirements.
(3) The energy transferred to the high-rise conjoined structure by the seismic action is influenced by the location of the conjoined corridor, but the effect is small. Some energy transferred to the high-rise conjoined structure by seismic waves is dissipated through modal damping, and some are consumed through structural deformation energy. However, we should focus on the extent of damage to the elements to meet performance-based design requirements.

6 LIMITATIONS AND PROSPECTS OF THIS PAPER

The connection method of the connecting corridor has a great influence on the seismic performance of the conjoined structure, but the influence of the connection method is not considered in this study for the time being. In addition, this paper only investigates the regular conjoined structure and has not considered the effect of the connection corridor on the shaped structure. Therefore, the next step is to focus on studying the seismic performance of the connection method and the shaped connection body to give seismic design suggestions for the connected structure.

REFERENCES

Liu Jingbo, Li Zhengyu, Shi Meng, et al. Dynamic analysis of long-span high-rise connecting building [J]. *Journal of Building Structures*, 2004, **25(1)**: 45–52.

Lu Xiao, Lu Xinzheng, Guan Hong, et al. Collapse simulation of RC high-rise building induced by extreme earthquakes[J]. *Earthquake Engineering Structural Dynamics*, 2013, **42(5)**: 705–723.

Lu Xilin, Chen Linzhi, Zhou Ying, et al. Shakingtable model tests on a complex high-rise building with two towers of different heights connected by trusses[J]. *The Structural Desing of Tall Special Build*, 2008, **18(7)**: 765–788.

Rajmani A, Guha P. Analysis of wind & earthquake load for different shapes of high-rise buildings[J]. *Civil Engineering Technology*, 2015, **6(2)** : 38–45'.D

Shi-shun zhang. Dynamic response analysis of multi-tower connected high-rise building under earthquake action [D]. Wuhan: Huazhong University of Science and Technology, 2005.

Xu Liwei. Influence of structural stiffness on seismic response of asymmetric tower structures [J]. *Journal of Heilongjiang University of Science and Technology*, 2005, **15(1)**: 31–34.

Zhou Wenkai. Seismic analysis of a high-rise twin tower connected structure [J]. *Industrial Construction*, 2016, **46(suppl.)** : 283–288.

Structural and seismic analysis of conjoined buildings

Ranran Zhang*
College of Civil Engineering, Southwest Forestry University, Kunming, Yunnan, China

ABSTRACT: In recent years, due to the continuous changes in building functions and the increasingly diverse requirements for building appearance, the application of conjoined structures in engineering has become increasingly widespread, and their connection methods have become increasingly diverse. The conjoined structure of high-rise buildings is formed by connecting towers. Compared with the traditional single tower, the force is more complicated, so the analysis and design of the structure are very difficult. Taking a high-rise conjoined structure as an example, this paper analyzes the selection and design of the conjoined structure from the perspectives of overall stress and deformation and analyzes the stress characteristics, applicable conditions, and design principles of various connection methods. The objective of this paper is to provide a reference for similar projects.

1 INTRODUCTION

With the development of the construction industry, people have a new demand for modern residential buildings, and corresponding improvement measures and countermeasures are also produced. [Ma 2022] In order to meet the needs of residents for high-rise residential buildings, communication, and activities, a platform is set at the interval between the two residential buildings, and its structure is conjoined. As stipulated in "Technical Regulations for Concrete Structures of High-rise Buildings," a rigid connection is adopted between the conjoined structure and the main structure.

Stressing between components is complicated by the close connection between the connecting bodies. In addition, under the action of the earthquake, the connecting part of the conjoined structure is easily disconnected from the main structure, and may collapse in severe cases. This makes the current one-piece structure design a difficult problem for current designers.

2 PROJECT OVERVIEW

The site used in this case is Kunming. It has a conjoined structure with residential areas on both sides and a platform in the middle. [Wang 2021] It covers an area of 957.96m^2, with a total construction area of 13913.28m^2. There are 18 floors above ground, with a floor height of 3m and a total building height of 54m. See the previous chapter for floor plans of buildings. The design service life of the main structure is 50 years, the fire resistance class is first-class, the building structure class is second-class, and the structural importance coefficient is 1.0. The seismic fortification intensity of this project is 8 degrees, the seismic design acceleration is 0.2g, and the design earthquake is grouped into the second group for class B.

3 STRUCTURAL SYSTEM AND LAYOUT

For the convenience of use, the residential buildings on both sides of the project adopt a shear wall structure system, and in order to obtain more space for activities in the middle platform, the frame-shear wall structure floor slab is a cast-in-place reinforced concrete beam-slab system.

---

*Corresponding Author: 535255631@qq.com

The two towers and their conjoined parts are in a left-right symmetrical relationship. The vertical components, plane layout, number of floors, and rigidity of the two towers from floors 1 to 16 are completely consistent. The residential buildings on both sides of 17 and 18 are consistent with floors 1 to 16. No shear walls and frame columns are provided, and the standard floor plan is shown in Figure 1.

The concrete strength grade of structural beams and columns is C40, the concrete strength grade of the 1st to 4th floors is C45, the 5th to 18th floors are C40, and the structural slab concrete strength grade is C35. Frame columns, frame beams, coupling beam longitudinal bars, shear wall distribution bars, and stirrups are of HRB400 grade. The shear walls of the 1st to 4th floors in the residential area are 0.3m thick, the 5th to 18th floors are 0.25m thick, and the platform area uses 0.3m thick shear walls, 800mm×800mm columns, and 800mm×800mm side columns. The thickness of the floor slab is 0.18m. This paper selects Midas Gen and PKPM software for comparative analysis.

The plane shape of the structure is rectangular, and the overall height-width ratio of the conjoined body is 54/22.8=2.37, which meets the requirements of the "High-level Regulations."

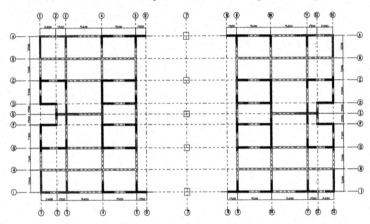

Figure 1. Standard floor plan.

4 SEISMIC PERFORMANCE TARGETS

According to the different importance of structural components, combined with the seismic performance targets of the structure, the seismic performance targets of the tower components are determined, as shown in Table 1.

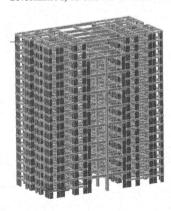

Figure 2. MIDAS design model.

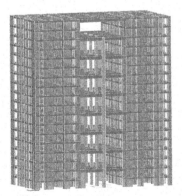

Figure 3. PKPM design model.

5 STRUCTURAL OVERALL ELASTICITY ANALYSIS

5.1 Self-resonance characteristics

Table 1. Overall seismic performance design objectives.

Earthquake impact		Earthquakes abound	Fortify against earthquakes	Severe earthquake
Structure of the overall performance	Performance level macroscopic damage	1 Intact, generally do not need to repair can continue to use	3 Mild damage and general repair can continue to use	4 Moderate damage, repair or reinforcement before continued use
	Displacement angle limit	1/800	1/400	1/100
Component performance	key components Normal vertical components Siamese	No damage No damage Elasticity (stress ratio<0.7)	Minor damage Minor damage Elasticity (stress ratio<0.8)	Mild damage Some components are moderately damaged Stress ratio ≤ 1.0
	Analytical methods	Elastic time history analysis	Equivalent elasticity	Dynamic Elastoplastic Time History Analysis
	Analysis software	PKPM/MIDAD GEN	PKPM	PKPM

On the basis of the calculation model, vertical and horizontal load cases are defined. Among them, the vertical load cases mainly include the self-weight of the structure, the additional fixed load, and the live load. There are two main types of horizontal load cases: seismic and wind loads. [Liu 2021].

It can be seen from Table 2 that the analysis results of the two calculation methods are similar. The first and second-order modes are all translational vibration modes, and the torsional period ratio is less than 0.9 required by the specification, while the first three-order modes are shown in Figure 4 [Yuan 2013]. Since the structure is a high-rise conjoined structure, its torsion effect is unavoidable, and its torsion period is relatively long.

Table 2. Self-resonance period/s.

Software	MIDAD GEN	PKPM
Order 1	0.792	0.9404
Order 2	0.6693	0.7952
Order 3	0.5546	0.6532
Order 4	0.2258	0.2705
Order 5	0.1884	0.2283
Order 6	0.1664	0.1985
Cycle ratio	0.7	0.69

(a) The first mode shape diagram (X-direction translation)

(b) The second mode shape diagram (Y-direction translation)

(c) Third mode diagram

Figure 4.　Structural mode pattern diagram.

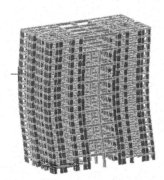
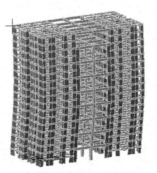

Figure 5.　Overall displacement in X direction under earthquake.

Figure 6.　Overall displacement in the Y direction under seismic action.

113

5.2 Overall displacement and deformation

The overall displacement and deformation of the structure are obtained by MIDAS/GEN. It can be seen from the deformation curve of the structure that the lateral displacement of the structure is relatively uniform as the floor changes. The overall deformation and displacement curve of the structure is shown in the figure. At the same time, it also shows that the stiffness of the structure is uniform, and the internal force distribution of the shear wall and the frame column is more reasonable.

5.3 Analysis of structural deformation

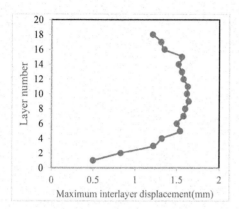

Figure 7. X-direction seismic maximum interlayer displacement diagram under small seismic action.

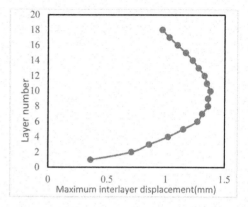

Figure 8. Maximum interlayer displacement diagram of Y-direction seismic conditions under small earthquakes action.

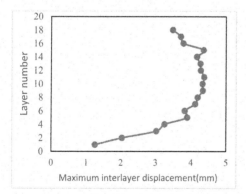

Figure 9. X-direction seismic maximum interlayer displacement diagram under the action of medium earthquakes.

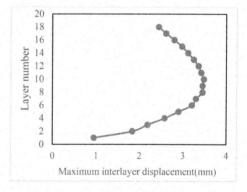

Figure 10. Maximum interlayer displacement map of Y-direction seismic conditions under the action of medium earthquakes.

The overall displacement and deformation of the structure and the control of the inter-story displacement angle are relatively macroscopic requirements. When calculating the displacement, in order to control the regularity of the plane layout and reduce the influence of the torsional effect on the structure, the influence of accidental eccentricity should not be considered. For high-rise buildings specified in 3.7.3 of the "High Regulations," the ratio u/h of the maximum displacement between floors to the floor height should not exceed 1/800 [Li 2013].

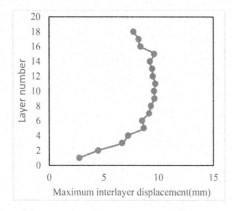
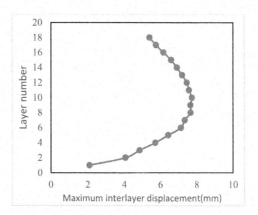

Figure 11. X-direction seismic maximum interlayer displacement diagram under the action of large earthquakes.

Figure 12. Maximum interlayer displacement diagram of Y-direction seismic conditions under the action of large earthquakes.

Through software analysis, it can be seen that the maximum floor displacement of the whole building is 23.74mm under multiple earthquakes, and the maximum inter-floor displacement angle of the whole building is 1/1828; the maximum floor displacement of the whole building is 63.58mm under the fortification earthquake, and the maximum inter-floor displacement angle of the whole building is 1/684; the maximum floor displacement of the whole building is 141.11mm under rare earthquakes, and the maximum inter-floor displacement angle of the whole building is 1/308.

6 CONCLUSION

The case belongs to the A-class height over-limit high-rise building, which adopts the conceptual design method to integrate the performance design concept into the entire structure and components and analyzes the elastoplastic dynamic time history of the small, medium, and large earthquakes according to the different performance indicators. After calculation and analysis, it is proved that the structure meets the design requirements of "not damaged when small earthquakes occur, repairable when medium earthquakes occur, and not collapse when large earthquakes occur," and the requirements are met by its cycle ratio, overall displacement and deformation, and interlayer displacement analysis, and the structural system is safe and feasible, reasonable and effective.

REFERENCES

Li Ya, Yan Jianghong. The application of design software in building structure design[J]. *Science and Technology Innovation and Application*, 2013, (21):69.

Liu Pei, Ding Jiemin, Wu Honglei, etc. Analysis and design of large-span contiguous structure of henan construction building[J]. *Building Structure*, 2021, 51(S2):259–266.

Ma Dajie, Yuan Binbo. Research on the design of flexible connected conjoined structures[J]. *Engineering Construction and Design*, 2022, (07):23–25.

Wang Peng, Xu Ping, Du Mingjun, etc. Seismic response analysis of a high-level large-span conjoined structure[J]. *Sichuan Architecture*, 2021, 41(06):189–193.

Yuan Liangliang. *Theoretical analysis and case design of frame-shear wall structure*[D]. Handan: Hebei University of Engineering, 2013.

Numerical simulation study on the influence of lattice anchor rod on rock slope stability

Yunpeng Xie*

School of Civil and Traffic Engineering, Guangdong University of Technology, Guangzhou, China

ABSTRACT: In slope protection technology, geotechnical anchoring technology is the most widely used one. Bolt support has high technical content, low construction cost, good support effect, and simple and fast operation. It is an advanced and common form of support at home and abroad. In order to explore the influence of lattice bolt support on improving slope stability, this paper takes a rock slope in Guangzhou as an example and uses the finite element software Midas to numerically model and calculate the lattice bolt support scheme. The results show that: (1) The slope has self-stable properties under natural conditions and is in a stable state; however, under the unsupported excavation condition, it is in an under-stable state and needs to be supported to ensure the stability of the slope. (2) The support scheme of lattice bolts with 2m spacing can control the deformation of the plastic zone, improve the safety factor, and the support effect is good.

1 INTRODUCTION

The stability evaluation and treatment of rock slope has always been the focus of slope engineering research. In recent years, computers have been widely used in rock slope stability evaluation (Chang 2020; He 2013; Li 2006; 2007) and failure mode analysis (Chen 2015; Huang 2015; Lin 2008; Wu 2010; Zheng 2004), and have many incomparable advantages over traditional calculation methods. When there is a complex combination of factors, such as uneven material properties, arbitrary boundary conditions, complex geometric shapes, etc., the finite element method can flexibly process and solve. Some scholars at home and abroad have carried out related research on the stability analysis of rock mass slopes. Zheng Yingren introduced the strength reduction method into finite element calculation to analyze the stability of rock mass slopes, which opened up a new path for studying rock slope problems (Zheng 2002). Jiang carried out discrete element numerical simulation of jointed rock slope and the influence of environmental degradation factors on the strength of non-through jointed rock mass (Jiang 2017). The discrete element method (DEM) was proposed by Cundall (2020) on Newton's second law. Each block or particle moves according to the force state and can move independently, reflecting the contact, separation, and dumping of the rock blocks. Equal displacement problem, suitable for stability analysis of jointed rock slopes. Nishimura used discrete element commercial software PFC2D to simulate and analyze the sliding mechanism of completely homogeneous rock slopes (Nishimura 2010).

Based on the above discussion, the stability analysis of high and steep slopes is an indispensable part of design and construction. The establishment of model elements requires the assistance of finite element software, and the lattice bolt elements involved in the model can be modeled in finite element software to participate in the calculation. Relying on an actual engineering case of a high slope, this paper conducts numerical modeling of the slope based on Midas/GTS software, and analyzes the slope stability and the development trend of deformation and failure under different

---

*Corresponding Author: xyypfzzfl3@126.com

working conditions from the calculation results. The rationality of the support method is discussed, effective suggestions are put forward from the perspective of finite element analysis, and the support scheme that illustrates the rationality of finite element analysis in engineering practice provides theoretical support for the optimization of safe construction design at the construction site of high and steep slopes.

2 PROJECT OVERVIEW

This project is located on the southwest side of a project in Guangzhou. The construction site of the rock slope is shown in Figure 1. The artificial fill layer in the rock slope site is widely distributed, the medium weathered rock core is relatively complete, and the strongly weathered rock has obvious weathering difference, which is easy to soften and disintegrate when exposed to water. The rock slope selected by the model established in this paper is on the southwest side of the proposed project. Meteorological disasters include tropical cyclones, heavy rain, and strong convection. When typhoons land, storm surges, and rainstorms often follow one after another, which is easy to cause flooding. Construction (structures) should pay attention to drainage, ventilation, and cooling in summer.

Figure 1. Site construction drawing.

3 NUMERICAL SIMULATION CALCULATION AND ANALYSIS OF HIGH AND STEEP SLOPES

3.1 *Finite element strength reduction method*

Stability refers to the ability of the slope to resist the force that moves the earth material down the slope. The finite element SRM is used to calculate the safety coefficient of the slope at the accident location or instability location. The strength reduction coefficient F_s is adopted to reduce the cohesion C and internal friction angle φ, and the sum value of C' and φ' of the reduced virtual anti-shear strength index is used to replace the original cohesion C and internal friction angle φ to analyze until the instability conditions are calculated. When the system reaches an unstable state through strength reduction, the finite element calculation will not converge, and the reduction coefficient at this time is the safety coefficient. Suppose the finite element method is kept to maintain a sufficient calculation accuracy. In that case, it will have the following advantages over the traditional method:

(1) It can calculate a slope with complex landform and geology. (2) It considers the nonlinear elastoplastic constitutive relation of soil mass and the influence of deformation on stress. (3) It can simulate the instability process of soil slope and the shape of the sliding surface. The sliding surface is roughly in a strip shape when the horizontal displacement changes suddenly and where the plastic deformation develops seriously. (4) There is no need to assume the shape of the sliding surface and slice when solving the safety coefficient. The calculation formula for the safety coefficient is as follows:

$$C' = \frac{C}{F_s}$$

$$\tan \varphi' = \frac{\tan \varphi}{F_s}$$

$$\tau' = C' + \sigma \tan \varphi'$$

Where: F_s is the strength reduction coefficient; C' is the cohesion after reduction; φ' is the internal friction angle after reduction; τ' is the anti-shearing strength after reduction.

3.2 Relevant modeling parameters

In the modeling and numerical simulation analysis, the relevant modeling parameters of materials are shown in Table 1 below.

Table 1. Relevant modeling parameters.

Model materials	Bulk density/	Modulus of elasticity/MPa	Poisson's ratio	Cohesion/ kPa	Internal friction angle/(°)
Plain fill	19.1	15.1	0.3	13.5	11.6
Silty clay	18.9	33.2	0.3	14.2	30.8
Completely weathered granite	19.4	94.5	0.3	22.6	22.2
Strongly weathered granite	19	115.6	0.3	80	30
Moderately weathered granite	21	5000	0.3	150	35

3.3 Stability analysis of numerical simulation

The established model is a simplified three-dimensional model. The boundary constraints, dead-weight load, anchor prestress, lattice beam contact, and other analysis conditions were set, and the material parameters and establishment attributes in Table 1 were input to divide the grid, as shown in Figure 2.

The simulation software is used to model and input relevant parameters, select the Mohr-Coulomb strength criterion, and use the strength reduction method (SRM) to continuously reduce its cohesion and internal friction angle, and use this principle to analyze the stability of rock slopes, to simulate the boundary conditions and stress conditions of the rock slope to judge the stability of the slope. The rock mass of the selected project is of good quality. Under the natural stress state, the calculated safety and stability factor is 1.95, and during the excavation, the rock slope is stable, and there is no major slippage on the slope.

With the implementation of the project, the high and steep side slopes are excavated, and the construction method is divided into steps and excavated multiple times. In the excavation process, the real-time detection of the detection point is set to be in a safe state. After completion, due to the redistribution of the ground stress and the retained soil gravity, the rock mass after the excavation

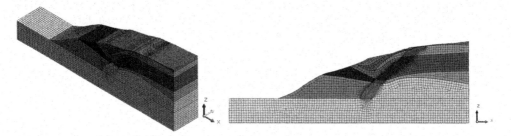

Figure 2. Grid division for high and steep slope model.

is completed on the left will have a certain extrusion and shear effect, resulting in the formation of a potential slide the belt from the top of the slope to the toe of the slope. The penetration of the sliding zone directly affects the stability of the high and steep slopes. Once penetration, the sliding zone will slide down along the tangent position of the left rock mass slope angle. The high and steep slope after excavation is shown in Figure 3 below.

Table 2. Slope safety coefficient.

	Slope type	Level I	Level II	Level III
Permanent slope	General working condition	1.35	1.30	1.25
	Seismic working condition	1.15	1.10	1.05
	Temporary slope	1.25	1.20	1.15

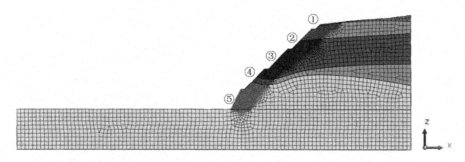

Figure 3. Unsupported slope after excavation.

Table 3. Classification of slope stability state.

Safety coefficient	$F_s < 1.00$	$1.00 \leq F_s \leq 1.05$	$1.05 \leq F_s \leq F_{st}$	$F_s \geq F_{st}$
Slope stability state	Unstable	Understable	Basically stable	Stable

Since the high and steep slope is in a safe state after excavation, but it is far from meeting the requirements of the specification, the following support scheme is designed according to the actual situation:

Among the common support measures in China, cast-in-place concrete lattice beams and anchor rods can be used for joint support in the case of poor slope stability. For the high and steep slopes in this paper, only the cast-in-place concrete lattice beams and prestressed anchors are needed to meet the stability requirements. The parameters of the lattice anchors are shown in Table 4, and the layout of the lattice anchors is shown in Figure 4.

Table 4. The parameters of the lattice anchors.

Anchor rod	25	30000	0.2
C30 concrete	25	30000	0.2
Lattice beam	25	30000	0.2

As shown in Figure 5, the advantage of this scheme is that it solves the problem of partial shearing of the slope during bolt support, and there is a developed plastic zone. Partial displacement is generated, preventing large-scale overall sliding of the slope. The maximum deformation of the plastic zone is 6.7×10^{-1}. At this time, the stability safety factor of the slope is 1.32, which is in a stable state and greater than the stability factor required by the specification design.

Figure 4. Arrangement of lattice bolt support.

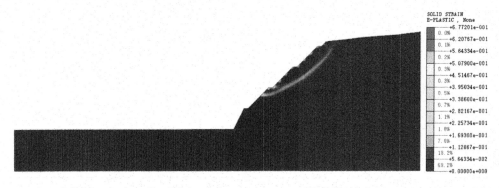

Figure 5. Effective plastic strain of high and steep slope supported by lattice bolts.

The safety factor of the slope under different working conditions is shown in Figure 6 below. It can be seen from the chart analysis that the safety factor of the slope is the highest, which is 1.95, due to its self-stabilizing property under natural stress. As the construction progresses, the soil body is disturbed after the slope is excavated, and the stability drops sharply. The specific performance is that the safety factor decreases, which is 1.1, and the slope is in an unstable state. As a tension member deep into the stratum, the anchor rod improves the overall stability of the slope through the anchoring effect of the anchor rod body; when the lattice anchor rod is combined for support, it can effectively exert the respective advantages of the lattice beam and the anchor rod. The main function of the lattice is to distribute the residual sliding force or earth pressure and rock pressure of the slope body to the anchor rods or anchor cables at the lattice structure points and then transmit them to the stable stratum through the anchor cables, so that the slope body can be stabilized. Under the action of the anchoring force provided by the anchor rod or the anchor cable, the safety factor reaches 1.32 and is in a stable state. In the process of playing a supporting role, lattice beam anchors play a major role, and lattice beams play a secondary role.

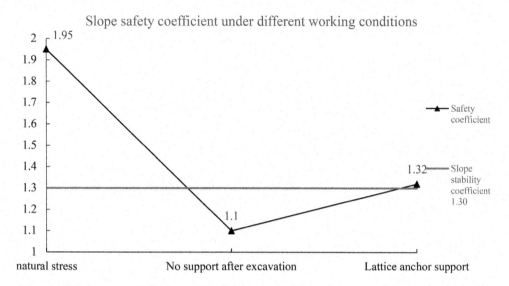

Figure 6. Slope safety coefficient under different working conditions.

4 CONCLUSION

This paper takes the actual engineering case as the analysis and research object and uses Midas-GTS finite element software to analyze the stability of a rock slope. The main conclusions are as follows:

(1) Through numerical simulation analysis, it is concluded that the high and steep slope is stable before excavation and becomes slightly unstable after excavation, with a certain penetration of the plastic zone. After the lattice beam is supported, there will be a plastic zone. If it is subjected to stress concentration, the plastic zone may be penetrated, resulting in unstable factors of the slope, which is relatively stable after bolt support. When lattice beams and prestressed bolts are used for joint support, there is no penetration area on the effective plastic strain diagram. The safety factor reaches 1.32, which meets the safety standard design specifications.

(2) When the lattice bolt combination is used for support, the advantages of lattice beams and bolts can be effectively exerted. The main function of the lattice is to distribute the residual sliding force or earth pressure and rock pressure of the slope to the lattice. The anchor rod or anchor cable at the structural point is then transmitted to the stable formation through the anchor cable, so that the slope body is in a stable state under the anchoring force provided by the anchor rod or anchor cable plays a supporting role. In the process, the lattice beam anchors play a major role, and the lattice beams play a secondary role.

(3) The arrangement of bolt support proposed in this project is only limited to the stage of numerical analysis, and there is still a lack of relevant actual engineering data verification. In the later stage, the bolt design parameters of this rock slope project can be further based on actual

engineering for engineering practice. Optimizing design, monitoring results of slope top displacement monitoring, deep horizontal displacement monitoring and bolt stress monitoring, to achieve better economic benefits.

DATA AVAILABILITY STATEMENT

The data that support the findings of this study are available from the corresponding author upon reasonable request.

ACKNOWLEDGMENTS

This work was supported by the National Natural Science Foundation of China (grant number 52078142).

REFERENCES

Chang Siyuan, Chen Zhezhou, Chai Lijie, et al. Application example of finite element method in rock slope stability analysis [J]. *Urban Geology*, 2020, 15(4): 380–387.

Chen Pengyu. *Slope structure characteristic analysis and stability research of high rock slope* [D]. Wuhan: China University of Geosciences, 2015.

Guotao Meng, Christine Detournay, Peter Cundall. Formulation and application of a constitutive model for multijointed material to rock mass engineering[J]. *International Journal of Geomechanics*, 2020, 20(6).

He Chuanren. *Stability analysis and comprehensive treatment of high rock slopes* [D]. Changsha: Central South University, 2013.

Huang Ping, Li Xiaochao. Application of numerical calculation in geotechnical engineering [J]. *Electric Power Survey and Design*, 2015(S1): 144–149.

Jiang Mingjing, Liu Wei, Sun Ya, et al. Discrete element simulation of direct shear test for non-through jointed rock mass considering environmental degradation[J]. *Geotechnical Mechanics*, 2017, 38(9):2728.

Li Kegang. *Stability analysis and deformation prediction of rock slopes* [D]. Chongqing: Chongqing University, 2006.

Lin Zhongming. Slope stability analysis of a mountain substation [J]. *Electric Power Survey and Design*, 2008(4): 14–17.

Liu Jie, Li Jianlin, Hu Hailang, et al. Research on fuzzy evaluation method of rock slope stability based on finite element analysis [J]. *Chinese Journal of Rock Mechanics and Engineering*, 2007(S1): 3438–3445.

Nishimura T, Fukuda T, Tsujino K. Distinct element analysis for progressive failure in rock slope [J]. *Soils & Foundations*, 2010, 50(4):505.

Wu Qin. *The collapse failure mechanism of rock slope and its stability analysis method* [D]. Chongqing: Chongqing Jiaotong University, 2010.

Zheng Yingren, Zhao Shangyi, Zhang Luyu. Slope stability analysis using finite element strength reduction method [J]. *China Engineering Science*, 2002(10):57–61+78.

Zheng Yingren, Zhao Shangyi. Application of finite element strength reduction method in soil and rock slopes [J]. *Chinese Journal of Rock Mechanics and Engineering*, 2004(19): 3381–3388.

Analysis of the influence of foundation pit excavation on adjacent metro section

Haiyan Ju*, Xingxing Liu*, Chen Yang*, Yan Liu*, Meng Hu*, Mingfu Fu* & Xiaoyong Fang*
Nanchang Institute of Technology, Jiangxi Provincial Engineering Research Center of the Special Reinforcement and Safety Monitoring Technology in Hydraulic & Civil Engineering, Nanchang, Jiangxi, China

ABSTRACT: Taking a foundation pit project in Nanchang as an example, the influence of foundation pit excavation on the adjacent subway station was analyzed by establishing a finite element model for numerical simulation, and the displacement of the main structure, wind pavilion structure, and interval structure due to foundation pit excavation was analyzed. The displacement change is compared with the on-site monitoring data. The analysis results show that the simulation data are similar to the monitoring data. The research results have certain reference significance for the determination of the numerical model, the selection of parameters, and the analysis of the impact on the adjacent buildings for similar new projects in this area.

1 INTRODUCTION

With the development of the city, major real estate projects around the subway station are also booming, and underground foundation pit projects appear near the subway. The foundation pit excavation is bound to bring certain harm to the subway section in the operation period, which will threaten the safety of subway tunnels and station structures. Therefore, it is necessary to adopt a reasonable foundation pit support type and excavation method and systematically evaluate the influence of foundation pit excavation on subway interval, which has guiding significance for engineering design and construction (Chen & Li 2005; Wang et al. 2010).

Many scholars have studied the impact of foundation pit excavation on surrounding buildings. Zhang and Zhu (2013) predicted and evaluated the stability of the foundation pit construction process and its impact on the surrounding environment based on finite element simulation. Tian and Chen et al. (2012) analyzed the settlement of adjacent shallow foundations caused by deep foundation excavation and precipitation. Zhang and Huang (2013) proposed a method to analyze the influence of excavation unloading on the deformation of adjacent buildings in excavation engineering. But the research and analysis on the excavation of the foundation pit on the adjacent subway section are still relatively small.

In this paper, the numerical simulation is done with the Midas finite element analysis software based on the data of the monitoring points taken in the subway section. The displacement change results of the subway tunnel are obtained. It is judged that the construction of the foundation pit will cause adverse effects on the existing subway station and tunnel structure, which provides a reference for the design and construction of other foundation pit works.

---

*Corresponding Authors: 2005992511@nit.edu.cn, 1303129723@qq.com, 1046566510@qq.com, 1184315944@qq.com, 2422483989@qq.com, 809380293@qq.com and 1144165318@qq.com

2 PROJECT OVERVIEW

The proposed project is located in Nanchang City, Jiangxi Province. The proposed buildings are two office buildings, one office service apartment, and corresponding ancillary buildings.

The east side of the project is adjacent to Guanzhou Station of Line 4, and the south side is adjacent to the interval between Guanzhou Station and Dingjiazhou Station. The horizontal net distance between the basement outside line and the main structure of Line 4 station is about 21.9m, and the distance between the main structure of Line 4 is about 21.9m. The horizontal net distance of the structure is about 10.1m, and the horizontal net distance from the interval structure is about 18.2m. The basement sideline is about 63.0m from the center line of Yunjin Road.

According to the drilling data, the underlying bedrock in the survey area is mainly the tertiary argillaceous siltstone group and mudstone group, and the lithology is mainly purple-red argillaceous siltstone, occasionally mudstone or sandstone, terrigenous clastic structure, medium-thick layered structure, mainly argillaceous cementation, local calcareous cementation. The rock mass is relatively complete, and the strongly and moderately weathered rock layers are distributed in interlayered form.

3 DESIGN AND CONSTRUCTION OF DEEP FOUNDATION PIT SUPPORT

In order to ensure the progress and construction safety of foundation pit excavation and basement structure construction and to reduce or avoid adverse effects on the surrounding environment, it should take corresponding protective measures during foundation pit construction.

The excavation depth of the foundation pit is between 8.4 and 9.4m, and the excavation depth of the foundation pit near the subway side is about 9.4m. Soil-cement mixed walls and steel supports are used to support the surrounding structure on the side of the foundation pit adjacent to the subway. The stirring piles are double-controlled according to the pile length of 22.90m and the strong weathering of not less than 0.5m; the stirring piles form a closed water-stop system. The three-axis mixing pile is double-controlled according to the pile length of 20.18m and the strong weathering of not less than 0.5m. The side away from the subway is supported by double rows of cast-in-place piles, and a row of stirring piles is set between the piles. The mixing pile is double-controlled according to the pile length of 22.90m and the strong weathering of not less than 0.5m; the mixing pile forms a closed water-stop system.

4 NUMERICAL MODELING

According to the actual engineering geological conditions, the soil is divided into six layers according to the actual soil stratification. The corresponding geomechanical parameters of each soil layer are shown in Table 1.

Table 1. Geotechnical mechanical parameters of each layer.

Surrounding rock stratification	Volumetric weight (kN/m^3)	Poisson's ratio	Cohesion (kPa)	Internal friction angle (°)	Compression modulus (Mpa)
Plain fill	18.39	0.18	6	23	20
Silty clay	19.02	0.25	20	6	24
Fine sand	19.52	0.31	10	26	28
Coarse sand	20.03	0.31	12	20	30
Gravel sand	21.04	0.31	18	21	35
Argillaceous Siltstone	22.98	0.36	42	38	40

Similarly, the elastic modulus of the retaining pile in the SWM construction method is 7800 MPa. The equivalent thickness of the retaining pile is 80cm. The material parameters of steel pipe support are selected according to steel, and the material parameters of pillar and segment are selected according to the corresponding grade of concrete. The specific mechanical parameters are shown in Table 2.

Table 2. Structural calculation parameters.

Material	Gravity (kN/m^3)	Elastic Modulus(MPa)	Poisson's ratio	Cross-sectional area (m^2)
SWM fencing pile	24	7800	0.2	0.75
Steel pipe support	78	200000	0.2	0.05
column	24	28000	0.2	0.025
Tunnel segment	25	345000	0.2	0.25

A three-dimensional numerical model is established based on the actual distribution of the foundation pit and the subway tunnel section. The influence range of foundation pit excavation in the numerical calculation is fully considered. The overall model is 180m long (x-direction), 240m wide (y-direction), and 30m deep (z-direction). The foundation pit is 120m long, 100m wide, and 9.5m deep. The three-dimensional network model is shown in Figure 1.

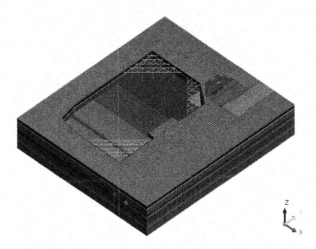

Figure 1. Calculation model.

After the initial stress field of the soil layer is stable, the displacement of the subway interval structure is cleared, and then the soil layer of the foundation pit excavation and the construction steps of adding SWM continuous wall and building internal support is simulated. Since the change of elastic modulus with the unloading of the foundation pit needs to be considered, the modified Mohr-Coulomb constitutive model is selected to calculate the displacement of the adjacent subway interval structure caused by foundation pit excavation in three directions. After the initial stress field of the soil layer is stable, the displacement of the subway section structure is reset to zero, and then various construction steps such as excavating the soil layer of the foundation pit, adding the SWM method diaphragm wall, and building internal supports are simulated. Because the change of the elastic modulus with the unloading of the foundation pit needs to be considered, the modified Mohr-Coulomb constitutive model is chosen to calculate the displacement of the adjacent subway section structure caused by the excavation of the foundation pit in three directions. The construction scheme steps with working conditions are shown in Table 3.

Table 3. Construction steps.

Serial number	Construction content	Outline
1	Initial stress field analysis	Calculation of soil gravity stress field
2	Tunnel construction	Excavation of eastern subway tunnel and construction of initial lining structure
3	Subway station construction	Establishment of the subway station and wind pavilion structure
4	Zero displacement	Displacement changes of shield tunnels and subway stations cleared to zero
5	Continuous wall construction	Construction of SWM continuous wall
6	Excavation of the first layer of soil	Excavation depth – 3m
7	Internal support	First internal support
8	Excavation of the second layer of soil	Excavation depth – 9.4 m

4.1 *Displacement of foundation pit envelope*

The existing subway station is located on the northeast side of the plot, and the shield tunnel is on the east side, so the horizontal displacement of the enclosure structures on the east and north sides is the key to control. Figures 2 and 3 show the horizontal displacement of the pile envelope in the SWM construction method of the foundation pit. According to the finite element calculation results, the maximum horizontal displacement of the east enclosure structure in the X direction is -13.5mm, and the maximum horizontal displacement of the north enclosure structure in the Y direction is -12.3mm. The main reason is that under the action of soil unloading, the SWM enclosure piles on the east and north sides of the adjacent subway section have a certain degree of horizontal lateral displacement towards the inside of the foundation pit.

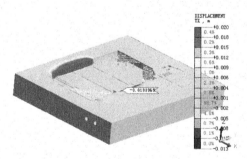 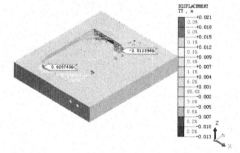

Figure 2. Cloud diagram of horizontal displacement of the east enclosure.

Figure 3. Cloud diagram of horizontal displacement of the north enclosure.

4.2 *Displacement of the subway station*

The maximum displacement of the main body of the subway in the X direction is -1.0mm, the maximum displacement in the Y direction is -0.2mm, and the maximum displacement in the Z direction is 2mm due to foundation pit construction. The displacement in the x-direction of the main structure of the station is shown in Figure 4. Compared with the wind pavilion and the tunnel, the main structure of the station has a smaller change in horizontal displacement, but its final vertical displacement is larger. The reason may be that the main structure is greatly affected by the buoyancy force during the unloading process of the soil, and its structural stability is worse, so the response to the excavation of the foundation pit is more sensitive.

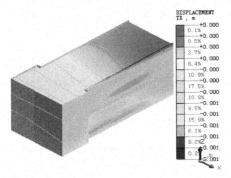 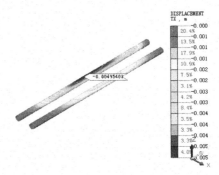

Figure 4. Cloud diagram of X-direction displacement of the main structure of station.

Figure 5. Cloud diagram of X-direction displacement of the subway tunnel structure.

4.3 *Displacement of subway shield tunnel*

The maximum displacement in the X direction of the tunnel structure in the subway section caused by the foundation pit construction is -4.9mm, the maximum displacement in the Y direction is -0.3mm, and the maximum displacement in the Z direction is 0.9mm. The displacement of the subway tunnel structure in the x direction is shown in Figure 5. The tunnel has a certain degree of horizontal displacement and vertical uplift towards the inside of the foundation pit, mainly in the horizontal lateral displacement.

5 COMPARATIVE ANALYSIS OF SIMULATION RESULTS AND MONITORING RESULTS

According to numerical analysis results, it can be seen that the excavation of the foundation pit causes the earth pressure on the outer wall of the SWM method diaphragm wall structure in the east and north side of the foundation pit adjacent to the subway section to change, which causes the tunnel segment structure on the left side of the subway to a certain degree lateral displacement of leveling to the inside of the foundation pit. The maximum horizontal displacement of the enclosure structure on the east side adjacent to the tunnel is 13.5mm, and the maximum horizontal displacement on the north side near the subway station is 12.3mm. Compared with the actual monitoring values, it can be seen from Table 4 that the actual deformation of the enclosure structure is similar to the finite element analysis results, and the finite element analysis result is about 10% smaller than the deformation value ratio, which is mainly caused by the fact that the finite element simulation cannot fully reflect the complex situation of the actual construction.

Table 4. Displacement results of foundation pit retaining structure.

Serial number	Horizontal displacement of east retaining structure (mm)	North retaining structure (mm)
Simulation maximum value	−13.5	−12.3
Maximum monitoring value	−15.1	−14.8

After the foundation pit is excavated to the base, the deformation of each structure in the subway section reaches the maximum value, and the maximum deformation results in all directions are shown in Table 5. In the actual monitoring displacement change of the main body of the subway station, the horizontal displacement in the x direction is 0.9mm larger than the finite element analysis result. The horizontal displacement in the y direction is 0.2mm larger than the finite element analysis result. The vertical displacement in the z direction is larger than the finite element analysis result. The analysis result is 0.2mm larger. The actual monitoring displacement of the shield tunnel is 1.8mm (x direction), 1.0mm (y direction), and 0.8mm (z-direction) larger than the finite element analysis results in three directions. The comparison results show that when the foundation pit is excavated to the base, the actual monitoring data are basically similar to the numerical simulation calculation results of the subway structure.

Table 5. Additional displacement results of subway structure.

Serial number	Structure	X direction displacement (mm)	Y direction displacement (mm)	Z direction displacement (mm)	Displacement control value (mm)	Whether the additional displacement is satisfied
Maximum value of numerical simulation	Station main body	−1.0	−0.2	2	10	meet
	Shield tunnel	−4.9	−0.3	0.9	10	meet
Maximum value of actual monitoring	Station main body	−1.9	−0.4	2.2	10	meet
	Shield tunnel	−6.7	−1.3	1.7	10	meet

6 CONCLUSION

The following conclusions can be drawn from the numerical analysis of the influence on the adjacent subway section by excavation and unloading of foundation pits in Nanchang.

(1) Comparing the calculation results of finite element analysis and the actual monitoring results, it can be seen that the data of the two are relatively similar. Therefore, it is effective to analyze the impact of foundation pit excavation on the structure of adjacent subway sections by using Midas GTS finite element analysis software before foundation pit construction. It has a certain guiding significance for practical engineering.
(2) The displacement of the main structure and tunnel structure of the Station of Metro Line 4 during the construction process of the deep foundation pit is small, and the displacement changes are all within the range of the displacement control value of 10mm. Therefore, the construction of the foundation pit of the local block poses little threat to the adjacent subway section and will not greatly impact the normal subway operation. However, in the actual project, the construction of a deep foundation pit is still the main factor affecting the safety of the subway tunnel structure. Therefore, in order to ensure the safety of the subway section structure, it is necessary to strengthen the real-time monitoring of the main structure of the subway station and the tunnel structure in the construction of the foundation pit and basement.

ACKNOWLEDGMENTS

Supported by the Jiangxi provincial education department of science and technology project (GJJ211907), the Jiangxi provincial science and technology project (20202BABL214041, 20192BAB206032), Nanchang Institute of Technology graduate Innovation Special Fund Project (YJSCX202128, YJSCX202109).

REFERENCES

Chen Y, Li YS. Calculation method of underlying tunnel uplift caused by excavation unloading [J]. *Underground space and engineering*, 2005, (1): 91–94.

Tian ZQ, Chen R, Wang ZZh, etc. Settlement Analysis of Adjacent Shallow Foundation Caused by Deep Foundation Excavation and Precipitation [J]. *Underground Space and Engineering Journal*, 2012, 8: 1483–1490.

Wang C, Yan SW, Zhang QB. Study on the influence mechanism and control measures of deep foundation pit excavation on adjacent bridge piles [J]. *Rock mechanics and engineering*, 2010, 29(1): 2994–3000.

Zhang Y, Zhu G. Research on the influence of deep foundation pit excavation on adjacent buildings based on monitoring information [J]. *The Journal of Underground Space and Engineering*, 2013, 9(2): 1975–1980.

Zhang Z, Huang M, Wang W. Evaluation of deformation response for adjacent tunnels due to soil unloading in excavation engineering[J]. *Tunneling and Underground Space Technology incorporating Trenchless Technology Research*, 2013, 38(3): 244–253.

Zhou JK, Li ZH. Numerical analysis of the influence of foundation pit engineering adjacent to subway tunnel on tunnel deformation [J]. *Journal of Underground Space and Engineering*, 2010, 6(1): 1398–403.

Numerical analysis on settlement of high fill subgrade of high-speed railway

Xiaolei Liu*

Ningxia Institute of Science and Technology, Ningxia, China

ABSTRACT: China has witnessed a rapid development of high-speed railroad construction. As high-speed railroads often traverse mountainous areas, there are many road sections filled and excavated, and high-fill subgrades are not uncommon. According to the *Construction Quality Acceptance Standards of High-speed Railway Subgrade Engineering*, the high-speed railway subgrades with high fills need to meet the requirements of being close to zero settlement after construction. Based on the settlement of the subgrade in the high fill section of a high-speed railway in China, this paper analyzes the subgrade settlement mechanism and uses numerical simulation analysis to determine the area with the largest subgrade settlement, which provides data references for later engineering construction.

1 INTRODUCTION

High-speed railways generally require the subgrade filling height (Jia 2013) to be no greater than 8m. However, given the construction and development of high-speed railways in China, it is inevitable that high-fill subgrades with a filling height greater than 8m will appear. There are two important technical issues in high-fill subgrades (Cai et al. 2017), stability control during construction and post-construction settlement control, which require accurate prediction of the settlement of high-fill subgrades. The ballastless track of high-speed railway requires "zero settlement" of high-speed railway foundation and puts forward requirements for settlement control of high-fill subgrades. In order to ensure the quality of the project, it is necessary to strengthen the control of subgrade settlement and comprehensively adopt effective technical means and strict management strategies to ensure the subgrade's strength, stiffness, and overall stability.

In order to deeply study the settlement of the high-fill road section, this paper mainly relies on the actual project of a high-speed railway in China. The highest filled section of subgrade, with a height of 11.21m, belongs to the high-fill section. The relevant calculation data can be obtained from the engineering site geological survey report, related engineering construction documents, and raw material monitoring reports. The MIDAS-NX software is used to simulate and analyze the settlement and deformation of the foundation during the construction phase to analyze and grasp the settlement law.

The works are carried out using mechanical layered filling. Therefore, the proposed model needs to consider the settlement simulation of the subgrade under different working conditions. Under simulation calculation, the law of subgrade settlement can be preliminarily grasped, and the maximum position of settlement can be found, which is convenient for proposing suggestions for engineering construction.

*Corresponding Author: 29257826@qq.com

2 NUMERICAL MODEL ESTABLISHMENT

2.1 Conditional assumptions and model simplification

The properties of subgrade fillers are relatively complex. The model in this paper adopts the continuous medium finite element method to analyze the settlement of high-fill subgrade during construction. The assumptions of this model are as follows:

(1) The mechanical properties of the same material are consistent, and the material itself is uniform, continuous, and isotropic;
(2) No parameters are set at the contact surface between different formation materials, the displacement of the two is coordinated, and there is no relative slip;
(3) This model is a plane strain model;
(4) The effect of groundwater is not considered.

2.2 Calculation parameters

In the example subgrade, there are subgrade sections and embankment sections, respectively. Considering that the embankment section has the largest settlement, and the fill height is 11.21m, the paper focuses on the settlement analysis of the embankment section. The combined effects of filler, train, and rail loads are considered in the calculation. The designed subgrade structure of this subgrade section is that the excavated subgrade section is 1.5m thick graded crushed stone mixed with 5% cement base bed; the fill subgrade section is 2.7m thick graded crushed stone mixed with 5% cement base bed + below the base bed of A and B fillers.

The main difference between the deformation modulus and the compression modulus of soil comes from the different confinement conditions when it is compressed. The dynamic deformation modulus is used for calculation, and concerning the three-dimensional space problem in the field, consideration should be given to the recoverable and unrecoverable deformation of the soil. Therefore, the compressive modulus was used for the calculation in this study, considering the one-dimensional deformation case with confinement conditions. Since there is no compressive modulus in the measured data, it is needed to refer to the calculation method in Zhang Qianli et al. (2005). Taking E=3X0.23K30, the compressive modulus of the foundation bed is 135.24MPa, and below the foundation bed is 119.37 MPa. Its value is about twice the dynamic deformation modulus, which is consistent with the experimental data of Wang Wenliang (2009).

The mechanical parameters of each geotechnical material of graded crushed stone, fillers of groups A and B, marl intercalated with shale W3(IV), and marl intercalated with shale W2(IV) can be calculated by looking up the on-site investigation report and on-site inspection results, thereby obtaining model-related parameters, as shown in Table 1 below.

Table 1. Calculation model in the investigated parameter table.

Soil	Weight capacity γ/kN/m^3	Cohesion c/kPa	Friction angle φ/°	Elastic modulus E/MPa	Poisson's ratio/μ
Graded crushed stone	23.7	15	36	135.24	0.3
Fillers of groups A and B	22.8	10	35	119.37	0.3
Marl intercalated with shale W3	23	25	20	11000	0.3
Marl intercalated with shale W2	23	25	20	11000	0.3

2.3 Model establishment

Most of the problems in the field of geotechnical engineerings, such as slope problems, underground engineering, etc., involve infinite or semi-infinite fields when establishing numerical models, and the discrete areas in the actual modeling process are limited. In order to prevent this discrete processing from generating large errors, the calculation range must be large enough, and the boundary should be as close to the actual state as possible.

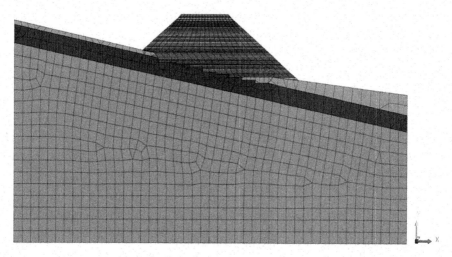

Figure 1. The calculation model for the grid figure.

A large amount of literature and calculations show that when a certain soil is excavated or treated in engineering, the range in which it has a large influence on the stress and displacement of the surrounding soil is 2.5-3 times the contour size of the excavation or the interaction surface between the structure and the soil body. Soil bodies outside this range have little impact, which can be ignored. The boundary conditions of the finite element model are: in the model, the upper surface and roadbed are free boundaries, the two sides of the soil below the ground surface constrain the horizontal displacement of the model, and the bottom boundary of the model constrains the vertical displacement of the model. The initial stress field is considered the self-weight stress field. The mesh of the model is divided by 4-node elements. In the upper part, the mesh division of the graded crushed stone and filler that needs to be analyzed is relatively fine, while the settlement of the lower soil body is small, and the mesh division of the lower soil body can be larger. Therefore, the model establishment mainly considers the weight of each layer of soil and the influence of the upper rail and train loads. The computational mesh division diagram is shown in Figure 1.

3 SUBGRADE DEFORMATION ANALYSIS

Generally speaking, railway subgrade settlement includes foundation settlement and subgrade settlement. The subgrade is filled with a large number of rock bodies, such as graded crushed stone and fillers of groups A, B, or C. These rockfills are granular materials composed of a large number of solid particles. From a microscopic analysis, their settlement deformation is mainly composed of three parts: (1) the compression deformation of the particle skeleton; (2) the continuous extrusion between the particles; (3) creep deformation that occurs continuously due to the refinement and slip of fine particles to fill the pores. From the macroscopic analysis, railway subgrade settlement mainly includes subgrade settlement during construction and post-construction settlement. The settlement and deformation laws are analyzed by MIDAS-NX finite element modeling. The layered filling thickness of the subgrade section is calculated as 30cm for each layer, and the slope gradient is set according to the actual engineering situation. The subgrade deformation law in this process is analyzed by layer filling. The filling process is simulated according to different filling and construction conditions, as shown in Figures 2–6.

3.1 Settlement analysis during construction

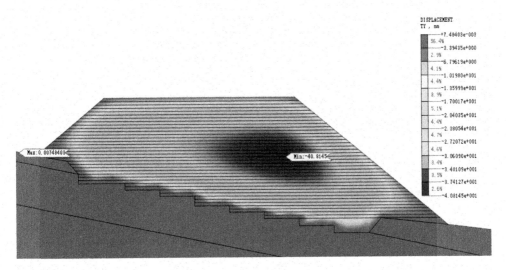

Figure 2. Settlement of A and B materials.

From the settlement situation after filling A and B materials, it can be seen that the maximum settlement after the filling is 40.1mm, which mainly occurs at the height of about 2–6 m, and the settlement mainly occurs in the area on the right side of the subgrade center.

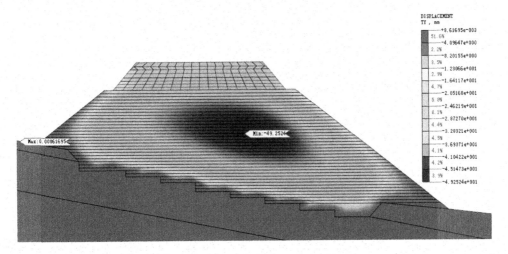

Figure 3. Loading and preloading stage settlement.

For the settlement after the completion of the loading and preloading stage, the maximum settlement at this time is 49.3mm, the settlement continues to increase due to the upper loading, and the settlement position moves to the center of the subgrade due to the upper uniform load.

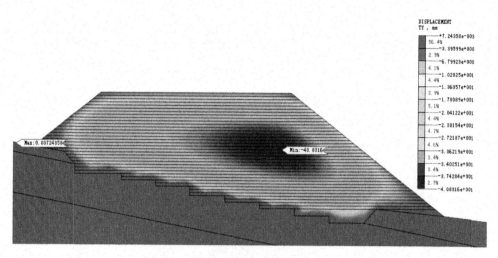

Figure 4. Loading and unloading stage settlement.

The settlement after unloading the loading stages shows that the maximum settlement is 40.8mm, and the position of the maximum settlement returns to the right of the center of the subgrade after the upper uniform load is removed.

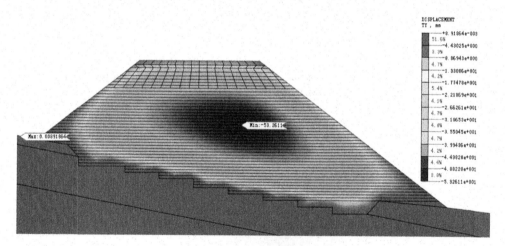

Figure 5. Stage settlement after the filling stage of graded crushed stone.

The settlement after the filling of graded crushed stone was completed showed that the maximum settlement was 53.3mm, and the settlement increased by 12.5mm after the upper part was filled with gravel. The maximum settlement position was higher than the settlement position of the heap preloading stage, increased to about 4-8m, and maintained in the right position of the subgrade center.

For the settlement after the completion of the upper part of the subgrade laying rails and considering the load caused by the train, the surface layer of the subgrade filled with gravel also begins to settle. It can be seen that the maximum settlement is 56.7mm, and the position with the maximum settlement is still at the right position of the center of the subgrade, but the maximum settlement occurs at the height of about 4m-10m, which is caused by the load of the upper rail and train considering the concentrated stress.

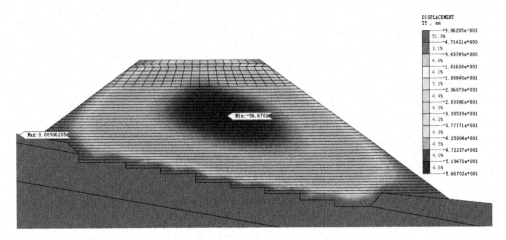

Figure 6. Rail and train load settlement.

Analyzing the settlement of each construction stage is of great significance to construction guidance. The paper analyzes the settlement of the subgrade filling process according to each construction condition. After filling AB fillers, loading equivalent uniform load, unloading load, filling graded crushed stone, upper rail, and train load, the deformation state, the law of foundation settlement, and the location of deformation can be observed by simulating the deformation state during the construction stage, and the detailed analysis and calculation results are shown in Table 2.

Table 2. Working conditions of different filling process settlement results summary table.

Working condition	Construction process	Y overall direction displacement (mm)	Monitoring value (mm)
Working condition 1	Natural settlement of foundation soil	0	0
Working condition 2	A and B materials completed filling	40.8	45.1
Working condition 3	Loading and preloading	49.2	52.5
Working condition 4	Unloading and loading	40.83	41.2
Working condition 5	Filling of graded crushed stone	53.3	56.3
Working condition 6	Rail and train loads	56.7	57.9

From the subgrade displacement analysis of the above working conditions, the following can be obtained: the maximum displacement in the horizontal direction, the maximum settlement in the vertical direction of the subgrade during the layered filling process, and the position of the maximum settlement. Through the simulation results, the construction process can be predicted well. The deformation curve is shown in Figure 2, from which it can be seen that the numerical simulation value is the same as the monitoring value. The monitoring settlement is larger than the simulation value in the initial stage. Still, the two are almost equal in the later compaction stage, indicating that the simulation model is more accurate and can be used to predict the subgrade settlement in other stages.

From the analysis of the calculation results of the subgrade displacement under different working conditions, we can get:

During the layered filling process of the subgrade, the maximum settlement after the completion of the A and B fillers is 40.8mm, which mainly occurs at the height of about 2-6m, and the settlement mainly occurs in the area on the right side of the center of the subgrade. Due to the upper loading effect, the settlement continues to increase, the settlement position moves to the center of the subgrade due to the uniform load on the upper part, and the maximum settlement position after the heap unloading stage returns to the right position of the subgrade center. After the completion of graded crushed stone filling, the settlement increased by 12.1 mm, and the maximum settlement increased to about 4-8 m, which remained at the right side of the subgrade center. After the subgrade filling is completed, the maximum settlement is 56.7 mm by considering the laying of the rails on the upper part and the load caused by the train. At this time, the filling height is 11.21m, the settlement per unit height is 5.06 mm/m, and the maximum position is still at the right position of the center of the subgrade. Due to the slope at the bottom of the subgrade, the thickness of the soil layer on the right side of the subgrade is large, resulting in a larger settlement on the right side.

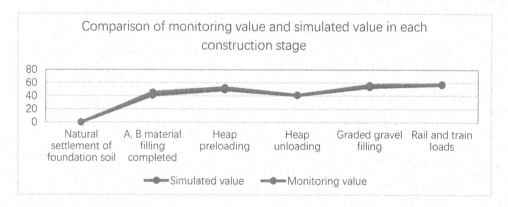

Figure 7. Deformation of the subgrade construction phase of the figure.

3.2 *Post-construction deformation analysis of subgrades*

Many experimental studies show that from the macroscopic level, the settlement of railway subgrade mainly includes subgrade settlement during construction and post-construction settlement. The previous section analyzed the basic laws of subgrade settlement during construction. This chapter specifically analyzes the post-construction settlement law.

Figure 8 shows the displacement in the X direction (that is, the horizontal direction) of the roadbed settlement after construction. The maximum deformation is 1.16mm, and the maximum deformation is located at the boundary between the slope ratios of 1:1.5 and 1:1.75 on the long side. The slope stability coefficient calculated by simulation is 2.06, which is much larger than the specified value in the specification.

Figure 9 shows the displacement in the Y direction of the roadbed settlement after construction. The maximum deformation is 5.83mm, located on the upper surface of the right side of the roadbed.

Through the analysis of the post-construction displacement calculation results of the subgrade, the following can be obtained:

(1) The post-construction displacement in the horizontal direction has a decreasing trend, indicating that the settlement in the horizontal direction tends to be stable, and the maximum settlement occurs at the junction of different slope ratios. After calculation, the slope stability coefficient meets the standard requirements. During the construction process, strict attention

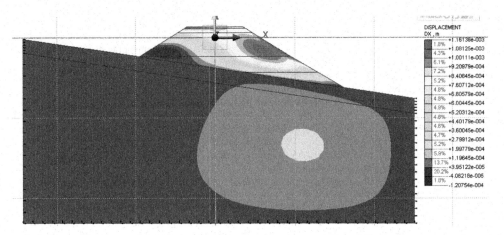

Figure 8. The X-direction displacement nephogram of roadbed.

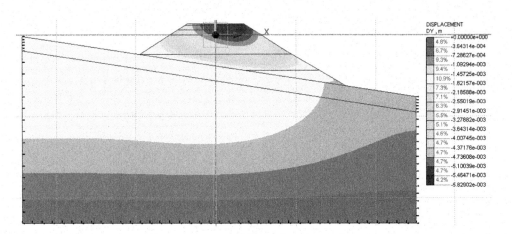

Figure 9. The Y-direction displacement nephogram of roadbed.

should be paid to the filling technology and lateral displacement control at the junction of this section to ensure the stability of the slope.
(2) The maximum filling height of the high fill section is mainly on the right side of the subgrade. Considering the non-horizontal subgrade of the original foundation, the maximum post-construction displacement of the subgrade in the vertical direction is at the upper right surface of the subgrade.

4 CONCLUSION

By using the MIDAS-NX finite element software, the paper establishes a finite element model, selects the constitutive model and parameters of each material, and simulates and analyzes the deformation of the high-fill subgrades of high-speed railways. The analysis and calculation results provide the corresponding practical engineering construction. The technical guidance and suggestions provide a good data description for the subsequent construction of the process.

REFERENCES

Cai W X, Liang H, Zhu Y P, et al. Analysis of settlement and deformation factors of high-fill roadbed based on FLAC3D [J]. *Chinese Journal of Hydraulic and Architectural Engineering*, 2017, 34(3): 15–19.

Jia L H. *Key technology of coarse particle filler for high-fill subgrade of high-speed railway*[D]. Changsha: Master's Thesis of Central South University, 2013.

Jia L, He S K, Zhu Y P, et al. Experimental study on post-construction settlement monitoring of high-filled embankments [J]. *Highway Traffic Science and Technology*, 2017, 34(3): 15–19.

Wang W L. Construction technology of Group A and B packing for railway passenger dedicated line foundation [J]. *Science and Technology Information Development and Economy*, 2009, 13(9): 197–199.

Wang Y C. *Calculation analysis and research on settlement and deformation law of high fill roadbed*[D]. Chongqing: Chongqing Jiaotong University, 2006.

Zhang Q L, Han Z L, Lv B L. Structural analysis and design method of high-speed railway subgrade bed[J]. *China Railway Science*, 2005, 6(26): 53–57.

Numerical simulation of interface slip of steel-concrete composite beam

Shirap Tenzin, Nima Ciren & Yuandan Duoji
The Highway Construction Project Management Center, Transport Department of the Tibet Autonomous Region, Lhasa, Tibet, China

Jiacheng Zhao
School of Civil Engineering, Beijing Jiaotong University, Beijing, China

Guangming Wang
Beijing Municipal Engineering Research Institute, Beijing, China

Li Zhu*
School of Civil Engineering, Beijing Jiaotong University, Beijing, China

Haolin Guo
CCCC Highway Bridges National Engineering Research Centre Co. Ltd., Beijing, China

ABSTRACT: There is a problem that the stud load capacity is affected by the strength of the concrete slab of the steel-concrete beam being damaged during the stressing process. In this paper, relying on the composite beam bridge on National Highway 345, the theoretical analysis method of static load calculation of reinforced concrete composite beam is used, and different models are established for comparison through Abaqus to simulate the bending process of the static load of the composite beam and obtain the simulated values of each parameter of the composite beam. The simulated values of the parameters of the composite beam are used to obtain the relative slip at the intersection of the composite beam as the load increases. This study provides a reference for the finite element analysis of steel-concrete composite beams.

1 INTRODUCTION

The steel-concrete composite beam is a combined structure in the bridge sector, where two materials, concrete and steel, are combined and jointly stressed using shear connectors (e.g., PBL connectors, pins, and sections) (Huang 2017; Nie 2017, 2007). Shear connectors play a key role in effectively transferring shear forces in steel-concrete composite beams as an important force transfer element. There has been a great deal of research and theoretical analysis on the fatigue performance of shear connectors in composite beams, and formulas suitable for design calculations have been introduced, including shear bearing capacity, slip performance, and fatigue performance. A few studies exist on the degradation law of the load-carrying capacity and stiffness of shear connectors after corrosion or high temperature (Ju 2019; Mirza 2021; Wang 2017). However, there are few studies on the influence of stud load-bearing capacity due to the strength damage of concrete slabs.

Using mathematical approximations, large-scale finite element calculation and analysis methods are used to simulate real physical systems (including geometry, loads, and other working conditions). From the bridge field, with the combination of the computer field and the engineering field, the development and use of large general finite element software have led to an increasingly refined finite element model, summarizing the numerical model for the composite beam, which

---
*Corresponding Author: zhuli@bjtu.edu.cn

is divided into three main categories: all components are built using beam cell (Zeng 2013; Zou 2013); concrete slab and steel beam in the composite beam is simulated using shell units, and shear connectors are simulated using spring stiffness (Nie 2005); all components are built using solid units (Jia 2011; Li 2018). All three modeling methods have their own advantages and disadvantages, as well as their scope of application. The suitable modeling method is chosen reasonably according to the content of the engineering study during the numerical simulation. Compared with other finite element software, Abaqus has the advantages of a rich library of material models and the ability to build arbitrary structural models, interaction types, and constraint types (Shi 2006).

In this paper, based on the analytical method of static load theory calculation for composite beams, different solid unit models and beam unit models are established by Abaqus for comparison to explore the accuracy of the model establishment and whether it can analyze the mechanical characteristics of composite beams under normal use conditions, and to comprehensively examine the changes of the relative slip at the intersection of composite beams with increasing load.

2 ABAQUS MODEL BUILDING

The model in this paper refers to the experimental content of the literature (Ma 2020) and is analyzed by comparing the calculated data from this model with the experimental beam data. The main structure of the composite beam consists of a concrete slab, steel beam, and studs. Because the analysis of this paper focuses on the stress of the studs and the stress of the connection part of the 1/4 span high-strength bolts, the solid unit is used for analysis and simulation. Due to the complicated calculation process of the solid unit, the beam unit can be used for modeling and analysis when stress analysis of the internal structure is not required. The material of the connecting plate is the same as the material type of the steel beam. The high-strength bolts are 10.9s M20 high-strength bolts, and according to the material provided by the manufacturer, the yield strength of the high-strength bolts is set to 932MPa, which also meets the elastic-plastic ideal model. The holes are cut in the corresponding steel beam, and the connecting plate and high-strength bolts are added. The front and rear are connected with the 8mm thick steel plate, and the lower flange connection plate is a homogeneous 8mm steel plate. The correct contact and loading conditions are used to analyze the high-strength bolt connection area.

In the establishment of concrete slabs, since solid units establish both concrete slabs and studs, it is necessary to reserve stud holes at the corresponding positions of concrete slabs and establish contact relations with the concrete interior. The exact build process is shown in Figure 1.

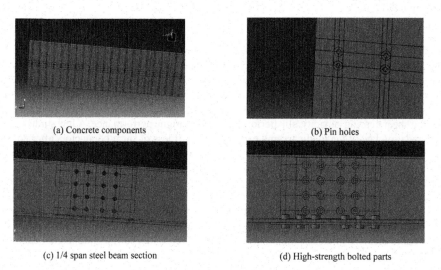

Figure 1. Component of composite beam solid model.

The concrete composite beam model is shown in Figure 2.

Figure 2. Composite beam solid element model.

3 INTERFACE SLIP STUDIES

In this paper, solid unit studs, studs, and concrete holes are contacted in the form of normal hard contact, and tangential "penalty" friction, and the plastic damage model is used for the concrete intrinsic relationship, so there are large stresses in the concrete and stud contact area.

The beam end slip and the stress variation in the compressive and tensile sides of the studs along the length of the beam are given below.

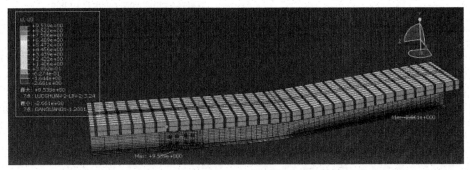

(a) Slip of the composite beam along the length of the beam

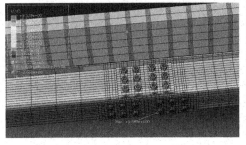

(b) Slip at the intersection (with bolt side)   (c) Slip at the intersection (unbolted side)

Figure 3. Cloud-based slip of composite beam along the beam length.

The composite beam in the maximum load-bearing capacity along the beam length direction of the slip cloud chart is shown in Figure 3. Because the steel beam top plate with bearing static load bearing capacity of the pressure state, the two sides 1/4 span presents the span of the slip situation, with the bolt side U3 direction of the displacement negative, no bolt side U3 direction of the displacement is positive, both to the span of the direction of loading slip. The steel beam bottom plate of the composite beam is subjected to tensile action, then it is a case of slipping toward both ends, while because the composite beam intersection interface is not a rigid connection, the concrete bottom plate is subjected to tensile action and also presents a case of slipping toward the end of the beam. At the composite beam intersection, the concrete bottom slab is displaced toward the beam end, and the steel beam top slab is displaced toward the span, so the composite beam intersection will produce relative slippage, subjecting the shear joints in the composite beam to the shear force along the beam length.

The change in the slip of the cross-section of the composite beam along the length of the beam as the load increases is shown in Figure 4, where the trend in the slip at the end of the composite beam

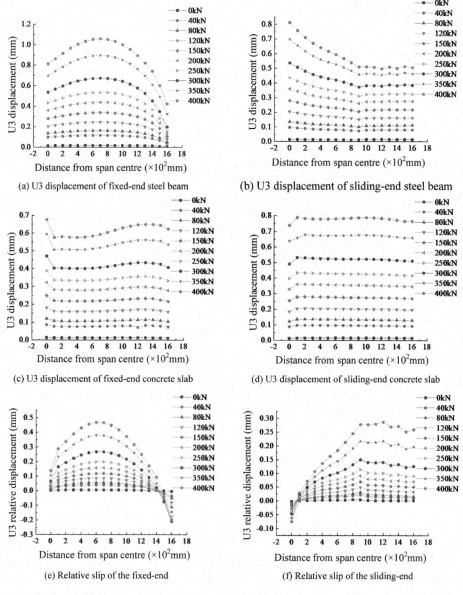

Figure 4. Trend of relative slip at the fixed-end and sliding-end of composite beam.

can be seen. The data was collected from the nodes in the cloud chart. The displacement in the U3 direction (longitudinal direction of the beam) of the steel beam was selected at the displacement of the edge node of the upper flange plate of the steel beam. The displacement in the U3 direction of the concrete was selected at the displacement of the node of the concrete base plate near the upper flange plate of the steel beam. The displacement in the U3 direction of the concrete is selected as the displacement of the node of the concrete base plate near the upper flange of the steel beam. The displacements of the concrete and steel beam along the U3 direction in this model are presented separately, and their displacements are analyzed with the change in load, and then the relative slip of the composite beam is calculated by subtracting the two. On the left is a graph of the data from the span to the fixed end direction, and on the right is a graph of the displacement change from the span to the sliding end. The graph shows the magnitude of the slip in the U3 direction of the steel beam and the composite beam's concrete slab.

From Figure 4, it can be concluded that the maximum displacement value of the composite beam along the beam length direction (U3 direction) is at 1/4 span near the fixed end. Because the fixed end of the composite beam only imposes a boundary constraint on the displacement of the steel beam in the U3 direction, the bottom of the concrete slab is in tension throughout the longitudinal direction, and the displacement of the bottom of the concrete slab in the U3 direction along the length of the beam is not large, and they are all displaced toward the sliding end, as shown in Figure 4 (a) and (b). The relative slip of any node of the composite beam can be obtained by subtracting the displacement in the U3 direction at the bottom of the concrete slab and the top of the steel beam at the same position, as shown in Figure 4(e) and (f). Because the boundary constraint condition in Abaqus sets the entire fixed end of the steel beam as a constraint, it is not consistent with the test situation, so the relative slip of the fixed end of the composite beam shows a convergence in 0. The relative slip at the sliding end of the beam for each section along the length of the beam is consistent with the experimental values, as shown in Figure 4(f) and Figure 5. Both figures show a trend of 0 slip at the mid-span and a maximum slip at the beam end. From the U3 directional displacements of the steel beam and concrete slab extracted by Abaqus, it is concluded that the difference in relative slip in either section is due to the difference in the U3 displacements of the fixed and slipped ends of the steel beam of the composite beam along the length of the beam, which is what causes the relative slip at the intersection of the composite beam, and the underlying cause of the relative slip is the difference in the U3 directional displacements of the same section of the concrete slab and steel beam at the intersection.

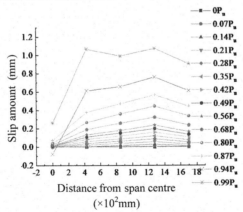

Figure 5. Relative slip of test beam.

It is derived from Figure 5 that the relative slip of the combined beam changes greatly and shows nonlinear changes when approaching the ultimate load. Along the beam length direction, the relative slip of the cross-section near the middle of the span shows linear growth, the relative slip of the cross-section from 1/4 span to the beam end position tends to be stable, and the relative slip of the 1/8 span combination beam near the beam end reaches the maximum, and the slip reaches 1 mm when approaching the ultimate load.

4 CONCLUSION

This paper uses Abaqus to simulate the bending process of the composite beam numerically under static load and gives the simulated values of the finite element data of the parameters of the composite beam. The steel beam nodes were selected from the edge nodes of the flange plate on each section of the steel beam, the concrete slab nodes were selected from the concrete nodes adjacent to the steel beam nodes, and the relative slip of the section was the difference between the U3 displacement of the concrete nodes and the U3 displacement of the steel beam nodes. When approaching the ultimate load, the relative slip of the composite beam varies greatly and shows a nonlinear change. Along the beam length direction, the relative slip of the cross-section near the middle of the span shows linear growth, the relative slip of the cross-section from 1/4 span to the beam end position tends to be stable, and the relative slip of the 1/8 span combination beam near the beam end reaches the maximum, and the slip reaches 1 mm when approaching the ultimate load. The relative slips of the concrete slab and steel beam unit nodes in the U3 direction of the composite beam are in good agreement with the test values.

ACKNOWLEDGMENTS

The authors gratefully acknowledge the financial support from the Science and Technology Project of Transportation of Tibet Autonomous Region (Study on Key Technology of Construction of Weathering Steel-concrete Composite Beam Bridges with Cast-in-situ Deck in Tibet).

REFERENCES

Huang Qiao. *Design principles of steel-concrete composite structures for bridges* [M]. Beijing: China Communications Press, 2017.

Jia Yuanlin, Chen Shiming & Wang Xindi. Non-linear numerical analysis of in vitro prestressed steel-concrete continuous composite beams[J]. *Journal of Tongji University* (Natural Science Edition), 2011, 39(09): 1258–1265.

Ju Chen, Zhang Haipeng & Yu Qian-Qian. Static and fatigue behavior of steel-concrete composite beams with corroded studs[J]. *Journal of Constructional Steel Research*, 2019, 15618–27.

Li Wenxian. *Theoretical and experimental study of steel-concrete composite beams with different connection degrees*[D]. Southeast University, 2018.

Ma Guanling, Ni Yongjun & Luo Xinyuan. Static performance analysis of steel-concrete composite beams under positive and negative moment loads[J]. *Transportation Science & Technology*, 2020(05): 1–5.

Mirza Olivia, Shill Sukanta Kumer, Rashed M.G. & Wilkins Kathryn. Experimental and numerical studies on the shear connectors in steel-concrete composite beams at fire and post-fire exposures[J]. *Steel and Composite Structures*, 2021, 39(05): 529–542.

Nie Jianguo & Tian Chunyu. Analysis of effective width of simply supported composite beam-slab system[J]. *China Civil Engineering Journal*, 2005, (02): 8–12.

Nie Jianguo. *Application of composite girder bridges in small and medium span bridges*[A]// Papers of the 11th Annual Meeting of Sub-association for Steel-Concrete Composite Structures [C]. Harbin, Heilongjiang, China: 2007: 684–688.

Nie Jianguo. *Steel-concrete composite bridges* [M]. Beijing: China Communications Press, 2011.

Shi Yiping & Zhou Yurong. *ABAQUS finite element examples in detail* [M]. China Machine Press, 2006.

Wang, Bing. *Study on the residual mechanical properties of steel-concrete composite girder bridges based on fatigue cumulative damage effect* [D]. Southeast University, 2017.

Zeng Xinggui, Zhou Donghua, Li Longqi, et al. Computational analysis of interface slip of composite beams[J]. *Engineering Mechanics*, 2013, 30(06): 162–167.

Zou Yang. *Study on the effect of slip on the mechanical behavior of steel-concrete composite beams*[D]. Chongqing Jiaotong University, 2013.

Numerical analysis of the impact of deep foundation pit excavation induced ground and pipeline responses

Ren Qiang* & Wei Kuang Min*
Nanjing Hydraulic Research Institute, Nanjing, Jiangsu Province, China

ABSTRACT: Based on the pipeline sheet pile deep foundation pit project on a soft soil foundation, the numerical simulation calculation model of support structure-pipeline-soil interaction is established, and the behaviors of the excavation-induced ground and pipeline responses are analyzed. The process of pipeline burying and soil backfilling is simulated, and the deformation laws of ground and pipeline before and after foundation treatment are also studied and revealed. The results show that the foundation reinforcement scheme of the project has a good control effect on the horizontal and vertical displacements of pipelines. The research results can play a reasonable reference for relevant problems and similar projects.

1 INSTRUCTIONS

Foundation excavation engineering is complex engineering of interaction and interaction between soil and retaining structure. It is generally recognized that soil mass excavation could inevitably cause ground stress relief and movements, and hence additional buildings and underground pipelines deformations and internal forces. In adverse conditions such as weak soil properties, the nearby existing pipelines may suffer from appreciable deformations and even damages like cracks, dislocations, and leakages (Ahmed 1990; Calvetti et al. 2004; Sharma et al. 2001; Vorster et al. 2005).

Therefore, how to ensure excavation during construction without affecting the normal use of adjacent pipelines is a very important problem. Taking the foundation excavation engineering on soft soil foundation as the background, this paper establishes a numerical simulation calculation model, in an attempt to analyze the behaviors of the excavation-induced ground and pipeline responses, including settlement and deformation in the process of foundation pit excavation and pipeline embedding, where its deformation law is revealed and studied, which can play a reasonable reference for the relevant problem and the construction of similar projects.

2 PROJECT OVERVIEW

The project is a new sewage pipe with a buried depth of 8m. The pipeline is DN1200 reinforced concrete pipe with a wall thickness of 120mm. The excavation width of the foundation pit is 2 m, and the excavation depth is 12m. The stratum passes through the fill and silt of the subgrade and belongs to an unstable construction disturbance structure.

The 12m Type-V Larssen Sheet Pile and $\Phi 250 \times 10$ steel pipe inner support are combined to form the retaining structure of the foundation pit, three supports are provided for the foundation

---

*Corresponding Authors: qren@nhri.cn and kmwei@nhri.cn

pit with a horizontal spacing of 3m. According to the report of geotechnical engineering geological investigation, the strata in the field area are divided from top to bottom: ①artificial soil layer; ②-1 coarse sand layer; ②-2 silt soil layer; ②-3 coarse sand layer; ③-1 strong weathered granite. The section is shown in Figure 1 below.

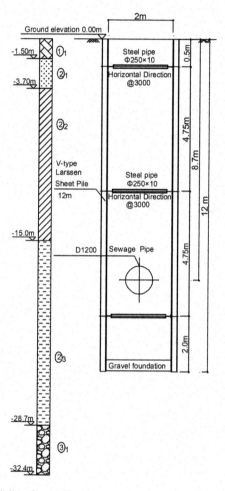

Figure 1. Plan of model and the referential section.

3 FINITE ELEMENT MODULE

3.1 *Computational model*

The boundary range of the calculation model is that the side boundary is 4 times the excavation depth of the foundation pit, and the bottom boundary is 5 times the excavation depth of the foundation pit. The size of the model is 170 m×50m.

The material of each soil layer is simulated by a 4-node isoparametric solid element, the steel sheet pile and pipeline are simulated by beam element, while the steel pile support is simulated by rod element. The boundary condition of the model is the constrained horizontal displacement on both sides, set fixed constraint at the bottom. The plane mesh model of the calculation and analysis area after subdivision is shown in Figure 2.

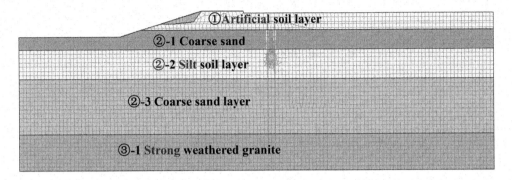

Figure 2. Plane finite element model.

3.2 Calculation parameters

The ideal elastoplastic model with Mohr-Coulomb yield condition as a failure criterion is adopted for soil. The calculation parameters include elastic modulus E, Poisson's ratio μ, cohesion c, and internal friction ϕ. The values of various parameters are shown in Table 1. Generally, elastic modulus $E = (2.5 \sim 3.5) E_s$ (Wang Chenghua 2002). For safety, it is taken as 3 in the calculation. Considering the unloading of foundation pit excavation, the unloading modulus is adopted for the calculation of elastic modulus. The loading and unloading test results can be referred, ① artificial soil layer, ②-1 coarse sand, ②-3 coarse sand layer, and ②-1 strong weathered granite take 2 times the initial loading modulus, while ②-2 silt soil layer takes 3 times the initial loading modulus.

Table 1. The values of various parameters for soil material.

Material name	Thickness m	γ (kN/m³)	γ_{sat} (kN/m³)	c (kPa)	φ °	E (MPa)	v
①Artificial soil layer	1.5	17.90	18.50	22.0	23.0	14	0.25
②-1 Coarse sand	2.2	21.50	22.00	0	35.0	126	0.25
②-2 Silt soil	11.3	16.70	17.30	8.8	7.5	5.8	0.45
②-3 Coarse sand	13.3	22.00	22.50	0	35.0	135	0.25
③-1 Strong Weathered Granite	3.7	21.00	21.60	20.5	32.0	5700	0.30

The elastic model is adopted for steel sheet piles and pipelines. The values of parameters are shown in Table 2.

Table 2. The values of parameters for pipe.

Material name	γ (kN/m³)	E (GPa)	v
Pipeline	25.0	30	0.25
Larssen Sheet Pile (Q295P Steel Plate)	78.5	206	0.28

3.3 Excavation process simulation

In order to realize the dynamic simulation of the whole construction process, the construction steps are simulated according to the actual working conditions. The specific numerical simulation steps are shown in Table 3.

Table 3. Construction steps of the pit excavation.

Step	Content	Descriptions
Step-1	Initial in-situ stress balance	
Step-2	Foundation reinforcement	Cement mixing Pile
Step-3	Steel sheet pile construction	
Step-4	The first layer is excavated The first steel brace is applied	The soil is excavated to −0.5 m The height of the steel brace is −0.5 m
Step-5	The second layer is excavated The second steel brace is applied	The soil is excavated to −3.5 m The height of the steel brace is −5.25m
Step-6	The third layer is excavated The third steel brace is applied	The soil is excavated to −6.5 m The height of the steel brace is −8.0m
Step-7	The fourth layer is excavated	The soil is excavated to the bottom of the pit
Step-8	Backfill the first layer of the foundation pit Remove the inner support	Backfilling to −6.5m
Step-9	Backfill the second layer of the foundation pit Remove the inner support	Backfilling to −3.5m
Step-10	Backfill the third layer of the foundation pit Remove the inner support	Backfilling to −0.5m
Step-11	Backfill the fourth layer of the foundation pit Pile pulling	Backfilling to 0.0m
Step-12	Roadbed Filling	Filling to 2.0m
Step-13	Traffic loads applying	Uniformly distributed load of 7.8kPa

4 ANALYSIS OF NUMERICAL SIMULATION RESULTS

4.1 Analysis of foundation pit excavation and pipeline embedding process

Figure 3 shows the settlement distribution of pavement observation points at various stages. With the deepening of excavation depth, the pavement settlement increases continuously. When the

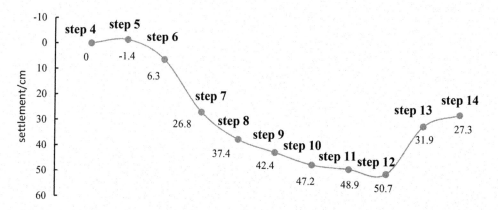

Figure 3. The development process of subgrade settlement in each stage.

excavation reaches the bottom of the foundation pit, the settlement is 26.8mm. When the foundation pit is backfilled, the settlement continues to increase. When the backfill reaches the top of the pit, the maximum settlement deformation caused by pavement settlement is 50.7mm. With the filling of the subgrade and the application of vehicle load, the deformation of the embankment top rebounds, and the final settlement deformation is 27.3mm.

Figure 4 shows the horizontal and vertical deformation of the pipeline. It can be seen from the figure that the pipeline is buried in the soil, the foundation pit is backfilled, the subgrade is filled, and the vehicle load is applied. The maximum horizontal deformation of the pipeline caused by the construction process is 59.5mm and the vertical deformation is 122.2mm, exceeding the allowable deformation of the pipeline.

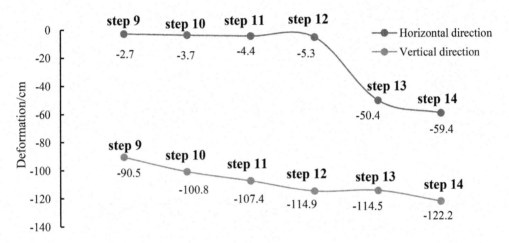

Figure 4. The horizontal and vertical deformation of the pipeline.

4.2 Relevant calculation and analysis after foundation treatment

The cement mixing pile reinforcement method is used to treat the foundation of the underlying layer of the pipeline, and the influence of foundation pit excavation and pipeline embedding on the deformation of the pavement and pipeline after the foundation reinforcement treatment is analyzed. The preliminarily proposed reinforcement scheme of the pipeline foundation is a cement mixing pile with a pile diameter of 500mm and spacing of 1m, which is arranged in a regular triangle.

The soil within the treatment range is simulated by a composite foundation. The equivalent composite modulus of pile and soil between piles is calculated according to the area weighting method in foundation reinforcement. The elastic parameters of the pile-soil equivalent body after reinforcement can be expressed by the area replacement rate is:

$$\alpha = \frac{\pi d_0^2}{2\sqrt{3}s^2} \tag{1}$$

Where d_0 = pile diameter; s = pile spacing

Based on the basic numerical model in Section 1, before the excavation steps, replace the soil material in the corresponding reinforcement area with the material in the reinforcement area, that is, the purpose of reinforcement is achieved by changing the mechanical properties of the soil. The physical parameters of solid materials are shown in Table 4.

Table 4. Physical parameters of reinforcement materials.

material name	Unreinforced material		Reinforced material	
	Elastic modulus E(MPa)	Poisson's ratio μ	Equivalent elastic modulus E(MPa)	Equivalent Poisson's ratio μ
①Artificial soil layer	14.0	0.25	56.0	0.23
②-1 Coarse Sand	126	0.25	145	0.23
②-2 Silt Soil	5.8	0.45	50.0	0.38
③-3 Coarse Sand	135	0.25	150	0.23

Figure 5 shows the settlement distribution diagram of pavement observation points after foundation treatment. For comparison, the results of no treatment scheme are given. It can be seen that the settlement of pavement decreases significantly. When the foundation pit is excavated to the bottom of the pit, the settlement deformation is 21.2mm.

With the backfilling of the foundation pit, the settlement deformation increases. After the backfilling of the foundation pit, the maximum settlement deformation of pavement is 24.2mm and the final settlement deformation is 13.7mm.

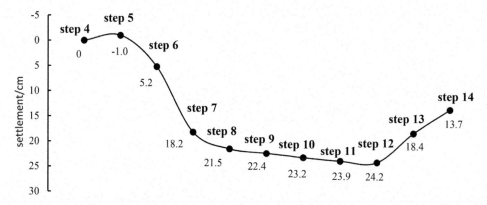

Figure 5. Distribution diagram of embankment top settlement in typical stage (Unit: mm). (Foundation Treatment Scheme).

Figure 6 shows the deformation diagram of sewage pipe after foundation treatment, and the results of no foundation treatment scheme are listed in the figure. The comparative analysis shows that the pipeline deformation after foundation treatment is significantly reduced, and the maximum horizontal deformation of the pipeline caused by the whole construction process is reduced to 28.6mm, which is 21.2% lower than that without reinforcement, while the vertical deformation is reduced to 38.1mm, which is 15.5% lower than that without reinforcement.

Therefore, the reinforcement scheme has a good control effect on the horizontal displacement and vertical displacement of the pipeline. According to the requirements of the owner of the project for deformation control, this method can be used to strengthen the pipeline.

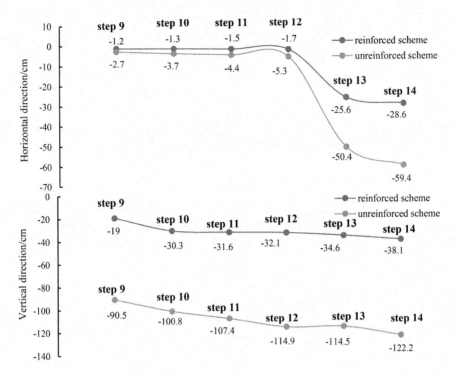

Figure 6. The deformation diagram of sewage pipe.

5 CONCLUSION

Based on the plane finite element method, the behaviors of excavation-induced ground and pipeline responses are discussed, and the foundation treatment measures and effects are analyzed.

(1) With the deepening of the excavation depth of the foundation pit, the horizontal displacement and vertical displacement of the pipeline are accordingly increasing;
(2) Compared with that before reinforcement, the horizontal displacement is reduced by 21%, while the vertical displacement decreased by 15.5%. The cement mixing pile can reduce the horizontal and vertical displacement of the pipeline and protect the pipeline effectively.

ACKNOWLEDGMENTS

This research has been funded by the special fund for basic scientific research business expenses of central public welfare scientific research institutes NHRI (NO. Y320001).

REFERENCES

AHMED I. (1990). *Pipeline response to excavation-induced ground movements*. Ph.D. thesis. Cornell University, New York.
Calvetti F., di Prisco C. & Nova R. (2004). Experimental and Numerical Analysis of Soil–Pipe Interaction. *J Geotech Eng Div ASCE*. 130(12), 1292–1299.
Sharma J.S., Hefny A.M., Zhao J. & Chan C.W. (2001). Effect of large excavation on deformation of adjacent MRT tunnels. *Tunn Undergr Space Technol*. 16(2), 93–98.
Vorster, T.E.B. & Klar, A. & Soga, K., et al. (2005). Estimating the effects of tunneling on existing pipelines. *J. Geotech Geoenviron*, 131(11), 1399–1410.
Wang Chenghua (2002). *Principles of soil mechanics*. Tianjin University Press, China.

Seepage pressure prediction model of concrete dam based on EEMD-GRU

Haishan Qiao*, Zhi Zhang*, Zhigang Wu* & Zhenghua Wen*
State Power Investment Corporation Yellow River Electric Power Technology Co., Ltd., Xining, China

Shengfei Zhang*
Institute of Water Resources and Hydroelectric Engineering, Xi'an University of Technology, Xi'an, China

ABSTRACT: In order to more accurately predict the seepage pressure change trend of the Laxiwa high hyperbolic arch dam to ensure dam safety, in view of the non-linear and non-stationary characteristics of the seepage pressure monitoring data of the concrete dam, and the data sequence contains certain noise, the prediction accuracy of the model is not high. Therefore, an EEMD-GRU prediction model based on ensemble empirical mode decomposition (EEMD) and gated recurrent unit (GRU) is proposed. Firstly, the model decomposes the seepage pressure data into eigenmode function components (IMF) with different frequencies by empirical mode decomposition, takes each component as the input of the GRU model and forecasts it, and adds the prediction results to obtain the final seepage pressure prediction value. Taking the measured monitoring data of the osmometers of the Laxiwa arch dam as an example, the modeling analysis is carried out. EEMD-GRU is used to predict with a single GRU model, EEMD-LSTM model, and single LSTM model, and its accuracy is compared. The results show that the EEMD-GRU model effectively improves the accuracy of seepage pressure prediction.

1 INTRODUCTION

With its unique advantages in design, construction, operation, and management, the concrete dam has become one of the main dam types in dam construction in China. However, with the rapid development of water conservancy and hydropower, the safety of reservoir dams is becoming more and more prominent. The topography, geology, hydrology, and other engineering conditions faced by the development and construction of high dams and large reservoirs are becoming more and more complex. The dam is subjected to various dynamic, static, and special cyclic loads in the operation process, which makes the construction and operation safety of the reservoir dam more uncertain (Wu & Chen 2016).

Seepage is a common problem in concrete dams. The dam break events caused by seepage account for 20% ~ 40% of the total number (Fang & Duan 2007). Because the seepage control and drainage structure and water level upstream and downstream of the concrete dam change with time, the seepage will also change with time. The seepage effect is used to reflect the seepage situation of the concrete dam (Wu et al. 1990). It is an important way to predict the seepage of concrete dams by using the measured data series. However, the high randomness, complexity, and uncertainty of seepage have brought challenges to accurate prediction (Zhang et al. 2018). Due to the limitation of current monitoring technology and analysis theory, the effects of water pressure, temperature, and aging are mainly considered in the conventional statistical model. However, the

---

*Corresponding Author: memory20200925@163.com, study200925@163.com, mliscm20200925@foxmail.com, hydroproject@163.com and Chinaxutzsf@163.com

influence of uncertain information such as structural damage, fluid-solid coupling, joint fissure, and measurement is not well considered, so it is difficult to further improve the fitting accuracy and prediction ability (Wei et al. 2018).

In recent years, with the development of artificial intelligence, machine learning algorithms, such as neural networks and support vector machines, have been applied to dam safety monitoring. However, the structure of the common neural network model needs to be modified by the algorithm specified in advance in the training process, so it is difficult to ensure the optimal structure. Moreover, it is easy to fall into local optimal solution, while the SVM model is difficult to deal with large-scale samples. Therefore, improving the prediction ability of seepage pressure of concrete dams is an important link to monitoring the seepage safety of the concrete dam. The deep learning method has good feature extraction ability and data fitting ability, which has been widely used in image, speech, and natural language processing. More and more fields begin to pay attention to the practicability of deep learning (Lu & Zhang 2013; Sun et al. 2013; Zhang et al. 2018). Among machine learning methods, the neural network is widely used in nonlinear system prediction because of its powerful multi-mapping ability and has achieved good prediction accuracy. The recurrent neural network (RNN) inputs the state values of the previous time into the current neuron. The time series data mining is realized. On the basis of the RNN neural network, Gru neural network solves the defects of gradient explosion and disappearance of RNN by adding gate structure to control the influence degree of the previous time, so that Gru neural network can better process and mine time series (Deng et al. 2020) than RNN. Due to the uncertainty in the actual operation of the dam. The seepage pressure data series have obvious non-linear and non-stationary characteristics, and there are inevitably some noises in the series. The non-linear and non-stationary data are mainly composed of information of different scales. It is of great significance to mine hidden information and reduce noise for the accurate prediction of seepage pressure data. At present, the common signal processing methods include wavelet transform, empirical mode decomposition (EMD), and ensemble empirical mode decomposition (EEMD). For wavelet transform, when there is white noise in the data, the denoising effect is not ideal. In EMD decomposition, mode aliasing is easy to occur, which leads to poor prediction results. The EEMD decomposition improves the mode aliasing phenomenon by adding white noise to improve the prediction ability of seepage pressure (Han et al. 2015).

To sum up, this paper decomposes the seepage data into intrinsic mode function (IMF) components with different frequencies by using ensemble empirical mode decomposition (EEMD). Each component is taken as the input of the Gru model and predicted. The final seepage pressure prediction value is obtained by superimposing the predicted results, and the EEMD-GRU seepage pressure prediction model is proposed.

2 RESEARCH METHOD

2.1 *Ensemble empirical mode decomposition (EEMD)*

EEMD is an improved method of EMD, which can overcome the mode aliasing defect of EMD. EEMD eliminates the intermittence in the original time series by adding auxiliary noise and suppresses the influence of noise in the decomposition result (Zhang & Liang 2013).

2.2 *Gated recurrent unit (GRU)*

The difference between a recurrent neural network (RNN) and common feedforward neural network (FNN) is that the input timing information is taken into account. It is commonly used in speech recognition (Mesnil et al. 2015) and image classification (Mou et al. 2017). In order to solve the problem of gradient vanishing in RNN, Hochreite and Schmiduber proposed long short memory neural network (LSTM) (Hochreiter & Schmiduber 1997).

GRU is a variant of LSTM (Gao et al. 2020), as shown in the figure. GRU has two control gate units, which are the reset gate and the update gate. The computational complexity of GRU is much smaller than that of LSTM, but the performance of the model is not significantly different.

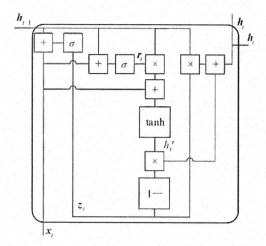

Figure 1. GRU unit structure.

The output vectors of the update gate and reset gate determine which information can be used as the output of the gating loop unit. Therefore, they can keep the information in the long-term sequence and not remove it with the increase of time, which shows that it is feasible to replace LSTM with GRU in principle.

2.3 *EEMD-GRU prediction model*

The seepage pressure of the concrete arch dam is affected by temperature, water level, and other factors, and the monitoring data are typically non-linear and non-stationary signals. In this paper, the seepage pressure prediction model based on EEMD-GRU is constructed to realize the seepage pressure fitting prediction analysis of a concrete dam. The specific steps are as follows:

(1) Acquisition and processing of data sets: the seepage pressure data and environmental data of the dam are obtained through the safety monitoring system, and the data sets are preprocessed.
(2) Decomposition of seepage pressure data series: the seepage pressure data series are decomposed by EEMD to obtain the IMF component.
(3) Reconstruction data preprocessing: due to the different dimensions of different environmental impact factors, in order to improve the prediction accuracy of the model, the reconstructed data are normalized.
(4) Seepage pressure data prediction: GRU model is established to predict the seepage pressure of the processed data. The obtained seepage pressure values are inversely normalized, and the predicted values of each component are accumulated to obtain the final prediction results of the model.

3 EXPERIMENT AND RESULT ANALYSIS

3.1 *Engineering examples and selection of measuring points*

Laxiwa Hydropower Station is located on the mainstream of the Yellow River at the junction of Guide county and Guinan County in Qinghai Province. It is the second cascade hydropower station close to

Longyangxia Hydropower Station among the large and medium-sized hydropower stations planned for the section from Longyangxia to Qingtongxia in the upper reaches of the Yellow River. The main water retaining structure is the normal concrete logarithmic spiral variable thickness double curvature thin arch dam with dam foundation elevation of 2210m, dam crest elevation of 2460m, and maximum dam height of 250m. Comprehensive monitoring items including deformation, seepage, temperature, stress, and strain are arranged in the dam.

In this paper, the measured values of piezometers P8-11 with an elevation of 2229m and p10-11 with an elevation of 2270m at the upstream side of typical dam section 11 from January 2, 2019 to March 10, 2021 are selected for analysis. See Figure 2 for the seepage pressure-time sequence process lines of P8-11 and p10-11 measuring points.

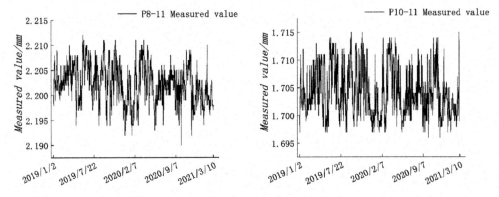

Figure 2.   P8-11 and p10-11 osmotic pressure sequence hydrograph.

70% of the data were selected as the training set and 30% as the test set for prediction and comparative analysis. The data selection table of three test points is shown in Table 1.

Table 1.   Margin settings for A4 size paper and letter size paper.

Measuring point	The corresponding date of the training set	Days	Corresponding date of the test set	Days
P8-11	2019.1.2~2020.7.17	548	2020.7.18~2021.3.10	235
P10-11	2019.1.2~2020.7.15	546	2020.7.16~2021.3.10	234

It can be seen from Figure 2 that the seepage pressure data series of the two measuring points have obvious non-linear and non-stationary characteristics. The data of the two measuring points are reliable and the series are relatively complete. On this basis, the seepage pressure prediction research of concrete arch dams based on EEMD-GRU is carried out.

3.2 Influence component selection

The research shows that the seepage pressure of the dam is affected by many factors, which are mainly composed of three influencing components: water pressure component P_H, temperature component P_T, and aging component P_θ. Therefore, the seepage pressure of the dam can be expressed as follows:

$$P = P_H + P_T + P_\theta \tag{1}$$

Considering the selection of dam type, the water pressure component $X_1 = (H - H_0)$, $X_2 = (H - H_0)^2$, $X_3 = (H - H_0)^3$, $X_4 = (H - H_0)^4$, where H is the monitoring day upstream water level, H_0 is the upstream water level on the initial measurement date. Considering the lag effect of water pressure on dam seepage, the average value $X_5 = (H_{1-3} - H_0)$ of 1-3 days before the monitoring day, the average value $X_6 = (H_{4-10} - H_0)$ of 4-10 days, the average value $X_7 = (H_{11-30} - H_0)$ of 11-30 days and the average value $X_8 = (H_{31-60} - H_0)$ of 31-60 days are selected. The temperature component is related to the ambient temperature and the temperature field inside the dam body. When the temperature monitoring data are discontinuous, it can be expressed by a simple harmonic function. Therefore, four multi-period simple harmonic waves are selected as the temperature factor in this paper:

$$\sin\left(\frac{2\pi it}{365}\right) - \sin\left(\frac{2\pi it_0}{365}\right) \quad (2)$$

$$\cos\left(\frac{2\pi it}{365}\right) - \cos\left(\frac{2\pi it_0}{365}\right) \quad (3)$$

$$\sin\left(\frac{4\pi it}{365}\right) - \sin\left(\frac{4\pi it_0}{365}\right) \quad (4)$$

$$\cos\left(\frac{4\pi it}{365}\right) - \cos\left(\frac{4\pi it_0}{365}\right) \quad (5)$$

Where t_0 is the cumulative number of days from the model selection start date to the first day of the monitoring sequence, and t is the cumulative number of days from the monitoring date to the model selection start date. In addition, the stress generated by the concrete dam body under the action of load will change the pores in the dam body, improve or deteriorate the seepage state of the dam body, and the transmission or dissipation of seepage pressure will also have an impact on the seepage. Therefore, the following two aging factors are selected: θ-θ_0, $\ln\theta$-$\ln\theta_0$ ($\theta = t/100$, $\theta_0 = t_0/100$).

3.3 Decomposition of seepage pressure data

Firstly, due to the different dimensions of different environmental impact factors, in order to improve the prediction accuracy of the model, the measured values of seepage pressure are normalized first, and then the EEMD decomposition of the seepage pressure time series is carried out. The decomposition results are shown in Figure 3. The original osmotic pressure time series is decomposed into 9 IMF components with different scales, and the frequency is from high to low, and the corresponding IMF image becomes smoother and smoother.

3.4 Seepage pressure prediction based on EEMD-GRU

3.4.1 Model parameter selection

After the decomposition of measuring point data, the GRU prediction model is established for 9 new data series (IMF1 ~ 9). To establish the model, four hyperparameters are needed: maximum number of iterations, initial learning rate, number of layers of hidden layers, and number of hidden units. In GRU neural network, the hidden layer, number of hidden units, initial learning rate, and maximum number of iterations have a great influence on model training and prediction accuracy. If the number is small, the forecast effect will be worse due to too little training. Too much will lead to the over-fitting of the model. After many experiments, the model has set up a layer of the hidden layer with 64 hidden units, 120 maximum iterations, and a 0.08 initial learning rate.

In order to verify the performance of the forecasting model proposed in this paper, the LSTM model, GRU model, and EEMD-LSTM model are used to verify and compare the seepage pressure data of the two measuring points.

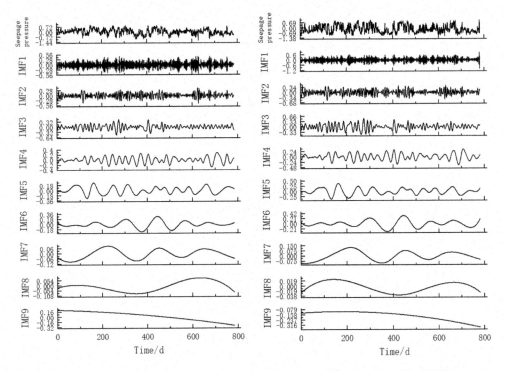

Figure 3. Decomposition results of P8-11 and P10-11 osmotic pressure sequence based on EEMD.

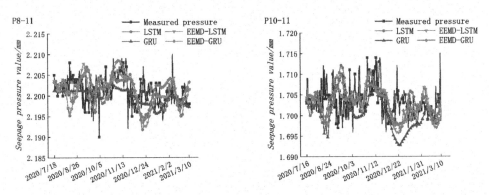

Figure 4. Prediction results of each model (P8-11).   Figure 5. Prediction results of each model (P8-11).

3.4.2 *Evaluation index of the prediction model*
In order to compare the predictive effects of different models, mean absolute error (MAE), root mean square error (RMSE), and mean absolute percentage error (MAPE) are used as evaluation indexes to analyze the predictive accuracy of the models.

3.5 *Analysis of prediction results*

The comparison between the predicted results of each model at the two measuring points and the actual seepage pressure sequence is shown in Figures 4 and 5. Table 2 depicts prediction performance evaluation indexes.

157

The analysis data shows that the magnitude of the variation of the osmotic pressure value is smaller than that of the osmotic pressure value itself. Therefore, by comparing the predicted value with the measured value curve in the figure, the error magnitude of various neural network models is smaller. In contrast, the error magnitude of a single LSTM and GRU model is significantly larger than that of the two combination algorithms. Although the EEMD-GRU predicted value is different from the actual value at some inflection points. However, the overall result is basically consistent with the sequence of osmotic pressure values, which can well reflect the change of seepage pressure at the measuring point, and has a better prediction effect and fitting accuracy than the other three models.

Table 2. Comparisons of prediction performance indexes for each prediction model.

Model	LSTM	GRU	EEMD-LSTM	EEMD-GRU
MAE /mm (P8-11)	0.0034	0.0026	0.0022	0.0021
MAPE/% (P8-11)	0.1523	0.1167	0.0976	0.0887
RMSE/mm (P8-11)	0.0043	0.0033	0.0029	0.0026
MAE/mm (P10-11)	0.0038	0.0045	0.0027	0.0025
MAPE/% (P10-11)	0.2207	0.2642	0.1380	0.1253
RMSE/mm (P10-11)	0.0049	0.0059	0.0043	0.0042

From Table 2, we can see that there are two single models which do not use EEMD to decompose the data, and the three evaluation indexes are obviously slightly higher. When the LSTM network is used to predict seepage pressure value, it is slightly worse than the GRU network, and the calculation speed of the GRU-related model is significantly faster than LSTM. The three evaluation indexes of the EEMD-GRU osmotic pressure prediction model proposed in this paper are the lowest in the three groups of osmometer measuring points and the speed is faster. It shows that the prediction accuracy of the model processed by EEMD-GRU is significantly improved, the hidden information in non-linear data can be excavated more effectively, and different information can be predicted more accurately, which further verifies the better performance of the prediction model.

4 CONCLUSION

The time series of concrete arch dam seepage pressure has typical non-linear characteristics, and the data contains certain noise, which easily leads to the low accuracy of the prediction model. In this paper, an EEMD-GRU seepage pressure prediction model is proposed. Through an experimental study on the measured values of the seepage pressure gauge of the Laxiwa concrete hyperbolic arch dam, it is concluded that several IMF components with different frequencies can be obtained by decomposing the effects of EEMD, which can excavate some hidden information in the non-linear data and improve the calculation accuracy. Compared with conventional models, the EEMD-GRU seepage pressure prediction model proposed in this paper has a better prediction effect. Each evaluation index is better than a single neural network, which can give full play to the improvement of calculation power brought by artificial intelligence algorithms and provide a new method for concrete arch dam seepage pressure prediction.

REFERENCES

Deng, D.Y. et al. (2020) Short-term load forecasting based on EEMD-GRU-MLR. *Power grid technology*. 44 (02), 593–602.

Fang, C.H. & Duan, Y.H. (2007) Statistical analysis and warning of dam break events. *People's Yangtze River* 41 (11), 96–100.

Gao, M.Y. et al. (2020) Real-time dynamic earth-pressure regulation model for shield tunneling by integrating GRU deep learning method with GA optimization. *IEEE Access*. 8:64310–64323.

Han, Q.Y. et al. (2015) Using EEMD to eliminate high-frequency noise and baseline drift in pulse blood-oximetry measurement simultaneously. *Journal of Electronics & Information Technology*. 37 (6), 1384–1388.

Hochreiter, S & Schmidhuber, J. (1997) Long short-term memory. *Neural computation* 9(8), 1735–1780.

Lu, L. & Zhang, A.J. (2013) Application of least squares support vector machine model in dam monitoring. *People's Yellow River* 35 (11), 99–100,103

Mesnil, G. et al. (2015) Using recurrent neural networks for slot filling in spoken language understanding. *IEEE/ACM transactions on audio, speech, and language processing*. 23 (3),530–539.

Mou, L. et al. (2017) Deep recurrent neural networks for hyperspectral image classification. *IEEE transactions on geoscience and remote sensing*. 55 (7), 3639–3655.

Sun, P.X. & Zhao, K.P. (2013) Application of combined model based on entropy weight method in dam seepage prediction. *Hydropower energy science* 31 (12), 70–73.

Wei, B.W. et al. (2018) Multi-scale deformation combination forecast model for concrete dam based on BP-ARIMA. *Hydro-Science and Engineering*. 2018(02), 52–60.

Wu, Z.R. & Chen, B (2016) A review on the development of dam safety monitoring models. *Modern Surveying and Mapping* 39(5), 1–3, 8.

Wu, Z.R. et al. (1990) *Safety monitoring theory of hydraulic structures and its application.* Nanjing: Hohai University Press.

Zhang, H.L. et al. (2018) Study on seepage monitoring model of concrete faced rockfill dam. *Journal of Three Gorges University* (Natural Science Edition). 40 (3), 24–28.

Zhang, X.Q. & Liang, J. (2013) Chaotic time series prediction model of wind power based on ensemble empirical mode decomposition-approximate entropy and reservoir. *Acta Physica Sinica* 62 (5), 1–10.

Deep-water rubble mound breakwater construction in the open Mediterranean Sea under adverse conditions: Main breakwater extension of Hadarom Port, Ashdod, Israel

Ran Tao*
China Harbour Engineering Co., Ltd., Beijing, China

Rui-yi Huang* & Xian-dao Feng*
CCCC Second Harbour Engineering Co., Ltd., Wuhan, China

Yue-ji Huo*
China Communications Construction Co., Ltd., Beijing, China

ABSTRACT: To solve the problems of limited construction window due to the adverse wave condition, large quantity and high acceptance requirement of rock dumping, and also the difficulties of temporary protection during construction, this paper acquires the wave condition limit for different layers of rock to optimize the construction schedule and winter protection structure design based on 2D & 3D physical model test, and in addition apply visualization technique for rock slope and armor unit installation, to ensure that the project is carried out successfully as a reference for deep-water rubble mound breakwater construction under similar wave conditions.

1 INTRODUCTION

Open-sea marine works involve many risks (Van der Meer 2005). The Ashdod Port Main Breakwater was designed in the late fifties and constructed during the period from 1962 to 1965 with a rubble mound type, composed of different rock layers and armored with concrete tetrapods of 10 and 16 cubic meters in the trunk and round-head respectively (Stadler 1989). The performance of this 2200-meter breakwater was considered to be satisfactory until 1978. But the stone berm was shown to have lost an average of 30% of its mass with a maximum of 50% between stations 1400-1600 after full profiles measurements of the seawards slope. Then damage to the end section and round-head was caused by the March 1980 storm (Hm=5.4m, Tp=12s) and extensive breakage of tetrapods was caused by the December 1980 storm (Hm=6.30m, Tp=12s).

The existing Main Breakwater of Ashdod port was extended for Hayovel (Eitan) Port by the construction of a 1,150-meter-long rubble-mound breakwater in the open sea, reaching the depth of 22 meters at the round-head. During the construction in November 2004, various damages to the uncompleted Main Breakwater under construction were produced by a 1 in 10-year class storm occurred with a significant wave height of approximately 6.70 meters (Hoch 2011).

As an extension of Ashdod port and Hayovel port in Israel, Hadarom port is designed for Maersk Triple E-class container vessels, and the existing main breakwater is extended by 600 meters as a shield for the new container terminal and berths. The main breakwater extension is reaching the depth of 25 meters at the round-head and is armored with a 2-layer of 40-ton Antifer cubes. The

---

*Corresponding Author: rtao@chec.bj.cn, 13947605@qq.com, 283218530@qq.com and huoyueji@ccccltd.cn

model testing which was carried out during the design period predicted that the major damaging forces from wave attack would take place on the inner side (the land side) of the round-head.

The general layout of the Hadarom port and the design section of the main breakwater extension is shown in the following Figures 1 and 2.

Figure 1. The general layout of Hadarom port.

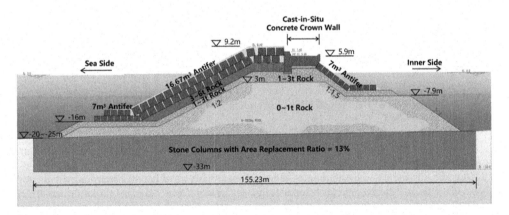

Figure 2. Design section for main breakwater extension of Hadarom port.

2 WAVE DATA ANALYSIS

According to the wave data recorded by the Coastal and Marine Engineering Research Institute (CAMERI) and verified by the data from the European Centre for Medium-Range Weather Forecasts (ECMWF), both the most frequently occurring wave direction and the strongest wave direction is

WNW and the swell plays a leading role in summers while wind wave is for winters. The summer-based and winter-based wave height and wave period directional distribution in the deep water of Ashdod port by 1992 to 2009 time-series with the data coverage up to 99% is shown in the following Figures 3 and 4, where calm means the significant wave height is lower than 0.5 meter.

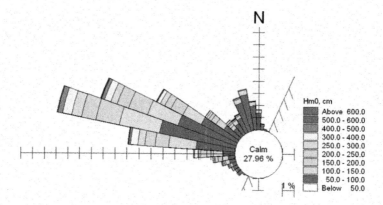

Figure 3. Annually based wave height directional distribution of Hadarom port. (1992-2009 time-series). Data Coverage = 99.16%.

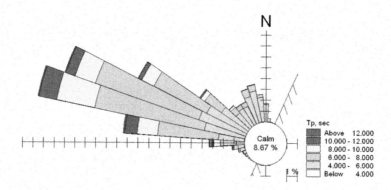

Figure 4. Annually based wave period directional distribution of Hadarom port. (1992-2009 time-series). Data Coverage = 99.16%.

The adopted criteria for water levels and wave conditions for main breakwater extension are summarized in the following Table 1.

Moreover, the monthly distribution of recorded maximum wave height occurrence frequency shows that annually the average occurrence frequency of significant wave height lower than 0.5m is not much higher than 30%.

3 PHYSICAL MODEL TEST

3.1 *2D model test for critical instability wave condition*

In order to have a more intuitive understanding of the critical instability wave condition for different types of rocks, a 1:50-scale 2D physical model test is carried out with the incident wave enlarging by 0.5m from Hs=0.5m, Tp=7.9s, with the conversion parameter of spectral peak period and effective period to be 1.05.

Table 1. Water levels and wave conditions.

Parameter	Value
Mean High Water Spring (MHWS)	+0.38m
Mean Sea Level (MSL)	+0.081m
Mean Low Water Spring (MLWS)	0.22m
Extreme High Water Levels	1 yr = +0.72m
	50 yr = +1.12m
	100 yr = +1.18m
Extreme Low Water Levels	1 yr = -0.30m
	50 yr = -0.66m
	100 yr = -0.79m
Sea Level Rise	0.008m/yr (0.40m for 50 years)
Wave Conditions (1 yr RP)	H_m=5.6m, T_p=11.8s, MWD=295°
Wave Conditions (100 yr RP)	H_m=8.3m, T_p=12.0s, MWD=295°

During the model test, the critical instability wave height for different types of rock sections is identified by the amount of rock rolled and the deformation of sections as shown the following Figure 5 and the test results are concluded in the following Table 2.

a. Type E rock (0-1 ton)   b. Type D rock (1-3 ton)   c. Type C rock (3-6 ton)

Figure 5. Photos taken during the model test for critical instability wave condition.

Table 2. Critical instability wave height for different types of rock.

	Type E rock	Type D rock	Type C rock
Rock Weight	0-1 ton	1-3 ton	3-6 ton
Section Top Level	–3.0m	+0.6m	+3.5m
Critical instability wave height (Hs)	2.0m	3.0m	4.5m

From the test, it additionally could be concluded that type E rock is stable under –8.0m level under the incident wave up to be Hs=6.7m, and when the type E rock is dumped to –6.0m level, about 20% of the cross-section will be lost. If the type E rock dike is covered by type D rock up to a –2.6m level, the cross-sectional loss is reduced to 10%.

Therefore, it is recommended that during the winter stormy weather, type E rock dumping should be strictly below –8.0m level, moreover, the uncompleted rock round-head is unstable and should be protected carefully.

3.2 3D model test for a temporary protective structure

In order to achieve a stable and economical protective structure plan for the uncompleted rock round-head during winter, a 1:50 scale 3D physical model test is carried out under the incident wave condition with a 10-year return period with the wave height to be 6.2 meters. Irregular wave with JONSWAP spectrum as $\gamma=7$ from three different directions as 270°, 295°, and 330° is used for the test.

During the construction of the main breakwater extension for Hayovel port, after the November 2004 storm damage, temporary protective groins were placed. Therefore, the rock gabion was tested comparatively with antifer cubes as shown in Figure 6.

a. Rock Gabion b. Antifer Cubes

Figure 6. Photos taken during the model test for temporary protective structure.

According to the test results shown in the following Table 3, the destabilization position of 1 layer 40-ton Antifer cubes is usually in the interval between the wave height above and below the mean sea level, and it is recommended as an integrated solution with 1 layer and 2 layers of Antifer cubes for temporary protective structure for the round-head of the main breakwater during the winter stormy season.

Table 3. Observation results of the 3D model test for temporary protective structure.

Protective Structure		Test Results	Experimental Findings
Rock Gabion Chain	5×8-ton	Unstable	Ineffective protection, not recommended.
	2×16-ton	Stable	Large amount of work, not recommended.
Precast Concrete Blocks	1-layer 40-ton Antifer Cubes	Slightly Collapsing	Integrated solution recommended.
	2-layer 40-ton Antifer Cubes	Stable	

4 REAL-TIME MULTIBEAM-BASED UNDER-WATER SURVEY

The underwater level of rock dumping of type E is surveyed by multi-beam sonar. However, usually, the multi-beam data process is manual and takes a long time of data cleaning and data QC to exclude the anomalies.

Based on the Combined Uncertainty and Bathymetric Estimator (CUBE), which provides a mechanism for automatically processing the multi-beam data by estimating the depth plus a confidence interval directly on each node point of a bathymetric grid, a real-time multi-beam-based under-water survey system was developed for on-site quick decision-making of underwater rock dumping as shown in the following Figure 7.

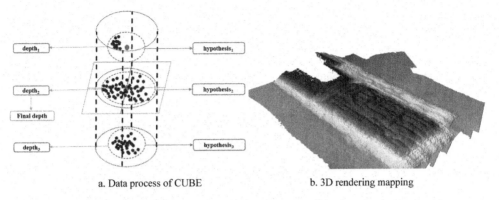

a. Data process of CUBE b. 3D rendering mapping

Figure 7. Data Process of CUBE-based real-time multi-beam survey system.

5 VISUALIZED CONSTRUCTION

5.1 Rock sloping

Generally, the tolerance of level deviation for rock dumping is from ±40cm to ±90cm. With the consideration to assurance of a better order for amour unit placement according to the specification of breakwater construction for Hadarom port, which brings a challenge for the massive rock dump and sloping, since the tolerance for type D rock is -20cm to +30cm above water level and -40cm to +60cm below, moreover, for type C rock, it is -30cm to +40cm above and -50cm to +70cm below.

Trimble® GCS900 grade control system is used for assistance to excavators' operators with underwater rock sloping as shown in the following Figure 8. This system integrates a variety of different sensors to provide elevation and reach guidance for the bucket cutting edge, by manually guiding the bucket to a specified position relative to a benchmark position or measuring a slope between two points.

a. System installed on the excavator b. The system provides bucket guidance

Figure 8. Trimble® GCS900 grade control system used on site.

5.2 Amour unit installation

According to the specification of breakwater construction for Hadarom port, the placement order for 2-layer Antifer cubes is semi-random based on the placement grid, which is usually assisted by divers. However, the work window period of divers is subject to the environmental condition of the wave, turbidity, and work depth, which makes the construction efficiency greatly constrained by the competence and experience of divers.

Echoscope® real-time 3D sonar is used for assistance to crane operators with underwater Antifer cubes installation as shown in the following Figure 9, since it provides real-time geo-referenced mapping and images by producing over 16,000 beams per ping, which enable operators to make immediate assessments.

Figure 9. Echoscope® real-time 3D sonar used for underwater Antifer cubes installation.

6 CONSTRUCTION PROCESS AND PROGRESS

Based on the physical model test results, the cross-section of the main breakwater extension is breakdown into about 13 steps including the concrete pouring of the crown wall on the top of the breakwater as shown in the following Figures 10 and 11. The main breakwater extension for Hadarom port was commenced in May 2016 and accomplished in December 2019.

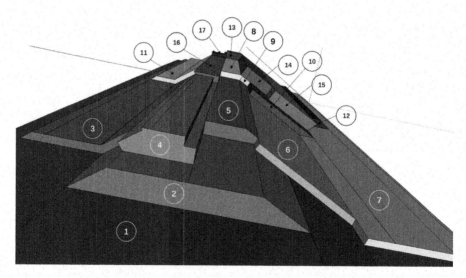

Figure 10. Work breakdown and construction flow for breakwater construction.

    a. Existing round-head dismantling   b. Construction flow of rock dumping   c. Main breakwater extension accomplished

Figure 11. Photos taken during the construction process.

7 CONCLUSIONS AND PROSPECTS

The execution of deep-water rubble mound breakwater construction in the Open Sea is complicated and full of risk, and it should be carefully according to the model test and weather forecast. The visualized tools could provide efficient support for construction on site.

Due to the reason of shape, size, and porosity of the massive rock, the CUBE-based real-time multi-beam survey system still cannot provide accurate data processing and clean for the massive rock bed larger than type D rock.

REFERENCES

Jentsje van der Meer. (2005). Hayovel port development, construction in winter: An acceptable risk. *Ashtrom Dragados Hayovel Port Joint Venture, Internal Memorandum* 2005.

L. Stadler, M. Radomir. (1989). Main breakwater repair at the port of Ashdod, Israel. *Design of Breakwaters, Thomas Telford*.

Oren Noa, Radomir Max, Di Castro Dan F. (2018). Protecting port construction works in open sea – Hadarom Port, Ashdod, Israel. *Coasts, Marine Structures and Breakwaters*.

V.N. Valdecantos, P.F. Carrasco. (2007). Structural and geotechnical failure under wave attack in the crown wall of rubble mound and caisson breakwaters. *Proceedings of Coastal Structures 2007 Conference*.

Zeev Hoch. (2011). The construction of an open-sea port in the mediterranean sea under adverse conditions: The Eitan Terminal, Port of Ashdod, Israel. *Proceedings of Coastal Structures 2011 Conference*.

Finite element analysis of pile-soil-structure dynamic interaction on layered soil site

Ziqiong Yang* & Wenhao Qi*

Key Laboratory of Earthquake Engineering and Engineering Vibration, Institute of Engineering Mechanics, China Earthquake Administration
Key Laboratory of Earthquake Disaster Mitigation Mitigation, Ministry of Emergency Management, China

ABSTRACT: Based on the current situation of the lack of theory and experience in the construction of nuclear power plants on non-bedrock sites, it is necessary to carry out the seismic design of pile foundations in non-bedrock sites. In order to study the mechanics of pile-soil-structure dynamic interaction with large mass and stiffness in nuclear island, a detailed numerical simulation program was carried out using a pile-soil-structure ABAQUS FEM model on layered soil sites. Based on a free field model, the result of the ABAQUS FEM model was compared with the result of the EERA model, which proved that the ABAQUS FEM model is suitable for solving pile-soil-structure problems. In the program, 5 types of layered soil sites with actual soil mechanics parameters were set up, 2 types of group-pile models with and without upper structure were established, and 3 El Centro waves with different intensities were taken as input seismic motion. Then the seismic response of the piles was calculated by ABAQUS software. Some conclusions could be drawn: (1) the inner force of piles change rapidly at the interface between different strength soils; (2) the upper structure only influence the inner force at the pile head; (3) piles at different location suffered different intensity seismic force in group piles, the side piles were easier to be damaged than the middle piles. Sites with layered soils will have a disadvantageous effect on the force of the pile group foundation, especially at the interface of the soil layer, which should be considered in pile foundation design.

1 INTRODUCTION

With the increasing economic development of our country, the demand for energy consumption is increasing day by day. As a new type of energy, nuclear power has the advantages of large energy, low pollution, and controllable cost, and has been widely promoted. However, the construction of nuclear power plants has very high requirements on the foundation, so bedrock sites are generally selected. In recent years, the nuclear power industry has developed rapidly, and site resources have become increasingly tight. In order to meet the needs of nuclear power development, the construction of nuclear power plants on non-bedrock sites has become a key concern at this stage. The pile foundation is a widely used form of deep foundation with good seismic performance, but there are also some examples of seismic damage. The large mass and stiffness of nuclear power structures have a great influence on the dynamic interaction of the structural system. The use of pile foundation in non-bedrock sites puts forward higher requirements for the seismic design of pile foundation.

For the safety of nuclear power plants, the design and construction safety level of nuclear power structures are the highest. The superstructure of nuclear power plants often has a high seismic capacity, and it is difficult to damage during earthquakes. In order to ensure the safety of nuclear

---

*Corresponding Authors: yangzqgz@126.com and qwhtky@163.com

power structures in an earthquake, the seismic design of pile foundations in the non-bedrock site is very important.

Scholars have discussed the numerical simulation analysis of seismic resistance of underground structures and pile-soil interaction. Nogami (Nogami & Konagai 1986) used the time domain method to analyze axial single pile response and established time domain pile-soil interaction force in an ideal foundation soil medium. Penzien (Penzien et al. 1964) first used the Winkler foundation beam method to analyze the seismic response of bridge pile foundations in clay sites. Boulanger R W (Boulanger et al. 2004) used openness to carry out pile-soil dynamic interaction in liquefiable sand foundation; Von Arx (Wolf & Von 1978) used axisymmetric the finite element model establishing the first complete dynamic analysis method for pile groups. S K (Kuecueukarslan et al. 2003) used the mixed numerical model method to analyze the nonlinear contact between pile and soil and compared it with the test results. For the superstructure, Behrouz Asgarian (Asgarian et al. 2012) established the interaction system of pile-soil-structure in ABAQUS. The most commonly used soil elastic-plastic models in ABAQUS are the Mohr-coulomb model and the Druker-Prager model (Panaghi & Mahboubi 2010), while the linear viscoelastic model (Soules, Busbey, Rekhson, Markovsky, Burke, 1987) is mostly used for asphalt pavement, there are few simulations on soft clay foundations (Liu 2007).

In this paper, in order to study the interaction characteristics of pile-soil-structure in non-bedrock sites, a finite element model with the actual site as a parameter is designed for numerical simulation, and the dynamic characteristics of rock-socketed piles in the core island foundation model under the action of actual ground motion are discussed. Summarized the law of vibration response and the influence of ground motion parameters and site on dynamic characteristics and dynamic response. Pile groups are always used in practical pile foundations. In order to explore the dynamic response of pile body based on pile-soil-structure interaction, a layered soil finite element model of the pile group is designed in line with the actual situation, and the kinematic interaction (PSI effect) and inertial interaction (PSSI effect) of the pile group in layered soil foundation were analyzed respectively.

2 LAYERED SOIL FINITE ELEMENT MODEL

Natural foundation in China generally shows layered characteristics, and most soil sites are layered soil. Therefore, in the dynamic analysis of pile foundation under horizontal load, it is necessary to consider the difference between different soil layers. In order to obtain more realistic research results, a pile-soil interaction system in a layered soil site is established. Numerical simulation is carried out for layered soil, and the pile-soil interaction analysis is completed in the case of two-layer soil and three-layer soil, and the influence of different sites on the dynamic response of piles and soil is considered.

2.1 *The establishment of the finite element model*

In this paper, a two-dimensional finite element model is used, and five piles are selected for the number of piles in the pile group. According to the results of the field engineering geological survey and the local typical soil distribution, the soil layers are merged in the model. According to the relevant literature (Lu et al. 2005; Maravas et al. 2007) and their results, it can be seen that the horizontal deformation of the pile under horizontal load is more obvious at the end of the pile in shallow soil. Therefore, the soil layer is simplified to the different situations of two layers and three layers, and it is approximately regarded as extending from the bedrock down to the bottom.

In order to facilitate the follow-up study of the dynamic response characteristics of the piles at different positions, the five piles are named piles 1 to 5, as shown below.

The size of the finite element model is 60m*60m, the number of group piles is five, and it is designed as a rock-socketed pile. The upper layer of the model site is 30 meters of overburden, and the lower layer of bedrock is 30 meters. The depth of the pile is 40 meters, and it is embedded in

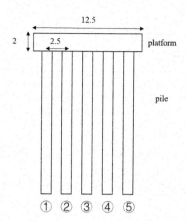

Figure 1. Pile group diagram.

the bedrock for 10 meters. The size of the pile cap is 12.5m*2m; the diameter of the pile is 0.5 meters, and the distance between the pile centers is 5 times the pile diameter.

When studying the inertial interaction of the structural system, the pile group, pile cap, and soil model are used to maintain consistency with the dynamic interaction model in size, material parameters, and constitutive model. In order to reduce the influence of centroid height variation of the superstructure on the bending moment and shear force of the pile body under dynamic load, the upper structure is fixed in the numerical simulation, and the structural quality is changed by changing the material density.

The layered soil model of the pile group is meshed as shown in the following figure. In order to reduce the mesh difference between the soil near the pile and the pile body, the mesh of the soil near the pile is refined. Considering the pile-soil deformation coordination, the grid is more and more sparse from the center position outward.

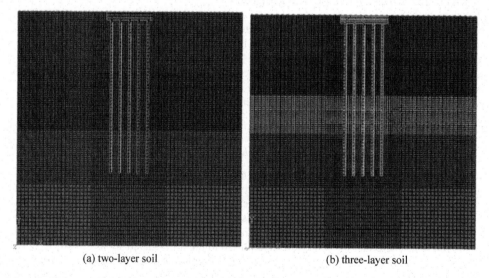

(a) two-layer soil   (b) three-layer soil

Figure 2. Finite element model of the pile group in layered soil.

The finite element model pictures are shown above, which are the schematic diagrams of the two-layer and three-layer soil sites respectively.

2.2 Boundary condition settings

In this paper, the lateral artificial boundary (Liu et al. 2006) of the model is set as the bounding degree of freedom boundary. The degree of freedom of the corresponding nodes at the same horizontal height of the lateral boundary conditions of the finite element model with binding constraints is realized by the MPC binding command in ABAQUS software. The artificial boundary of the bottom surface is set with viscosity, which is established by the infinite element in ABAQUS.

2.3 Numerical simulation parameter selection

The soil layer data calculated in this paper comes from a pumping station in Dongsheng Village, an important site of Shuangyashan's water supply project. Geological parameters refer to the site engineering geological survey report of the pumping station. The topography of the pumping station is a floodplain on the right bank of the Songhua River, the surface is flat, and the surface elevation is 65.18 m-65.64 m.

According to the 'Code for Seismic Design of Buildings' GB50011 – 2010 Section 4.3.1, the project site is located in the area of seismic fortification peak acceleration of 0.05g (equivalent to seismic fortification intensity VI).

The measured soil samples were numbered from soft to hard as 1 to 4, and were combined to form different site conditions of layered soil. In addition, the parameters of the overburdened soil layer are also optimized to a certain extent, and the material parameters of the pile and soil layer are shown in the following table.

Table 1. Material parameters.

Number of soil layer	Soil type	Soil Category	Density (t/m^3)	G_{max} (KPa)	C_s(m/s)	Poisson's ratio
1	Medium soft soil	Silty clay	1.921	51.064e3	163.04	0.35
2	Medium soft soil	Medium sand	1.947	72.006e3	192.31	0.35
3	Medium hard soil	Gravelly sand	1.993	128.823e3	254.24	0.30
4	Medium hard soil	Gravelly sand	2.038	259.945e3	357.14	0.30
/	Rock	Basalt	2.244	3336.48e3	1219.2	0.25
Concrete pile			2.5	3.45e7	/	0.20
Quality mass			7.8	2.06e8	/	0.20

2.4 Loading ground motion

El Centro wave is selected as the ground motion load input. PGA is selected as the strength index, and the three input amplitudes are 0.05 g, 0.1 g, and 0.2 g. The duration of ground motion is 50 s, which is more than five times the structural period.

2.5 Validation of the free field model

In this paper, a finite element model of free field is established in ABAQUS, and the EERA program is used to compare and verify whether the numerical method in ABAQUS is correct. The results of EERA output at the surface (0 meters) and bedrock surface (-30 meters) are compared with the free field model established by ABAQUS, as shown in the following figure. Including acceleration time history, velocity time history and pseudo-acceleration response spectrum.

2.5.1 Acceleration time history comparison

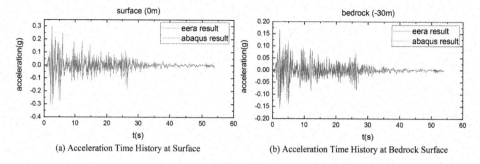

Figure 3.　Comparison chart of acceleration time history.

2.5.2 Velocity time history comparison

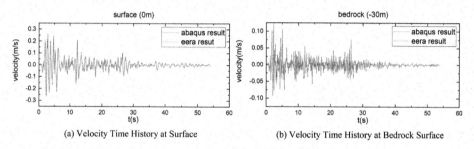

Figure 4.　Comparison chart of velocity time history.

2.5.3 Pseudo-acceleration response spectrum comparison

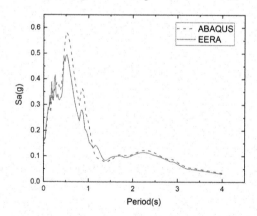

Figure 5.　Pseudo-acceleration response spectrum.

Results of comparison verified that the results of the finite element free field model are reasonable, and this numerical simulation method can be used for subsequent analysis in this paper.

2.6 Loading ground motion

The finite element numerical simulation conditions completed in this paper are shown in the following table.

Table 2. Working State Table for Numerical Simulation.

Serial number	Layer number	Type of soil site	Upper structure quality	PGA
1	Two	Soft-hard	0	0.05g
2			0	0.1g
3			0	0.2g
4			200t	0.05g
5			200t	0.1g
6			200t	0.2g
7		Hard-soft	0	0.1g
8			200t	0.1g
9	Three	Soft-hard-hard	0	0.05g
10			0	0.1g
11			0	0.2g
12			200t	0.05g
13			200t	0.1g
14			200t	0.2g
15		Soft-hard-soft	0	0.1g
16			200t	0.1g
17		Hard-soft-hard	0	0.1g
18			200t	0.1g

3 PILE-SOIL INTERACTION ANALYSIS

Numerical simulation is carried out on the finite element model of the pile group in layered soil, and the influence of the layered soil site, on the dynamic response of the pile group is obtained. The working conditions of the layered soil site include soft-hard soil site, hard-soft soil site, soft-hard-soft soil site, hard-soft-hard soil site and soft-hard-hard soil site. At the same time, it is needed to input different magnitudes of ground motion amplitude, analyze the kinematic interaction and inertial interaction of pile groups, and explore the dynamic characteristics of pile groups at different positions.

Due to a large amount of numerical simulation data in the test conditions, limited by the length of this paper, the 0.1g ground motion amplitude condition is selected as the illustration below.

3.1 Acceleration response characteristics of pile body

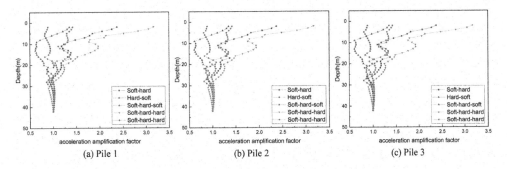

Figure 6. Pile acceleration amplification factor diagram under kinematic interaction.

It can be seen from figure 6 and figure 7 that the acceleration response of the pile body is affected by the site and the mass of the superstructure under different site conditions, the trend of acceleration amplification factor of pile 1, pile 2 and pile 3 is basically the same.

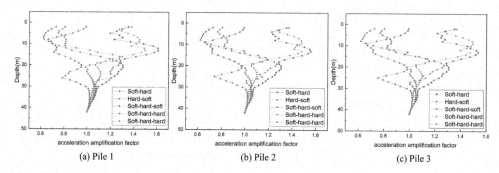

Figure 7. Pile acceleration amplification factor diagram under inertial interaction.

In the kinematic interaction, the acceleration amplification factor of the pile body in the hard-soft site is about 1. The acceleration amplification factor of the soft-hard-soft site is increasing in the range from the top of the pile to 10m, and the amplification factor is less than 1 at the bedrock surface of 10m to 30m, showing a decreasing trend. The acceleration amplification factor of the pile body in the hard-soft-hard site is slightly larger than 1, and it gradually increases. The magnification coefficients of the soft-hard site and the soft-hard site have the same trend, the growth rate is large above the bedrock surface, and the acceleration amplification factor of the pile body is the largest in the soft-hard site. Without the action of the upper mass block, the growth rate of the acceleration amplification factor of the pile body in the soft soil layer is larger than that of the hard soil layer.

During inertial interaction, the magnification coefficients of hard-soft sites and hard-soft-hard sites have similar trends, and the magnification factor is less than 1 in the range of 0 to 10 m. The trend of the acceleration amplification factor of the pile body in the soft-hard site and the soft-hard-hard site is the same, and the amplification factor of the pile is the largest in the soft soil layer. The magnification factor is also less than 1 in the hard-soft-hard site, and the magnification factor increases rapidly in the first layer of soft soil. Therefore, when the pile-soil-superstructure interacts, the acceleration amplification factor of the pile body in the soft-hard site and the soft-hard-hard site is greater than 1.

3.2 *Internal force distribution characteristics of pile body*

Under the input of 0.1g ground motion, the bending moment of the pile body in the layered soil site is obtained as shown in the figure above, and the following conclusions can be concluded:

1) The peak value of the bending moment occurs at the soil layer boundary and at the pile cap. The maximum bending moment in PSI is generally at the bedrock surface; but when the first layer is soft soil, the maximum bending moment position appears at the top of the pile. When the pile is affected by the upper mass, the internal force at the pile cap will increase, so the pile head is the weak place for earthquake resistance.

2) For a layered soil site, the softer the soil layer where the pile is located, the greater the bending moment of the pile body; the greater the difference in the stiffness of the soil in contact with each other between the two layers, the greater the value of the pile force.

3) By comparing the effect of upper mass on layered soil site, it can be seen that the bending moment values of piles in different sites are only significantly different at the pile-cap site.

3.3 *Deformation analysis of pile foundation structure*

The relative displacement is the absolute value of the displacement of the pile body relative to the pile bottom. Table 3 shows the peak displacements of the pile body at the top of the pile, the layered position, and the bedrock surface on the soft-hard site model of the pile group.

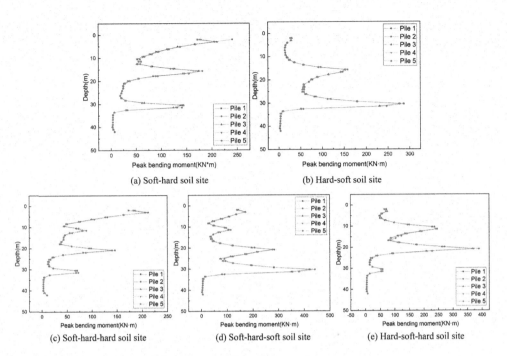

Figure 8. Bending moment of pile body under kinematic interaction.

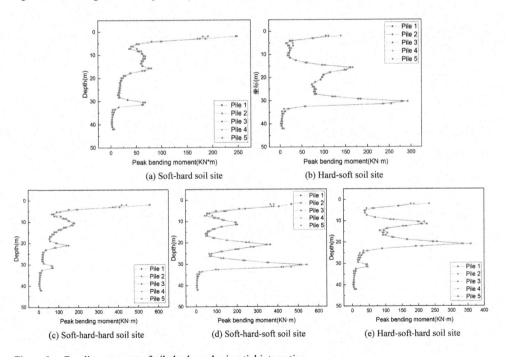

Figure 9. Bending moment of pile body under inertial interaction.

It can be seen from table 3 that under the action of horizontal ground motion, the displacement of the pile body at different positions is inconsistent, which reflects that the displacement of the foundation pile during the deformation of the pile group is affected by the position of the pile. The displacement peak size of each foundation pile in the pile group is as follows: pile 3> pile 2, 4> pile 1, 5.

Table 3. The horizontal relative displacement of the pile group in soft-hard soil site under 0.1g working condition.

Interaction type	Serial number	Peak displacement at pile top (mm)	Peak displacement at soil layer junction (mm)	Peak displacement at bedrock surface (mm)
Kinematic interaction	1	85.957	72.243	68.478
	2	85.966	72.269	68.489
	3	85.971	72.276	68.493
	4	85.966	72.269	68.489
	5	85.957	72.242	68.478
Inertial interaction	1	86.593	70.483	64.794
	2	86.614	70.459	64.831
	3	86.618	70.447	64.845
	4	86.613	70.461	64.830
	5	86.593	70.486	64.794

Figure 10 shows the peak relative displacements of the pile body on the hard-soft-hard site. It can be seen from figure 10 that when the peak value of the input ground motion acceleration is 0.1g, in different layered soil sites, the pile body deformation modes of the foundation piles at different positions are similar, and the maximum displacement occurs at the pile-cap. The relative displacement of the pile body at different pile positions is different, but the displacement difference is very small.

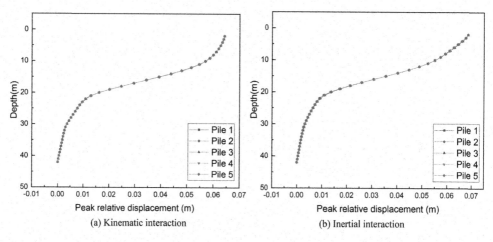

Figure 10. The peak value of relative displacement of pile body in hard-soft-hard soil site.

It is known that the displacement of the middle pile is the largest. Table 4 shows the horizontal displacement of the pile body at the top, each layer, and the bedrock surface of pile 3 at different sites. It can be found from the table that the maximum relative displacement is in the range of 70 mm to 90 mm. In PSI and PSSI, the horizontal displacement of the pile body is the largest in the soft-hard-soft sites, and the horizontal displacement of the pile body is the smallest in the hard-soft sites.

Table 4. Peak relative displacement of pile 3 under 0.1g working condition.

Interaction type	Site type	Displacement at pile head (mm)	Displacement at 10m (mm)	Displacement at 15m (mm)	Displacement at 20m (mm)	Displacement at bedrock surface (mm)
Kinematic interaction	Soft-hard	85.971	72.251	72.276	71.407	68.493
	Hard-soft	71.304	69.349	66.310	59.302	54.660
	Soft-hard-soft	91.751	81.689	75.475	72.114	70.293
	Soft-hard-hard	83.813	70.842	68.654	68.264	67.023
	Hard-soft-hard	88.170	83.024	77.881	75.462	73.018
Inertial interaction	Soft-hard	86.618	74.495	70.447	68.036	64.845
	Hard-soft	72.351	66.379	63.657	57.054	53.591
	Soft-hard-soft	94.195	81.185	77.7836	74.262	67.429
	Soft-hard-hard	87.622	80.780	77.887	74.101	70.084
	Hard-soft-hard	88.633	73.662	72.512	71.780	68.412

4 CONCLUSION

This paper takes the pile-soil system of the non-bedrock site foundation of the nuclear island as the research object and carries out the numerical simulation of the pile-soil interaction under the action of ground motion. The EERA equivalent linear model is used to process the site data, and the two-dimensional finite element model is established in ABAQUS. The kinematic interaction and inertia interaction of group piles in two-layer soil sites and three-layer soil sites are analyzed respectively, and the influence of different sites on the pile-soil interaction is discussed. As for the contribution of inertial interaction and motion interaction in pile-soil interaction, further in-depth research is needed to obtain consistent conclusions.

By analyzing the dynamic response characteristics of pile foundation underground motion, the laws of numerical simulation under different working conditions are summarized. The main research contents and research results are summarized as follows:

- Using ABAQUS viscoelastic constitutive model, introducing EERA and adopting an iterative calculation method to obtain the shear modulus and damping ratio compatible with the strain, and comparing the calculated results of the finite element free field with EERA. The numerical simulation results are in good agreement with the equivalent linear model results, which proves the validity of the numerical simulation method.
- Through the finite element analysis, the weak links of the seismic design of the pile body under each working condition are obtained. In the case of PSI, the weak part of the pile body is the boundary of the bedrock surface; in the case of PSSI, the weak part is the pile cap. At the same time, the internal force of the pile body at the soil layer in each layered soil site has a sudden change.
- Comparing the dynamic response laws of piles under the action of PSI and PSSI, the internal force of the pile body under different site conditions is only significantly different at the pile cap, and the internal force at the top of the pile under PSSI is nearly one time larger than that under PSI.
- In a layered soil site, when the elastic modulus of the two layers of soil differs greatly, the extreme value of the internal force of the pile body occurs in the layered soil. The greater the difference in soil stiffness between the two layers in contact with each other, the greater the value of the pile force at the boundary between the soil layers. Therefore, it is necessary to pay attention to whether the stiffness of the soil layer changes uniformly when selecting a layered soil site.
- The maximum horizontal displacement of the pile body occurs at the top of the pile. The displacement of the side piles of the group piles is small, and the displacement of the middle piles is large. The displacement of the foundation pile during the deformation of the pile group is

affected by the position of the pile. The displacement peak size of each foundation pile in the pile group is as follows: pile 3> pile 2, 4> pile 1, 5.
- In this paper, the seismic response characteristics of pile groups at different positions are studied. In the pile group model, compared with the three middle piles, the side piles on both sides are more likely to be damaged by ground motion due to their larger force. Subsequently, future research can focus on improving the pile strength of side piles, changing the pile material parameters, and discussing whether the overall seismic performance of pile groups has improved.

ACKNOWLEDGMENTS

This work was supported by the Scientific Research Fund of the Institute of Engineering Mechanics, China Earthquake Administration (Grant No. 2019B10); and the Natural Science Foundation of Heilongjiang Province of China (Grant No. LH2021E121).

REFERENCES

Asgarian B, Shokrgozar H R, Shahcheraghi D and Ghasemzadeh H 2012 Effect of soil pile structure interaction on dynamic characteristics of jacket type offshore platforms *Coup. Systems. Mech.* **1** 4.
Boulanger R W, Wilson D W and Kutter B L 2004 Nonlinear FEM analyses of soil-pile interaction in liquefying sand *Geo. Trans.* **126** 470–8.
Jingbo Liu, Yixin Du, Xiuli Du, Zhenyu Wang and Jun Wu 2006 3d viscous-spring artificial boundary in time domain *Earthq. Eng. Eng. Vib.* **5(1)** 93–102.
Kuecueukarslan S, Banerjee P K and Bildik N 2003 Inelastic analysis of pile-soil structure interaction *Eng. Struct.* **25(9)** 1231–9.
Lu X, Li P, Chen B, and Chen Y 2005 Computer simulation of the dynamic layered soil–pile– structure interaction system *Can. Geotech. J.* **42** 742–51.
Maravas A, Mylonakis G and Karabalis D L 2007 Dynamic characteristics of simple structures on piles and footings 4th International Conference on Earthquake Geotechnical Engineering (Greece: Thessaloniki).
Nogami T and Konagai K 1986 Time domain axial response of dynamically loaded single piles *J. Eng. Mech.* **112(11)** 1241–52.
Panaghi K and Mahboubi A 2010 Analysis of the effects of soil behavior law on the transfer and impedance functions in soil-pile interaction models *Geoflorida*. pp 2982–91.
Penzien J, Scheffey C F and Parmelee R A 1964 Seismic analysis of bridges on long piles *J. Eng. Mech. Div. Ase.* **90(3)** 223–54.
Soules T F, Busbey R F, Rekhson S M, Markovsky A and Burke M A 1987 Finite-element calculation of stresses in glass parts undergoing viscous relaxation *J. Am. Ceram. Soc.* p 70.
Wolf J and Von A G 1978 Impedance functions of a group of vertical piles *Proc. ASCE Conf.* vol 2 *Earthquake Eng. Soil Dyn. Pasadena.* pp 1024–41.
Zhifeng Liu 2007 Study on the rheology of clay and its applications in the evaluation of long-term stability of bridge's pile foundations *Tongji*.

Seismic vulnerability analysis of reinforced concrete frame structures built in different times

Lixin Shang, LingXin Zhang & JiaLu Ma*
Institute of Engineering Mechanics, CEA, Harbin, Heilongjiang, China

ABSTRACT: To explore the impacts of different codes, construction purposes, story number, and seismic fortification intensity on the seismic vulnerability of reinforced concrete frame structures, 6-story and 12-story non-residential buildings and 6-story residential buildings with a fortification intensity of 6, 7, 8, and 9 degrees are designed based on GB J11-89 Code of Seismic Design of Buildings (China Architecture & Building Press 1989.) (hereinafter referred to as "GB J11-89 Code") and GB 50011-2001 Code of Seismic Design of Buildings (China Architecture & Building Press 2001.) (hereinafter referred to as "GB 50011-2001 Code"). The Platform OpenSees is adopted for establishing corresponding nonlinear analysis models of these two groups of 22 reinforced concrete frame structures. The incremental dynamic analysis (IDA) method is utilized to explore the seismic vulnerability and seismic performance of the designed structures. The research results show that reinforced concrete (RC) frame structures designed with the old code still satisfy the seismic fortification level required by the GB 50011-2010 Code of Seismic Design of Buildings (China Architecture & Building Press 2010.) (hereinafter referred to as "GB 50011-2010 Code").

1 INTRODUCTION

Seismic vulnerability, one of the focuses of earthquake engineering and a core part of "performance-based earthquake engineering," mainly refers to the conditional probability for a structure to reach or exceed a destructive state under a ground motion intensity (Yu 2012). Empirical, analytical, and hybrid methods are generally adopted for seismic vulnerability analysis. Specifically, the empirical method can be used to evaluate a structure's seismic performance through statistical analysis of seismic damage data, which, though being quite efficient, only applies to the regions with sufficient seismic damage data (Whitman 1973). In the analytic method, the elastic-plastic finite element method is adopted to calculate the responses of a structure under the seismic action and further assess its seismic performance(Zhang et al. 2002). In contrast, the hybrid method is a combination of empirical and analytical methods. The analytical results are utilized as a supplement to the seismic damage data, or the seismic damage data are employed for correcting the analytical results; thereby, more authentic results can be secured (Kappos & Panagopoulos 2010).

Due to its advantages, such as flexible spatial distribution, the reinforced concrete frame structure is widely used in industrial and civil buildings. In recent years, the seismic performance of reinforced concrete frame structures has been vigorously explored. H. Hwang et al. (Hwang & Liu 2004) conducted a vulnerability analysis of the concrete-based continuous bridge structure on the seismic zone NewMadrid in the East-Central United States and proved that the proposed method applies universally to the vulnerability analysis of bridge structures in the similar regions. Lyu et al. (Lu et al. 2006) put forward the overall vulnerability analysis method for a structure in combination with its reliability method and performance-based seismic design idea. Based on

---

*Corresponding Author: d jialuma@163.com

IDA seismic vulnerability analysis, Lyu et al. (2012) evaluated the seismic performance of complex out-of-codes high-rise buildings, providing a basis for predicting their seismic damage and loss. Yu et al. (2012) proposed the "cloud atlas-strip method" to dissect the probabilistic seismic demand of the reinforced concrete frame structure, put forward the seismic vulnerability function by considering the uncertainty of essence and knowledge, and applied it to analyze the seismic vulnerability of the reinforced concrete frame structure. The analytical function of probabilistic seismic risk was then offered based on the vulnerability function for the eventual assessment of the seismic probabilistic safety level of this structure.

Although scholars have done extensive research on the seismic vulnerability of reinforced concrete frame structures, most of the research objects are designed based on the existing code. However, China's seismic design code has been updated several times, and the latest one is GB 50011-2010 Code. Reinforced concrete frame structures built based on the old codes in China still account for a large proportion. Among the current research results, the seismic performance of such buildings is still not investigated. To solve this problem, we designed a group of reinforced concrete frame structures with different seismic fortification intensities, story heights, and purposes based on GB J11-89 Code and GB 50011-2001 Code, and their seismic vulnerability was analyzed. The analytical results can be utilized for seismic damage prediction, post-earthquake emergency responses, and analysis of VC investment data in the insurance industry.

2 ANALYTICAL METHOD

2.1 *Analytical method of seismic earthquake for a structure*

A structure's seismic vulnerability is defined as the conditional probability for a structure to reach or exceed a limit state under a certain ground motion intensity, namely:

$$F_R(x) = P[D \geq C \mid IM = x] \quad (1)$$

where $F_R(x)$ refers to the seismic vulnerability function; D is the seismic demand; C is the seismic-resistant capacity; $D \geq C$ means that the structure reaches or exceeds a limit state; IM signifies the ground motion intensity parameter, including Peak Ground Acceleration (PGA), Spectral Acceleration (S_a), etc.

In this study, PGA is adopted as the earthquake intensity measurement; θ_D means the structure's maximum interlayer displacement angle when PGA=x; θ_C refers to the lower limit of the maximum interlayer displacement angle in a limit state. Thus, the following equation is obtained:

$$F_Rx = P[\theta_D \geq \theta_C \mid PGA = x] \quad (2)$$

Assume θ_D and θ_C obeys normal distribution, the probability can be obtained by the following equation:

$$p_f(PGA = x) = \Phi\left(\frac{-\ln\left(\frac{\theta_C}{\theta_D}\right)}{\sqrt{\sigma_{\ln C}^2 + \sigma_{\ln D}^2}}\right)$$

$$= \Phi\left(\frac{\ln(e^A(x)^B/\theta_C)}{\sqrt{\sigma_{\ln C}^2 + \sigma_{\ln D}^2}}\right) \quad (3)$$

where, $\sigma_{\ln C}$ and $\sigma_{\ln C}$ are the logarithmic standard deviations of θ_C and θ_D respectively. According to Reference (Lu, Su, Zhou, 2012), when PGA is a variable, $\sqrt{\sigma_{\ln C}^2 + \sigma_{\ln D}^2} = 0.5$.

For fragility analysis with the fitting statistical method, assume the structural damage parameters, peak inter-storey drift angle (θmax), and the input ground motion strength and peak acceleration (PGA) meet the equation:

$$\theta_{max} = \alpha(PGA)^\beta \quad (4)$$

Take the logarithm on both sides and simplify the equation, then:

$$\ln \theta_{max} = A + B \times \ln(PGA) \quad (5)$$

where, A and B are constants, which can be obtained by plotting the scatter diagram with ln(PGA) as the horizontal coordinate and $\ln(\theta_{max})$ as the vertical coordinate.

Values A and B can be obtained through linear fitting. They are substituted into Eq. (3) to calculate the conditional probability of a structure reaching or exceeding a limit state under different intensities of earthquake ground motions, and the seismic vulnerability curve is then drawn.

2.2 Incremental dynamic analysis (IDA) method

In seismic vulnerability analysis methods mostly based on elastic-plastic finite element analysis, the structure's responses are calculated by inputting earthquake ground motion loads. The results are analyzed to get seismic vulnerability. Commonly-used analytical methods include the simplified analytical method, cloud atlas-strip method, dynamic time-history analysis method, incremental dynamic analysis (IDA) method, etc. (Li et al. 2018). Among them, the IDA method is often used in the current seismic vulnerability research work as it considers the impact of the uncertainty of earthquake ground motion on structural response. Its calculation results can be easily used to analyze the whole process of structural responses from resilience development to elastoplasticity and the changes in the ground motion intensity, thus presenting the structure's seismic performance more comprehensively (Lu et al. 2012). As a result, the IDA method is utilized here for subsequent research.

Specifically, the IDA method advocates the selection of appropriate ground motions for amplitude modulation in a row based on a certain proportion, and different amplitudes of ground motions are applied to the structure for dynamic time-history analysis to calculate its respective responses. After that, the ground motion intensity parameter and structural response are utilized as the horizontal and longitudinal coordinates to get an IDA curve. Multiple strips of earthquake ground motions are selected to repeat the above steps and obtain the IDA curve family. The seismic vulnerability of the structure is acquired by substituting the vulnerability analysis equation after the curve family is treated with the statistical analytical method. The above method effectively eliminates the impact of uncertainty in the earthquake ground motion on the structure's analytical results.

2.3 Selection of ground motion intensity measurement (IM) and damage measurement (DM)

In essence, seismic vulnerability research focuses on the relationship between earthquake ground motion and structural response, so selecting appropriate IM and DM is especially important. PGA, as the most direct and simplest concept, is the most commonly-used ground motion intensity parameter by most countries across the world (Zhou & Li 2014). The maximum interlayer displacement angle (ISDA) can be obtained through numerical simulation and is directly correlated with node turning, interlayer deformation, and other capabilities to better reflect the structure's overall performance. This study chooses maximum ISDA as the DM, while PGA is adopted as the IM.

GB 50011-2010 Code stipulates that the reinforced concrete frame structure has an "elastic ISDA limit" of 1/550 and an "electro-plastic ISDA limit" of 1/50. In our study, the limit of 1/550 is adopted as an indicator for the state of "basically intact," and 1/50 as the lower limit of the "destruction state." Combined with the suggestions on state limits offered by Yang Shuo et al. (Zhou & Li 2014) based on numerous previous studies, the judgment criteria were finally chosen and are presented in Table 1.

Table 1. ISDA Limits of Concrete Frame Structures at the Ultimate States.

Damage level	Basically intact	Slight damage	Moderate damage	Destruction state
~1/550	1/550~1/275	1/275~1/135	1/135~1/50	1/50~

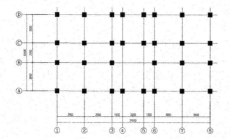

Figure 1. The gird-line layout of the residential building.

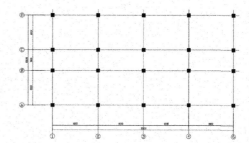

Figure 2. The gird-line layout of non-residential building.

2.4 *Selection of earthquake ground motion*

To reduce the impact of the uncertainty of earthquake ground motion on the structure, considering the influence of PGA and Peak Ground Velocity (PGV) we choose PGA/PGV as the indicator to classify a total of 30 earthquake ground motions into three categories: Category One: PGA/PGV < 0.8g/ms^{-1}; Category Two: 0.8g/ms^{-1} < PGA/PGV < 1.2g/ms^{-1}; Category Three: PGA/PGV > 1.2g/ms^{-1}; sites are divided into Categories C, D, and E with abundant earthquake ground motion records where the structure easily suffer damage.

3 ANALYTICAL MODEL

3.1 *Project overview*

To explore the influence of different seismic design codes and different fortification intensities, story heights, and purposes on the seismic vulnerability of reinforced concrete frame structure, a representative gird-line layout is chosen for residential and non-residential buildings, respectively, and a 6-story residential building, a 6-story non-residential building, and a 12-story non-residential building is designed in accordance with *GB J11-89 Code* and *GB 50011-2001 Code*, respectively, based on the fortification intensities 6, 7, 8, and 9 degrees. PKPM is used to design different sections of beams and columns of the same configuration, and 22 structural models are obtained.

Specifically, the gird-line layout of the residential and non-residential buildings is shown below:

The 6-story residential building has a story height of 3,700 mm, with a total height of 22.2 m. Due to the limited space, only the section sizes of beam and column are presented, while reinforced concrete members are designed by following the design codes and taking into account the economy and other factors in the actual projects:

The 6-story or 12-story non-residential building also has a story height of 3,700 mm, with a total height of 22.2 m and 44.4 m, respectively. Due to limited space, just like the residential building, only the section sizes of beam and column are presented:

3.2 *Analytical model*

In this study, the fiber model OpenSees is adopted for numerical simulations; Steel01 is utilized as the steel material; Concrete01 is employed as the concrete. Compared to the direct section

Table 2. Beam and column sections.

Seismic fortification intensity	Floor	89 code Beam	89 code Column	01 code Beam	01 code Column
6	6	250×500	450×450	250×500	500×500
7	6	250×550	500×500	250×600	500×500
8	6	250×600	550×550	300×600	550×550
9	6	300×700	700×700	350×700	700×700

Table 3. Beam and column sections.

Seismic fortification intensity	Floor	89 code Beam	89 code Column	01 code Beam	01 code Column
6	6	200×500	400×400	250×600	550×550
	1~6	250×550	700×700	250×600	700×700
	6~12		500×500		550×550
7	6	250×550	500×500	250×600	550×550
	1~6	250×600	700×700	300×600	700×700
	6~12				550×550
8	6	250×600	500×500	300×600	550×550
	1~6	250×600	700×700	300×600	700×700
	6~12		500×500		550×550
9	6	300×700	600×600	350×700	600×600

resilience model, the stress-strain relationship between fibers in the fiber section model decides the resilience and deformation relationship of the entire section, and the actual performance under stress for the section simulated is more objective and accurate. The basic principle lies in that the member is longitudinally divided into several segments. The deformation of a single section in the middle of each segment represents the deformation of this segment, and this section is subdivided into several fibers.

The constitutive relations between these two kinds of materials are shown below:

Concrete01 model is a uniaxial constitutive model based on the concrete material Kent-Scott-park, and four parameters shall be defined: peak stress and strain, ultimate stress, and strain, without considering the tensile strength of the concrete. To be specific, Concrete C40 has a standard compressive strength of 26.8 N/mm^2, a peak strain of 0.002, a residual strain of 0.0035, and residual strength of 10 N/mm^2. This model utilizes the simplest concrete material in OpenSees, yielding a higher computational efficiency.

Steel01 Model is a double broken line model with a high computational efficiency that supports massive computation in vulnerability research. Specifically, Steel HRB400 has a yield strength (Fy) of 400 N/mm^2 an elastic modulus (Es) of 2×10^5 N/mm^2 and a strain hardening rate (α) of 0.001.

3.3 *Validation of analytical model*

By simulating the structure in Literature (Yang 2016) for seismic vulnerability analysis, the reasonableness of the proposed model is verified, and the comparative results are shown below:

As indicated, 01-7-Yang Shuo and 89-7-Yang Shuo refer to the seismic vulnerability results of the non-residential buildings based on *GB 50011-2001 Code* and *GB J11-89 Code*, respectively;

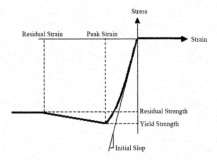
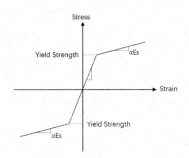

Figure 3. Constitutive relations for Concrete01.

Figure 4. Constitutive relations for Steel01.

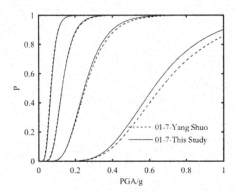
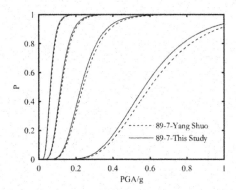

Figure 5. Comparisons of non-residential buildings based on GB 50011-2001 Code.

Figure 6. Comparisons of non-residential buildings based on GB J11-89 Code.

01-7-this study and 89-7-this study are the simulation results proposed in this paper. The analytical results are affected by different factors, such as the modeling software and the constitutive model of the material. It can be considered that the proposed Model here is accurate and reasonable despite a slight difference within the allowed range.

4 VULNERABILITY ANALYSIS RESULTS

Thirty earthquake ground motion loads with an amplitude adjusted to 0.1 g, 0.2 g, 0.3 g, 0.4 g, 0.5 g, and 0.6 g, respectively, are applied to the structure. The Platform OpenSees is adopted for analysis to get its displacement response. The IDA method is adopted for data processing to get the seismic vulnerabilities of the structure built at different times with different fortification intensities and different purposes. Moreover, these results are comparatively analyzed. Due to limited space, the vulnerability results in the structure with a fortification intensity of 7 degrees accounting for a large proportion in real life are displayed.

4.1 *Impact of different codes*

In the above graphs, "Non-residential" refers to the curve of non-residential buildings, and "residential" refers to the curve of residential buildings.

It can be seen from the vulnerability curve and damage probability matrix that for both residential and non-residential buildings, the buildings designed based on *GB 50011-2001 Code* have a better seismic performance than those based on *GB J11-89 Code*. With the increase in the fortification intensity, their seismic performance all enhances. Noticeably, the seismic fortification criterion

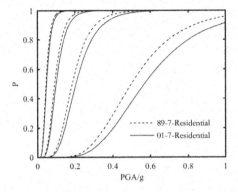
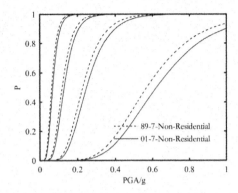

Figure 7. Comparisons of residential structures with a fortification intensity of 7 degrees based on the old and new codes.

Figure 8. Comparisons of non-residential structures with a fortification intensity of 7 degrees based on the old and new codes.

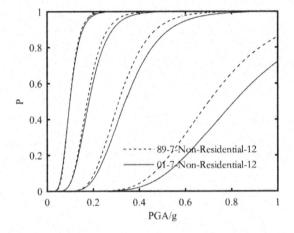

Figure 9. Comparisons of non-residential structures with a fortification intensity of 7 degrees based on the old and new codes (12 floors).

Table 4. Damage probability matrices for 6-story based on different codes reinforced concrete frame structures with a fortification intensity of 7(0.10g) degrees (based on GB 50011-2001 Code).

	Weak earthquake PGA=35gal		Weak~moderate earthquake PGA=55gal		Moderate earthquake PGA=110gal		Strong earthquake, PGA=220gal	
Damage Level	Non-residential structures	Residential structures	Non-residential structures	Residential structures	Non-residential structures	Residential structures	Non-residential structures	Residential structures
Basically intact	0.965	0.795	0.722	0.390	0.098	0.024	0.001	0.000
Slight damage	0.034	0.200	0.268	0.537	0.572	0.381	0.074	0.027
Moderate damage	0.000	0.005	0.010	0.073	0.316	0.533	0.557	0.413
Destruction state	0.000	0.000	0.000	0.001	0.013	0.062	0.365	0.550
Collapse	0.000	0.000	0.000	0.000	0.000	0.000	0.002	0.010

of "no collapse under strong earthquakes" is most affected by the fortification intensity. The underlying reasons lie in that the new code raises stricter and more rigorous requirements for seismic influence coefficient and seismic check and that seismic internal force combination coefficient increases compared to that in the old code(Dai 2002). This leads to an increased section or enhanced

Table 5. Damage probability difference matrices for 6-story based on different codes reinforced concrete frame structures with a fortification intensity of 7(0.10g) degree.

Damage Level	Weak earthquake PGA=35gal D-value	Weak~moderate earthquake PGA=55gal D-value	Moderate earthquake PGA=110gal D-value	Strong earthquake, PGA=220gal D-value
Basically intact	−0.171	−0.333	−0.074	−0.001
Slight damage	0.166	0.166	−0.191	−0.047
Moderate damage	0.005	0.005	0.216	−0.144
Destruction state	0.000	0.000	0.049	0.185
Collapse	0.000	0.000	0.000	0.007

Table 6. Damage probability matrices for 6-story different based on codes reinforced concrete frame structures with a fortification intensity of 7(0.10g) degrees (based on GB J11-89 Code).

Damage Level	Weak earthquake PGA=35gal Non-residential structures	Residential structures	Weak~moderate earthquake PGA=55gal Non-residential structures	Residential structures	Moderate earthquake PGA=110gal Non-residential structures	Residential structures	Strong earthquake, PGA=220gal Non-residential structures	Residential structures
Basically intact	0.944	0.750	0.640	0.322	0.064	0.014	0.000	0.000
Slight damage	0.056	0.242	0.342	0.576	0.519	0.306	0.047	0.014
Moderate damage	0.000	0.008	0.018	0.101	0.394	0.585	0.494	0.320
Destruction state	0.000	0.000	0.000	0.001	0.023	0.095	0.454	0.646
Collapse	0.000	0.000	0.000	0.000	0.000	0.000	0.005	0.020

Table 7. Damage probability difference matrices for 6-story based on different codes reinforced concrete frame structures with a fortification intensity of 7(0.10g) degree.

Damage Level	Weak earthquake PGA=35gal D-value	Weak~moderate earthquake PGA=55gal D-value	Moderate earthquake PGA=110gal D-value	Strong earthquake, PGA=220gal D-value
Basically intact	−0.194	−0.317	−0.050	0.000
Slight damage	0.186	0.186	−0.213	−0.033
Moderate damage	0.008	0.008	0.191	−0.174
Destruction state	0.000	0.000	0.071	0.192
Collapse	0.000	0.000	0.000	0.015

reinforcement ratio in the design process and improves the overall seismic performance of the structure. Additionally, the 12-story non-residential building has a better seismic performance than the 6-story non-residential building with the same seismic fortification intensity designed based on the same code.

4.2 Comparisons of different purposes

By comparing the structures with the same story number, the vulnerability curve and the damage probability matrix suggest that the non-residential building has better seismic performance than the residential building with the same fortification intensity designed based on the same code. The non-residential building is superior to a residential building in terms of seismic performance, and the difference in their seismic performance expands with the increase in the seismic fortification intensity. It can be attributed to the fact that a non-residential building has a simple layout and a

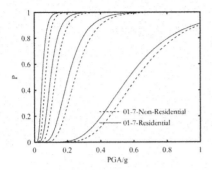 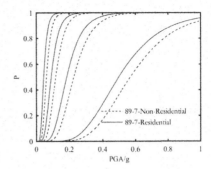

Figure 10. Comparisons of non-residential and residential buildings with a fortification of 7 degrees (based on GB 50011-2001 Code).

Figure 11. Comparisons of non-residential and residential buildings with a fortification of 7 degrees (based on GB J11-89 Code).

Table 8. Damage probability matrices for 6-story non-residential and residential reinforced concrete frame structures with a fortification intensity of 7(0.10g) degrees (based on GB 50011-2001 Code).

Damage Level	Weak earthquake PGA=35gal Non-residential structures	Weak earthquake PGA=35gal Residential structures	Weak~moderate earthquake PGA=55gal Non-residential structures	Weak~moderate earthquake PGA=55gal Residential structures	Moderate earthquake PGA=110gal Non-residential structures	Moderate earthquake PGA=110gal Residential structures	Strong earthquake, PGA=220gal Non-residential structures	Strong earthquake, PGA=220gal Residential structures
Basically intact	0.944	0.750	0.640	0.322	0.064	0.014	0.000	0.000
Slight damage	0.056	0.242	0.342	0.576	0.519	0.306	0.047	0.014
Moderate damage	0.000	0.008	0.018	0.101	0.394	0.585	0.494	0.320
Destruction state	0.000	0.000	0.000	0.001	0.023	0.095	0.454	0.646
Collapse	0.000	0.000	0.000	0.000	0.000	0.000	0.005	0.020

Table 9. Damage probability difference matrices for 6-story non-residential and residential reinforced concrete frame structures with a fortification intensity of 7(0.10g) degrees.

Damage Level	Weak earthquake PGA=35gal D-value	Weak~moderate earthquake PGA=55gal D-value	Moderate earthquake PGA=110gal D-value	Strong earthquake, PGA=220gal D-value
Basically intact	−0.194	−0.317	−0.050	0.000
Slight damage	0.186	0.186	−0.213	−0.033
Moderate damage	0.008	0.008	0.191	−0.174
Destruction state	0.000	0.000	0.071	0.192
Collapse	0.000	0.000	0.000	0.015

complete structure, and its designed roof load is greater than that of a residential building, leading to increased sections of beam and column and improving its seismic performance.

5 CONCLUSIONS

Based on *GB J11-89 Code* and *GB 50011-2001 Code*, 22 groups of reinforced concrete frame structures with different fortification intensities, purposes, and story numbers are designed. The Platform OpenSees is adopted for modeling and analysis, and the IDA method is adopted for seismic vulnerability research to draw the following conclusions:

(1) Reinforced concrete frame structure designed based on *GB 50011-2001 Code* is found to have improved seismic performance compared to the structure based on *GB J11-89 Code*; 6-story

frame structures with different purposes have realized a similar increase in seismic performance, while 12-story non-residential structures have their seismic performance enhanced more significantly.

(2) Non-residential structures are identified with better seismic performance than residential structures with the same seismic fortification intensity designed based on the same code; 12-story non-residential structures outperform 6-story non-residential structures in terms of seismic performance.

(3) It can be seen from the vulnerability curve that reinforced concrete frame structures designed based on *GB J11-89 Code* and *GB 50011-2001 Code*, no matter residential or non-residential structures, all satisfy the requirements of "no damage under minor earthquakes, repairable under moderate earthquakes, and no collapse under strong earthquakes."

ACKNOWLEDGEMENT

This research was funded by the Scientific Research Fund of the Institute of Engineering Mechanics, China Earthquake Administration (2019D03) and the Special fund for the basic scientific research business of the Institute of engineering mechanics, CEA. <Study on some problems of seismic design method of building structures based on behavior > (No. 2019A01)

REFERENCES

Dai Guoying. Some Comparison on the Regulation between 89 Edition and 2001 Edition of the Seismic Design Code [J]. *Building Structure*, 2002(12): 66–71.
GB 50011-2001 *Edition for Seismic Design of Buildings* [S]. Beijing: China Architecture & Building Press, 2001.
GB 50011-2010 *Code for Seismic Design of Buildings* [S]. Beijing: China Architecture & Building Press, 2010.
GBJ 11-89 *Edition for Seismic Design of Buildings* [S]. Beijing: China Architecture & Building Press, 1989.
Hwang H, Liu Jingbo. Seismic fragility analysis of reinforced concrete bridges [J]. *China Civil Engineering Journal*, 2004, 37(6): 47–51.
Kappos A .J., Panagopoulos G.. Fragility curves for reinforced concrete buildings in Greece[J]. *Structure and Infrastructure Engineering*, 2010, 6(1-2):39–53.
Li Hongnan, Cheng Hu, Wang Dongsheng. Review of advances in seismic fragility research on bridge structures[J]. *Engineering Mechanics*, 2018, 35(9):1–16.
Lou Sizhan, Ye Zhiming, Chen Lingli. Seismic Risk Assessment of Frame Structure Buildings [J]. *Journal of Natural Disasters*, 2005(05): 103–109.
Lu Dagang, Li Xiaopeng, Wang Guangyuan. Global seismic fragility analysis of structures based on reliability and performance [J]. *Journal of Natural Disaster*, 2006, 15(2): 107–114.
Lu Xilin, Su Ningfen, Zhou Ying. IDA-based seismic fragility analysis of a complex high-rise structure[J]. *Journal of Earthquake Engineering and Engineering Vibration*, 2012, 32(5):19–25.
Whitman R V. Damage probability matrices for prototype buildings[J]. *Structures Publication*, 1973, 380.
Yang Shuo. *Study on a Hybrid Method for Seismic Vulnerability Analysis of nonresidential RC Frame Structures* [D]. Institute of Engineering Mechanics, CEA, 2016.
Yu Xiaohui. *Probabilistic seismic fragility and risk analysis of reinforced concrete frame structures* [D]. Harbin: Harbin Institute of Technology, 2012.
Zhang Lingxin, Jiang Jinren, Liu Jieping. Seismic vulnerability analysis of multistory dwelling brick buildings [J]. *Earthquake Engineering and Engineering Vibration*, 2002, 22(1): 49–55.
Zhou Ying, Li MengJie. State-of-the-art Intensity Measures for Incremental Dynamic Analysis [J]. *Structural Engineers*, 2014, 30 (06) : 199–204.

Study on the influence of subway foundation pit excavation sequences on the deformation of retaining structure

Song Xu*, Changjie Xu, Lihong Tong* & Haibin Ding
State Key Laboratory of Performance Monitoring and Guarantee of Rail Transportation Infrastructure, Nanchang, Jiangxi, China
Institute of Geotechnical Engineering, School of Civil Engineering and Architecture, East China Jiaotong University, Nanchang, Jiangxi, China

Zhilong Wu
Shenzhen GongKan Geotechnical Group Co., LTD, Shenzhen, China

ABSTRACT: Based on the subway foundation pit project of Wenyi West Road in Hangzhou, this paper studies the problems of different excavation sequences, deformation of retaining structure, and surface settlement of foundation pit. Results show that the deformation of the retaining structure for the same foundation pit is significantly different on both sides. Furthermore, the soil layer cannot be simply regarded as the horizontal uniform soil layer during the analysis. The pile load of the foundation pit should be reduced on the side of the larger deformation, and the load should be distributed on the side of the retaining structure with smaller deformation as far as possible. The horizontal displacement of underground continuous wall and surface settlement increase gradually with the excavation of the foundation pit. It is not difficult to analyze that the deformation of the underground continuous wall is significantly affected by the excavation sequences, while the excavation from the middle to both sides has the least influence on the deformation of the ground wall. The conclusions obtained in this paper can provide theoretical guidance and technical support for the design and construction of subway foundation pit, and have good reference value and practical significance for foundation pit engineering.

1 INTRODUCTION

Due to the unremitting advancement of urbanization, urban land is increasingly scarce, which brings about an inevitable trend of urban sustainable development to vigorously exploit and utilize underground space and build rail transit. However, the foundation pit construction in the complex urban environment with numerous buildings and underground tunnels and pipelines will inevitably cause adverse effects on the existing nearby buildings and municipal pipelines.

Zheng (2022) analyzed the deformation mechanism of foundation pit construction and its impact on the environment from the perspective of the whole process control of foundation pit construction. Considering the two working conditions that the tunnel is located outside and below the foundation pit, Liu (Liu et al. 2021) summarized the latest research results from four aspects: the effect mechanism of foundation pit excavation on the adjacent tunnel, the influence area of tunnel deformation caused by foundation pit excavation, the prediction method of tunnel deformation affected by foundation pit excavation and the control method of foundation pit excavation on the tunnel, respectively. Zhang (Guo et al. 2021; Xie et al. 2014; Zhang et al. 2011) et al. studied the impact of foundation pit excavation on the existing surrounding tunnels and pipelines, and found that the

---

*Corresponding Author: sxu_delta@qq.com

impact of foundation pit excavation on the surrounding environment was significant. Zhu (Zhu et al. 2021) used PLAXIS numerical software to analyze the influence of pit and block excavation sequence on tunnel deformation. Results showed that the excavation sequence should be as follows: the far pit should be first followed by the near pit, the small pit should be first followed by the large pit, and the construction sequence of jumping excavation should be adopted when excavating the foundation pit adjacent to the rail transit. Shi (Shi et al. 2020) analyzed the characteristics and difficulties of deep foundation pit excavation adjacent to subway, and proposed corresponding solutions according to their own characteristics. Finally, the difficult problem of deep foundation pit excavation adjacent to the subway was solved by using an excavation method of "zoning, stratification and segmentation, time-limited symmetry and equilibrium". Lu (Lu et al. 2021) studied the distribution law of soil disturbance degree in the center of pit bottom and the depth of strong disturbance area under different excavation depths by using the finite element simulation method. The results showed that the disturbance would significantly increase the foundation settlement.

Based on the foundation pit project of the Hangzhou metro, this paper achieves the corresponding conclusions by analyzing the horizontal displacement of underground continuous wall and surface settlement during foundation pit excavation. Through the study of the excavation sequences of foundation pit, the impact of different excavation sequences on the deformation of retaining structure is analyzed in detail, which can provide a good reference value and practical significance for foundation pit engineering.

2 PROJECT OVERVIEW

The proposed station is located at the intersection of Wenyi West Road and Jing Teng Road, along the north-south layout of Jing Teng Road. As the starting point of the first phase of Line 3, the station is an island station with two floors underground. The standard section of the foundation pit is 21.7 m in width and 17.9 m in depth, the small end well is 25.8 m in width and 19.4 m in depth, and the large end well is 25.8 m in width and 18.3 m in depth, respectively. The main body enclosure adopts an 800 mm thick underground continuous wall. The toe of the continuous wall enters the weathered rock layer with an average depth of about 2.0 m and a depth of 24.5~35 m. The inner side of the continuous wall is set with a 700 mm thick lining wall while an 800 mm in shield well, and the design between the lining wall and underground continuous wall is based on a composite wall. The diameter of the column is 0.9 m, and the cross-section size of the concrete support is 800×800 mm.

3 MODEL PARAMETERS SELECTION

In this study, three-dimensional finite element software (PLAXIS 3D) was used to establish a numerical calculation model to analyze the deformation of enclosure structure and surface settlement during the construction process of the standard section of the Wenyi West Road subway station.

For the purpose of eliminating the boundary conditions' influence, this model size is set to 117m×130m×84.6m. The model grid is divided by spatial tetrahedral 10-node elements, and the finite element model is shown in Figure 1. HS-small modal is employed to simulate the stress-strain constitutive theory of soil, and the linear elastic constitutive model is utilized to simulate other components (such as the ground wall, column pile, support, etc.). The parameters of the constitutive model are shown in Table 1.

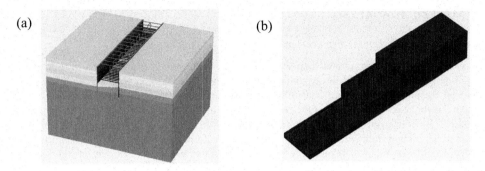

Figure 1. Finite element model diagram.

Table 1. Constitutive model parameters of soil.

Soil layer	γ (kN/m^3)	c' (kPa)	φ' (°)	E_{50} (MPa)	E_{oed} (MPa)	E_{ur} (MPa)	G (MPa)
① Plain fill	17.5	3	28	7.0	7.0	28.0	56.0
② Mucky silty clay	17.8	5	24	4.1	4.1	41.5	83.1
③ Silty clay	19.5	9	27	7.9	7.9	55.6	111.2
④ Silty clay sandwiched with silt	19.1	8	26	6.0	6.0	30.1	60.3
⑤ Silty clay	19.5	10	28	8.2	8.2	57.4	114.7
⑥ Sandy silty clay	19.4	8	26	6.5	6.5	38.7	77.5
⑦ Strong weathered sand conglomerate	21.0	90	25	40.0	40.0	120.0	240.0
⑧ Weathered conglomerate	21.5	110	30	70.0	70.0	210.0	420.0

4 VERIFICATION OF MODEL

Figure 2 shows the comparison between the measured and calculated values of the measured wall body of ZQT 17 and ZQT 31. It can be seen from the figure that the deformation modes of the calculated and measured underground continuous wall on both are the same, both of which are the realization modes of the inner convex enclosure structure. In the meanwhile, the calculated horizontal displacement of the underground continuous wall on both sides is basically consistent with the measured value. By comparing the calculated values with the measured values, the reliability of the finite element calculation model adopted in this study is proved.

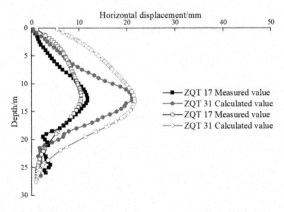

Figure 2. Comparisons between the calculated values with the measured values.

5 NUMERICAL ANALYSIS

5.1 *Analysis of horizontal displacement of underground continuous wall*

It's well known that the horizontal displacement of the underground continuous wall varies with the continuous advancement of subway station construction. Under the construction condition of steel bracing, the horizontal displacement of the underground continuous wall is reduced to a certain extent due to the reverse loading of the steel bracing, which is required to exert a certain amount of prestress. By comparing the cloud map of horizontal displacement of the underground continuous wall on the left and right sides in Figure 3, it can be found that the horizontal displacement of the underground continuous wall on the left side is significantly greater than that on the right side, which is mainly because there is poor silty clay in the depth range of the underground continuous wall on the left side, and the thickness of this layer near the pit bottom on the left side is obviously greater than that on the right side.

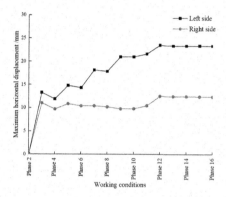

Figure 3. Maximum horizontal displacement of the underground continuous wall under different working conditions.

5.2 *Analysis of surface settlement*

The surface settlement on both sides of the foundation pit is depicted in Figure 4. It's clear that the maximum increment of surface settlement deformation outside the pit is -9.89 mm on the left side and -7.6 mm on the right side when the soil excavation to the first layer. The surface settlement deformation outside the pit on the left side increases to a certain extent in the excavation stage. However, when the construction of the middle slab of the station is completed, the variation of surface settlement deformation outside the pit is very small. In addition, the surface settlement deformation outside the pit on the right side did not change significantly after the completion of the excavation of the first layer. The maximum value of surface settlement on the left side is 22.9 mm, and that on the right side is 12.8 mm.

5.3 *Analysis of results caused by different excavation sequences*

This section conducts research based on the finite element model in the previous section and analyzes the horizontal displacement and surface settlement deformation of the enclosure structure by setting different excavation sequences. Besides, the left underground continuous wall is taken as the analysis object.

5.3.1 *Excavate from left to right*

According to Figure 5, the horizontal displacement of the central underground continuous wall is close to 0 due to the failure to reach the focus point during excavation. Subsequently, the horizontal

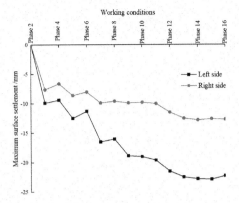

Figure 4. Maximum surface settlement under different working conditions.

displacement of the underground continuous wall enhances gradually with the unloading of soil, and its maximum value is 18.20 mm in the six excavation conditions, which is about 5.9 mm less than that in the simultaneous excavation conditions. The maximum value is 13.64 mm, and its maximum value is about 8.2 mm less than that of simultaneous excavation. The main reason is that the initial excavation displacement is the largest due to the delay of bracing.

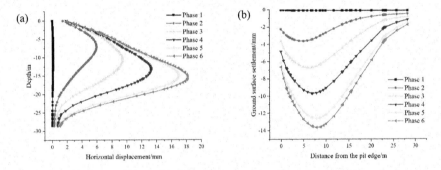

Figure 5. Deformation diagram of surface and the underground continuous wall on the left.

5.3.2 Excavate from the middle to the sides
The horizontal displacement diagram and surface settlement diagram of the underground continuous wall under different working conditions are shown in Figure 6. It can be reflected from Figure 6 that the horizontal displacement of the underground continuous wall grows gradually with the unloading of soil, and its maximum value reaches 13.76 mm, which is reduced by about 10.34 mm compared with the simultaneous excavation conditions. The maximum value of the ground surface settlement is 9.08 mm, and its maximum value is 12.76 mm less than that of simultaneous excavation. In other words, the horizontal displacement of the underground continuous wall on both sides is larger than that in the middle, mainly because the two sides of the excavation are not supported in time.

5.3.3 Excavate from the sides to the center
It can be obviously known from Figure 7 that the horizontal displacement of the underground continuous wall grows with the unloading of soil, and its maximum value is 13.91 mm in the five excavation conditions, and its maximum value is about 10.19 mm less than that in the simultaneous excavation conditions. The maximum value of the ground surface settlement is 9.03 mm, and its

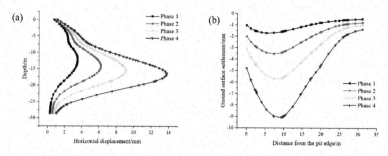

Figure 6. Deformation diagram of surface and the underground continuous wall on the left.

maximum value is 12.81 mm less than that of simultaneous excavation. What's more, the horizontal displacement of the underground continuous wall on both sides is larger than that in the middle because the excavation site is not supported in time.

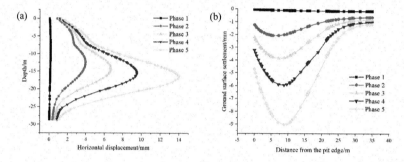

Figure 7. Deformation diagram of surface and the underground continuous wall on the left.

6 CONCLUSIONS

This paper studies the influence of the excavation sequence of the subway foundation pit on the horizontal displacement of the underground diaphragm wall, and we can draw some conclusions as follows: (1) The deformation of the left and right sides of the retaining structure of the same foundation pit is significantly different, so the soil layer cannot be regarded as a horizontal uniform soil layer for analysis. It is necessary to reduce the pile load of the foundation pit on the side with large deformation and distribute the load on the side with small deformation of the retaining structure as far as possible. (2) The horizontal displacement of underground continuous wall and surface settlement increase gradually with the excavation of the foundation pit and the construction of the station. (3) Different excavation sequences have a vital influence on the deformation of the ground wall. According to the analysis, the excavation from the middle to both sides has the least impact on the deformation of the ground wall. (4) Through the study of this paper, the stress and deformation behavior of the foundation pit retaining structure under different excavation sequences can be understood, so as to guide construction and reduce engineering risks.

ACKNOWLEDGMENTS

This work was supported by Fund from the education department of Jiangxi province (GJJ210618), the National Natural Science Fund (52168049), the Joint Fund of NSFC-Railway Corporation for basic research of high-speed railway (Grant No. U1934208), National Science Fund for Distinguished Young Scholars (Grant No. 51725802), and Science and technology cooperation special project of Jiangxi Province (Grant No. 20212BDH81034).

REFERENCES

Guo Y H, Yan M, Song Q, Yuan G and Fu X B 2021 Influence of deep foundation pit excavation on adjacent existing high-pressure natural gas pipeline *Journal of Underground Space and Engineering.* **17**(S2):840–7.

Liu B, Fan X H, Wang Y Y, Zhang J B and Fan Z B 2021 Research progress of influence of foundation pit excavation on adjacent existing subway tunnel *Chinese Journal of Geotechnical Engineering.* **43**(zk2):253–8.

Lu T S, Liu S Y, Cai G J, Wu K and Xia W J 2021 Study on excavation disturbance and soil recompression deformation in soft soil layer *Rock and soil mechanics* **42**(02):565–73.

Shi C Z, Liu T, Le J, Tao W, Lu C D and Sun Y 2020 Comparison and analysis of excavation methods of one side adjacent to subway side *National Civil Engineering Construction Technology Exchange Con. Proc (Middle Volume) (Beijing)* pp 76–81.

Xie X Y, YU H J, Wang Q G and Wang C 2014 Research on deformation control technology of existing power tunnel caused by foundation pit excavation *Journal of Geotechnical Engineering.* **36**(1):88–97.

Zhang Z G, Zhang M X and Wang W D 2011 Two-stage analysis method for the influence of foundation pit excavation on adjacent subway tunnel *Rock and Soil Mechanics.* **32**(7):2085–92.

Zheng G 2022 Deformation control method and engineering application of foundation pit engineering in soft soil area *Chinese Journal of Geotechnical Engineering.* **44**(1):1–36.

Zhu G Q, Lu X, Si Y H and Ye J N 2021 Analysis of the influence of excavation sequence of adjacent foundation pit on deformation of existing tunnel *Journal of Ningbo University (Science and Technology).* **34**(05):89–94.

Analysis of full support structures of bifurcation tunnel based on finite element method

Yu Peng
Hubei Institute of Water Resources Survey and Design, Wuhan, China
School of Water Resources and Hydropower Engineering, Wuhan University, Wuhan, China

Li Ruiqing*, Yao Xiaomin*, Nian Fuxi & Zhang Bing
Hubei Institute of Water Resources Survey and Design, Wuhan, China

ABSTRACT: In this study, numerical simulations based on finite element software Ansys14.5 are carried out for the assessment of the full support structures of the bifurcation tunnel. The entire construction process including excavation, supporting, and the lining is simulated by the stratum structure method, using the "birth and death" element technique. Support structures including primary lining, system bolts, steel arch frames, and secondary lining are reasonably modeled. Both construction and operation periods are taken into account. Evaluations cover deformation and stress of surrounding rock and support structures, as well as reinforcement calculation of secondary lining. Based on calculation results, relevant suggestions are given for engineering.

1 INTRODUCTION

The water replenishment along the Yin-Jiang-Bu-Han project passes through Yichang, Jingmen and Xiangyang in Hubei, China. The project adopts pressurized gravity water conveyance mode and there are many bifurcation tunnels of large size. Support structure design for bifurcated tunnels is complicated, necessitating analogies with design codes and similar engineering projects. It is necessary to recheck the deformation and stress of bifurcation tunnels by numerical analysis method.

The numerical analysis method for rechecking and assessing support structure design in underground engineering is now widely utilized and acknowledged, considerably increasing the safety and dependability of underground engineering (Li 2008; Lin et al. 2013; Schweiger & Schuller 2003; Zhang et al. 2016). However, the construction process of underground engineering is fairly complex, there are numerous types of support structures, and non-convergence for plastic calculation is a relatively common issue in calculations. As a result, numerical analysis is simplified to some extent, and full support structures may not be fully reflected in some cases.

According to relevant provisions of the specification for hydraulic tunnels (China Water Power Press, 2016.) (SL 279-2016) and the design code for hydraulic concrete structures (China Water Power Press 2008.) (SL 191-2008), the finite element software Ansys14.5 is utilized to recheck and assess the full support structure design of bifurcation tunnels, including evaluating the deformation and stress of surrounding rock and support structures, and determining the reinforcement of secondary lining-based crack-limit calculation, so as to provide references for engineering design.

---

*Corresponding Authors: Lirq686@sohu.com and 316541582@qq.com

2 CALCULATION METHODS

2.1 Stratum structure method

In this study, the stratum structure method is used to simulate the entire excavation-supporting-lining process by using a "birth and death" element technique in Ansys14.5. The stratum structure method entails the rational simulation of stratum and supporting structures, as well as their interaction during construction.

2.2 Elastic-plastic constitutive relation

Herein, the plastic mechanical assumption is adopted and the elastic-plastic constitutive relationship can be written as (Crisfield 1991):

$$\{\sigma\} = [D_{ep}]\{\varepsilon\} \quad (1)$$

Where $\{\sigma\}$ and $\{\varepsilon\}$ are stress and strain of material, respectively. $[D_{ep}]$ represents elastic-plastic matrix.

The iterative formula of the balance equation is (Crisfield 1991):

$$\begin{cases} [K_0]\{\delta_1\} = \{F\} + \{R\}(i=1) \\ [K_0]\{\Delta\delta_i\} = \{F\} - \sum_e \int_{ve} [B]^T [D_{ep_{i-1}}](\{\varepsilon_i\} - \{\varepsilon_0\}) \\ [\delta_i] = \{\delta_{i-1}\} + \{\Delta\delta_i\}(i=2,3,4,\ldots) \end{cases} \quad (2)$$

Where $[K_0]$ is the initial stiffness matrix, $\{F\}$ is the external load, $\{R\}$ is the unbalanced force, $\{\Delta\delta_i\}$ represents the displacement increment between calculation steps.

For elastic-plastic calculation, it is required to solve the nonlinear equations (2) in order to obtain the displacement, strain, and stress under a certain load condition. In general, the incremental method, iterative method, and the hybrid method combining the above two methods are adopted. More efficient solvers, such as the wavefront technique, sparse matrix method, and PCG method (preprocessing conjugate gradient method), must be used for large-scale nonlinear calculations.

2.3 Yield criterion

The Drucker-Prager yield criterion is a smooth approximation of the Mohr-Coulomb yield criterion. It introduces an additional term into the von Mises yield criterion to account for the influence of hydrostatic pressure, namely:

$$F = \alpha I_1 + \sqrt{J_2} - k = 0 \quad (3)$$

Where α and k are material constants, depending on the choice of yield criterion. I1 and J2 are invariants of the stress tensor. In the case of the Drucker-Prager criterion, considering that the Drucker-Prager circle on each section coincides with the outer vertex of the Mohr-Coulomb hexagon, α and k can be calculated as follows (Shi 2011):

$$\alpha = \frac{\sin\phi}{\sqrt{3}(3-\sin\phi)}, \quad k = \frac{6c\cos\phi}{\sqrt{3}(3-\sin\phi)} \quad (4)$$

Where ϕ and c represent the internal friction angle and cohesion, respectively.

2.4 Stress release of the surrounding rock

In the construction of underground engineering, the release of in-situ stress of surrounding rock is not accomplished instantly. It is necessary to consider different support stages for load sharing. Furthermore, the current mainstream design concepts believe that surrounding rock has a self-supporting capacity to some extent.

The code for the design of road tunnel (China Communications Press 2004.) (JTG D70-2004) points out that when the stratum structure method is used for calculation, the stress of primary support can be controlled by setting the load release coefficient so that primary support and secondary lining can jointly bear the load according to a certain proportion.

According to the corresponding specification indicated above and the geological conditions of this project, the load sharing ratios of surrounding rock, initial support, and secondary lining of the typical calculation segment presented in this study are 70%, 15%, and 15%, respectively.

2.5 Safety assessment of surrounding rock and supporting structures

(1) Deformation evaluation for surrounding rock
Referring to reference (China Communications Press 2004.), the permitted deformation after primary support is completed should be determined according to tunnel size, geological condition, and buried depth. The diameter of the selected bifurcation tunnel is 7.0m, where the surrounding rock is class IV and the buried depth is 600 m. Thus, the horizontal deformation permitted is (0.8%~2.0%) ×B= (0.8%~2.0%) ×700=5.6~14.0cm, and the vertical deformation allowed is (0.8%~2.0%) ×H×0.5= (0.8%~2.0%) ×700× 0.5=2.8~7.0cm.

(2) Stress evaluation for primary support
The primary support mainly evaluates the stress of anchor rods and steel arch frames. It is believed that the stress of anchor rods and steel arch frames should not exceed the designed value of steel strength of 360MPa.

(3) Reinforcement for secondary lining
According to the design code for hydraulic concrete structures (China Water Power Press 2008.) (SL 191-2008), the designed tensile strength and compressive strength of C30 concrete are 1.43MPa and 14.3MPa. Reinforcements shall be arranged according to the tensile stress diagram approach when calculated tensile stress exceeds the designed strength.

3 CALCULATION MODEL

3.1 Calculation segment

Calculations in this study are performed for a typical bifurcation tunnel segment: circular main tunnel with a diameter of 7.0m is connected with branch tunnel of city gate section with a diameter of 7.0m, where the surrounding rock is class IV, buried depth is 600m and lateral pressure coefficient is 1.0.

3.2 Calculation conditions

Calculations are carried out for both construction and operation period. During the construction period, the deformation and stress of surrounding rock and primary support are evaluated; with respect to the operation period, it is mainly for evaluating the deformation and stress of secondary lining for reinforcement arrangement. The main loads include: self-weight, rock pressure, internal water pressure, external water pressure, and grouting pressure. Load combinations under different calculation conditions are listed in Table 1. The specific method for load application can refer to reference (Li 2008).

Table 1. Calculation conditions and load combinations.

Period	Self-weight	Rock pressure	Internal water pressure	External water pressure	Grouting pressure
Construction	✓	✓	—	✓	✓
Operation	✓	✓	✓	✓	—

3.3 Calculation parameters

(1) Geological parameters

The physical and mechanical characteristics of the surrounding rock are shown in Table 2:

Table 2. Physical and mechanical characteristics of the surrounding rock.

Classification	Density ρ(kg; m^3)	Elastic modulus E (GPa)	Poisson's ratio	Internal friction angle (°)	Cohesive force c (MPa)
IV	2350	3.0	0.35	35	0.5

(2) Calculation parameters of the support structure

The designed primary support structures mainly include: C20 shot concrete with a thickness of 20cm, system bolts at the crown arch and side wall with anchor rods Φ25 and spacing of 1.2×1.2m, depth into the rock of 6m, and I-18a steel arch frames with a spacing of 0.8m. The secondary lining is made of C30 concrete with a thickness of 50cm. Furthermore, filling grouting shall be carried out within the scope of the crown arch for densifying the contact between lining concrete and surrounding rock.

The main physical and mechanical parameters of support structures are shown in Table 3:

Table 3. Physical and mechanical parameters of support structures.

Support structures	Density ρ (kg; m^3)	Elastic modulus E (GPa)	Poisson's ratio	Internal friction angle (°)	Cohesive force c (MPa)
Primary lining (C25)	2500	28	0.167	59.6	1.35
Secondary lining (C30)	2500	30	0.167	60.6	1.62
System bolts and steel arch frames	7800	210	0.16	–	–

3.4 FEM model and boundary conditions

According to Saint Venart's principle, the computation domain should be three times larger than the bifurcation tunnel. Figure 1 depicts the finite element calculation model, with the z-axis horizontal and pointing to the left for positive, and the x-axis vertical and pointing upward for positive. A total number of 617598 solid185 elements with fine mesh are used to simulate surrounding rock, primary lining, and secondary lining. System bolts are represented via 4171 link180 elements, while steel arch frames are modeled by 1236 beam188 elements. The modeling of support structures is shown in Figure 2.

In calculations, the bottom is entirely restrained and lateral pressure is provided around the computation domain. The connection between system bolts and steel arch frames with surrounding rock is realized by displacement mapping coupling.

4 RESULTS ANALYSIS

Calculations are performed for a typical bifurcation tunnel segment with the surrounding rock of class IV and the buried depth of 600m. During the construction period, the external water head is set at 40m and the grouting pressure is 0.3MPa. As for the operation period, the internal water head is set as 80m. The surrounding rock's lateral pressure coefficient is set as 1.0, and load sharing ratios for surrounding rock, initial support, and secondary lining are 70%, 15%, and 15%, respectively.

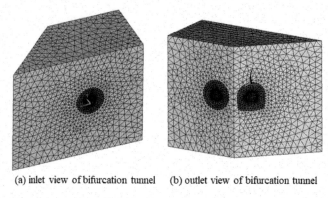

(a) inlet view of bifurcation tunnel (b) outlet view of bifurcation tunnel

Figure 1. The finite element calculation model.

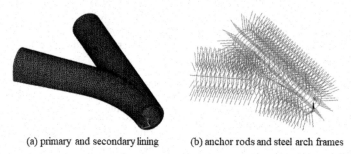

(a) primary and secondary lining (b) anchor rods and steel arch frames

Figure 2. The modeling of support structures.

4.1 *Surrounding rock*

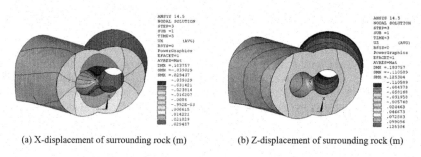

(a) X-displacement of surrounding rock (m) (b) Z-displacement of surrounding rock (m)

Figure 3. The displacement of surrounding rock (m).

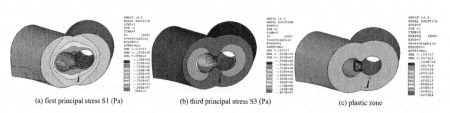

(a) first principal stress S1 (Pa) (b) third principal stress S3 (Pa) (c) plastic zone

Figure 4. Principal stress and plastic zone of surrounding rock.

Figures 3 and 4 respectively display the deformation and stress of surrounding rock after excavation and unloading. From calculation results, it can be found that in the case of high buried depth and lateral pressure, surrounding rock is squeezed and distorted inward. The maximum vertical downward displacement is 39 mm at the crown, while the maximum vertical upward displacement is 29 mm at the bottom. The transverse displacement around the excavation surface is roughly 20 mm. In general, the deformation of surrounding rock does not exceed the permitted displacements, which satisfies design requirements. The first principal stress of surrounding rock is generally negative. While the minimum third principal stress at the junction is around -89.8MPa, and plastic failure occurs. The plastic failure region does not exceed the depth of anchor rods. Attention should be paid to hazards such as rock falls, rock bursts, and rock instability during the construction period.

4.2 Primary support

(1) Stress analysis of system bolts

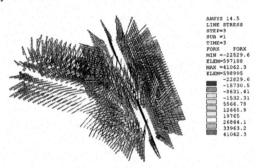

Figure 5. The axial force of anchor rods (N).

As illustrated in Figure 5, system bolts are mostly in tension at the inlet, outlet, and junction of the bifurcation tunnel, while some anchor rods are under compression due to extrusion of the surrounding rock. The overall axial force of anchor rods varies in a reasonable range, with the maximum tension of 41.1kN and the maximum compression of -22.8kN, which meets design requirements.

(2) Stress analysis of steel arch frames

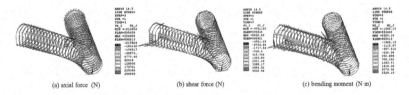

(a) axial force (N)   (b) shear force (N)   (c) bending moment (N·m)

Figure 6. Stress analysis of steel arch frames.

The bending moment, axial force, and shear force of steel arch frames are shown in Figure 6. Similarly, steel arch frames sustain obvious load at the inlet, outlet, and junction of the bifurcation tunnel due to the extrusion and induction of surrounding rock. At the intersection of the crown arch and side wall, the maximum bending moment is 2.5kNm. The distribution of axial and shear force is similar to that of bending moment, with the maximum axial force and shear force of 284.9kN and 5.4kN. Except for the stress concentration at the junction of the bifurcation tunnel, the overall support of steel arch frames meets the shear requirements.

(3) Deformation and stress analysis of primary lining

Figures 7 and 8 show the deformation and stress of the primary lining. Calculation results show that the deformation and stress of the primary lining are in harmony with that of the surrounding

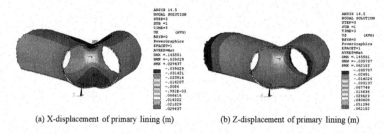

(a) X-displacement of primary lining (m)　　(b) Z-displacement of primary lining (m)

Figure 7.　The displacement of the primary lining (m).

(a) first principal stress S1 (Pa)　　(b) third principal stress S3 (Pa)　　(c) plastic zone

Figure 8.　Principal stress and plastic zone of the primary lining.

rock: the crown of the primary lining has the largest vertical downward displacement of 39 mm, and the bottom has the largest vertical upward displacement of 29 mm. Tensile stress exists at the crown and bottom of the junction, with the maximum first principal stress of 1.07MPa and the minimum third principal stress of -32.4MPa, and plastic failure occurs in a restricted range. It is critical to strengthen primary lining thickness and deformation monitoring at the junction of the bifurcation tunnel.

4.3　*Secondary lining*

(1) Construction period

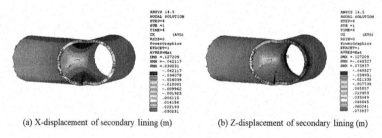

(a) X-displacement of secondary lining (m)　　(b) Z-displacement of secondary lining (m)

Figure 9.　The displacement of the secondary lining during construction (m).

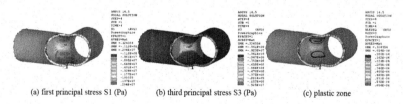

(a) first principal stress S1 (Pa)　　(b) third principal stress S3 (Pa)　　(c) plastic zone

Figure 10.　Principal stress and plastic zone of the secondary lining during construction.

The deformation and stress of secondary lining during the construction period are depicted in Figures 9 and 10. The vertical downward displacement at the crown arch is 42mm, while the vertical upward displacement at the bottom plate is 30mm. Due to the effects of rock pressure, external water pressure, and grouting pressure, the secondary lining is under compression and the first principal stress is negative in most locations. There exists a tensile stress zone at the crown arch and bottom plate of the junction, with a maximum tensile stress of 2.08MPa and a depth of less than 10cm. At the junction, the minimum third principal stress is -86.3MPa, and plastic failure occurs within a certain region. Similarly, enhancements of secondary lining and monitoring safety at the junction should be prioritized. The overall deformation of the secondary lining is minimal and conforms to design specifications.

(2) Operation period

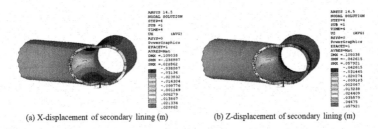

(a) X-displacement of secondary lining (m)   (b) Z-displacement of secondary lining (m)

Figure 11.　The displacement of the secondary lining during operation (m).

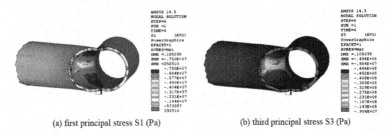

(a) first principal stress S1 (Pa)   (b) third principal stress S3 (Pa)

Figure 12.　Principal stress of the secondary lining during operation.

Figures 11 and 12 exhibit the deformation and stress of secondary lining during operation. Despite the internal water pressure, the secondary lining still shows an inward deformation under high rock pressure. The crown arch has the largest vertical downward displacement of 38mm, whereas the bottom plate has the largest vertical upward displacement of 28mm. The existence of internal water pressure offsets the compression deformation caused by rock pressure to some extent. As a result, the stress distribution of the secondary lining is more uniform. The maximum first principal stress is 0.29 MPa, while the minimum third principal stress is -49.6MPa, and no plastic failure occurs under this circumstance.

(3) Reinforcement calculation

It can be noticed that under the superposition of rock pressure, external water pressure, and grouting pressure during the construction period, the secondary lining has a certain region of tensile stress that exceeds the designed strength. While the internal water pressure during the operation period can partly counteract the extrusion of surrounding rock, the stress is relatively uniform. For deep tunnels with high lateral pressure, the construction period forms the control condition. In the region with low tensile stress, the secondary lining can be reinforced according to the minimum reinforcement ratio. The reinforcement to be configured according to the structure's minimum reinforcement ratio is $0.2\% \times 500 \times 1000 = 1000mm^2$ per unit width. For regions with high tensile stress, stress integral calculation is carried out using the tensile stress diagram approach:

the design value of tensile force sustained by reinforcements per unit width is 357kN, and the required reinforcements should be no less than $1.2 \times 357 \div 360 \times 1000 = 1488 mm^2$ per unit width. In general, it is suggested that the reinforcement amount should be no less than 1500mm^2 per unit width.

5 CONCLUSION

In this study, numerical calculations based on the finite element method are carried out for the assessment of the full support structures of the bifurcation tunnel. The whole construction process including excavation, supporting, and the lining is simulated by the stratum structure method, using the "birth and death" element technique in ansys14.5. Support structures including primary lining, system bolts, steel arch frames, and secondary lining are reasonably modeled. The main conclusions are as follows:

(1) Calculation results prove that the primary support design is basically reasonable. The deformation of the surrounding rock is minimal and stable and the plastic failure locally appears at the junction without further expansion. The stress of system bolts and anchor steel arch frames varies in a reasonable range.
(2) The deformation and stress of secondary lining show that: for the deep tunnel under high lateral pressure, the superposition of rock pressure with external water pressure and grouting pressure during construction behaves as the control condition. A certain range of plastic zone appears at the junction of the secondary lining. After the crack-limit calculation based on the tensile stress diagram approach, it is suggested that the reinforcement should be no less than 1500mm^2 per unit width.
(3) Calculation results indicate that the junction of the bifurcation tunnel is a major stress concentration region. The junction of the bifurcation tunnel shall be excavated to form a slow transition connection, and local support and thickness of the lining shall be strengthened. Furthermore, it is necessary to strengthen construction monitoring and pay attention to the hazards of collapse and rock bursts during construction.

ACKNOWLEDGMENTS

This study was financially supported by Key Scientific and Technological Projects of Hubei Provincial Water Resources Department under the grant of HBSLKY202119, Post-Doctoral Technology Innovation in Hubei Province.

REFERENCES

Code for design of road tunnel (JTG D70-2004). Beijing, China Communications Press, 2004.
Crisfield MA. *Nonlinear finite element analysis of solids and structures*. Volume 1: Essentials. 1991.
Design code for hydraulic concrete structures (SL 191-2008). Beijing, China Water Power Press, 2008.
Li W. *ANSYS case analysis of tunnel and underground engineering* (in Chinese). China Water Power Press, 2008.
Lin P, Zhou YN, Liu HY, et al. Reinforcement design and stability analysis for large-span tailrace bifurcated tunnels with irregular geometry, Tunnel. *Underg. Space Technol.*, 2013, 38(9): 189–204.
Schweiger HF, Schuller H. *A multilaminate model for finite element analysis of tunnel excavation*. Vienna, Springer, 2003.
Shi F. *Detailed explanation of secondary development and application examples of ANSYS* (in Chinese). China Water Power Press, 2011.
Specification for hydraulic tunnels (SL 279-2016). Beijing, China Water Power Press, 2016.
Zhang ZX, Liu C, Huang X, et al. Three-dimensional finite-element analysis on ground responses during twin-tunnel construction using the URUP method. *Tunnel. Underg. Space Technol.*, 2016, 58:133–146.

Study on strain of non-integrity prestressed concrete pipe pile in loess area

Wei Liu*, Guangli Sun* & Jianyang Fu*
School of Surveying and Exploration Engineering, Jilin University of Technology, Jilin Changchun, China

Meng Hu
School of Resources and Environmental Engineering, Jiangxi University of Science and Technology, Jiangxi, China

ABSTRACT: Prestressed concrete pipe piles (PHC) are widely used in the engineering construction industry because of their good construction characteristics. However, because of their different conditions in different regions, the change of the pile body stress with depth under different nonintegrity conditions makes a big difference. Demonstration and analysis are carried out using methods such as theoretical analysis, field tests, and numerical simulation. The results show that: 1) The impact of collapsible loess on the stress of the pile should be paid attention to during the construction of the loess area; 2) When the pile just enters the soil, the stress development trend of the soil is small; 3) When the pile enters A stress concentration phenomenon occurs in the middle of the pile body when it reaches 12 to 16m in the soil, and the stress increase trend is obvious. Therefore, special attention should be paid to the damage caused by the stress concentration phenomenon to the pile body during construction at this stage; 4) After the pile sinking is completed, there is a phenomenon of stress spreading at the top of the pile. According to the test results, the phenomena that should be paid attention to in the construction process are put forward to avoid damage to the shaped body.

1 INTRODUCTION

Prestressed concrete pipe piles are widely used in engineering projects due to their advantages such as their unique standardized production, high strength, high pile quality, and small environmental pollution. In recent years, with the vigorous development of the country and the promotion of prestressed concrete pipe piles, many scholars have conducted many research applications.

Y. Guo (Guo & Cui 2011), Y.m. Wang (Wang 2016) and P.sh. Xi (Xi et al. 2014) conducted a test of PHC pipe piles in the old vicious land area and a variety of methods such as finite element, respectively, and analytical research and mechanics; Z.Ding (Ding et al. 2021) conducted research on different test sites according to the unique characteristics of soft clay, such as low bearing capacity, and concluded that the application method suitable for pipe piles in soft soil areas. M.x.Tang (Tang et al. 2020), Z.h.Liu (2020) analyzed the load-bearing performance of different pipe types under sandy soil conditions and the applicable conditions of pipe piles in sandy soil layers by static load test and settlement analysis. J.g.Zheng (Liu et al. 2010; Liu & Zheng 2011) carried out the analysis and research of the axial force of the pile body, the lateral resistance of the pile, the bearing properties, and the internal force measurement of the prestressed pipe pile in the collapsible loess area.

---

*Corresponding Author: 1253009413@qq.com

At the same time, prestressed concrete pipe piles are also widely used in many aspects, Chen (Chen 2012) aiming at the frequent occurrence of natural disasters in the southern region, used the prestressed pipe piles in flood control embankments and studied their stability and stress characteristics. Zhou (2007) and Zhao (2008) studied the effects of soil squeeze on prestressed concrete pipe piles in deep foundation pits and the support and bolts of deep foundation pits respectively.

Although many domestic scholars have conducted various research on prestressed concrete pipe piles, they have also made significant research findings, and have also promoted the application and development of prestressed concrete pipe piles. However, few scholars in China have studied the joints of prestressed concrete pipe piles. Due to the actual needs of the project and the limitations of various conditions, the prestressed concrete pipe piles can't meet the actual needs of all projects in terms of pile length. Therefore, in engineering in the actual use process, the pile connection has to be used to meet the actual needs of the project. This paper mainly uses prestressed concrete to carry out the pile driving test analysis under the condition of the pile connection. The displacement of the node position changes with the depth of the pile body sinking, so the whole pile driving process fails due to the damage of the pile body node displacement in the actual application of the project later.

2 BASIC THEORETICAL ANALYSIS

Since the connection of the prestressed concrete pipe pile makes the pipe pile an incomplete body, the integrity of the pile body after the connection of the pile is first tested, and the low-strain reflected wave method is generally used (China Construction Industry Press 2003), By this method, the integrity of the pile body is detected, so as to check the welding quality of the connecting pile. Multisection pipe piles are spliced into a whole pile generally by end plate welding for connection. In manual welding, circular seam welding should be carried out symmetrically in more than three layers, and measures should be taken to reduce welding deformation. However, due to the difference in wave impedance at the flange, the nonholonomic pile vibration model is used in the numerical simulation analysis (Li et al. 2011).

It is assumed that the shaped body is a heterogeneous elastic system with variable cross-section. The action of the soil around the pile on the pile is simplified as a distributed elastic force proportional to the displacement and a distributed damping force proportional to the vibration velocity. At this time, the motion equation of the micro-section of the pile body under the action of the internal force of the pile body, the elastic force, and the damping force of the soil around the pile is given as follows (Chen et al. 2004)

$$F + \frac{\partial F}{\partial x}dx - F - c\frac{\partial u}{\partial t}dx - ku\,dx = \rho A\,dx\frac{\partial^2 u}{\partial t^2} \qquad (1)$$

In the formula, $F = AE\frac{\partial u}{\partial x}$ is the internal force of the pile;

$u = u(x, t)$ for the pile x in t particle displacement at the time;

c and k are the equivalent damping coefficient and equivalent stiffness coefficient of the soil surrounding the pile at unit depth, respectively.

$F = AE\frac{\partial u}{\partial x}$ and $u = u(x, t)$ are substituted into Formula (1), simplify to get

$$\frac{\partial}{\partial x}\left(AE\frac{\partial u}{\partial x}\right) - c\frac{\partial u}{\partial t} - ku = \rho A\frac{\partial^2 u}{\partial t^2} \qquad (2)$$

In the formula, $A = A(x)$ is the cross-sectional area of the pile;

$E = E(x)$ elastic modulus of the pile.

The boundary conditions at the bottom of the pile are

$$\left(AE\frac{\partial u}{\partial x}+c_b\frac{\partial u}{\partial t}+k_b u\right)\bigg|_{x=l}=0 \tag{3}$$

Pile top boundary condition is

$$AE\frac{\partial u}{\partial x}\bigg|_{x=0}=-P(t) \tag{4}$$

Taking the initial conditions, that is

$$u|_{t=0}=0,\ \frac{\partial u}{\partial t}\bigg|_{t=0}=0 \tag{5}$$

(2) In the formula, k and c are the soil density on the pile side ρ_s shear modulus G_s and radius γ_0;
(3) In the formula, k_b and c_b are the density of the soil under the pile ρ_b, shear modulus G_s and radius γ_0 determination;
(4) The exciting force in the formula $P(t)$ is determined by its impulse I and action time t_0;
Taking the first derivative of u in Formulas (2) to (5) with respect to time t, we get

$$\frac{\partial}{\partial x}\left(AE\frac{\partial v}{\partial x}\right)-c\frac{\partial v}{\partial t}-kv=\rho A\frac{\partial^2 u}{\partial t^2} \tag{6}$$

$$\left(AE\frac{\partial v}{\partial x}+c_b\frac{\partial v}{\partial t}+k_b v\right)\bigg|_{x=l}=0 \tag{7}$$

$$AE\frac{\partial v}{\partial x}\bigg|_{x=0}=-\frac{dp(t)}{dt} \tag{8}$$

$$v|_{t=0}=0,\ \frac{\partial v}{\partial t}\bigg|_{t=0}=0 \tag{9}$$

The v is the vibration speed of the Pile x at t moment, $v=v(x,t)$

3 OVERVIEW OF THE TEST SITE

The test site is located in Qing yang City, Gansu Province. The landform unit belongs to the Longdong Loess Plateau landform unit. The stratum distribution of the test site is relatively regular. The upper part is filled with soil, and the lower part is the Malan loess layer and the Lishi loess layer. Soil layer, the site stratum is evenly distributed. The main indicators of the soil layer of the test pile are shown in Table 1, and the pile end is located in the loess layer ⑤ of Lishi. According to the indoor test, the upper part of the Malan loess layer, paleosoil ① and Lishi loess ① layer in the proposed construction site of the test site are collapsible. The total amount of collapse is calculated to be 329.60~1100.30mm.

The piles used in the test site are both PHC 500 AB 125, the pile diameter of 500 mm, the pile length is 24m, and the pile is welded, the piles are from the top, and each single tube pile length is 8m long, respectively. The pipe pile bottom is closed by a cross-type steel pile tip, and static pressure is used.

Table 1. Index table of physical and mechanical properties of foundation soil.

Layer number	Soil layer name	Thickness h/m	Severe $\gamma/g \cdot cm^3$	Void ratio e	Compression modulus E_s/Mp_a
③	Malan loess	9.6	15.8	1.017	9.71
④	Ancient soil	3.5	16.6	0.946	10.11
⑤	Lishi loess	5.7	17.5	0.833	9.71
⑥	Ancient soil	4.8	18.3	0.763	9.78

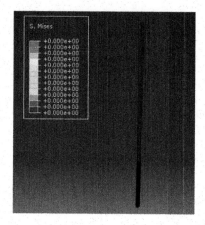

Figure 1. S_1 Working condition.

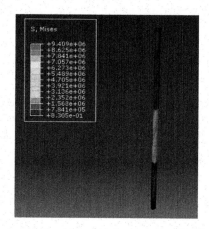

Figure 2. S_2 Working condition.

4 FINITE ELEMENT SIMULATION ANALYSIS

4.1 Analysis steps

Aiming at the data analysis of the above experimental site, the simulation analysis of the position of different nodes of prestressed concrete pipe piles by using the three-dimensional numerical simulation software ABAQUS. The experimental analysis steps are as follows:

(1) In order to meet the size effect of the model and consider the authenticity of the data, the total length of the pile is 24m, which is connected by three sections of pipe piles, the lengths of which are 8m, 20m and 24m respectively. $\sigma_2 \sigma_3 \sigma_4 \sigma_5$ and σ_6 represent the corresponding stress, where σ is the stress when no force is applied to the pile;
(2) The precast concrete pipe pile adopts the linear elastic model;
(3) The material of the concrete precast tubular pile is C80, the weight is 24 kN/m³, Young's modulus is $3.5 \cdot 10^3$ MPa, and the Poisson's ratio is 0.35;
(4) The applied force on the top of the pile is 3000KN;
(5) Pile driving will not be carried out when the bottom of the pile sinks into the bearing layer. The horizontal displacement and the influence of groundwater buoyancy on the pile will not be considered on the side of the pile. Only the reaction force of the soil and the friction of the side will be considered at the bottom of the pile resistance.

In the numerical simulation, each part corresponds to the dynamic change process of the pile body stress when the prestressed concrete pipe pile is not applied with force, and after the force is applied as the pile body enters the soil at different depths. These conditions are represented by S_1 to S_6, respectively.

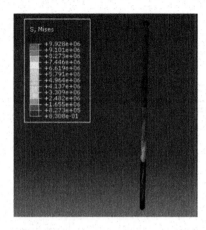
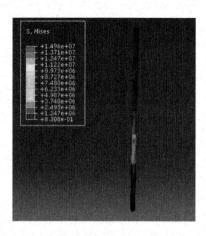

Figure 3. S₃ Working condition.   Figure 4. S₄ Working condition.

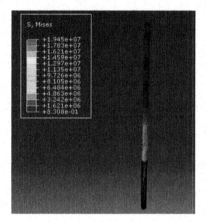
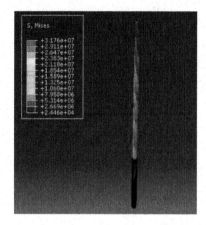

Figure 5. S₅ Working condition.   Figure 6. S₆ Working condition.

4.2 *Analysis of results*

Through numerical simulation and analysis of the cloud map, it can be clearly found that the stress of the prestressed concrete pile between 12 and 16 m is relatively concentrated, the stress change is relatively large, there is an obvious upward trend, and the stress at both ends of the pile is relatively scattered, especially in the pile body. At the top, the stress at the bottom of the pile is relatively large due to the diffusion of the stress to the bottom during the pile driving process, while in the middle of the pile, the reaction force at the bottom of the pile and the force exerted by the top of the pile makes the stress in the middle of the pile more concentrated, resulting in a larger change trend. Its specific analysis is given as follows:

(1) When the prestressed concrete pipe pile is sunk into the soil body for 8m, the changing trend of the pile body stress inside the soil body is about 4kN/M, and the overall stress change is not big;
(2) When the pipe pile body is sunk to 12m-16m, due to the influence of stress concentration, a large stress change occurs inside the pile body, and the stress is mainly concentrated at this position;

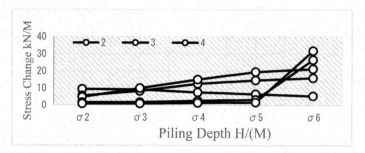

Figure 7. Stress change trend diagram of prestressed concrete pipe pile.

(3) When the pipe pile body sinks to 20m-24m, the stress at the bottom of the pile gradually decreases, and the stress at the top of the pile end increases suddenly due to the diffusion of stress, and presents a nonlinear change. The specific numerical changes are shown in Table 2.

Table 2. Stress changes of prestressed concrete pipe piles under different pile-driving depths.

Depth H(M)	Stress (kN/M) σ_2	σ_3	σ_4	σ_5	σ_6
8	9.41	5.50	4.70	1.56	0.78
12	9.10	8.27	9.93	1.65	0.82
16	7.48	12.47	14.96	2.49	1.25
20	6.48	14.59	19.85	3.24	1.60
24	5.31	15.89	21.18	26.47	31.76

5 CONCLUSION

In this paper, in the formation environment of the prestressed concrete pipe pile, in the formation environment of the loess test site, the on-site soil layer test, and the use of numerical simulations have analyzed the change in stress with the depth of the pile in the non-intact state. Impact, finally analyzed the cause of stress changes in piles according to the data of the numerical simulation, and the main conclusions have the following points:

(1) Under the condition of applying a certain force, the changing trend of the pile bottom stress shows a decreasing trend with the increase of the depth of the pile body, and the overall change shows a certain regularity;
(2) As the depth of the sink increases, the pile sinks into the soil, the pile presences a stress concentration, and the generation of this phenomenon is due to the application of force at the top of the pile body, due to the pile body. The reaction force generated at the bottom makes it stressful in this stage, and the increase in the increase in stress increase in the central portion of the pile body should be particularly paid special attention to the actual engineering application, so as to avoid the inclination of the piles and piles;
(3) In the range of 20–24m from the top of the pile body, since the bottom of the pile body has entered the bearing layer, the stress change of the pile body has been reduced. A part of the stress in the body suddenly and sharply increases, resulting in certain damage to the ring;
(4) Based on the application of prestressed concrete pipe piles in the loess area, theoretical analysis, field soil test, and numerical simulation are carried out according to some unique characteristics

of the loess area. Changes resulting from increasing pile depths are discussed and points to be noted in different pile-sinking processes are presented.

Finally, the basis of the basics is applicable to the work in similar areas, and further research discussions should still be conducted in terms of soil layer changes and the application force.

REFERENCES

F. Liu and J.g. Zheng. Experimental study on PHC pile of moisture loess field [J]. *Journal of Geotechnical Engineering*, 2011,33 (S2): 362–366. http://mtw.so/5GmNkk

J.f. Zhou. Application of PHC pipe pile in deep foundation pit project [D]. *Wuhan University of Technology*, 2007. http://mtw.so/6hdJRp

JGJ 106-2003 Construction patch testing technical specification [S]. *Beijing: China Construction Industry Press*, 2003. http://mtw.so/5Vpgow

M.x. Tang, H.s. Hu, C.l. Liu, Y.p. Yue, Z.k. Hou and H. Chen. Comparative experimental study on bearing performance of different pipe pile types in sandy soil[J/OL]. *Rock and Soil Mechanics*, 2020(S2):1–9[2021-10-12]. http://mtw.so/5y6q3O

P.s. Xi, X.k. Sun, X.t. Zhang and B. Liu. Numerical Analysis of the horizontal bearing force in the PHC pipe pile in the old clay area [J]. *Journal of Anhui Institute of Architecture (Natural Science Edition)*, 2014, 22 (03): 47–51. http://mtw.so/6oJTk4

X. Zhao. Research on engineering application of PHC pipe piles in deep foundation pit support [D]. *Xi'an University of Architecture and Technology*, 2008. http://mtw.so/5GmQa8

Y. Guo and W. Cui. Experimental study on the application of PHC pipe piles in old clay area[J]. *Chinese Journal of Geotechnical Engineering*, 2011, 33(S2):108–115. http://mtw.so/5y6lqI

Y.m. Chen. Application and research of PHC pipe pile in Wenzhou flood control dio project [D]. *Zhejiang University*, 2012. http://mtw.so/62RhmB

Y.m. Wang. The carrying characteristics of PHC pipes in Hefei Laojiao area [J]. *Anhui Geology*, 2016, 26 (03): 225–227. http://mtw.so/6hdG9T

Y.q. Chen, Z.g. Ren and D.j. Liu. Simulation calculation of transient longitudinal vibration of nonholonomic piles[J]. *Journal of Hefei University of Technology(Natural Science Edition)*, 2004(10):1210–1214. http://mtw.so/5GmQro

Z. Ding, X. Zhang, F.y. Liang, D.j. Cheng and L.q. Wang. Research and prospect of soft soil silk excavation on neighboring tunneling [J]. *Journal of China Road*, 2021, 34 (03): 50–70. http://mtw.so/5y6pWI

Z.g. Li, Z.b. Ke, D.j. Liu, Z.t. Lu, Y. Guo. Research on the quality of PHC pipe pile joints judged by the low-strain reflected wave method[J]. *Chinese Journal of Geotechnical Engineering*, 2011, 33(S2):209–212. http://mtw.so/5VpgKC

Z.h. Liu, J.g. Zheng, Y.t. Yu. Experimental study on vertical bearing properties of PHC piles in collapsible loess sites[J]. *Chinese Journal of Geotechnical Engineering*, 2010, 32(S2):111–114. http://mtw.so/5VpdDy

Z.h. Liu. Application and research of PHC pipe pile composite foundation with thin sand level [D]. *Shenyang Building University*, 2020. http://mtw.so/6hdGBD

Study on the thermal temperature field of hydration of prefabricated box girders at an early age and its effects

Li Yan & Gu Chuanyao*
University of Jinan, Shandong, Jinan, China

Wang Youzhi
Shandong University, Shandong, Jinan, China

ABSTRACT: Based on the Jining section of Jiwei High-speed Expressway, finite element software was used to analyze the temperature field of the box girder in the early stage, and the temperature field distribution of the box girder bearing section at the key time node is obtained. The early hydration heat of concrete was monitored for 8 consecutive days during the process of pouring the box girder, and the temperature changes of the top web and bottom plate were analyzed in combination with the numerical simulation results. The present results showed that after about 40 hours, the temperature reached the peak value, and the concrete temperature rose fastest at the top-web junction at this time. In the cement hydration and heating stage, the heating rate of the concrete was greatly accelerated and formed a temperature difference from the atmospheric temperature. And the heat diffused from the inside to the atmosphere along the beam thickness direction, and the temperature was highest at the top web node of the box girder, resulting in temperature cracks. The maximum tensile stress of 4.85 MPa occurred during the temperature rise phase from 20h-30h, and the maximum tensile stress of 10.55MPa appeared during the temperature drop stage. The stress change was consistent with the temperature difference and had an insignificant relationship with the absolute value of the temperature. Our result demonstrated that tensioning the prestressed steel bundles of the box girder could effectively reduce the tensile strain at the junction of the concrete top web, and effectively reduced the cracking risk of the box girder.

1 INTRODUCTION

As reinforced concrete is increasingly used in bridge engineering, more and more problems have gradually been exposed. The concrete produced a large amount of hydration heat due to cement hydration, and a temperature gradient was generated in the process of heat transfer inside the box girder, which increased as it is closer to the surface of the box girder, thus leading to the generation of temperature cracks. This became the most common research topic in the engineering community, and it was also an urgent problem to be solved in engineering and academia (Zhong & Zhu 2021). The cracks would occur in the structure, when the temperature stress generated by the hydration heat rise effect exceeded the allowable tensile stress of concrete, which would have an adverse effect on the safety and durability of the structure, or cause the entire structure to collapse (Wang 2021; Wu 2020). Therefore, temperature control measures should be taken when pouring concrete box girders to avoid serious damage to the quality of the box girders.

For the study of hydration heat temperature and stress, many scholars at home and abroad first started from the study of large-volume concrete, especially for the temperature stress and crack resistance of concrete dams (Han 2020; Ozylidirim & Gormez 1996; Zia & Caner 1993). However,

---

*Corresponding Author: cea_gucy@ujn.edu.cn

for the research on the distribution law of the hydration heat temperature field of the box girder, domestic scholars generally refer to the empirical formula of mass concrete. And the research on the early temperature field and temperature crack cracking mechanism of the concrete box girder is still in the imperfect stage (Wang et al. 2020; Yao 2020; Zeng 2019). Yang Menggang et al. (2001) conducted a detailed study on the heat release phenomenon of concrete hydration heat and the distribution law of temperature field through on-site data collection, and according to the research results, reasonable suggestions for reducing the thermal temperature of hydration were given. But there was no systematic study of the concrete temperature field and stress field distribution.

Compared with ordinary large-volume concrete, the concrete box girder section will be more complex, there are many factors affecting the hydration heat (Myers & Carrasquillo 2000; Nie 2013; Xiang & Yang 2003), and the boundary conditions are complicated. It is difficult to accurately predict the temperature field change law of the box girder section through the relevant calculation parameters of the concrete (Chen et al. 2021; Xiang et al. 2003; Yang et al. 2022; Zhao et al. 2004). In this present study, the method of mutual confirmation of numerical simulation and measured data were adopted. and a large amount of monitoring data was obtained by burying temperature sensors in the section of the box girder. The model parameters were constantly adjusted through the actual measurement data compared with the simulation so that the measured data and simulation data were more appropriate. Our results provided theoretical data for similar projects, and the layout of monitoring points could be reduced in the future, to save costs.

2 NUMERICAL SIMULATION AND FIELD TESTING

2.1 Project overview

The Jining section of the Jiwei High-speed Expressway is equipped with 4 small box girders with C50 concrete. The specifications of each box girder are: the beam height is 1.60m, the middle beam width is 2.40m, the side beam width is 2.850m, the top plate thickness is 0.18m, the thickness of the cross-middle section bottom plate is 0.18m, the thickness of the bottom plate of the web thickening section is 0.30m, the thickness of the web is 0.30m, the thickness of the web is 0.30m, and the thickness of the horizontal partition is 0.20m. The support section of the box girder was shown in Figure 1.

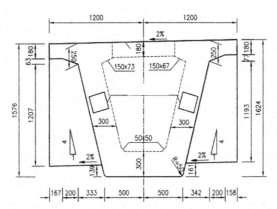

Figure 1. Cross-sectional view of the box girder support.

2.2 Calculation model and parameter settings

The thermal temperature field of hydration of concrete box girder is essentially a three-dimensional unsteady temperature field problem, and it is practical to use a three-dimensional finite element solid model to simulate and calculate (ignoring the longitudinal temperature gradient). In our research, a beam section with a cross-section of 2 meters at the support of the box girder was selected for finite element analysis. The support section was divided into a total of 1680 nodes and 1064 units. The time-dependent properties and thermal coefficients of the material were especially concerning the definition of the material. The set boundaries included a foundation fixed boundary, symmetric boundary, convective boundary, and fixed temperature. The load includes a heat source and tube cooling. We found the heat source in the heat of hydration module in the load, enter the heat source function and assign the heat source. We defined a fixed temperature boundary which was constant and defined the heat exchanged with the outside at each moment by convection coefficient. The input part of the DX and DY symmetric boundary was the setting of the adiabatic boundary. When no data associated with external heat transfer was input, it was automatically considered as an adiabatic boundary, and heat transfer was only performed inside the unit, not externally dissipated. The finite element model was shown in Figure 2.

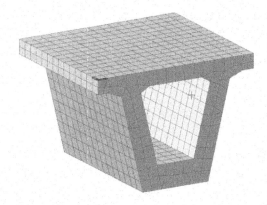

Figure 2. Box girder support cross-section meshing model.

The main calculation parameters of the finite element of the hydration thermal temperature field of the box girder were shown in Table 1.

Table 1. Main finite element calculation parameters.

Concrete model		C50
Specific heat (kcal/kg°C)		0.225
Specific gravity (kgf/m^3)		2470
Thermal conductivity (kcal/m hr°C)		2.62
Coefficient of thermal expansion		$1.0*10^{-5}$
Cement content per unit volume (kgf/cm^3)		476
Poisson's ratio		0.2
28-day compressive strength (MPa)		60
Maximum adiabatic temperature rise (K)		65.36
Atmospheric temperature (°C)		20
Pouring temperature (°C)		25
Convection coefficient (kcal/m^2 hr °C)	Cover the protective layer surface	13
	Steel formwork	14

2.3 Field trials

The arrangement of measuring points in the test section should follow the principle of symmetry to ensure the accuracy of the test. On the symmetrical section, three points (measuring points 1, 2 and 3) were evenly arranged along the axis from inside to outside. On the symmetrical section of the bottom plate of the box girder, three points (measuring points 4, 5, and 6) were evenly arranged from the inside to the outside along the axis. Another three measuring points (measuring points 7, 8, and 9) were evenly arranged in the middle of the left web of the box girder from inside to outside. Three measuring points (measuring points 12, 11 and 10) were evenly arranged from the inside to the outside at the junction of the top web at the upper left of the box girder. A schematic diagram of the measurement point distribution was shown in Figure 3.

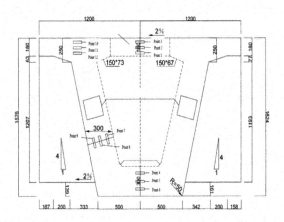

Figure 3. Schematic diagram of the cross-sectional measurement point of the box girder support.

XHX-21x buried strain gauge was selected for this project, which was widely used in bridges, construction, railways, hydropower, dams, and other engineering fields to measure the surface and internal strain temperature of various concrete structures, which could fully understand the force status of the measured components.

Technical parameters: Strain range ± 2000 με
Sensitivity: 1 με (0.1Hz).
Temperature measurement range: −20°C–125°C
Temperature measurement sensitivity 0.25°C Accuracy: ±0.5°C

3 RESULTS AND ANALYSIS

3.1 Comparison of results

In order to visually analyze the internal and surface temperature changes of concrete box girders over time, 4 key nodes were selected from each representative section for analysis, as shown in Table 2.

Table 2. Selected node numbers and locations.

Serial number	The node number	Place	Serial number	The node number	Place
1	285	The box girder roof was centered on the symmetrical axis	8	416	The middle of the left web of the box girder
2	377	The bottom plate of the box girder was symmetrical in the middle of the axis	11	547	The apical web is in the middle of the junction

The model calculated data and the measured data of the field test of the representative four nodes were summarized to calculate the deviation between the model and the actual test data, and the deviation value was: [(measured value - calculated value) ÷ measured value]×100%. The detailed data was shown in Table 3.

Table 3. Comparison between the measured temperature and the calculated temperature of some measured points.

Node		Time (h) 10	30	45	50	96	128	160	192
285	Measured values	37.00	41.75	42.50	45.00	43.00	41.75	37.75	34.75
	Calculate the value	37.18	42.37	43.36	43.31	41.15	39.88	38.71	38.00
	Deviation (%)	−0.4	−1.4	−2.0	3.7	4.3	4.4	−2.5	−9.3
377	Measured values	34.00	36.00	38.50	42.75	41.75	41.00	40.75	35.25
	Calculate the value	35.74	39.87	41.90	44.34	41.62	39.12	38.46	38.56
	Deviation (%)	−5.1	−9.7	−8.8	−3.7	0.3	4.5	5.6	−9.3
416	Measured values	38.00	39.00	42.75	43.25	41.25	40.00	42.50	38.00
	Calculate the value	35.85	41.75	44.24	44.69	42.00	39.50	39.66	39.92
	Deviation (%)	5.6	−7.0	−3.4	−3.3	−1.8	1.2	6.6	−5.0
	Measured values	39.50	43.50	44.00	48.75	46.75	44.25	43.75	42.25
	Calculate the value	37.68	43.62	45.81	46.50	43.25	42.13	40.63	40.34
	Deviation (%)	4.6	−0.2	−4.1	4.6	7.4	4.7	7.1	4.5

From the analysis in Table 3, it could be seen that:

(1) The deviation between the measured temperature of each internal measurement point and the calculated temperature was within 10%, which showed that the finite element model established by this calculation method could well simulate the hydration heat temperature field of a concrete box girder.

(2) The calculation and measured value of node 547 was relatively high, which was attributed to the fact that the node was located at the junction of the top plate and the web of the box girder and the middle part of the bottom plate, which had a large amount of cement pouring in the prefabrication process, the outer edge of the close box girder was farther away, a large amount of hydration heat gathered was not easy to dissipate. The temperature of node 285 was low because the section of the box girder in this position was relatively thin, the outer edge of the box girder was closer, and it was easy to exchange heat with the external connection.

3.2 Temperature field analysis

Hydration heat was generated in the first three days, so special attention should be paid to the study of the distribution of hydration heat in prestressed concrete box girders at an early age. We intended to take the thermal temperature field of hydration of the box girder within a total period of 8 days for 192h for finite element simulation analysis. After the model operation was completed, the calculation results of the thermal temperature field of the hydration of the box girder at different times could be obtained. The temperature field cloud diagram of the key time node of the box girder support section was shown in Figure 4.

Because there were many measuring points, in order to facilitate the analysis of the temperature, 12 measuring points were divided into four areas: the top plate of the box girder, the box girder web, the junction of the bottom plate, and the top box girder web. The measurement points of each area were divided into three cross-sections: the inner area, the middle of the area, and the surface of the area, which were denoted as JM1, JM2, and JM3 for convenience. Figure 5 showed the variation of hydration heat temperature with age at each monitoring section of the box girder.

We can collect the following points from Figures 4 and 5:

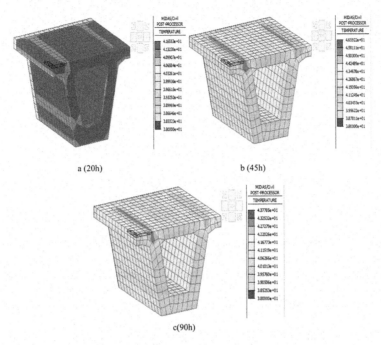

Figure 4. Partial-time box girder support cross-section temperature field cloud diagram.

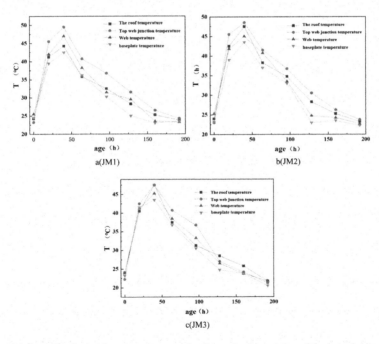

Figure 5. Variation of hydration heat temperature of each monitoring section of the box girder with age.

(1) The hydration heat temperature of each section of the box beam was generally consistent with the aging period. The change process was basically to heat up rapidly first, reaching the highest point at 40h, and then the temperature dropped to equilibrium, which was generally consistent with

217

the room temperature. From the graph, it could be seen that the fastest rate of hydration reaction of cement occurred during the temperature rise stage.

(2) The temperature of the concrete at the junction of the top web plate rises the fastest, and this position was the temperature peak compared with other locations in the same section. The temperature peak at the junction of the top web plates of all three sections was around 50°C. There was a temperature gradient at this position, which was easy to produce large temperature stress, resulting in the generation of temperature cracks, which was one of the key points in box girder engineering.

(3) Due to its proximity to the junction of the roof and the relatively small amount of concrete pouring, the position of the roof plate of the box girder was obviously affected by the ambient temperature, and the temperature of the top plate position showed a rapid temperature and cooling trend.

3.3 Stress field analysis

The key time node stress field cloud diagram of the box girder support section was shown in Figure 6. The monitoring results of each section were taken as the representative values of the early age strain of the concrete in this area, and the prestressed steel bundle tension was stretched when the maintenance age reached 80h, and the variation of the strain of each monitored section of the box girder with age was shown in Figure 7.

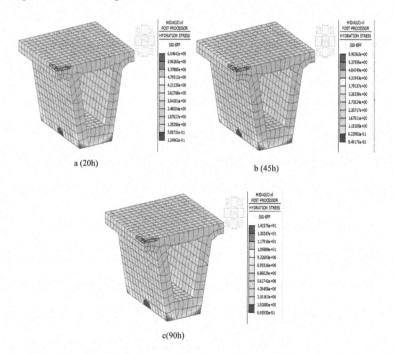

Figure 6. Partial-time box girder support cross-section stress field cloud diagram.

We can collect following points from Figures 6 and 7:
The maximum tensile stress 4.85MPa appeared in the temperature rise stage from 0h to 30h. And the maximum tensile stress that appeared in the temperature drop stage was 10.55MPa. The generation of concrete cracks mainly depended on the temperature stress caused by the temperature difference between the inside and outside. The stress change was consistent with the temperature difference and had little to do with the absolute value of the temperature.

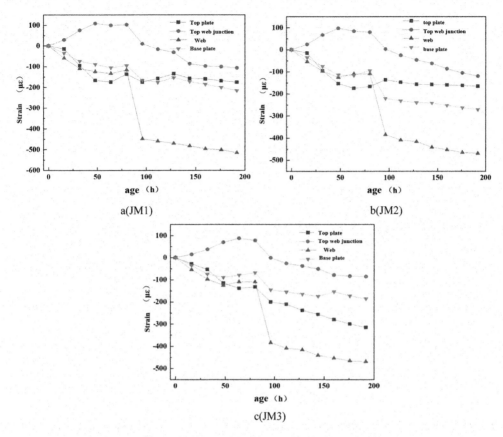

Figure 7. Variation of the strain of each monitoring section of the box girder with age.

(2) Before the prestress tension, each corresponding position of each section was basically in a compressive state, and the strain of the concrete decreased first and then increased with the growth of aging. After the prestressed tension, the strain of the concrete in the four monitoring areas of each section was first significantly reduced and then stabilized. The prestressed tension had a significant influence on the strain of the beam concrete. The measuring points 10, 11, and 12 located at the junction of the top web were in the tensile state in the early stage of concrete pouring. But under the influence of the prestressed steel beam, the tensile strain at the junction of the top web plate was significantly reduced, which greatly reduced the possibility of cracking.

4 CONCLUSION

By analyzing the monitoring results of the hydrothermal temperature field and the strain field of the prefabricated box girder in the pouring process in the early stage, the following main conclusions were drawn:

(1) Compared with other locations in the same section, the temperature rises fastest at the junction of the top of the box girder, and the peak value was also the highest. Therefore, the temperature at the position was much greater than the atmospheric temperature, forming the temperature difference with the atmospheric temperature, where the heat transfer ability was poor and convenient to produce temperature cracks.

(2) The prestressed tension had a significant impact on the strain of the beam concrete. Affected by the prestressed steel bundles, the tensile strain at the junction of the top web was significantly reduced, which greatly reduced the possibility of cracking.

REFERENCES

Chen Zonghui, Wu Di, Dong Xiaobing. Analysis of the causes of bottom plate cracking during the construction process of prestressed concrete continuous box girder bridge[J]. *World Bridge*, 2021, 49(03):103–107.

Han Jiahao. *Study on the force performance of wet joints of simple branched continuous girder bridges under complex constraints*[D]. Shandong University, 2020. DOI:10.27272/d.cnki.gshdu.2020.001327.

Myers J J, Carrasquillo R L. Influence of Hydration Temperature on Durability and Mechanical Property Performance of Prestressed and Precast High-Performance Concrete Beams[C], Fifth International Bridge Engineering Conference, *Journal of the Transportation Research Board*, No. 1696, 2000(1):131–142.

Nie Yudong. *The temperature field and temperature effect analysis of large-span concrete box girder bridge in the cold area*[D]. Harbin Institute of Technology, 2013.

Ozylidirim C, Gormez J R. Design of High-Performance Concrete Mixtures and Test Beams for a Bridge in Virginia[C]. *Virginia Transportation Research Council RePort* No. FHWA/VA-96R27, 1996.

Wang Fuxing. Monitoring and analysis of heat temperature and strain of hydration of asymmetrical prestressed concrete box girder[J]. *Railway Construction*, 2021, 61(06):41–43.

Wang Xiangguo, Peng Yifan, Yang Menggang. Research on hydration heat of mass concrete at arch support and temperature control measures for a high-speed railway tied-arch bridge[J]. *Journal of Railway Science and Engineering*, 2020, 17(03):549–555. DOI:10.19713/j.cnki.43-1423/u.T20190605.

Wu Guixian. Study on temperature characteristics of concrete box girder based on field test[J]. *Gansu Science and Technology*, 2020, 36(11):93–96.

Xiang Min, Liao Likun, Wang Xinmin. Analysis of thermal temperature field of hydration of concrete box beam[J]. *Journal of Shijiazhuang Railway Institute*, 2003(03):82–86. DOI:10.13319/j.cnki.sjztddxxbzrb.2003.03.023.

Xiang Min, Yang Congjuan. Study on the exothermic law of hydration of high-strength concrete[J]. *Concrete*, 2003(03):27–29+43.

Yang Menggang, Wen Yongkui, Chen Zhengqing. The hydration temperature monitor and the cracking control of concrete box girder[J]. *Journal of Railway Science and Engineering*, 2001(03):40–44. DOI:10.19713/j.cnki.43-1423/u.2001.03.010.

Yang Zeying, Zhao Fengjin, Zhang Peng, Liu Yangyudong, Sun Yinglin. Analysis of out-of-plane deformation of thin-walled closed-mouth curve box girder under temperature gradient[J/OL]. *Journal of Shandong University* (Engineering Edition), 2022, 52(01):47–57.

Yao Rui. *Study on the thermal temperature effect of hydration of large-volume concrete on bridge structure pile*[D]. Chang'an University, 2020.

Zeng Chengyu. *Research on the application of crack prevention and control of large-volume concrete in practical engineering*[D]. Nanchang University, 2019.

Zhao Wangda, Duan Fangying, Xu Zhisheng. Development of concrete temperature stress monitoring system in railway mega bridge construction[J]. *China Railway*, 2004(11):25–27+10. DOI:10.19549/j.issn.1001-683x.2004.11.006.

Zhong Yongxin, Zhu Qimin. Analysis of shrinkage changes and prestress loss during prefabricated assembly of section beam[J]. *Sino-Foreign Highway*, 2021, 41(01):126–132. DOI:10.14048/j.issn.1671-2579.2021.01.026.

Zia P, Caner P. Cracking in Large-Sized Long-SPan Prestressed Concrete AASHTO Giders[C]. Final RePort-Center for Transportation Engineering Studies, North Carelina State University, RoPort No. FHWA/NC/94-003,1993.

Crack detection of T700 composite specimen based on the natural frequency

Hao Yang, Yu'e Yang* & Cheng Liu
College of Mechanical Engineering, Jinan University, Jinan, Shandong, China

ABSTRACT: Since the occurrence of cracks will largely weaken the stiffness of the composite structure itself, it is easy to cause major accidents. Therefore, in order to improve the service life of the composite material and ensure the safety of people's life and property, it is particularly important to seek an accurate and efficient quantitative identification method for the location of composite cracks. In this paper, the second-order response surface model and MIGA algorithm are used to optimize the simulation model of T700 carbon fiber epoxy resin matrix composites to accurately grasp the mechanical properties of the specimens in the actual working conditions. Secondly, the variation law of natural frequency and other parameters affected by composite cracks is analyzed by numerical analysis and image processing, and then the distribution characteristics of natural frequency and other parameters are established. Based on this feature, the influence of crack depth on the accuracy of crack location and identification is discussed. Finally, through the quantitative analysis of the influencing factors of composite crack identification, the quantitative prediction equation of crack location is established. The results show that the average error between the predicted value and the measured value of the optimized model decreases from 8.63% to 3.53%, which effectively improves the accuracy of the simulation model. The natural frequency and other parameters have a good characterization relationship with the development of cracks, which can be used as a sensitive characteristic index of crack extension trend. The cracks appearing at the symmetrical position of the specimen have the same distribution characteristics of the natural frequency change ratio of any two orders. The square of the natural frequency change decreases monotonously with the increase of the crack depth. The method based on the numerical solution of the prediction equation narrows the range of sample residuals and significantly improves the identification accuracy of composite crack defects. This study improves the crack location quantification.

1 INTRODUCTION

These guidelines, written in the style of submission to *J. Phys.: Conf. Ser.*, show the best layout for your paper using Microsoft Word. If you don't wish to use the Word template provided, please use the following page setup measurements. Carbon fiber composites are widely used in various industries with their excellent material properties, especially in the aerospace and rail transportation industries, and have gradually replaced many traditional structures (Sannamani & Tallman 2021). Due to the dispersion of material properties, manufacturing process and other aspects of the impact, composite materials in the use process will always be affected by various factors, resulting in the emergence of cracks (Bolf et al. 2020), and the emergence of cracks in a large extent will weaken the stiffness of the structure itself, resulting in major accidents, so it is necessary to find an effective method to detect cracks. Since it is relatively easy to obtain the natural frequency, the damage detection method based on the frequency response function is the most common damage detection

---

*Corresponding Author: me_yangye@ujn.edu.cn

and identification method, and it can display the overall vibration characteristics and meet the requirements of global damage detection (Khan et al. 2020; Valašková Veronika & Melcer Jozef 2022; Abedin Mohammad used the frequency change before and after the damage to detect the fracture damage of the bridge and proved the effectiveness(Abedin & Mehrabi 2021) of this method for the damage identification of component structure. Cawley estimated the structural damage by using the measured natural frequency change and derived the functional relationship(Cawley & Adams 1979) between any two-order frequency change ratio before and after the damage and the damage location. Hearn obtained the conclusion that the square ratio of the natural frequency change before and after the damage of any two-order modal structure can be used to identify the damage location of the structure by deducing the characterization relationship between the square of the frequency change of different evolution orders and the damage (Hearn & Testa 1991).

In this paper, the optimized simulation model is used to identify and detect the crack of T700 carbon fiber epoxy resin matrix composite specimens, and the mapping relationship between crack damage and natural frequency change is described. Combined with numerical analysis and image processing, the relationship between the square ratio of any two-order natural frequency change and the crack location and the quantitative relationship between the square of natural frequency change and the crack depth is obtained by the curve fitting method.

2 THEORETICAL MODEL (HEARN & TESTA 1991)

Usually, the single plate composite structure system under free suspension is excited. Due to the perturbation theory, the composite material produces a variety of vibration modes (including moving and rotating along x, y, and z directions). Under the condition of ignoring the damping effect, the vibration characteristic equation is:

$$(K - \omega^2 M)\varphi = 0 \tag{1}$$

M is a mass matrix; K is stiffness matrix; ω^2 is the inherent frequency the square of the rate; φ is the regularized vibration mode.

When cracks in the structure will cause minor changes in the stiffness and mass of the composite material, it is represented by ΔK and ΔM. It can be obtained from Equation (1):

$$[(K + \Delta K) - (\omega^2 + \Delta \omega^2)(M + \Delta M)](\varphi + \Delta \varphi) = 0 \tag{2}$$

Since the change of mass and vibration mode is very small and can be ignored, Equation (2) can be simplified as the absolute value of the ratio of any first-order natural frequency change to the first-order natural frequency change, so as to characterize the crack location of composite materials. The calculation formula is as follows:

$$\left|\frac{\Delta \omega_i}{\Delta \omega_1}\right| = \sqrt{\frac{\frac{\varepsilon_n^T(\varphi_i) K_n \varepsilon_n(\varphi_i)}{\varphi_i^T M \varphi_i}}{\frac{\varepsilon_n^T(\varphi_1) K_n \varepsilon_n(\varphi_1)}{\varphi_1^T M \varphi_1}}} \tag{3}$$

In the formula, $\varepsilon_n(\varphi_i)$ represents the deformation of the n position calculated by the i-mode φ_i.

And because the square $\Delta \omega_i^2$ of natural frequency changes is a function that can define the location n and depth of cracks α_n, namely:

$$\Delta \omega_i^2 = \alpha_n \frac{\varepsilon_n^T(\varphi_i) K_n \varepsilon_n(\varphi_i)}{\varphi_i^T M \varphi_i} \tag{4}$$

After determining the location of the crack, for any first order natural frequency, $= \frac{\varepsilon_n^T(\varphi_i)K_n\varepsilon_n(\varphi_i)}{\varphi_i^T M \varphi_i}$ is a certain value, the degree of crack is

$$\alpha_n = \frac{\Delta\omega_i^2}{k} \qquad (5)$$

From the above, it can be concluded that the crack depth of composite materials can pass through The square of natural frequency change is obtained.

3 FINITE ELEMENT SIMULATION ANALYSIS

The finite element simulation software ABAQUS2016 is used to model and analyze the structure of CFRP veneer. The 3D solid model of the CFRP veneer is established by the solid element, and the 16-layer CFRP veneer processed by T700 epoxy fabric prepreg is simulated. The stacking sequence is [45 / 0 / -45 / 90] 2 s. The material parameters provided by the manufacturer are shown in table 1. In order to improve the analysis accuracy and convergence speed, the global seed size is set to 10 mm, and the single CFRP plate structure is divided into 110 elements and 276 nodes. The element is divided into 8-node linear hexahedron elements of C3D8R by structural mesh technology. The finite element model of the CFRP plate is shown in Figure 1.

Table 1. CFRP material parameters.

ρ (kg/m^{-3})	E_1 (GPa)	$E_2 \approx E_3$ (GPa)	$v_{12} \approx v_{13}$	v_{23}	$G_{12} \approx G_{13}$ (GPa)	G_{23} (GPa)
1600	67	63	0.06	0.45	4.5	3.48

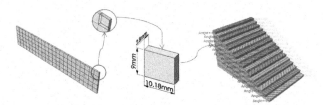

Figure 1. Finite element model of CFRP single plate.

Since the Block Lanczos method is often applied to the analysis of models with solid elements, it can well deal with the vibration modes of rigid bodies, and can effectively analyze components with large analysis models and a large number of vibration modes. Therefore, based on the Block Lanczos method, the finite element model of CFRP single plate is established to analyze the inherent characteristics under free boundary conditions, and the first four order bending and torsional modal characteristics of simulation and test are obtained (Table 2).

The second-order response surface model and MIGA algorithm are used to optimize the four material parameters to make the simulation model closer to the experimental test data (Zhang et al. 2019). Table 3 is the corrected material parameters, and Figure 2 is the error comparison before and after the model correction.

It can be seen from Figure 2 that in addition to the limitation of the third-order natural frequency due to the combined effect of each order of simulation, the error increases slightly, and the error of each order decreases significantly. The maximum error decreases from 15.69 % to 7.11 %, and the average error decreases from 8.63 % to 3.53 %. The simulation model is effectively optimized. Next, the optimized model is used to identify the crack damage.

Table 2. Comparative analysis of simulation and experimental modal vibration modes.

	Modal shape from simulation	Modal shape from text	Description
Mode 1			The first bending mode (Bending along y-zais)
Mode 2			The first torsion mode (Translation along x-zais)
Mode 3			The second bending mode (Bending along y-zais)
Mode 4			The third bending mode (Bending along y-zais)

Table 3. Material parameters after model modification.

ρ (kg/m^{-3})	G_{12} (GPa)	G_{13} (GPa)	G_{23} (GPa)
1798	5.16	3.65	4.13

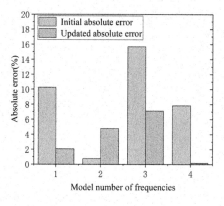

Figure 2. Error comparison before and after model correction.

4 RESEARCH ON FRACTURE LOCATION IDENTIFICATION

The geometric model of crack damage of CFRP plate studied in this paper is shown in Figure 3. The size of the CFRP plate is: length × width × height (224 × 45 × 2.6mm). A long × wide (24 × 2mm) crack was set at a distance of 30mm from the left end to simulate the fracture damage of composite materials.

The influence of crack location on natural frequency is analyzed by ABAQUS. In this part, the same crack depth is used to simulate different crack location identification (that is, 5-224mm away from the left, 5mm interval, respectively, as shown in Figure 3). Comparing the working conditions before and after damage, the absolute value of the ratio of natural frequency change (the absolute value of the ratio of the first four natural frequencies change to the first natural frequency change) is taken, and the obtained data are plotted in Figure 4.

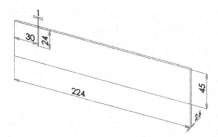

Figure 3. Geometric model of CFRP cracks.

It can be seen from Figure 4 that the absolute value of the natural frequency change ratio of each order changes symmetrically from both ends to the middle. Therefore, it is only necessary to analyze the first half, and the second order shows a downward trend. The third order shows a concave type that decreases first and then increases. The fourth order shows a double concave type, and the closer to the center, the smaller the amplitude. The crack position of the composite structure can be accurately characterized by Figure 4.

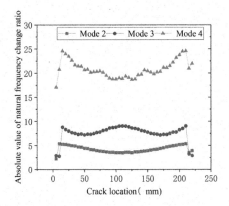

Figure 4. The absolute value of the natural frequency change ratio at different damage locations.

In this paper, the absolute value of the natural frequency change ratio in Figure 4 is fitted by a polynomial, and the fitting effect of each order polynomial and the natural frequency change ratio of each order is judged by the determination coefficient. As shown in Table 4, the residual error of the six-order polynomial fitting is analyzed, as shown in Figure 5.

Table 4. Polynomial fitting effect.

	Second-stage	Third-stage	fourth-order
Polynomials of degree 2	0.26	0.39	0.44
Polynomials of degree 3	0.26	0.39	0.46
Polynomials of degree 4	0.66	0.47	0.67
Polynomials of degree 5	0.67	0.47	0.69
Polynomials of degree 6	0.81	0.81	0.83

The polynomial fitting effect of table 4 shows that the higher the polynomial degree is, the better the absolute value fitting effect of the natural frequency change ratio of each order is. Therefore, the fitting curve of the sixth-order polynomial is selected for residual evaluation.

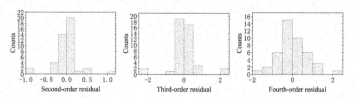

Figure 5. Residuals of polynomial fitting.

It can be seen from the residuals fitted by a polynomial in Figure 5 that the residual range of the second order is the smallest, most of which are between (−0.5,0.5), and the range of the third and fourth orders is large, most of which are between (−1,1). Therefore, selecting the fitting formula $= -7.49x_1^6 + 5.16x_1^5 - 1.4x_1^4 + 1.88x_1^3 - 0.01x_1^2 + 0.37x_1 + 1.62$ of the second order natural frequency change ratio to identify the crack position can effectively improve the recognition accuracy of the crack position, which has important guiding significance for the subsequent crack detection test research.

Under the condition of controlling the crack position unchanged, the crack depth is studied to analyze the influence of crack depth on natural frequency. In this part, the same crack position is used to simulate different crack depth identification (that is, the damage condition with a width of 2 mm, depth of 1-43 mm, and interval of 1 mm is set at 30 mm from the left end) for finite element simulation, and the absolute value of the natural frequency change ratio of Figure 6 is drawn.

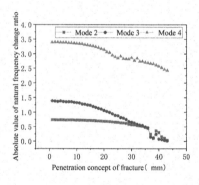

Figure 6. The absolute value of the natural frequency change ratio at different damage locations.

It can be seen from Figure 6 that when the depth is less than 50 % of the specimen width, the influence of different crack depths on the absolute value of the natural frequency change ratio changes regularly. Third, the fourth-order natural frequency shows a significant downward trend with the increase in crack depth, and the second-order natural frequency shows a weak downward trend. However, when the depth is greater than 50 % of the specimen width, the natural frequencies of each order fluctuate significantly, resulting in an increase in the error.

It can be seen from Figure 4 that the minimum influence of crack location on the change ratio of any two-order natural frequency is about 5. The influence of crack depth on any two-order natural frequency change ratio is about 3.5, as shown in Figure 6. Therefore, based on any two-order natural frequency change ratio identification index, the influence of crack depth on crack location can be ignored.

5 QUANTITATIVE IDENTIFICATION OF CRACKS

The natural frequencies of the specimens under different crack depths are analyzed by the finite element method, and the relationship between the square of the first four natural frequencies and the crack depth is obtained. Since the square value of the frequency change is relatively large, it is difficult to distinguish the trend of the natural frequency change of each order. Therefore, Figure 7 is drawn by using the natural frequency difference (with or without damage).

It can be seen from Figure 7 that for the identification of crack depth, the difference representation of natural frequency change is similar to the absolute value representation of natural frequency and any two-order natural frequency change ratio, but the accuracy is different. In this paper, the curve in Figure 7 is fitted to meet the accurate identification of fracture depth.

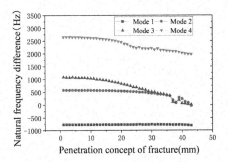

Figure 7. The natural frequency difference of different damage degree.

Table 5. Polynomial fitting effect.

	First-order	Second-stage	Third-stage	Fourth-order
Polynomials of degree 2	0.61	0.92	0.99	0.97
Polynomials of degree 3	0.82	0.95	0.99	0.98

In this paper, the polynomial fitting of the natural frequency change ratio in Figure 7 is carried out, and the fitting effect of each order polynomial and the natural frequency change ratio of each order is judged by the determination coefficient R^2, as shown in Table 5. The polynomial fitting effect of Table 5 shows that the higher the polynomial degree is, the better the fitting effect of natural frequency changes of each order is. The determination coefficient R^2 of the cubic polynomial fitting is more than 0.95 except for the first order of 0.82. Therefore, the cubic polynomial is selected for fitting. The third-order polynomial fitting effect of each natural frequency change is shown in Figure 8.

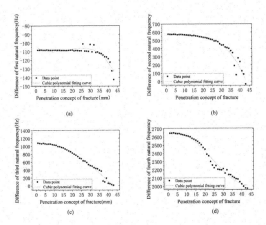

Figure 8. Polynomial fitting curve.

227

It can be seen from the polynomial fitting curve in Figure 8 that the first-order fitting curve has the largest fluctuation. The error caused by the increase in the damage degree of the second-order and fourth-order fitting curves leads to a poor fitting effect, and the third-order fitting curve has the best effect. Therefore, selecting the fitting formula$= 0.005x_2^3 - 0.9x_2^2 + 4.21x_2 + 1070.67$ of the third-order natural frequency change ratio for crack depth identification can effectively improve the identification accuracy of crack depth, and has important guiding significance for subsequent crack depth test research.

6 CONCLUSION

(1) Based on the optimized simulation model, this paper reduces the error between simulation and test data and improves the accuracy of simulation data. Furthermore, the absolute value of the natural frequency change ratio is used to identify the global damage location, and it is concluded that the absolute value of the natural frequency change ratio has a good characterization relationship with the development of cracks. The fitting formula of the second-order natural frequency change ratio with the best fitting effect is used to identify the crack location, which effectively improves the identification accuracy of the crack location.

(2) In this paper, the square of natural frequency change is used to identify the damage degree, and it is concluded that the square of natural frequency change decreases monotonically with the increase of crack depth. The fitting formula of the third order natural frequency change ratio with the best fitting effect is used to identify the crack depth, which effectively improves the recognition accuracy of the crack depth.

The results of this study show that this method can effectively identify the location and degree changes of single factor cracks in the actual working conditions. The study of crack identification for multi-factor, multi-position interaction, and nonlinear damage law needs more scholars to further study.

REFERENCES

Abedin, M., & Mehrabi, A. B. (2021) Bridge damage identification through frequency changes. *Sensors and Smart Structures Technologies for Civil, Mechanical, and Aerospace Systems*.

Bolf, D., Zamarin, A., & Basan, R. (2020) Composite material damage processes. *Journal of Maritime & Transportation Science*, 3(3), 307–323.

Cawley, P., & Adams, R. D. (1979) The location of defects in structures from measurements of natural frequencies. *The Journal of Strain Analysis for Engineering Design*, 14(2), 49–57.

Hearn, G., & Testa, R. B. (1991) Modal analysis for damage detection in structures. *Journal of Structural Engineering*, 117(10), 3042–3063.

Khan, M. W., Din, N. A., & Haq, R. U. (2020) Damage detection in a fixed-fixed beam using natural frequency changes. *Vibroengineering PROCEDIA*, 30(4), 38–43.

Sannamani M. & Tallman T. N. (2021) The Effect of Sensitivity Matrix Formulation on Damage Detection in Carbon Fiber Composites With Surface-Mounted Electrodes via Electrical Impedance Tomography. (eds.) ASME 2021 Conference on Smart Materials, Adaptive Structures and Intelligent Systems(pp.). *American Society of Mechanical Engineers*.

Valašková Veronika & Melcer Jozef. (2022) Bridge Natural Frequencies, Numerical Solution versus Experiment. *Applied Sciences*(3). doi:10.3390/APP12031765.

Zhang, Y., Yang, Y., Du, W., & Han, Q. (2019) Research on finite element model modification of carbon fiber reinforced plastic (cfrp) laminated structures based on correlation analysis and an approximate model. *Materials*, 12(16).

Analysis of seismic damage phenomena and causes of frame structures with external verandah

Zeren Tang*
Key Laboratory of Earthquake Engineering and Engineering Vibration, Institute of Engineering Mechanics, China Earthquake Administration, Harbin, China
Key Laboratory of Earthquake Disaster Mitigation, Ministry of Emergency Management, Harbin, China

Jianing Gu
Longfor Group Holdings Limited, Beijing, China

Di Liu
Key Laboratory of Earthquake Engineering and Engineering Vibration, Institute of Engineering Mechanics, China Earthquake Administration, Harbin, China
Key Laboratory of Earthquake Disaster Mitigation, Ministry of Emergency Management, Harbin, China

Zijian Liu
Department of Information Engineering, The Chinese University of Hong Kong, Hong Kong SAR, China

ABSTRACT: Frame structure with an external verandah is a common building style in southern China. This unique structural form, which reveals its unique existence in the Chinese southern region, is mostly used in densely populated areas such as teaching buildings and dormitories. However, this structural style has shown poor seismic performance in earthquake sites, causing certain casualties and property losses. This paper summarizes the common seismic damage phenomena of frame structures with an external verandah and analyzes the causes of damage, taking two typical double-span frame structures with an external verandah in Wenchuan and Lushan earthquakes as examples. Numerical simulations of a frame structure with an external verandah are performed using Abaqus software, and the results are obtained by the on-site seismic damage phenomenon. Eventually, specific suggestions, including increasing part of the column cross-section and the spacing of the bottom hoop reinforcement, are proposed based on seismic damage and numerical simulation results for optimization and strengthening of such type of structure.

1 INTRODUCTION

Unlike balconies and terraces, verandahs are free spaces in front of the external walls of a building that are covered by a roof and can be used by multiple people. The buildings with external verandahs originated from the classical temple-style architecture in Greece, but it was not widely popular and used because of the high dimensional region in which Europe is located. With the global invasion of European colonies in the modern era, this architectural style took root and developed rapidly in Southeast Asia, which had a hotter and more humid climate than that of Europe. The first appearance of buildings with verandahs in China was in Guangzhou's Thirteen Houses, after which it took root and developed very rapidly in the southern part of China. It was the only form of architecture when modern Chinese architecture began to be built, and it occupies a very important position in the development process of modern architecture in China (Fujimori 1993). Meanwhile,

---

*Corresponding Author: 840601388@qq.com

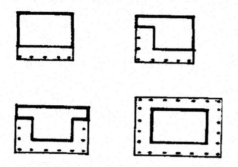

Figure 1. Common layout of the buildings with verandah.

Figure 2. The buildings built in modern China.

the sotto portico, which is common in South China including Taiwan Province, is not a kind of buildings with a verandah (Jessie 1971). The common layout of the buildings with verandahs and the buildings built in modern China are shown below.

Liu, Y. (2011) points out that the external verandah in these buildings can be used for shading and ventilation in the south of China to avoid the heat, and it is conducive to increasing indoor lighting. While in northern China the external verandah is mostly closed to become a sunroom to resist drought and cold climate. The external verandah in southern China is both a part of the indoor function and an indispensable living space. In recent decades, China's buildings with external verandah are mainly constructed in school buildings, dormitories, part of office buildings, and other places. The collapse of this type of building will cause serious casualties and property damage after earthquakes. The serious collapse of the school buildings in Xuankou Town High School in the 5.12 Wenchuan earthquake in 2008 exposed the poor seismic performance of this type of building, and the damage mechanism of this type of building deserves further study.

This paper will summarize the earthquake damage phenomenon of buildings with external verandahs in several earthquake sites, establish numerical models for calculations, analyze the causes of damage, and make some suggestions on the reinforcement methods for such buildings.

2 ANALYSIS AND SUMMARY OF COMMON EARTHQUAKE DAMAGE

The frame structures with external verandahs can be divided into single-span external and double-span. Single-span buildings with external verandahs have low structural redundancy and only one seismic line of defense, which does not conform to the concept of multiple lines of defense, with the poor structural seismic performance and the degree of seismic damage is much greater than that of multi-span frame structures (Sun et al. 2008). In contrast, the seismic damage phenomena in the Chichi earthquake (21st, September 1999) in Taiwan Province and the Wenchuan earthquake (12th, May 2008) showed that although double-span buildings with external verandahs had additional external verandah columns than single-span buildings, they also had serious seismic damage (Li et al. 2008).

Detail analysis will be taken in this section pertaining to seismic damage to the teaching building of Xuankou Town Middle School in the Wenchuan earthquake and the teaching building of Baosheng Town Center School in Lushan County during the Lushan earthquake. Numerical models are also built using Abaqus for comparison.

2.1 *The teaching building of Xuankou Town middle school*

Buildings with external verandahs in the teaching building of Xuankou Town Middle School mostly collapsed toward the corridor side on the first floor, and toward the classroom side with a larger

Figure 3. Single-span buildings with external verandah collapsed in the Chichi earthquake.

Figure 4. Double-span buildings with external verandah collapsed in the Wenchuan earthquake.

span on the second floor and above. The damage to the buildings is shown in Figure 5. At the same time, the earthquake damage phenomenon of Buildings with external verandahs generally shows the phenomenon of "strong beam and weak column," which means damage to the column is more serious than the beam. Moreover, the damage at the top of the column is much more serious than the damage at the bottom of the column, and the concrete at the top of the column may spill or even break, and the rebar may be pulled off. The study concluded that the crowded and large openings on the large span side led to a larger load on the large span side than on the corridor side, which caused different degrees of seismic damage, in other words, the structural plane and inside arrangement had a great impact on the seismic performance of the external corridor frame structure (Guo 2009). Meanwhile, the design of the buildings with external verandah does not fully consider that the axial pressure ratio will increase under seismic action, and thus ignore the resulting overturning moment (Huang et al. 2016).

Studies have also pointed out that different arrangements of infill walls also affect the seismic performance of frame structures (Huang 2017). Tasnimi et al. (Tasnimi & Mohebkhah 2011) explored the effect of infill wall openings on the overall seismic performance and meticulously investigated the effect of masonry strength, etc. on frame damage modes, strength, stiffness, and energy dissipation performance. The results showed that the structural strength and stiffness with infill walls increased, but the ductility decreased.

(a) Seismic damage to the whole structure

(b) Seismic damage to part of the structure

Figure 5. The teaching building of Xuankou Town Middle School.

2.2 *The teaching building of Baosheng Town Center School*

The teaching building of Baosheng Town Center School is a double-span building with an external verandah. horizontal cracks at the connection between the wall and beam beneath the windows on the ground floor and crosses diagonal cracks in the wall between the window and door openings on the ground floor have appeared in the building, which is shown below.

(a) Horizontal cracks in the ground floor

(b) Cross diagonal cracks in the wall between the window and door

Figure 6. The teaching building of Baosheng Town Center School.

The teaching building of Baosheng Town Center School is a double-span building with an external verandah. horizontal cracks at the connection between the wall and beam beneath the windows on the ground floor and crosses diagonal cracks in the wall between the window and door openings on the ground floor have appeared in the building, which is shown below.

2.3 *Damage to the whole building*

The double-span buildings with external verandahs mostly collapse toward the corridor side on the first floor and the larger span of the classroom side on the second floor and above. The collapse direction is shown in Figure 7. It is believed that the crowded and large openings on the large span side lead to a larger load on the large span side than on the corridor side, thus causing this collapse trend (Ma et al. 2011; Ye et al. 2009).

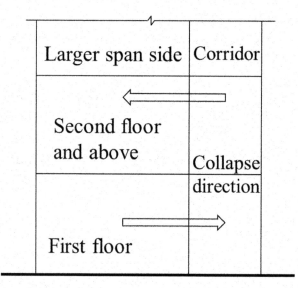

Figure 7. Collapse direction of the buildings with external verandah.

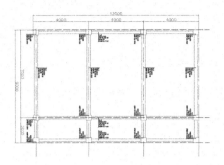

Figure 8. Structural dimensions and reinforcement information.

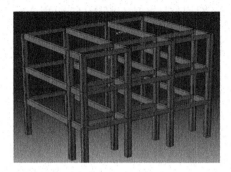

Figure 9. Structure model.

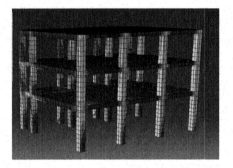

Figure 10. Concrete cloud map.

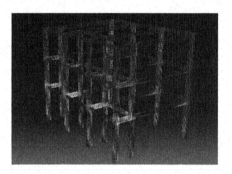

Figure 11. Rebar cloud map.

2.4 *Numerical simulation by abaqus*

A building in Guangyuan County, Jiange City, Sichuan Province is used as a prototype and numerical simulation is performed using Abaqus software.

The structural plan dimensions are 12m (3×4m) in length, 9m (7-2m) in width, and 9.5m in height with three floors. The height of the first floor is 3.5m and that of the remaining two is 3m. The structural dimensions and reinforcement information are shown in Figure 8.

The concrete of the model is C30, the section type of the RC frame is solid units and the floor slab is shell unit. The hoop and longitudinal reinforcement are used in the truss unit to represent the HPB235 and HRB335 materials. The solid units are connected to the shell units by tie connections, and the solid units are connected to the truss units by embed interaction. The structural model is shown in Figure 9.

The results of the nonlinear time history analysis of the model are as follows.

In the concrete cloud map Figure 10, the column stress on the ground floor of the external verandah is significantly higher than that of the middle and large span side column, while the column stress on the second and third floor of the large span side is higher than that of the middle and external verandah column. The simulation results are in good agreement with the overall structural seismic damage phenomenon summarized above.

In the rebar cloud map, it can be seen from Figure 11 that the hoop reinforcement at the short span of the ground floor is obviously stressed, while the hoop reinforcement in some areas of the joints of the ground floor beams and columns received shear forces. This is caused by the uneven span distribution and the large seismic horizontal force on the first floor.

3 STRUCTURAL OPTIMIZATION AND REINFORCEMENT RECOMMENDATIONS

Given the above summarized seismic phenomena of the frame structure with external verandah, this section makes a few suggestions on structural optimization and reinforcement.

3.1 *Recommendations for infill walls*

When arranging the infill wall of the frame structures with an external verandah, it should be kept as reasonable as possible to avoid the unreasonable distribution of the structural internal forces. At the same time, the infill wall's material can choose new material of high strength.

3.2 *Recommendations for the whole structure*

Most of the frame structures with external verandahs have the same column cross-section size, which makes the structure's originally unevenly distributed internal forces more unreasonable. Meanwhile, local encryption of longitudinal reinforcement or hoop reinforcement can be carried out for the vulnerable parts of the structure to improve the local seismic performance.

As shown in the concrete cloud map above, the cross-sectional dimensions of the verandah side columns can be increased. From the rebar cloud map above, it can be seen that the hoop reinforcement at the short span of the ground floor and at the joints of the beams and columns is under greater stress, and the hoop spacing can be reduced at these locations to improve the structural shear resistance and thus enhance the seismic performance.

4 CONCLUSIONS

This paper summarizes and analyzes the common seismic damage phenomena of the frame structures with external verandah, selects two seismic damage examples for detailed elaboration, and makes specific comments on the optimization and strengthening of such structures. The following conclusions are obtained.

1. Due to the uneven span and load distribution of the frame structures with external verandah, the internal force distribution of the structure is uneven, and the whole structure shows the phenomenon of "strong beam and weak column." The damage to the top of the column is higher than the bottom of the column, and the column will break when it is serious.

2. The infill wall arrangement of the frame structures with external verandah should be as reasonable as possible, and the materials can select the new and high-strength materials.

3. The cross-section of columns on the same floor of the frame structures with external verandah should not be designed to be uniformly the same size, and the cross-section should be varied according to the law of internal force distribution. While the two-span length ratio of this type of structure should be as small as possible.

4. In this paper, the structural model is studied and analyzed by numerical simulation methods, and the results are more consistent with the seismic phenomena, but no experimental studies are conducted. Future research should further investigate the overall damage mechanism of the frame structures with external verandah as well as reasonable and effective reinforcement methods.

REFERENCES

Fujimori, T. 1993. External verandah-the origin of modern Chinese architecture. *Architectural Journal*, **33**(5).
Guo, X. 2009. Characteristics and mechanism analysis of the great Wenchuan earthquake. *Journal of Earthquake Engineering and Engineering Vibration*, **29**(06):74–87.
Huang, Q. 2017. Study on improvement of seismic performance of side corridor frame with infill wall. *(Hunan University)*.

Huang, S., Guo, X., Sun, D., et al. 2016.Shaking table test on failure mechanism of RC frame with an exterior corridor. *Engineering Mechanics*, **33**(12):63–71+85.

Jessie, L. 1971. *China and Christian Colleges, 1850–1950*. (Ithaca and London: Cornell University Press).

Li, H., Xiao, S., Huo, L. 2008. Damage investigation and analysis of engineering structures in the Wenchuan earthquake. *Journal of Building Structures*, **04**:10–9.

Liu, Y. 2011. Categorization and Distribution of Verandah Style Architecture in China. *South Architecture*, **02**:36–42.

Ma, Y., Lu, X., Ye, L., et al. 2011. Seismic damage simulation and analysis of typical RC frames of Xuankou school. *Engineering Mechanics*, **28**(05):71–7.

Sun, B., Yan, P., Hu, C., et al. 2008. Overview of seismic damage to different structures in Yingxiu Town during the Wenchuan Earthquake. *Journal of Earthquake Engineering and Engineering Vibration*, **05**:1–9.

Tasnimi A.A., Mohebkhah A. 2011. Investigation of the behavior of brick-infilled steel frames with openings, experimental and analytical approaches. *Engineering Structures*, **33**(3):968–80.

Ye, L., Li, Y., Pan, P. 2009. Seismic damage to building structures of Xuankou Middle School in Yingxiu Town. *Building Structure*, **39**(11):54–7+29.

Large underground cavern excavation scheme design and surrounding rock stability influence

Tian He*
College of Civil Engineering, Chongqing Jiaotong University, Chongqing, China

Hao Ding
College of Civil Engineering, Chongqing Jiaotong University, Chongqing, China
Chongqing Transportation Research and Design Institute Co., Ltd, Chongqing, China

Zhenhua Peng
CNOOC Petrochemical Engineering Co., Ltd., Qingdao, Shandong, China

Renjing Zhu, Xinghong Jiang & Liang Cheng
Chongqing Transportation Research and Design Institute Co., Ltd, Chongqing, China

ABSTRACT: The establishment of large underground gas storage is of great significance for China's natural gas reserves and regulation, and the excavation of large underground gas-storage caverns is the key to underground gas storage. Reasonable excavation scheme selection can improve the stability of surrounding rock and save the construction period. Aiming at the excavation problem of large underground gas storage with a cylindrical dome structure, this paper puts forward three excavation schemes of a single construction channel, two construction channels, and three construction channels, and establishes a numerical calculation model based on excavation step by FLAC, and analyzes the stability of surrounding rock. The results show that the excavation process has little effect on the stability of surrounding rock after the excavation of the cavern, which mainly affects the stability of surrounding rock in the excavation process. After the excavation of the cavern, the vertical displacement of the surrounding rock of the single construction channel is 9.76 mm, and the horizontal displacement is 7.76 mm. The maximum vertical displacement in the excavation process of two construction channels is 14.2 mm, and the maximum vertical displacement in the excavation process of three construction channels is 11.4 mm. At the same time, by analyzing the crack range of the numerical model cell, the crack range of the single construction channel scheme is the smallest, and the scheme has little influence on the top and bottom of the gas storage, and the fractured rock mass caused by excavation is less. On this basis, the three schemes are compared comprehensively. Compared with the other two schemes, the single construction channel scheme has the lowest cost of civil construction, fewer safety hazards, less engineering quantity, and faster construction speed. It is reasonable to comprehensively recommend a single construction channel.

1 INTRODUCTION

Natural gas is an important energy for today's social development, and the demand for natural gas is increasing all over the world. China is a major energy consumption country, and its demand for natural gas is also increasing. All countries in the world continue to expand their natural gas reserves. With the development of the economy, the world's demand for natural gas is increasing. However, China's s current gas storage capacity is very limited, and there is still a certain gap with

---

*Corresponding Author: 1647636435@qq.com

the world average level. Therefore, underground gas storage has the advantages of large gas storage, saving ground resources, being safe and reliable, being prone to small environmental pollution, and being free from the weather (Lei 2018).

Large-scale permanent underground caverns are developed with the need for electricity, the larger scale of Canada's Lagrangian secondary power station, underground powerhouse size 483m, 26m wide, 47.3m high. In 1988, Telata's underground hydropower station was built in Indonesia. Its underground cavern is 253 m long, 35 m wide and 49.5 m high, which became the largest underground cavern in the world at that time. Zhang Jianshan and others did research on the large underground cavern group excavation scheme and proposed large underground cavern anchor cable construction technology, large underground cavern dome fine safety excavation technology, rock anchor beam fine excavation support technology, large section deep shaft small diameter slag chute type rapid safety excavation technology (Zhang 2020). The vertical chamber is a combination of a spherical crown dome and cylindrical tank, which adopts the construction scheme of the one-shaped guide pit method, cross-shaped guide pit method and circular guide pit reserved rock column method (Liu 2016). The rapid excavation construction method for a large underground cavern was proposed by Yang et al. (2018). In the future, the scale of the underground powerhouse in the project will be larger and the technical difficulty will be greater. It can be seen that the research on the stability of surrounding rock of large underground cavern engineering is imminent. The surrounding rock stability analysis method of underground caverns puts forward three kinds of analysis methods: surrounding rock classification method, analytical method, physical simulation method, and numerical simulation method (Chen 2020; Xiao 2000). Mu and Sun et al. applied ANASYS to conduct a nonlinear finite element simulation analysis on the influence of surrounding rock stability in three excavation processes (Mu 2004; Sun 2006). Li Lu, Gao Qiao, Wang Hui, and Wei Yun carried out a comparative analysis of the stability of surrounding rock of underground powerhouse under different excavation schemes by combining the elastoplastic damage finite element method with plane geomechanical model test and 3D nonlinear finite element method (Gao 2019; Li 2016; Wang 2017; Wei 2015).

In view of the stability of the surrounding rock of underground storage, Jan Johansson and Xia Caijun et al. selected the typical burial depth of the underground cavern for the selection of the scheme and the tightness requirements of the underground cavern for the compressed air energy storage. Considering different cavern forms and cavern sizes, they used Abaqus finite element software to calculate the plastic zone and the strain around the cavern of the surrounding rock of the compressed air energy storage cavern under high internal pressure (Jan 2003; Xia 2014). In view of the stability of the oil storage cavern of the underground water-sealed oil storage cavern, Zhang Chengbin and Hu Mupeng et al. took the oil storage cavern of an underground water-sealed oil storage cavern project as the research object, adopted the value selection method of surrounding rock parameters based on the GSI system, and carried out a numerical analysis on the stability of surrounding rock with the aid of FLAC3D software. The displacement criterion and stress criterion were used to explain the numerical analysis results, and then the stability of the surrounding rock was judged (Hu 2013; Wang 2011; Zhang 2019). Li used mathematical statistics and numerical calculation to determine the factors affecting the deformation of surrounding rock and deformation characteristics; in order to reasonably and comprehensively evaluate the effect of cavern support, the effect of supporting in maintaining the stability of surrounding rock is evaluated by the stability state of surrounding rock, the deformation of surrounding rock and the stress of supporting structure (Li 2018). Sun studied the stability of the oil storage cavern under the actual construction excavation conditions through FLAC3D numerical analysis and studied the stability of the cavern from the two aspects of surrounding rock stress and displacement deformation (Sun 2017).

In this paper, the excavation method of a large underground gas storage chamber with a total height of about 100m is studied based on the top of a hemispherical chamber with a diameter of about 35m, an ellipsoidal shape at the bottom, and a cylindrical connection in the middle. Three construction excavation schemes are proposed, and the impact of the stability of the surrounding rock is compared and analyzed to determine the most reasonable excavation method for the design and construction of similar large underground gas storage chamber projects.

2 STUDY ON EXCAVATION SCHEME OF GAS STORAGE CAVERN

2.1 Excavation scheme of single construction channel

The reverse drilling rig is used for a positive pilot hole to the construction channel position; the lower construction channel is constructed to the interface position, and the construction is continued to the side wall according to the outline of the lower construction channel; the construction of guide well (pipeline well) by reverse drilling rig; the reverse pilot shaft construction was carried out by using the reverse drilling rig, and the drilling and blasting method was used to expand the excavation four times from the inside to the outside. Finally, the design size of the chamber was formed by expanding excavation, and three drillers were equipped to drill at the same time. The excavation scheme is shown in Figure 1.

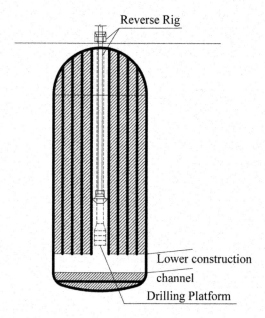

Figure 1. Facade of single channel construction.

2.2 Excavation scheme of two construction channels

The first layer uses the upper construction channel to excavate according to the construction sequence plan of the first layer. After the excavation is completed, the rotary excavator is used to construct the second slag chute according to the first layer working face; then, the lower channel is excavated according to the construction process plan of the third layer; when the ballast well is connected with the lower construction channel, the positive expansion method is used to excavate the main body of the gas storage cavern, and the blasting construction is controlled from top to bottom according to the amplitude and division of the excavation process in step IV in the figure. Finally, the bottom of the main body of the construction gas storage structure is excavated. The excavation scheme is shown in Figure 2.

2.3 Three construction channel scheme

2.3.1 Excavation scheme

The first layer uses the upper channel to construct according to the construction sequence plane of the first layer; the middle and lower construction channels to the interface position, continue to be

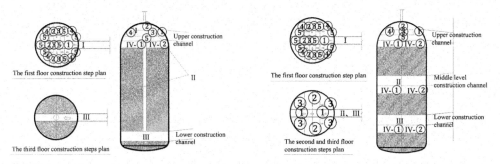

Figure 2. Two-channel construction drawing.   Figure 3. Three-channel construction drawing.

constructed to the side wall according to the outline of the construction channel, and then expand excavation according to the upper layer of the construction sequence plan of the second and third layers; according to the upper, middle and lower construction channels, three working faces are constructed respectively, and the top-down control blasting is used to construct the main structure of the gas storage cavern. The excavation scheme is shown in Figure 3.

2.4 *Construction excavation scheme comparison*

The estimated construction period and approximate excavation volume of the three construction schemes are shown in Table 1.

Table 1. Comparison of excavation schemes.

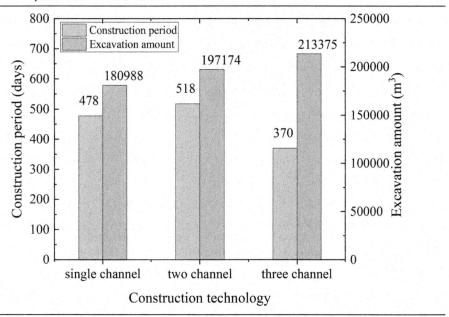

Advantages and disadvantages of single construction channel: Only one construction channel is needed, the civil construction cost is the lowest, it is not easy to plug the well, the amount of slag is small, the safety hazard is small, and the construction speed is fast; it has large quantities and high construction cost of temporary shotcrete support.

Advantages and disadvantages of two construction channels: Only two construction channels are needed, the cost of civil construction is relatively low, and the cost of slag utilization is low; easy plugging, need to control blasting particle size, a large amount of slag, long construction period.

Advantages and disadvantages of three construction channels: The three working faces are constructed simultaneously, and the construction period is fast; Construction of 3 construction channels, high cost of civil construction; slag lifting equipment shall be set up for slag discharge, with the high cost and slow slag discharge efficiency.

Note: This study proposes that the construction period is the theoretical construction period, which is obtained by referring to the construction progress and work efficiency of similar construction methods. The actual construction period should be combined with the detailed construction organization and mechanical matching to calculate the efficiency of each process, and then calculate the construction period.

3 STABILITY ANALYSIS OF CONSTRUCTION SURROUNDING ROCK

3.1 *computation module*

The research object of this paper is about 35 meters in diameter hemispherical top, the bottom adopts ellipsoid, the middle adopts cylinder connection height about 100 meters large gas storage cavern as the foundation structure. In order to explore the most reasonable excavation method among the three excavation methods, without considering the influence of construction channels on structural safety and stability, it is necessary to study the influence of various excavation methods on the stability of the surrounding rock of the cavern. The cavern calculation model with model grid division, and monitoring points G1, G2, G3, and G4 are shown in Figure 4.

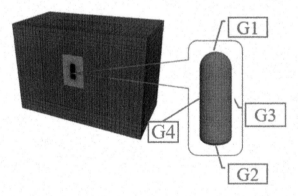

Figure 4. Calculation model.

3.2 *Boundary conditions*

The horizontal boundary of the calculation model is constrained by the displacement of the x-axis and y-axis respectively; the lower boundary of the model is constrained by the displacement in the z-axis direction; the surface is a free boundary without any constraint. The actual buried depth above the top of the cavern is taken to calculate the surface deformation.

The value of grade III surrounding rock material parameters used in the stability calculation of surrounding rock by construction method in this paper refers to the average value in the design specification of highway tunnel (JTG 3370-2018), as detailed in Table 2.

3.3 *Constitutive model*

In this paper, the classical Mohr-Coulomb (MC) criterion is used to determine the yield failure behavior of materials under shear and tension modes. The criterion is simple in structure and easy

Table 2. Physical and mechanical parameters of surrounding rock.

Parameter	Values
Gravity/$kN \cdot m^{-3}$	24
Coefficient of elastic resistance/$MPa \cdot m^{-1}$	900
Elastic modulus/GPa	13
Poisson ratio	0.28
Angle of internal friction/°	45
Force of cohesion/MPa	1.1
Calculation of friction angle/°	65

to obtain parameters, which is widely used in geotechnical engineering. For the shear-level tension mode, the MC criterion is expressed as:

$$F_S = \sigma_1 - N_\varphi \sigma_3 + 2c\sqrt{N_\varphi} \quad (1)$$

$$F_t = \sigma_3 - \sigma_t \quad (2)$$

where, σ_1 and σ_3 are the maximum and minimum principal stresses, MPa; c is the cohesive force, MPa; φ internal friction angle, °; N_φ the expression is $N_\varphi = \frac{1+\sin(\varphi)}{1-\sin(\varphi)}$; σ_t for the tensile strength of the rock, MPa.

After the rock material reaches yield, the magnitude and direction of plastic strain are determined by the plastic flow law. According to the plastic potential, the plastic strain increment can be obtained as follows:

$$d\varepsilon_{ij}^p = d\lambda \frac{dg}{d\sigma_{ij}} \quad (3)$$

where, $d\lambda$ is a non-negative plastic factor, whose value can be determined by the consistency condition; the plastic potential function g is described by Eq. (1) and Eq. (2) (associated flow rule) for shear and tensile failure.

From the plastic strain, the second partial strain invariant of plastic strain can be obtained, which is used to measure the degree of shear damage to rock, as follows:

$$D_S = \sqrt{\frac{(\varepsilon_1^p - \varepsilon_2^p) + (\varepsilon_2^p - \varepsilon_3^p) + (\varepsilon_3^p - \varepsilon_1^p)^2}{6}} \quad (4)$$

The extent of rock tensile damage can be measured by maximum principal tensile strain:

$$D_t = \varepsilon_3^p \quad (5)$$

To determine whether the rock element is damaged or not, it is necessary to set the maximum plastic damage of the element, namely the maximum plastic shear/tensile strain. In the calculation process, if the element reaches the maximum plastic damage, the element failure is determined.

3.4 Analysis of calculation results

3.4.1 Single construction channel scheme

The horizontal displacement distribution increases with the excavation, and the maximum horizontal displacement of rock and soil around the tunnel is 10.18 mm, which is distributed in the middle of the tunnel. The absolute value of horizontal displacement is small, and during the excavation process, the surrounding cave collapse risk is small. Vertical displacement distribution. When the excavation of arch rock mass is completed, the vertical displacement is almost stable. Finally, the

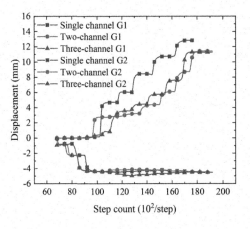 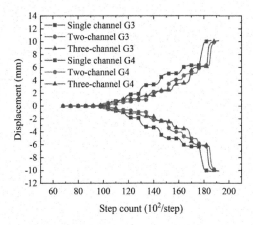

Figure 5. Vertical displacement comparison chart.

Figure 6. Horizontal displacement comparison chart.

maximum vertical settlement of rock mass around the tunnel is 4.84 mm, which is distributed at the top of the tunnel. The maximum vertical uplift of rock mass around the tunnel is 8.79 mm, which is distributed at the bottom of the tunnel, as shown in Figure 5 and 6.

3.4.2 *Two construction channel schemes*

The horizontal displacement distribution increases with the excavation, and the maximum horizontal displacement of rock and soil around the tunnel is 10.22 mm, which is distributed in the middle of the tunnel. When the excavation of arch rock mass is completed, the vertical displacement is almost stable. Finally, the maximum vertical settlement of rock mass around the tunnel is 5.04 mm, which is distributed at the top of the tunnel. The maximum vertical uplift of rock mass around the tunnel is 8.86 mm, which is distributed at the bottom of the tunnel, as shown in Figure 5 and 6.

3.4.3 *Three construction channel scheme*

The horizontal displacement distribution. With the excavation, the horizontal displacement increases continuously. Finally, the maximum horizontal displacement of rock and soil around the tunnel is 9.65 mm, which is distributed in the middle of the tunnel. Vertical displacement distribution. When the excavation of arch rock mass is completed, the vertical displacement is almost stable. Finally, the maximum vertical settlement of rock mass around the tunnel is 4.56 mm, which is distributed at the top of the tunnel. The maximum vertical uplift of rock mass around the tunnel is 8.46 mm, which is distributed at the bottom of the tunnel, as shown in Figure 5 and 6.

3.5 *Comparison of calculation results*

1) Comparison of plastic zones

A comparison of the plastic zone of the three construction solutions is shown in Figure 7. With the completion of the excavation, three kinds of through construction plan plastic zone mostly concentrated in the side wall of the cavity, the top and bottom of the cavity have a small number of appearances. As the construction program changed, the areas causing damage to the cavern sidewalls surrounding the rock continued to increase. However, the comparative diagram of the plastic zone shows that the single construction channel causes the least damage to the surrounding rock of the cavity sidewall

Through the plastic zone volume comparison graph shown in Figure 8, the single construction channel plastic zone volume is significantly less than the other two construction options. Therefore, under the three construction methods, the single construction channel construction method causes the least damage to the surrounding rock, which is mainly concentrated in the cavity sidewalls. The thickness and strength of the initial support and secondary lining should be strengthened in the later construction, which can effectively change the damage to the surrounding rock of the cavity side wall.

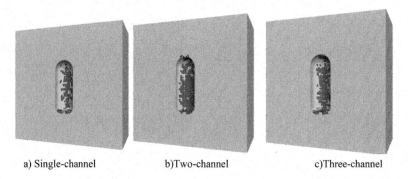

a) Single-channel b)Two-channel c)Three-channel

Figure 7. Plastic zone comparison chart.

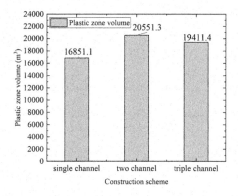

Figure 8. Volume comparison of plastic zone.

2) Fracture morphology

In the calculation process, the failure mode of the calculation unit is determined according to Section 2.3. In this paper, a new mathematical method is used to construct the cracks generated in the calculation process. It is assumed that the cracks are planar polygons, and the crack surface is controlled by the center point position of the crack surface and the normal vector of the crack surface. Assuming that the center point of the calculation unit is the crack center point; for the normal vector of the fracture surface, it is closely related to the failure mode of rock. In the traditional rock mechanics theory, the failure mode of rock will affect the direction of crack formation: the crack formed by tensile failure is perpendicular to the direction of the maximum tensile principal strain; the shear fracture is located at the weakest shear stress-strength ratio of rock, which is related to the direction of internal friction angle and main strain. Accordingly, the direction vector of the fracture surface can be determined, and then the fracture surface can be generated by controlling the center point of the fracture surface and the normal vector. The comparison of the three-dimensional morphology of cracks in three construction schemes is shown in Figure 9. The three-dimensional morphology of the fracture extends along the outdoor surface of the gas storage cavern. The fracture morphology of the single construction channel scheme is only distributed at the top of the gas storage cavern. The fracture morphology of the two construction channel schemes is mainly distributed in the top area of the gas storage cavern and gradually decreases along the wall of the cavern. The fracture morphology of the three construction channel schemes is filled with the surrounding rock of the whole gas storage cavern. Therefore, the fractured rock mass caused by scheme one excavation is less, and construction scheme one is better than scheme two and scheme three.

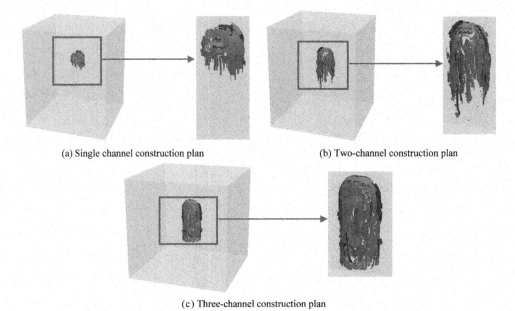

(a) Single channel construction plan   (b) Two-channel construction plan

(c) Three-channel construction plan

Figure 9. Comparison of three-dimensional crack morphology of three different construction schemes.

4 CONCLUSIONS

The proposed three construction excavation schemes of underground gas storage can meet the requirements of construction organization design and the stability of the surrounding rock of gas storage. Through the comparison of construction excavation schemes and numerical simulation, the stability of the surrounding rock of three construction excavation schemes is compared and analyzed. The results show that:

1) The comparison results of the construction excavation scheme show that the single construction channel scheme is suitable. Compared with the other two schemes, the construction cost of the scheme is the lowest, which is not easy to plug the well, the amount of slag is small, the safety hazard is small, and the construction speed is fast; engineering quantity is less and construction period is shorter, saving time.
2) The comparison of calculation results shows that the single construction channel scheme is better. The influence on the top and bottom of the gas storage is small, and the fractured rock mass caused by excavation is less. However, in comparison, the influence of the scheme on the surrounding rock around the gas storage is smaller, and the stability of the surrounding rock is slightly better.

The construction scheme of this study is feasible in theory, basically can meet the requirements of the overall stability of the gas storage, but at present for the expansion scheme of large diameter underground space structure is less, in the use of the implementation phase must be a specific analysis of the specific construction environment, this three kinds of scheme research only for this kind of large gas storage for reference. In order to enhance the feasibility and safety of the scheme, it is necessary to conduct in-depth research on the construction organization, the design of the vertical rotatable lifting (basket) system, and the design of the expansion blasting scheme in the implementation stage.

REFERENCES

Chen Zijian, Yan Zihai, GAN Penglu, Zuo Kaihua. Study on a fuzzy probability model for stability improvement of tunnel surrounding rock and its application [J]. *Tunnel construction* (English and Chinese), 2020, 40(04):504–511.

Gao Qiao, Mark, Tang Chunan, Ma Tianhui. Study on microseismic activity characteristics and stability of surrounding rock during excavation of huanggou pumped storage power station [J]. *Tunnel Construction* (Chinese & English), 2019, 39(05):775–782.

Hu Mou peng, Liang Jiu zheg, Xu Jie. Numerical analysis of the stability of surrounding rock for underground water-sealing oil storage in rock caverns[J]. *Oil & Gas Storage and Transportation*, 2013, 32(4), 370–375.

Jan Johansson. *Design principle of high-pressure gas storage cavern wall in lined cavern* [D]. Royal Institute of Technology, Sweden: Dissertation.

Lei Hong. Opportunities and challenges in the construction of underground gas storage in China [J]. *Oil & Gas Storage and Transportation*, 2018, V. 37; No. 355(07):728–733.

Li Jian. *Deformation characteristics of surrounding rock and support effect evaluation of large underground water-sealed cavern* [D]. Hebei University of Geosciences, 2018.

Li Lu, Chen Xiutong. Excavation sequence and stability analysis of surrounding rock of large underground power plant [J]. *Chinese Journal of Safety Science and Technology*, 2016 (12):5–12.

Liu Xiaogang. Excavation and construction technology of spherical crown domes in large underground caverns under complex geological conditions [J]. *Railway Construction Technology*, 2016, (7): 25–28.

Mu Chuang, Zhang Hong, Xia Haojun. *Journal of Northwest A&F University* (Natural Science Edition), 2004, (S1):139–143.

Sun Kaichang, Sun Zhiyu. Stability analysis of surrounding rock of underground powerhouse cave group in xiangjiaba hydropower station [J]. *Journal of Yangtze River Scientific Research Institute*, 2006, (5):29–32.

Sun Mingzong. *Stability analysis of super-large underground caverns: A case study of Zhanjiang National Strategic Petroleum Reserves* [D]. Hebei University of Geosciences: Master's thesis.

The world's largest underground gas storage and water sealing cavern has been successfully put into operation [J]. *Tunnel Construction*, 2015, 35(09):890.

Wang Hui, Chen Weizhong, Zheng Pengqiang, Wen Zhijie, Li Nan, Wang Qingbiao. *Journal of central south university* (science and technology), 2017, 48(04):1096–1103.

Wang Zhe Chao, Li Shucai, Xue Yiguo, Qiao Liping, Lin Chunjin. Analysis of integrity, deformation, and stability of surrounding rock of large underground water-sealed petroleum caverns [J]. *Journal of Shandong University* (engineering science), 2011, 41(03):112–117+125.

Wei Yun. Stability analysis of surrounding rock of dome under different excavation schemes [J]. *Subgrade Engineering*, 2015(6):128–132.

Xia Caichu, Zhang Pingyang, Zhou Shuwei, et al. Stability, and circumferential strain analysis of large-scale pressurized gas storage caverns. *Rock and Soil Mechanics*, 2014 (5): 1391–1398.

Xiao Ming. Numerical simulation of the three-dimensional dynamic process of excavation of underground caverns [J]. *Chinese Journal of Geotechnical Engineering*, 2000, 4 (7): 421–425.

Yang Ge, Lin Zhiwang, Peng Wei. Research on construction method of fast excavation of large underground caverns [J]. *Sichuan Hydropower*, 2018, 37 (4):22–26.

Zhang Chengbin, Zhang Yaqin. Simulation of stability of large section underground water sealing oil cave [J]. *Oil and Gas Storage and Transportation*, 2019, (07): 827–833.

Zhang Jianshan, Zhang Chuanhu, Song Haijie, Qi Jieyi. Excavation and construction technology of super-large underground caverns in wudongde hydropower station [J]. *Electric Power Survey and Design*, 2020, (6):12–16.

Building protection restoration technology and construction transformation technology

Analysis of reverse modeling techniques for BIM application in different construction projects

Yu Zhang & Dehai Zhang
School of Management, Shenyang Jianzhu University, Shenyang, China

Daguang Han*
Department of Building and Energy Technology, Oslo Metropolitan University, Oslo, Norway

Long Chen
School of Architecture, Building and Civil Engineering, Loughborough University, Loughborough, UK

Kaixin Hu
Chongqing Smart City and Sustainable Development Academy, Chongqing, China

Di Tao
College of Civil Engineering, Chongqing Jiaotong University, Chongqing, China

Mingshuo Gao
School of Management, Shenyang Jianzhu University, Shenyang, China

Ming Chen
Chongqing Smart City and Sustainable Development Academy, Chongqing, China

ABSTRACT: In recent ten years, the building information model (BIM) has been focused on various stages and scenes of construction engineering, but there is no consensus on the practical application of BIM. This paper introduces the principle and process of three-dimensional laser scanning and image-based modeling technology (IBM), the critical reverse modeling technology. Then, the reverse modeling technology meets the demands of different architectural objects, such as different application scenarios, architectural characteristics, and the actual needs of the project site. The paper will explore the reverse modeling technology suitable for different engineering requirements. At the same time, the fourth chapter of this paper will give some practical cases to illustrate the problems encountered in practical work and provide a specific reference value for similar projects. The source data required for reverse modeling can be roughly divided into design information of existing buildings and reality capture. Combined with specific projects, the feature analysis table provides scientific decision-making for reverse modeling technicians, improves efficiency, and saves costs.

1 INTRODUCTION

Accompanying the boom in computer-aided engineering (CAE), BIM or digital twin (DT) technology is applied in construction engineering everywhere. Whether it is based on BIM or DT technology, the initial task of the project is to create a visual model. For a large number of existing buildings, it is possible that BIM was not used at the beginning of the project, that factories and hospitals needed to be upgraded, and those ancient buildings needed to be digitally restored,

---

*Corresponding Author: daguangh@oslomet.no

when infrastructure needed to be managed and maintained digitally, a visual model needs to be re-established. In the actual project implementation, the existing reverse building modeling methods (RBM) are mainly divided into 2D drawing modeling, 3D laser scanners, photography, oblique photography, and other reality capture reverse modeling technology.

This paper mainly introduces the different technology, equipment, and principle of building a 3D model of an intelligent building and the combination of technology to improve the maintenance level of an intelligent building. This paper focuses on the detailed analysis of how to choose the method of creating a model when a BIM or DT project is required.

2 CURRENT METHODS OF REVERSE MODELING TECHNIQUES

2.1 Modeling with 2D drawings

CAD is a general term for designing, drawing, analyzing, and writing technical documents of products and projects using a computer as a tool. There are still a lot of 2D drawings for BIM applications around the world, and about 90% of all 2D drawings are still used in the United States today that are based on CAD technology and then combined with modeling software for building BIM models (Ragia et al. 2016). BIM software creates models that are not simple 3D models but relatively standard data sets in the construction industry. So the difference between BIM models and 3D models is whether or not they support IFC. In buildingSMART, a list of certified software that supports IFC is given. BIM Software can be roughly divided into modeling Software and using modeling Software. The core modeling Software (BIM Authoring Software) is the basis of BIM (Standard modeling software: Autodesk Revit, Bentley, and ARCHICAD).

2.2 3D laser scanning

As a new technology for 3D data acquisition, the basic principle of a 3D laser scanner is laser ranging. The laser emitter sends out the laser, hits the object surface, and then reflects on being received by the receiver and calculates the reflectivity of the object surface according to the energy received. It uses the principle of laser pulse ranging to obtain the characteristic surface information of the scanned object by processing the data. The working principle is to obtain the 3D coordinate information of the reflection point by internal recording and calculating the reflectivity, recording and storing the D information of the scanned object in Figure 1.

Due to its wide scanning range, high precision, fast scanning speed, and adaptability to different scanning scenes, it is mainly used in reverse engineering, responsible for surface copy number, 3D measurement of a workpiece, for the existing 3D object (sample or model) without the relevant 2D drawing, the data of the object's contour collection can be quickly measured, constructed and edited, surface digitizing model modified to generate general output format.

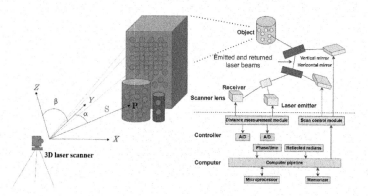

Figure 1. Working principles of 3D laser scanner and imaging.

2.3 Photograph and oblique photography

Actual scene modeling starts from nature photography, mainly close-up and tilts photography (Guo et al. 2020). Tilt photography real scene modeling is a new 3D modeling technology in the field of Surveying and mapping, design, and construction in recent years. The UAV is equipped with a high-resolution tilt camera and other equipment to collect aerial data from different angles and then use the 3D modeling software to solve the collected photos, point clouds, videos, and other data and quickly create a centimeter-level actual scene model. Camera modeling uses a camera to take several photos around a scene and import them into the software. After combining algorithms, a 3D model that can be rotated and browsed is generated (Lu & Brilakis 2019). The following points should be paid attention to when modeling with photos.

1. UAV is used to collect a large number of photos in the air, and there must be an inevitable overlap between every two photos to find the matching points in the later stage.
2. The original data of each photo (such as shooting coordinates, shooting angle, and focal length) should be obtained in advance as much as possible to reduce the amount of calculation in the later stage:
3. The software is used to sort out a large number of photos, automatically select matching points, and calculate the original data that cannot be obtained.
4. The spatial coordinates of each matching point are calculated, and then the coordinates of other vital points are supplemented through the algorithm, and the material is pasted to form the model.

3 LITERATURE RESEARCH AND CONTENT ANALYSIS

3.1 Research on application requirements of BIM model for engineering

By searching the Web of Science (WOS) for the frequency of the keyword in Table 1 to find the project in the development BIM facing different scenarios, with "engineering application" and "BIM" as the keyword, a total of 371 articles were searched in the past five years. Then the basic application scenarios and directions were determined by the literature clustering analysis (see Figure 2) with VOSviewer. Then searched "BIM"+ "Factory", "BIM"+ "Infrastructure (bridge, road, and tunnel)", and "BIM"+ "Historic building" by WOS to get the rest. In the same way, the literature analysis is used to get the value of running and managing BIM models for different application scenarios.

Table 1. WoS search for specific content.

Keywords	Year	Count
"BIM"+ "Engineering application"	Nearly five years	371
"BIM"+ "Factory"		28
"BIM"+ "Infrastructure (bridge, road, tunnel)"		365
"BIM"+ "Historic building"		104

3.2 Determining basic indicators

4 CASE STUDY

4.1 Case description

Case 1: The bridge can be scanned by three-dimensional laser scanning technology (Yang et al. 2015). The Leica P50 scanner is installed at the bridge construction site to scan the precise 3D

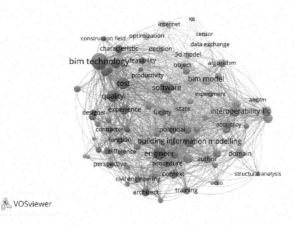

Figure 2. Clustering analysis results for "Engineering application + BIM" using VOSviewer.

Table 2. Generality and personality are collated.

Building category	Generality	Personality
Factory	BIM	Predictive maintenance
	Information technology	Framework
	Digital twin	Reliability
	Algorithm	Productivity
	Point cloud	Automation
	Asset management	Effectiveness
	Whole life cycle	Algorithm
	(design/construction/operation/maintenance phase)	Cost
	Data analysis and processing	Detection
	Availability	
	Integration	
	Sensor	
Infrastructure (Mainly for bridges, roads, and ports)	IoT	FEM/FEA
	Sustainability	Inspection

geometry of the components after noise reduction and cutting (see Figure 3). To work with the structural analysis team, the model will be further analyzed and simulated using the pylons and trusses of cable-stayed bridges in Geomagic Control (see Figure 4).

Case 2: The 3D laser scanning technology is used to scan the factory to obtain the complete point cloud data of the workshop. The complete point cloud data will be more convenient to compare with the scene and compared with the CAD drawings in the design stage. Factory piping modeled with BIM software facilitates the organization of MEP (Lu et al. 2018) related content and provides quick access to a list of pipe sizes and materials (see Figure 5).

Case 3: In the case of a small pavilion in an ancient building, a combination of oblique photography and photography can be used to obtain more precise coordinates and corresponding texture images (see Figure 6).

4.2 *Analysis of the application of modeling methods in different scenarios*

From the literature review and project experience, we can roughly divide BIM modeling into two methods. The first method uses CAD drawing-based modeling software (Method A), and the second is reverse modeling based on reality capture (Method B).

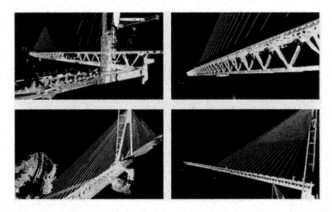

Figure 3. Large-span cable-stayed bridge point cloud.

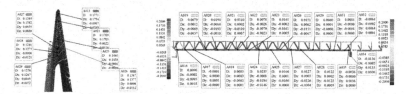

Figure 4. Data analysis of cable-stayed bridge tower and truss.

Figure 5. A car production workshop point cloud.

4.2.1 *Combing method A and method B*

The two completely complement each other. Method B of the modeling is complicated, and the process is complex, and the application of Method B on the object is relatively simple, and the modeling is not intricate. Method A is better than Method B in modeling complex buildings; however, because Method A is based on CAD drawings rather than reality, there is a lack of accuracy.

4.2.2 *Taking method B as the dominant method, while method A as the auxiliary method*

A is more suitable for infrastructure projects such as bridges or historic buildings (Cho & Liu 2017), as infrastructure often requires as much dimensional information as is realistic to facilitate later finite element analysis. The central part of the bridge focuses on the point cloud, and the remaining auxiliary settings of the bridge can be modeled directly with CAD drawings. More suitable for housing construction projects, oriented and facilities management, the integrity of various equipment is more substantial, but at the same time, precision requirements are not high. However, something is missing in the diagram for a renovation project, and a point cloud is needed.

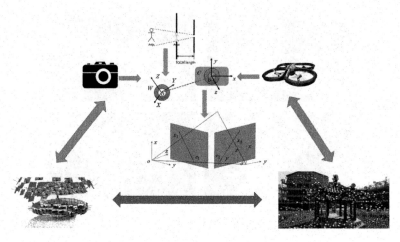

Figure 6. The picture shows the combination of taking pictures and drones.

Unlike the first scan, the second scan has high-quality construction, building, and highly consistent design models. It is possible to use drawings that contain more information.

5 CONCLUSION

Combined with specific projects and literature analysis, it is concluded that different applications in different scenarios or the same scenario may need different modeling requirements to guide the technical staff to model.

It is important to note that even if the reader chooses the recommended collocation based on the matrix summarized in this article, there will still be problems based on different stages and scenarios. For example, party A's work plan in the factory to be released to the new products needs to be kept confidential so that the site can not be typical arrangements for work. This situation recommends that parties B and A communicate entirely, advance each other's work plans, etc.

In a similar project in the future, technicians can conduct demand research in the initial stage of the project to generate the owners' needs opinion matrix to fully consider its particularity of it.

REFERENCES

Cho C Y, Liu X. (2017) An automated reconstruction approach of mechanical systems in building information modeling (BIM) using 2D drawings. *Asce International Workshop on Computing in Civil Engineering.*, 0: 236–244.
Guo J, Wang Q, Park J H. (2020) Geometric quality inspection of prefabricated MEP modules with 3D laser scanning. *Automation in Construction.*, 111: 103053.
Lu Q, Lee S, Chen L. (2018) Image-driven fuzzy-based system to construct as-is IFC BIM objects., *Automation in Construction.*, 92 (AUG.): 68–87.
Lu R, Brilakis I. (2019) Digital twinning of existing reinforced concrete bridges from labelled point clusters. *Automation in construction.*, 105 (SEP.): 102837.1–102837.16.
Ragia L, F Sarri, Mania K. (2016) 3D Reconstruction and visualization of alternatives for restoration of historic buildings. *International Conference on Geographical Information Systems Theory*, IEEE.
Yang X, Qin X, Wang J, et al. (2015) Building Façade recognition using oblique aerial images., *Remote Sensing.*

Information acquisition method of steel bridge manufacturing process oriented to intelligent construction

Jizhuang Hui*, Yafei Wang*, Chao Li, Xiaodong Yang & Jinlong Zhang
National Engineering Research Center of Highway Maintenance Equipment, Chang'an University, Xi'an, Shaanxi, China

ABSTRACT: To solve the information problem of steel structure bridge manufacturing process management, we proposed an event-driven steel structure bridge manufacturing information collection method based on Web, two-dimensional code, and database technologies, and established a steel structure collaborative construction decision-making information platform. Firstly, the code system of the steel structure bridge is constructed based on the construction resource code rules in the framework of BIM technology, and the two-dimensional code is produced by the unique code of the component of the code system. Secondly, QR code and steel structure bridge components/segments are combined to form an "intelligent entity", and its production factors are defined. Finally, an event-driven steel structure bridge information model is constructed, and the information collection of spatial location, state, time, and other factors in the manufacturing process of the steel structure bridge is realized by combining the Web information management platform. The whole information collection process is marked by the component/segment code, and the component/segment two-dimensional code is used as the unified carrier to form a complete data chain of manufacturing, quality inspection, and transportation process. The application of the case shows that the application of the information model can solve the problem of isolated information resources in the prefabricated production and construction management of steel bridges, and improve the characteristics of the traditional information record with low timeliness and poor accuracy.

1 INTRODUCTION

With the increasing application of emerging technologies such as cyber-physical fusion systems and digital twins in the manufacturing industry, real-time collection, processing, and analysis of the operation status data of the manufacturing process have been preliminarily realized in the traditional manufacturing workshop of the parts manufacturing process, and the transparency of production process has been improved. However, at present, the network collaborative manufacturing technology for industrial construction of steel structure bridges is still vacant, and it is difficult to realize the construction of a real-time information model in the manufacturing process of steel structure bridges, and then it is difficult to realize the autonomous intelligent production and management of steel structure bridge manufacturing.

Liu Zhaoqiu et al. (2020) constructed a building structure information model system for the engineering design stage by analyzing the information integration process and characteristics of BIM technology, which provided support for collaborative design and integrated building engineering software development. Xi Quanquan (Xi 2020) built a prefabricated beam production information management platform by combining mobile Internet technology, two-dimensional code technology, Baidu map API, and other technologies, and realized the production progress and quality

---

*Corresponding Authors: huijz@chd.edu.cn and wangyafei052@163.com

control of prefabricated beam production units by the headquarters. Liu Hao et al. (2020) proposed to combine BIM and two-dimensional code technology for information management of traditional prefabricated buildings and use the component code as a unique mark for information exchange, which solves the problem of information islands in traditional prefabricated buildings to a certain extent. Shi Zhankuan et al. (2017) developed the two-dimensional code technology based on the Web platform, and its application in construction management can effectively improve the efficiency of construction management. Zhong Kangjian et al. (2021) combined BIM, digitalization, and Internet of Things technology to build a smart bridge management platform. This platform can effectively improve the timeliness and accuracy of relevant data during information collection, and realize efficiency improvement and resource-saving while controlling the construction schedule. Chen Ning et al. (2017) developed a 3D visualization bridge disease information collection and management system by using the 3D visualization characteristics of the BIM model, which provided an intuitive and convenient working method for bridge maintenance.

To sum up, the current research work mostly focuses on the information management of traditional buildings, and the research on bridge information management is mostly in the stage of bridge maintenance and management, and there is less research on the key information management system in the bridge manufacturing process. This paper takes the manufacturing process of steel structure bridges as the research object, constructs an intelligent entity of steel structure bridges driven by bridges, and uses two-dimensional code, web, database, and other technologies to realize the information collection, interaction, and effective circulation of steel structure bridges in the manufacturing process.

2 BIM-BASED CODING SYSTEMS FOR STEEL STRUCTURE BRIDGES

The building information model (BIM) integrates the geometric model information, functional requirements, and component performance of the building project. It integrates all the information in the entire life cycle of the building project into a single building model and uses the BIM three-dimensional model as the information carrier. It can realize information exchange, sharing, and collaborative work in the whole life cycle of the project, and promote the informatization and intelligent development of the project construction process (He & Han 2011). The inconsistency of the bridge coding system brings a series of problems to the application of BIM technology and hinders the transmission and management of information in the construction process. Therefore, a unified and standardized coding system is an important basis for realizing informatization, the basis for information tracking, and the starting point for multi-professional, multi-department, and multi-field collaboration.

At present, there is no uniform standard for the coding of steel structure bridges in engineering. The coding rules in BIM technology are aimed at buildings, and there is no uniform standard for the classification and coding of bridge engineering components. Code steel structure bridges should follow the BIM coding rules (Zhang, Dong, Yepes, 2019). Steel structure bridge components or segments belong to construction resources. Based on the coding rules for construction resources in BIM, a coding system for steel structure bridges is built with engineering breakdown structure (EBS) coding (Liu, Lu, 2020). The compilation rules for establishing coding are shown in Figure 1. The symbols in Figure 1 ("*", "-", and ".") refer to connectors.

The specific part of the code and meaning examples are shown in Table 1 below.

3 BUILDING AN INTELLIGENT ENTITY FOR STEEL BRIDGES

3.1 *Brief introduction of two-dimensional code technology*

A two-dimensional code is a black and white graphic that uses a specific geometric graphic to distribute on a plane according to a certain rule, it is a barcode format for recording data symbol

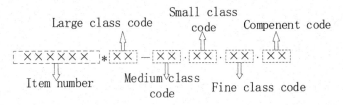

Figure 1. Encoding rules.

Table 1. Meaning of codes.

Category	Code	Meaning
Large class	10	Bridge and culvert
Medium class	10-03	Superstructure
Small class	10-03.10	Beam
Small class	10-03.20	Connection
Fine class	10-03.10.10	Main beam

information (Lu, 2020); two-dimensional code uses the concept of "0, 1" bit stream that constitutes the internal logic basis of the computer in the code compilation, and the data information is represented as a plane geometric figure by computer coding technology. In other words, the information is directly stored in the two-dimensional code. The two-dimensional code graphic is the content after the information is binarized (0, 1). QR code is selected as the research object in this study.

3.2 Build smart entities

The intelligent entity corresponds to the physical entity, which is an organic combination of information, models, and objects. Real-time sharing and collection of information can be achieved by constructing intelligent entities, and QR codes are used to generate two-dimensional codes for steel structure bridge components or sections. Each two-dimensional code contains the corresponding component coding information. The two-dimensional code is marked to the corresponding component or segment to be manufactured. Segment/component and two-dimensional code constitute an intelligent entity.

The construction of intelligent entities needs to further determine the information collection objects and definition elements, the information collection objects of intelligent entities are changed physical quantities, and the actual conditions of the entities are reflected in real time through the changed physical quantities. The change of entity in the process of machining is mainly divided into state change and spatial position change. The state change can reflect the progress of machining and manufacturing; during the construction of a bridge, spatial position change can efficiently monitor the machining and manufacturing process and provide real-time information regarding the spatial position, providing necessary information support for bridge construction.

The status of the intelligent entity mainly includes the status to be processed, the status in processing, the status of processing completed, the status of inventory and delivery, the status of transportation, and the status of acceptance. In each status, key manufacturing information needs to be uploaded.

The spatial position changes of intelligent entities mainly involve three scenarios—equipment, storage, and transportation. In the equipment and storage scenarios, the intelligent entities have no continuous changes in spatial points. In the transportation scenario, the intelligent entity is bound to the transportation tool, and the spatial position is constantly changing. Due to the correspondence between processes and equipment, the same equipment may correspond to multiple processes, but the flow of the process cannot reflect the flow of the actual spatial position, so the equipment and the process are coupled, which is space = {*equipment*∩*craft, storage, transportation*}, thereby forming a matching relationship between space and scene.

The elements of an intelligent entity are defined as follows:

Definition 1: Spatial location (*I*)

The spatial position (*I*) identifies the location of the intelligent entity at the time of an event, arranged and numbered according to its chronological sequence. The spatial position of the intelligent entity k increases sequentially and is expressed as $I_i^k = \{i_1^k, i_2^k, \cdots, i_n^k\}$.

Definition 2: Event (*E*)

Event (*E*) contains a series of operations on the intelligent entity, with the operation on the database as the sign of the event occurrence. $E_{i,j}^k$ represents an event *j* that occurs on space *i* by an intelligent entity k "$j = 1, 2, 3, 4, 5, 6, 7$" represent events to be processed, events in the process, events completed, events in storage, events out of storage, events in transportation, and events in acceptance, respectively.

As a set of operations, events can be described as follows:

$$E_{i,j}^k = \{ID_{tag}^k, I_i^k, t_{i,j}^k, R_{i,j}^k\} \tag{1}$$

where ID_{tag}^K is the number of the two-dimensional code; $t_{i,j}^k$ represents the moment when event *j* occurs on space *i* of intelligent entity k; $R_{i,j}^k$ represents the executor of event *j* that occurs to intelligent entity k on space *i*.

Definition 3: State (*S*)

State (*S*) is a process quantity that represents the state of the intelligent entity within the two events. $S_{i,m}^k$ means that the intelligent entity k is in the *m* state on space *i*. Among them, "$m = 1, 2, 3, 4, 5, 6, 7$" represents the status of pending processing, processing, completion of processing, inventory, warehouse delivery, transportation, and acceptance, respectively.

Definition 4: Event time (*T*)

$T_{i,j}^k$ represents the duration of the intelligent entity in the state $S_{i,m}^k$. The event time $t_{i,j}^k$ represents the moment when the event *j* occurs in space *i* of the intelligent entity k.

Definition 5: Event Executor (*R*)

Event executor $R_{i,j}^k$ represents the executor of event *j* that occurs on space *i* to intelligent entity k.

Definition 6: Process Status (S_t)

The technological state S_t represents the current technological state of the intelligent entity k.

4 EVENT-DRIVEN MANUFACTURING PROCESS INFORMATION COLLECTION

4.1 Intelligent entity information model

The intelligent entity information model of the steel structure bridge is driven by events. The operation of the two-dimensional code and the database is completed instantaneously, so it is regarded as an event, and the state of the intelligent entity is a process quantity, which is judged by two consecutive events, and the state changes when the next event occurs.

The information flow chart of the intelligent entity in three states is shown in Figure 2 The information of a certain state process is represented by $C_{i,j}^k$, which is abbreviated as:

$$C_{i,j}^k = \{S_{i,j}^k, E_{i,j}^k, E_{i,j+1}^k, T_{i,j}^k\} \tag{2}$$

After expansion and merger, it is expressed as:

$$C_{i,j}^k = \begin{cases} \{ID_{tag}^k, S_{i,j}^k, I_i^k, t_{i,j}^k, R_{i,j}^k, t_{i,j+1}^k, T_{i,j}^k\} & j = 1, 2 \\ \{ID_{tag}^k, S_{i,j}^k, I_i^k, t_{i,j}^k, R_{i,j}^k, t_{i+1,1}^k, T_{i,j}^k\} & j = 3 \end{cases} \tag{3}$$

where $T_{i,j}^k = t_{i,j+1}^k - t_{i,j}^k$ represents the duration of a state.

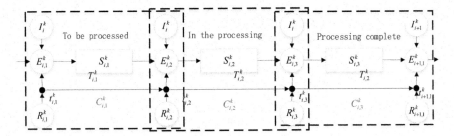

Figure 2. State information.

For the set of information on the same space I_i^k, they are respectively expressed as $E_i^k = \{E_{i,1}^k, E_{i,2}^k, E_{i,3}^k\}$, $S_i^k = \{S_{i,1}^k, S_{i,2}^k, S_{i,3}^k\}$, $t_i^k = \{t_{i?1}^k, t_{i,2}^k, t_{i,3}^k\}$, $T_i^k = \{T_{i,1}^k, T_{i,2}^k, T_{i,3}^k\}$, and $R_i^k = \{R_{i,1}^k, R_{i,2}^k, R_{i,3}^k\}$.

The information model is further made, as shown in Figure 3.

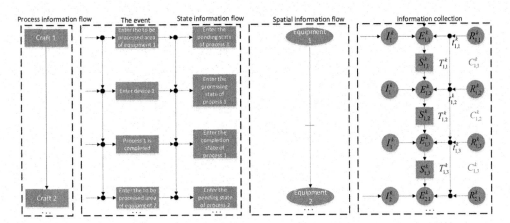

Figure 3. The information model.

It can be seen from the above information model that the information model of steel structure bridge includes process, state, and space changes.

1. There are three information flows in the manufacturing process: state, space, and process.
The spatial information flow I^k is expressed as:

$$I^k = i_1^k \to i_2^k \to \cdots i_n^k \qquad (4)$$

The state information flow S^k is represented as:

$$S^k = \underbrace{S_{1,1}^k \to S_{1,2}^k \to S_{1,3}^k}_{S_1^k} \to \underbrace{S_{2,1}^k \to S_{2,2}^k \to S_{2,3}^k}_{S_2^k} \to \underbrace{\cdots, \cdots,}_{\cdots} \to \underbrace{S_{n,1}^k \to S_{n,2}^k \to S_{n,3}^k}_{S_n^k} \qquad (5)$$

The process information flow S_t^k is expressed as:

$$S_t^k = S_k^1 \to S_k^2 \to \cdots S_k^n \qquad (6)$$

2. The total manufacturing time is equal to the sum of the individual state durations, and is equal to the manufacturing end time minus the manufacturing start time, as shown in Equation 7.

$$T^k = T_1^k + T_2^k + \cdots + T_n^k = \sum_{j=1}^{3} T_{1,j}^k + \sum_{j=1}^{3} T_{2,j}^k + \cdots + \sum_{j=1}^{3} T_{n,j}^k = t_{n,3}^k - t_{1,1}^k \qquad (7)$$

3. The set of total manufacturing person-times is the set of processing and manufacturing personnel, including the set of personnel in various states, as shown in Equation 8.

$$R^k = \left\{ \underbrace{R_{1,1}^k, R_{1,2}^k R_{1,3}^k}_{R_1^k}, \underbrace{R_{2,1}^k, R_{2,2}^k R_{2,3}^k}_{R_2^k}, \cdots, \underbrace{R_{n,1}^k, R_{n,2}^k R_{n,3}^k}_{R_n^k} \right\} \qquad (8)$$

4.2 *Manufacturing process information collection*

Steel structure bridge components/segments need to go through multiple process steps from raw materials to finished products, and the typical processing states to be experienced by different processes are the same. Since the component position information is determined by the current process state, collecting the manufacturing process information of the typical machining state is necessary to complete the collection of the physical quantity of the intelligent entity change.

The information collection process is dynamic, and the human-computer interaction collection process is shown in Figure 4. This requires developing a bridge component/segment database, where the table structure is a one-to-many relationship, and the segments contain component-related information. The device can scan the two-dimensional code of components to decode the two-dimensional code of components and submit the code to the back-end through the web front-end. The back-end queries the corresponding information in the database through the encoded information and returns it to the front-end, and the front-end renders the information and presents it to the user.

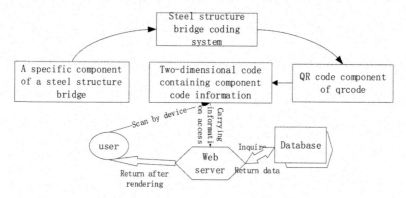

Figure 4. Information collection process.

5 ENGINEERING EXAMPLE

Take the manufacturing process of a steel structure bridge S as an example. The project number is 17-24 K. The main beam adopts welded I-beam section, with six main beam structures, four holes, and a total of 24 main beams. Through the establishment of a prototype system based on B/S architecture, the function of collecting the manufacturing information of steel structure bridges is realized, and the feasibility of the model is verified. The MySQL database is used to store data information, and PyCharm is used as the development tool. First, the monitoring variables and element information of the intelligent entity are entered into the database, connected to the web, the two-dimensional code number is corresponding to the manufacturing information in the database, and the corresponding data table is established for the manufacturing requirements and manufacturing information. Some functions of the prototype system developed according to the steel bridge information model are as follows:

1. Two-dimensional code pre-management. Project managers code the components according to the steel structure bridge coding system, and generate Two-dimensional code labels on the web page according to the component codes.
2. Create database tables. After the designer establishes the building model of the steel structure bridge, the management personnel establish the data table under the project database according to the minimum processing unit's manufacturing requirements and manufacturing information for the steel structure bridge.
3. Manufacturing process information collection. During the manufacturing process, the manufacturing process is recorded by scanning the QR code, triggering events and recording the manufacturing process in the form of events, and storing the information in the database at the same time.
4. Information statistics. The current manufacturing information is statistically analyzed and processed to obtain factors such as manufacturing time, personnel, and progress that are important to the current manufacturing process.
5. Judgment of illegal operation. For example, according to the manufacturing requirements, the steel structure is subjected to non-destructive testing by a class-A qualified testing agency 24 hours after welding. At this time, $t_{9,3}^{01} = 2022 - 01 - 26\ 10:53:21, t_{10,1}^{01} = 2022 - 01 - 27\ 08:30:45 t_{10,1}^{01} - t_{9,3}^{01} < 24h$. Therefore, it is an illegal operation, and the platform issues a warning. As shown in Figure 5, administrators can implement remote monitoring of illegal operations.

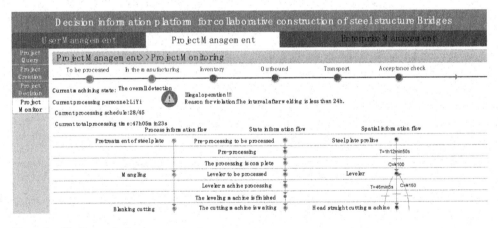

Figure 5. Platform warning.

6 CONCLUSION

This paper establishes a steel structure bridge coding system by analyzing the coding rules of construction resources under BIM technology and realizes the connection between steel structure bridges and BIM technology, providing a guarantee for the further realization of the information transmission of the intelligent construction of steel structure bridges. Based on the establishment of the steel structure bridge coding system, an intelligent entity of steel structure bridge segments/components based on QR code is established. As a result, an event-driven information model is built for steel structure bridges by defining the spatial location, time, process status, and other elements of intelligent entities. By updating the database information for the operation of the two-dimensional code at different stages, the monitoring of the status, space, process, and quality of the intelligent entity and the collection of key manufacturing information is realized, improving the real-time and reliability of construction process information tracking; the relevant information registered in each link provides a guarantee for the traceability of information in the later operation and maintenance stage. At the same time, the digital representation of bridge entities and information features improves the shortcomings of traditional information records such as low timeliness and poor accuracy.

ACKNOWLEDGMENT

This study was partly funded by the Tibet Autonomous Region Science and Technology Project (Grant No. XZ2019TL-G-03), and partly by the Shaanxi Provincial Department of Transportation (Grant No. 17-21K).

REFERENCES

Chen Ning, Ma Zhi-hua, Bo Ping, et al. Bridge disease information 3D based on BIM technology visual acquisition management system [J]. Journal of China & Foreign Highway, 2017, 37(01): 305–8.
He Qing-hua, Han Xiang-yu. The framework construction and process design of progress management system based on BIM [J]. Project Management Technology, 2011, 9(09): 96–9.
Liu Hao, Hong Jie-ru, Zhang Meng-xia, Wang Jin-yang, et al. Research on the management for the information of prefabricated building combining BIM and QR code technology [J]. Construction Technology, 2020, 49(02): 110–4+8.
Liu J, Lu M. Synchronized optimization of various management-function schedules in a multiproject environment: Case study of planning steel girder fabrication projects in bridge construction [J]. Journal of Construction Engineering and Management, 2020, 146: 05020002.
Liu Zhao-qiu, Li Yun-gui, Lv Xi-lin, Zhang Han-yi. BIM-Based integrated information framework for architectural and structural design model[J]. Journal of Tongji University(Natural Science), 2010, 38(07):948–953.
Lu L. Research on anti-counterfeiting technology based on encrypted two-dimensional code [J]. Insight – Information, 2020, 2(2).
Shi Zhan-kuan, Qiao Wen-tao, Leng Ping, et al. Research on application of QR code technology based on web platform in construction management [J]. Building Structure, 2017, 47(S1): 1193–6.
Xi Quan-quan. Research and development of production information management platform for precast beams of city road and bridge[D]. Zhengzhou University, 2020.
Zhang L, Dong L, Yepes V. Application study on building information model (BIM) standardization of chinese engineering breakdown structure (EBS) coding in life cycle management processes [J]. Advances in Civil Engineering, 2019, 2019.
Zhong Kang-jian, Ma Chao-fan. Analysis of intelligent bridge construction management guided by building information model+digitization+internet of things technology [J]. Highway, 2021, 66(07): 203–8.

The evolution roadmap of building carbon emissions based on scenario analysis method

Hongkai Wang, Dong Mao* & Hanyu Rao
State Grid Zhejiang Electric Power Corporation Information & Telecommunication Branch, Hangzhou, Zhejiang, China

ABSTRACT: Based on the fact that the construction industry accounts for a considerable proportion of the total greenhouse gas emissions, the control of building carbon emissions has become the focus of energy conservation and emission reduction. The establishment of "a carbon emissions trading market" has also become the main environmental policy tool for countries to achieve a low-carbon economy. In this paper, the method of scenario analysis is used to identify the influencing factors, and the number of factors is controlled by setting the frequency of the concept of factors adopted in the scenario to highlight the "criticality" of the identified influencing factors. Firstly, the connotation and content of building carbon emission rights are analyzed in depth. Secondly, the feasibility and implementation steps of the method are determined based on the identification method of influencing factors. Finally, the carbon evolution route model of each influencing factor is constructed according to the identification results. Under the possibility of improving carbon emission reduction technologies, the effect of enterprises' control on carbon emissions from buildings under various environmental systems is studied. In this paper, we studied the effectiveness of different market environments and institutional tools through comparative analysis based on controlling the total amount of carbon emissions. The research results showed that the construction of the carbon market trading system can effectively solve the negative externality of carbon emissions and internalize the external cost to achieve the Pareto optimality of the whole society. As a form of carbon pricing, carbon emission trading has proved the market mechanism's feasibility and superiority in solving the Coase theorem's externality problem. Under the current background, this paper makes an in-depth study on the market-based environmental policy tools for building energy conservation and emission reduction, which can provide a decision-making basis for environmental policymakers and promote the harmonious development of energy, economy, and environment.

1 INTRODUCTION

From an economic point of view, building energy conservation and emission reduction is an external problem. The internalization of external costs is the fundamental way to solve this problem, which generally covers two different ways, corresponding to planning means and market means respectively. To achieve more sustainable energy conservation and emission reduction, the more effective choice is to carry out market-oriented regulation, and the establishment of "a carbon emissions trading market" is the main environmental policy tool for countries to cope with climate change and low-carbon economy (Pozo et al. 2020). Building carbon emission refers to the right of building owners or users to discharge carbon into the atmosphere reasonably according to the law under the constraints of natural conditions and relevant laws and regulations to meet the normal functions of buildings and within the emission limits allocated by regulatory authorities following certain principles or methods (Pye et al. 2017). The building carbon emission trading mechanism is

*Corresponding Author: 641743819@qq.com

composed of two parts: carbon emission management and trading. The operation of the mechanism involves the main functional departments of the regulatory authorities, trading platforms, advisory bodies, and enterprises included in the carbon emission trading mechanism, each of which performs its duties and plays an executive role in the carbon emission trade mechanism (Qi & Cheng 2018).

This study adopts partial equilibrium and game theory analysis methods regarding the theoretical impact of environmental policy tools on corporate emission reduction behavior. To effectively avoid the problems and limitations in the practical application of the static game analysis method, because the development of the carbon emission trading system is still in the exploratory stage in China, this paper fully draws on and absorbs the current domestic and foreign-related research. Based on the perspectives of regulatory authorities and enterprises, this paper uses a game model to conduct a comparative study of two types of environmental policy tools, carbon tax and carbon emission trading rights and analyzes the evolution mechanism of building carbon emission behavior strategies.

2 EVOLUTIONARY ANALYSIS OF CARBON EMISSION BEHAVIOR STRATEGY

In the game relationship between the secondary market and the primary market under the carbon tax and carbon emission trading mechanism, based on the current situation, it is assumed that the secondary market and the primary market are both bounded rational game parties (Qian et al. 2018). According to the economic benefits of emission reduction, enterprises choose to implement or not to implement carbon emission reduction behavior strategies. The implementation of carbon emission reduction by enterprises will result in technology input cost I, and the same result will also reduce the carbon emissions e' of enterprises. After formulating the carbon tax policy, the primary market can choose two behavioral strategies of strict regulation or loose regulation (Qin et al. 2017). The strict supervision strategy adopted by the regulatory authorities will inevitably result in costs (C^g). If it is found that enterprises do not implement carbon emission reduction behavior, the regulatory authorities will impose πf penalty fees on them, and will also provide incentives (S) for enterprises that implement carbon emission reduction behavior. In addition, the result of reducing carbon emissions by implementing carbon emission reduction behavior will bring reputation benefits (R) to the regulatory authorities (Rogel et al. 2019). According to the above parameters with the game analysis, this paper constructs the "2 × 2" benefit payment matrix which is composed of the secondary market and the primary market in their respective strategies. The results are shown in Table 1.

Table 1. Benefit matrix of primary market and secondary market.

Game side		Primary market	
		Strict supervision	Loose regulation
Secondary market	Carry out	$-t(e-e')-I+S, R-C^g-S$	$-t(e-e')-I, R$
	Do not execute	$-te-\pi f, \pi f-C^g$	$-te, 0$

In the initial stage, the probability that the secondary market chooses to implement the carbon emission reduction strategy is $x(0 \leq x \leq 1)$. The probability that it does not implement it is $1-x$. At the same time, it is assumed that the probability of choosing a strict regulation strategy in the primary market is $y(0 \leq y \leq 1)$, and the probability of choosing loose regulation is $1-y$.

According to Table 1, the expected effects and population effects of the secondary market choosing to implement and not implementing carbon emission reduction strategies can be calculated as follows:

$$U_x = [-t(e-e')-I+S]y + [-t(e-e')-I](1-y) \quad (1)$$

$$U_{1-x} = (-te-\pi f)y + (-te)(1-y) \quad (2)$$

$$\bar{U}_x = xU_x + (1-x)U_{1-x} \quad (3)$$

Similarly, the formulas for the expected effects and population effects of local regulatory authorities choosing strict and loose regulatory strategies are as follows:

$$U_y = (R - C^g - S)x + (\pi f - C^g)(1 - x) \quad (4)$$

$$U_{1-y} = Rx + 0(1 - x) \quad (5)$$

$$\bar{U}_y = yU_y + (1 - y)U_{1-y} \quad (6)$$

According to the evolutionary game theory, this paper assumes that when the secondary market chooses to implement the carbon emission reduction strategy, the growth rate (dx/dt) is proportional to the difference between the effect obtained by choosing the strategy and the population effect.

$$\begin{aligned}\frac{dx}{dt} &= x(U_x - \bar{U}_{1-x}) = x(1-x)(U_x - U_{1-x}) \\ &= x(1-x)[te' - I + S + \pi f]y + [te' - I](1-y)\end{aligned} \quad (7)$$

As above, the replicator dynamic equation expression for the primary market can be obtained in this paper as follows:

$$\begin{aligned}\frac{dy}{dt} &= y(U_y - \bar{U}_{1-y}) = y(1-y)(U_y - U_{1-y}) \\ &= y(1-y)[(R - C^g - S)x + (\pi f - C^g)(1 - x)]\end{aligned} \quad (8)$$

Combining Formula (5) and Formula (6), the two-dimensional dynamic system composed of two populations of the primary market and the secondary market is as follows:

$$\begin{cases}\dfrac{dx}{dt} = x(1-x)[(te' - I + S + \pi f)y + [te' - I](1-y)] \\ \dfrac{dy}{dt} = y(1-y)[(R - C^g - S)x + (\pi f - C^g)(1 - x)]\end{cases} \quad (9)$$

Proposition 1: According to the carbon tax policy, in the dynamic system consisting of the primary market and secondary market, all equilibrium points where players adopt pure strategies are as follows: (0,0), (0,1), (1,0), and (1,1).

For Formula 9, let $\frac{dx}{dt} = 0$, and $\frac{dy}{dt} = 0$. Then, we can obtain: $x = 0; x = 1; y = 0; y = 1$;

There are four pure strategy schemes. Therefore, the stable points of their pure strategies are (0,0), (0,1), (1,0), and (1,1), respectively.

Proposition 2: The above dynamical system may have a mixed strategy equilibrium point: (x^*, y^*), and $x^*, y^* \in (0, 1)$.

For the dynamical system represented by Formula (10), let $Q(y) = (te' - I + S + \pi f)y + [te' - I](1 - y)$ and assume that $P(x) = (R - C^g - S)x + (\pi f - C^g)(1 - x)$. Set x and y equal 0 or 1, then we have:

$$\begin{cases}P(x) = (R - C^g - S)x + (\pi f - C^g)(1 - x) = 0 \\ Q(y) = (te' - I + S + \pi f)y + (te' - I)(1 - y) = 0\end{cases} \quad (10)$$

Let $\frac{dx}{dt} = 0$, and $\frac{dy}{dt} = 0$. The above equation is then solved for $x^* = \frac{C^g - \pi f}{R - C^g - S - \pi f + C^g}$ and $y^* = \frac{I - te'}{S + \pi f}$. If $x^*, y^* \in (0, 1)$, then (x^*, y^*) is the mixed strategy equilibrium point of the dynamical system.

In this paper, the evolutionary stability of the equilibrium point of the evolutionary dynamic system is analyzed to grasp the evolutionary asymptotic stability conditions of the system at each pure strategy stable point. In the multi-population evolutionary game, if the equilibrium point of the evolutionary game is an asymptotic stable state, then it must be a strict Nash equilibrium. The strict Nash equilibrium is a pure strategy equilibrium. According to the Lyapunov stability principle, the asymptotic stability of the equilibrium point of the system can be judged by solving the eigenvalues of the Jacobian matrix obtained from the dynamic system (Ryberg et al. 2020).

According to Equation (10), the Jacobian matrix of the two-dimensional dynamical system can be expressed as:

$$\begin{bmatrix} (1-2x)[(te'-I+S+\pi f)y+[te'-I](1-y) & x(1-x)(S+\pi f) \\ y(1-y)(R-S-\pi f) & (1-2y)[(R-C^g-S)x+(\pi f-C^g)(1-x)] \end{bmatrix} \quad (11)$$

Based on the Lyapunov stability theory, when the eigenvalues of the Jacobian matrix are all negative real numbers at the equilibrium point, then the equilibrium point is stable. When the eigenvalues of a point are positive and negative, it is referred to as a saddle point (Schneider et al. 2020). If they are all negative, the point is the source point. The evolutionary stability of the four equilibrium points in Proposition 1 is analyzed and verified below, and the results are shown in Table 2.

Table 2. Stability analysis of the two-agent evolutionary game.

(x,y)	Eigenvalue λ_1	Eigenvalue λ_2	Asymptotic stability condition
(0, 0)	$te'-I$	$\pi f - C^g$	$te' < I; \pi f < C^g$
(1, 0)	$I - te'$	$R - C^g - S$	$I < te'; R < C^g + S$
(0, 1)	$te' - I + S + \pi f$	$C^g - \pi f$	$te' + S + \pi f < I; C^g < \pi f$
(1, 1)	$I - te' - S - \pi f$	$C^g + S - R$	$I < te' + S + \pi f; C^g + S < R$

From the content of Table 2, this paper can find that if the stable state of strict supervision of the primary market and the implementation of carbon emission reduction in the secondary market is realized, the condition $I < te' + S + \pi f; C^g + S < R$ can be met at the same time. If the parameters satisfy the condition $te' < I; \pi f < C^g$, it is important to note that the evolving dynamical system may reach a steady state of (0, 0) (Stoerk et al. 2019). This would also be a most unacceptable situation. In addition, if the condition $I < te'; R < C^g + S$ is satisfied, it shows that the secondary market can consciously implement the carbon emission reduction strategy without the strict supervision of the regulatory authorities. To sum up, the key point for enterprises to implement environmental protection policies is to reduce the input cost and increase the penalty of the carbon tax πf (Tang et al. 2020).

3 SIMULATION EXPERIMENT ANALYSIS

To intuitively depict the evolution process of the primary market and the secondary market, this paper will use MATLAB software to simulate the dynamic system established above, and then verify the impact of key parameters on the stable state of the system. First, the parameters of the model are assigned, and the assignment results are shown in Table 3.

Table 3. System parameter assignment.

Parameters	t	e'	I	S	π	f	R	C^g
Value	0.4	10	6	2	0.6	8	4	5

The initial state (x_0, y_0) of the evolutionary dynamical system is set to be (0.5, 0.5) and (0.3, 0.5), respectively. When the parameter is set to be (0.5, 0.5), it means that both the secondary market and the regulatory authorities choose their strategic behavior with a half probability. However, when the parameter is (0.3, 0.5), this indicates that the willingness of enterprises to choose carbon emission reduction behavior is low, and the group is more inclined to choose not to implement carbon emission reduction. Therefore, this paper analyzes the evolution trend of the system from these two perspectives. The results are shown in Figures 1 and 2 below.

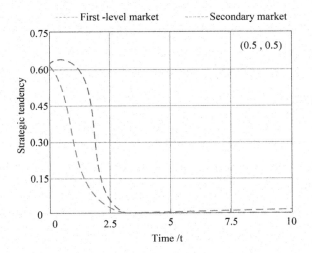

Figure 1. Diagram of behavior evolution when the parameter is set to be (0.5, 0.5).

Figure 1 depicts the evolution trend of the behavior strategy from time 0 to 10 in the primary market and the secondary market in the initial state (0.5, 0.5). The probability of choosing strict supervision in the primary market decreases rapidly from 0.5 and gradually tends to zero. The trend of the secondary market is to increase first and then decrease rapidly to zero.

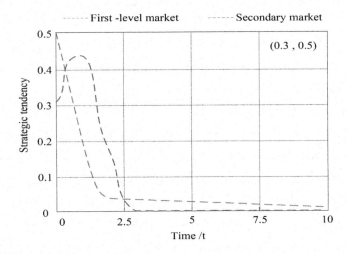

Figure 2. Diagram of behavior evolution when the parameter is set to be (0.3, 0.5).

Figure 2 depicts the behavior strategy evolution trend of the primary market and the secondary market in the initial state (0.3, 0.5). The evolution trend of the behavior strategy of the game players is consistent with Figure 1. When the regulatory authorities choose strict regulation with a high probability, the enterprises still tend to implement the carbon emission reduction strategy.

4 CONCLUSIONS

Based on the current grim situation of building energy conservation and emission reduction, this paper proposes that carbon emissions trading is an important market-based environmental tool to solve building energy conservation and emission reduction, and uses game theory to explore the mechanism of carbon emissions trading and other market-based environmental policy tools on building energy conservation.

(1) The benefit payment matrix composed of the secondary market and the primary market in their respective strategies is constructed. The game relationship between the secondary market and the primary market under the carbon tax and carbon emissions trading mechanism is studied.
(2) The asymptotic stability of the equilibrium point of the system is judged by solving the eigenvalues of the Jacobian matrix of the dynamic system. Then, the system simulation is carried out.

The transaction price is too much controlled by the regulatory authorities, and the auction with strong administrative color is generally used in the transaction. At present, there is no continuous and large amount of trading data, so it is impossible to conduct effective research on the whole market.

Since this article does not configure a reasonable quota, the selected allocation method is not straightforward, and the suggestions given are also one-sided. In the follow-up work process, it is necessary to analyze further the specific research tools and the various impacts on the construction industry to provide reasonable suggestions for price setting.

ACKNOWLEDGMENT

This study was financially supported by the Science and Technology Project Funding of State Grid Zhejiang Electric Power Corporation (Project title: Research on Energy Consumption Evaluation Control and Carbon Evolution Track Analysis Technology Based on Multi-source Energy Data Fusion and Sharing) (Grant No. B311XT210082).

REFERENCES

Pozo C, Galán-Martín Á, Reiner D M. (2020) Equity in allocating carbon dioxide removal quotas. *Nature Climate Change*, 6: 1–7.
Pye S, Li F G N, Price J. (2017) Achieving net-zero emissions through there framing of UK national targets in the post Paris Agreement era. *Nature Energy*, 2 (3): 17024.
Qi S, Cheng S. (2018) China's national emissions trading scheme: Integrating cap, coverage and allocation. *Climate Policy*, 18 (sup1): 45–59.
Qian H, Zhou Y, Wu L. (2018) Evaluating various choices of sector coverage in China's national emissions trading system (ETS). *Climate Policy*, 18 (sup1): 7–26.
Qin Q, Liu Y, Li X. (2017) A multi-criteria decision analysis model for carbon emission quota allocation in China's east coastal areas: Efficiency and equity. *Journal of Cleaner Production*, 2017, 168: 410–419.
Rogel J, Forster P M, Kriegler E. (2019) Estimating and tracking the remaining carbon budget for stringent climate targets. *Nature*, 571 (7765): 335–342.
Ryberg M W, Andersen M M, Owsianiak M. (2020) Down scaling the Planetary Boundaries in absolute environmental sustainability assessments–a review. *Journal of Cleaner Production*, 2020: 123287.
Schneider L, La Hoz Theuer S, Howard A. (2020) Outside in Using international carbon markets for mitigation not covered by nationally determined contributions (NDCs) under the Paris Agreement. *Climate Policy*, 20 (1): 18–29.
Stoerk T, Dudek D J, Yang J. (2019) China's national carbon emissions trading scheme: Lessons from the pilot emission trading schemes, academic literature, and known policy details. *Climate Policy*, 19 (4): 472–486.
Tang B J, Ji C J, Hu Y J. (2020) Optimal carbon allowance price in China's carbon emission trading system: Perspective from the multi-sectoral marginal abatement cost. *Journal of Cleaner Production*, 2020, 253: 119945.

Application of BIM technology in the process of construction under the development of internet of things

Bingran Chen*
Wuhan University of Technology, Wuhan, China

ABSTRACT: In the modern era when the Internet is widely used, digitalization has become an indispensable part of the Internet of everything. The application of technology in architectural engineering makes architectural engineering develop towards digitization and informationization, and solves the limitation of original CAD drawings. At the same time, it is easier to solve the differences between different departments in the standardization, integration, and visualization of engineering documents. And the use of construction simulation can solve a series of problems in the construction process. The application of BIM technology in construction engineering will better facilitate the implementation of the project.

1 INTRODUCTION

Since 2012, the added value of the construction industry has always accounted for more than 6.85% of the GDP, including accounting for 7.01% in 2021 (CCIA 2021). The construction industry plays an important role in promoting economic growth and promoting national urbanization construction. However, the problems such as extensive development mode, low labor productivity, low construction quality, and frequent engineering quality and safety accidents still exist objectively. Under the background of the transformation of the economy to high-quality development at the national level, the application of new technologies such as digital networking to realize the digital transformation of the construction industry in all stages of design, construction, operation, and maintenance is the main research direction of the construction industry at present. In the digitalization of the construction industry, the development of BIM is in the core position. At present, BIM is in Revit and Bentley internationally, and the application of these technologies in China is still in the initial stage of national call and local start.

The core and foundation of the Internet of Things is the Internet. The Internet of Things is an extended and extended network based on the Internet, and its client end extends to the exchange of information between goods. The definition of the Internet of Things is a network that combines radio frequency identification, infrared sensors, a global positioning system, a laser scanner, and other information sensing devices. According to the agreed procedures, the objects relate to the internet, information exchange, and communication, to achieve the intelligent identification, positioning, tracking, monitoring, and management of items. The basis of IoT is the wide application of various sensing techniques (Wang 2020).

2 DIGITAL TECHNOLOGY OF CONSTRUCTION ENGINEERING CONSTRUCTION

2.1 *Concept of engineering digitization*

Digital technology refers to the simulation of the physical world in the computer system, the use of digital technology to promote the progress of business model, and enterprise service

---

*Corresponding Author: 845248073@qq.com

upgrading, which is an important part of the high-quality development of the country. Engineering digitization technology is to expand the new graphics technology, computing technology, and engineering technology based on computer technology. In the era of drawing performance, engineering digitization is to use CAD technology to realize the transformation from manual drawing to computer-aided drawing. In the era of model performance, engineering digital technology uses BIM technology, based on the collaborative design of the 3D model, to replace the CAD drawing design mode, which improves the efficiency and quality of design work. In the era of data-driven, engineering data is constantly mined, integrated, and utilized. The digital twin concept was born. The whole engineering industry is moving toward the digital stage. Engineering digitization is to provide an intelligent service mode for the whole life cycle of engineering (Wang 2020).

2.2 Digital development status of construction in construction engineering in China

At present, most domestic architectural design enterprises have fully realized manual drawing to computer-aided drawing based on CAD software. After the CAD drawings are stamped with the drawing system of the design enterprise, they are uploaded to the drawing review organization through the Internet. The CAD drawings will be delivered for use after the examination of the drawing review organization and put on record by the relevant government. In addition to being delivered in the traditional form of the physical construction blueprint, the design drawings are also delivered in PDF format. The engineers will conduct the construction and production management according to the PDF version of the construction blueprint through the tablet computer. Although most design companies are currently vigorously promoting BIM technology and the final submission should be submitted as a BIM model in some areas. But specifically for engineering applications, few projects can abandon CAD-assisted drawing and perform the BIM forward design. Also, the BIM drawing review cannot be fully realized in the drawing review process. Not to mention the use of the BIM information model in the construction phase of material processing construction and management. In other words, at present, the digitalization of the domestic construction industry is still in the two-dimensional data model stage. The further development of digitization in the construction industry should rely on BIM technology simulation and integration of all building information. At the same time, the Internet technology should be used to realize information sharing of the BIM model between design enterprises' drawing review agencies and construction enterprises' relevant government supervision departments to achieve the purpose of greatly improving design quality and construction quality, and project management efficiency. Finally, we can achieve high-quality development in the construction industry.

At present, the building construction drawings are delivered in the form of PDF and the construction blueprint. And the construction organization and budget preparation are based on the reference and preparation of the CAD drawings corresponding to the construction blueprint. Given the limitations of two-dimensional drawings, they cannot clearly show component position, information, and spatial relationship. As a result, the BIM model can gather all the information of various professions in one location, such as building structure, water supply, drainage, machinery, heating, and ventilation. Material information, component information, and spatial relationships can be viewed simultaneously. Construction and production personnel can intuitively understand the design intention and concept.

2.3 Advantages of BIM technology

2.3.1 3D visualization and stereo

BIM technology is different from traditional CAD drawings. It can display architectural models in 3D. That way, the people involved do not have to build models in their brains solely on their imagination. With BIM models, people can more clearly express the design concept, present the future aspect of the project, and provide the tenderer with a clear understanding of what the designer intends. At the same time, in the 3D model of BIM, multiple modules can be integrated, which improves the inconvenience of providing three tripartite drawings, such as water, electricity, and heat. And the 3D models completely show the whole project in front of human eyes (Li 2021). BIM can separately extract the plane drawings of a certain piece of engineering that you need, thus avoiding the lack of cognition of the construction personnel in the application process of BIM technology situation.

Visualization will also improve the accuracy of the product. Through the actual scene simulation, we can observe the allocation of the site and site facilities and sites outside the existing infrastructure have space conflict. Technicians can check the professional components in the plane, facade, and section position, and complete the scope of the project pipeline layout and professional collision inspection, to avoid space conflict (Chen 2022).

2.3.2 *4D simulation technology*

Engineering designers can also simulate the elements that cannot be intuitively expressed through BIM technology, such as progress simulation, structure analysis, cost analysis, lighting, and energy consumption analysis, to further optimize the design. Through virtualization construction, technicians can observe the construction difficulties in the construction process, and design or modifier the construction scheme in advance. For example, they can simulate the route of construction machinery and the construction sequence of operation space engineering, the material equipment needed for construction, and the coordination of pipeline installation to optimize the use of large equipment to avoid repeated entry. And we could carry out fine management of the project, looking for the best scheme to ensure the smooth and safety of the construction process, to ensure the quality of the project (Li & Cao 2022). At the same time, the construction period required for the construction can be roughly obtained, and the actual construction period can be compared to analyze the deviation of the construction progress. Through BIM technology prospective and its complete database and good analysis ability, we can provide the owner, construction unit construction site all relevant information, and we can get the construction of material allocation, personnel allocation, task size, etc. In addition, BIM technology is convenient for cost analysis of human and material consumption, digitalization, and standardization, and is conducive to project management. Moreover, technicians can use light analysis to determine the placement of buildings and disaster simulation to optimize the structure.

2.3.3 *Compatibility*

Construction engineering will involve many fields of engineering blocks, so it often will be divided into many departments. And the professional design personnel will design their respective drawings. Traditional CAD drawings hinder the communication between the two sides, such as the inconsistency in the drawing notes. In BIM technology, the design drawings of multiple departments are integrated with a 3D model. In the case of a collision such as size, it can be marked on the model in real time, effectively avoiding the spatial-temporal error in the connection and reducing unnecessary trouble.

2.4 *Development trend of BIM technology*

With the continuous development of Internet of Things technology, the ability of various sensors to collect information is continuously improved. In this case, we transfer the collected information to the BIM model, and the BIM technology in the application layer can make full use of the information provided in the Internet of Things environment. In construction engineering, BIM technology can be used to assist various majors in deepening design and pipeline synthesis, simulating the construction process, improving the management ability and efficiency as well as the level of digitization of building. The application of BIM technology can also promote the realization of multi-professional collaborative design, fine management of materials, standardization of processing drawings, and the display of complex nodes. Through the in-depth application of the parametric building models in engineering, we were able to link progress review, resource review, program guidance, and risk

The application of BIM technology has achieved good economic benefits.451900 yuan was saved in cost.The labor cost,machinery cost and material cost saved 123,000 yuan,73,000 yuan and 255,900 yuan respectively.

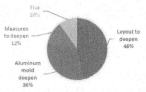
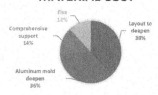

The surplus of labor cost mainly comes from the prefabrication of the support of the pipe harness, which is free of drilling installation, and the precise lofting of the steel curtain wall to reduce the secondary labor input. Measures to deepen the plan to disclose.

The remaining mechanical cost mainly comes from deepening the layout, quick construction, one-time survival of the same material, reducing the secondary entry of equipment, centralized processing of semi-finished products of pipeline comprehensive projects and so on.

The remaining cost of materials mainly comes from the reduction of secondary rectification by pipeline optimization and prefabrication of semi-finished products; Aluminum mold to deepen the structure of a survival and other aspects.

Figure 1. Economic benefits brought by the application of BIM technology.

Figure 2. Sunshine analysis and simulation.

management all together with BIM systems. Then the BIM working group could control the BIM data and the feedback of the on-site implementation, and actively collect data and analyze data to better guide the practice.

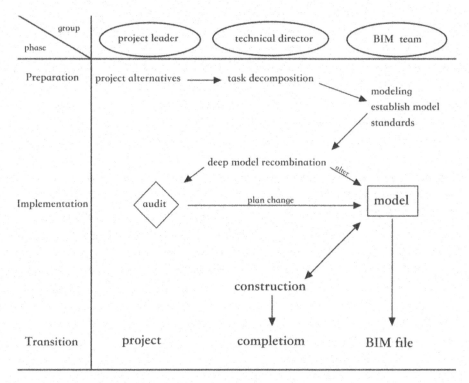

Figure 3. Process management of BIM technology in practical applications.

3 CONCLUSION

Internet of Things technology has a wide application prospect in the construction process of building engineering. The Internet of Things technology is used to sense various information data such as construction engineering site environment and link the data with the BIM model, which can realize automatic data collection and information update platform real-time monitoring of three-dimensional construction management with multi-party cooperation so that we can greatly improve the construction management of production efficiency and scientific. The application and popularization of BIM technology is the key factor in the digital transformation of the architectural engineering field. The delivery of design products in the form of a BIM model can promote the digital upgrading of engineering construction management and project operation and maintenance phase. The digital transformation and upgrading of the construction industry will only be possible by fully realizing the BIM forward design in the design industry, realizing the delivery of design products using the BIM model, and making full use of the development of BIM technology.

REFERENCES

Chen Qi et al. (2022). Volume 54 phase 2 BIM technology in the construction stage.
China Construction Industry Association. (2021). "*Statistical Analysis of Construction Industry Development in 2021*".
Li Peng and Cao Yiyun. (2022). *The Fine Management of BIM Technology Applied to Construction Cost*.
Li QingQi. (2021). *Analysis of BIM technology in the application of architectural engingeering design advantages*.
Wang Jinfeng. (2020). *From engineering digital application to smart city practice*.

Research on shield separate launching technology in limited space

Yang Lei*
Ningbo University, Ningbo, Zhejiang, China

ABSTRACT: Based on the shield tunnel project of Shenzhen Line 13, this paper optimizes the separate launching plan by using limited site conditions. It is suitable to choose the timing of vehicle transfer and adjust the horizontal transportation group synchronously, which improves the construction efficiency of each stage of departure. At the same time, a reasonable selection of excavation parameters and implementation of relevant control measures in composite strata ensure that the launching plan is safe, reliable, cost-effective, and efficient.

1 INTRODUCTION

1.1 Overview of the project

The Shiyan Section Shield Tunnel is located in Luozu Village, Shiyan Street, Bao'an District, Shenzhen. The pipe tunnel line exits the Shiyan shield starting shaft and goes south along the demolition area of Luozu Village. Parallel to the Luobao section tunnel of Line 13, during the period, it passed through several residential houses, passed through the planned Tianzhen River box culvert, passed through Luozu Community Workstation, passed through Guihang Metal Products Co., Ltd., and finally reached the shield receiving well. The total length of the shield tunnel is 430.1 m, the plane line is straight, the longitudinal section is a slope of one, the maximum slope is 40‰, and the buried depth of the tunnel is 12.2–21.4 m. The interval tunnel uses a Φ6,470 mm composite earth pressure balance shield machine to start from the shield starting shaft. The total length of the shield body of the shield machine in this project is about 9.3 m, and the total length of the whole machine including the supporting trolley is about 95 m. Because the shield starting well is located in a residential area, the total length is only 31.8 m, which does not meet the overall starting conditions for going down the well (Bu et al. 2018; Jiang et al. 2020; Zheng 2016; Zhong 2020). The shield machine is divided into 7 frames, the cutter head opening rate is 35%, the maximum propulsion speed is 8 mm/min, the maximum thrust is 42,550 KN, and the maximum climbing ability is 50‰.

1.2 Project geology

The shield tunnel mainly includes: plastic gravel clay, hard plastic gravelly clay, fully weathered biotite granite, strongly weathered biotite granite (soils), moderately weathered spherical weathered body (boulder), slightly weathered spherical weathered bodies (boulders), and other strata, the geological types of tunnel sections include full-section soft soils, soft soils combined with fully/strongly weathered rocks, boulders, and other complex situations.

---

*Corresponding Author: qc_fl17@163.com

1.3 Overview of originating working well

The shield starting well and receiving well of this project are in the form of independent working wells. The originating well is located in the open space between Luozu Avenue and Wencheng Road at the Dajiduan end after houses have been demolished. The surrounding environment of the originating well is complex and it is close to Metro Line 13 and is in a residential area. The total length of the shield starting well is 31.8 m, the length of the working well is 16.6 m, the length of the buried section at the rear is 14.2 m, and the depth of the well is about 19.2 m. The enclosure structure of the departure shaft consists of meat and vegetable occlusal piles with a diameter of 1 m and a spacing of 1.4 m and five vertical supports. During the shield construction period, a space of 11.75 × 7.5 m for shield hoisting and vertical transportation is reserved at the end of the starting shaft. The slope of the buried section at the rear of the originating well is 100‰. A soil collecting pit is set on the upper part of the buried section at the back of the working well. To meet soil disposal needs, the buried section is backfilled to a depth of three meters below the ground and a one-meter-high fence is built above the ground. Two soil box turning frames are also placed in the soil collection pit. The plane of the originating well is shown in Figure 1.

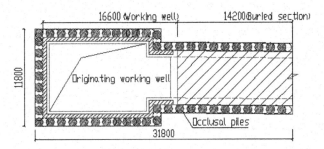

Figure 1. The layout of the shield starting shaft.

2 LAYOUT OF SEPARATE LAUNCHING

2.1 System of departure back-up

The shield backing system of the starting working shaft is assembled by 7 rings of reinforced concrete negative ring segments. To reserve the hoisting space, a 6-ring open ring and a 1-ring closed ring are used, and the segments are connected by bolts and matched with bolts. The gap between the backing structure, the negative ring segment, and the working well structure is filled with high-grade mortar to make the segment evenly stressed and the annulus smooth. The backrest structure is composed of two double 90# H-shaped steel combinations, lower eight-shaped braces, four 609 steel support, and π-type braces. The steel backrest is arranged between the last negative ring and the shaft wall structure, close to the structure. The shield backup system is shown in Figure 2. After the support setting of the backing system is completed, when the shield is advancing, attention should be paid to observing the deformation of the backing system to prevent damage caused by excessive displacement. Deformation observation points are set up on the back structure, which is measured once every time the distance is advanced at the beginning, and once for each ring when the back deformation is stable, and the observation can be stopped until the back is stabilized. Install 609 steel support and π-type braces immediately after shield tunneling reaches the +2 ring and the negative 1 ring segment emerges from the shield tail to improve the back support system.

2.2 Grading and transportation in launching well

Due to the limited space structure of the launching well, and the structural gradient of the buried section at the rear is 100‰, to make full use of the space of the originating well, the buried section

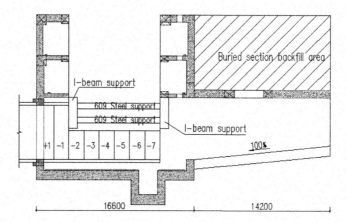

Figure 2. Starting back system diagram.

is elevated and graded to 40‰. The slope level transportation is in line with the flat slope tunnel of the shield starting section and meets the capacity requirements of electric locomotives. The width of sleepers with a height of 600 mm is placed in the tunnel to meet the conditions for placing turnouts in the later stage of separate launching, so there is no need to replace the sleepers during the construction process.

The vertical transportation of segments, construction materials, spoil, etc. is carried out by the ground wellhead or the vehicle at the reserved excavation opening. The normal propulsion stage of the horizontal transportation in the tunnel is completed by 2 sets of 45 T electric locomotives, one equipped with a pulp truck and 4×10 m^3 earth boxes, the other equipped with 2 flatbed trucks and 2×10 m^3 earth boxes, and the two vehicles complete a loop. To improve transportation efficiency and shorten the travel time for unearthed and transfer segments, two pairs of Y-shaped turnouts are set up in the tunnel near the wellhead, double rails are arranged, and signal lights are set at the turnouts.

3 SCHEME OF SEPARATE LAUNCHING

3.1 Stage of shield machine body goes down well

After the site layout is completed, first complete the installation of the starting base, and then hoist the backing system down to complete the installation, and at the same time pre-store 2-ring negative ring segments in the buried section. After that, each part of the shield body is hoisted down the well to complete the assembly, and correctly positioned on the shield base, and professional technicians complete the commissioning and acceptance work.

Limited by the space of the site, the 1#–5# frames are advanced in the field and are arranged in double rows. The installation is completed on the ground above the well and the connection and debugging work with the underground shield body is completed. The 6# frame is the air-conditioning and refrigeration system, and the 7# frame only has water pipe brackets, which are not needed in the separate tunneling stage, so the entry can be delayed. The hydraulic pipeline in the downhole section adopts a fixed pipeline, and other cables reserve sufficient length to meet the requirements of separate launching.

3.2 Stage of lateral excavation

Since there is no hoisting space in the well, the two-ring negative ring segment pre-stored in the hidden section at the back of the launching working well is assembled and then jacked forward, and then the -5-ring segment is hoisted from the side of the screw machine to go down the well, and the assembly is completed. The back shield can be jacked forward until it reaches the pile structure and starts to cut the fiberglass reinforcement in the range of the opening door.

Shield tunneling to -4 ring out of the shield tail, the front cutter head rests on the hole door, ready to cut the fiberglass fence pile. Shield excavation-3 rings came out of the shield tail, and after the cutter head entered the fencing pile, the unearthed began. At this time, there is no hoisting space on the rear side of the screw machine. It is planned to adopt a special small earth box and translation platform, which can realize the excavation from the side of the screw machine until the transition to the rear side of the screw machine has sufficient hoisting space. There are also applications and further development needs associated with maintenance wells.

Shield tunneling -2 rings, and the rear side of the screw machine has a hoisting space. At this time, sleepers and electric locomotive tracks can be laid in the negative ring segment and the buried section, and the horizontal and vertical transportation can be carried out through a flatbed truck and customized soil boxes. A hoist is set at the end of the buried section for traction. At this time, the front cutter head leaves the soil reinforcement area and enters the undisturbed soil.

3.3 The establishment of the backup system and the 1# trolley

Shield tunneling +2 rings, at the same time -1 ring segment is out of the shield tail, π-type braces and 609 purlins can be installed. In this way, a complete back force system is established. At this time, the cutter head is separated from the reinforcement area and enters the original soil. The hoisting space in the well is sufficient, and one electric locomotive can be hoisted down the well for dragging the flat plate for horizontal transportation.

A shield tunnel is excavated to the +14 ring, a bridge section is hoisted down the well, and the remaining frame section is left on the ground. Connect the belt conveyor to the rear of the 1# trolley, using the belt conveyor to unearth it. The horizontal transportation grouping is adjusted to 2 10 m³ muck trucks, 1 pulp feeder, and 1 electric locomotive. The muck truck is used as a segment transport vehicle after removing the soil box. At this stage, 4/5 round trips can complete the excavation of one ring segment.

3.4 Stage of 2#–5# trolley goes down the well

When the shield is tunneled to +42 ring, the 2#–5# trolleys are hoisted down and connected one by one, and the belt conveyor is connected to the 5# frame excavation position, and the excavation begins normally. The horizontal transport grouping is adjusted to 1 segment flat plate, 2×10 m³ muck trucks, 1 slurry feeder, and 1 electric locomotive, which can simultaneously complete segment transportation during the round-trip excavation process, further improving construction efficiency.

3.5 Stage of 6#–7# trolley goes down the well

When the shield is tunneled to +100 ring, and the turnout section can be accommodated in the tunnel, the 6# and 7# frames are hoisted down the shaft, and the turnout is installed at the rear of the frame in the tunnel during the frame transfer process, and a double-motor locomotive is used. Grouping for horizontal transportation further improves construction efficiency. Combining with the size limitation of the working well, the 1# group adopts 2 segment flat plates + two 10 m³ muck trucks +electric locomotive, and the 2# group adopts 1 section pulp truck +4 sections 10 m³ muck truck +electric locomotive. Two groups can complete the excavation work of one ring segment by entering and exiting once.

4 SEPARATE LAUNCHING CONTROL POINTS

4.1 *Stage of pass-through fencing piles and soil reinforcement areas*

When the shield passes through the enclosure piles and the soil reinforcement area after it has been launched because the glass fiber reinforced enclosure piles and the soil in the reinforcement area have a certain self-supporting capacity, the setting of the earth pressure can be low. Due to the strength of the fence pile, the initial installation knife is equipped with a full-disk hob for maximum cutting efficiency. At this stage, the propelling speed of the shield should be controlled within 1 cm/min to ensure that the jacking pressure of the shield and the torque of the cutter head will not greatly affect the performance of the shield and ensure the safety of the shield. At the same time, add a foaming agent or bentonite to the front of the shield as needed to improve the front soil. Synchronous grouting starts after the shield tail is about to enter the soil in the reinforcement area.

The pressure setting of the incision in the reinforcement area is selected according to the quality of the reinforcement and the abundance of groundwater displayed by the exploration holes in the tunnel door and should be controlled below 0.05 MPa. The total thrust of the shield starting in the reinforcement area should not exceed 1,000 t, the torque of the cutter head should not be larger than 4,000 kN.m, and the rotational speed of the cutter head should be controlled at 0.8 r/min to prevent the cutter head rotating speed when cutting solids. Excessive speed will cause damage to the cutter head. The deformation of the backrest during the advancing process should be paid attention to.

After the shield is out of the reinforcement area, to prevent the shield from suddenly "kowtowing" due to the change in the frontal soil quality, the balance pressure value is set slightly higher than the theoretical value, and the value of the balance pressure is adjusted in time according to the working conditions, according to the amount of stratum deformation, etc. The information feedback makes timely adjustments to the construction parameters such as the setting value of the balance pressure and the advancing speed to facilitate the smooth exit of the shield.

4.2 *Stage of shield tunneling normally*

Because the shield tunnel of this project is a mixed stratum of gravel clay soil and fully/strongly weathered rock, the composite earth pressure balance shield tunnel boring machine can be used in the excavation mode of the total soil pressure when excavating in the stratum with soft soil. The phase medium balances the external water and soil pressure. When excavating in the fully/strongly weathered granite stratum with hard soil, depending on the air tightness of the stratum, the auxiliary air pressure balance mode is used for excavation, that is, the injection is injected into the soil bin through the built-in pressure maintaining system of the shield or the foam air injection pipe. Part of the slag is replaced by air, and the solid phase + gas phase medium is used to balance the water and soil pressure on the outside of the excavation surface, which can reduce the excavation load, reduce the wear of the cutter head, and improve the excavation efficiency. The air-soil interface should be maintained to exceed $1/2$ of the height of the soil bin during the propulsion process using the air pressure assist mode to prevent the soil from collapsing due to the excessive height difference between the inside and outside of the soil bin, and to avoid over-excavation or frequent changes in the height of the air-soil interface leading to opening. The excavation surface is unstable. At the same time, according to the monitoring data of propulsion speed, excavation volume, and formation deformation, the grouting amount is adjusted in time to control the axis and formation deformation within the allowable range.

5 CONCLUSION

During the implementation of the interval shield tunnel project, the separate launching plan was optimized according to the limited site conditions. Through the adaptive transformation of the start-back system and the reasonable planning of in-well transportation, the space for the start-up work well was extremely limited on the site. Under various conditions, when the shield tunnel reaches +14 ring, +42 ring, and +100 ring, it is necessary to select the timing of vehicle transfer and adjust the horizontal transportation group synchronously. It is possible to improve the construction efficiency and ensure efficient slag removal and segment transportation. At the same time, in the face of composite strata, the selection of excavation parameters and the implementation of relevant control measures ensure that the launching plan is safe, reliable, economical, and reasonable, which has reference significance for similar projects.

REFERENCES

Bu Xingwei, Zeng Bocun, Wan Feiming, Du Peng, Quan Ziyang, Wang Lintao. Research on the construction technology of shield split starter under the condition of narrow space [J]. *Tunnel Construction* (Chinese and English), 2018, 38726–728.

Jiang Shaowu, Gao Peng, Qiu Chang. Research on the construction technology of split start of shield tunnel in ultra-narrow shaft [J]. *Construction Technology*, 2020, 49 (01): 79–82+112.

Zheng Yongjun. *A review of the shield tunneling method for split start construction* technology [J]. *Northern Architecture*, 2016, 1 (02): 65–68.

Zhong Zhiquan. EPB Shield split originating construction technology in narrow spaces—taking the shield tunnel of singapore metro C715 project as an example [J]. *Tunnel Construction* (Chinese and English), 2020, 40 (08): 1197–1202.

Moderate resolution imaging spectroradiometer (MODIS)-based internal wave detection in the East China Sea

Baisu Zhu* & Chen Li*
CCCC Tianjin Port Engineering Institute Co., Ltd., Key Laboratory of Coastal Engineering Hydrodynamic, CCCC, Tianjin, China

ABSTRACT: The Moderate Resolution Imaging Spectroradiometer (MODIS), in combination with fine spatial resolution and almost daily global coverage, allows for the use of sunlight to analyze and investigate high-frequency nonlinear internal solitary waves occurring at the near-global scale. The present study tries to delineate the distribution of internal waves in two hotspots in the East China Sea (ECS) using remote sensing observations with a spatial resolution of 250 m. The MODIS image shows internal wave packets propagating southwest to the Zhejiang coast adjacent to Changjiang Estuary, which may generate topography features. In addition, there are many internal waves around Jeju Island, spreading in different directions. Our results confirm the existence of two internal wave hotspots in the ECS and provide a basis for the study of the dynamic characteristics of this region in the future.

1 INTRODUCTION

Internal waves are a universal feature of the world's oceans, which may also play an important role in river plumes. Internal wave activity can originate from sea areas with significant topographic variation (Bourgault 2011; Holloway 1987; Jackson 2012; Xie 2015). The inflow process of plumes can also form internal waves in their front (Nash 2005). Previous studies have found that internal solitary waves generally exist in the nearshore sea where stratification occurs and play an important role in the generation of pycnocline turbulence (Alford 2012; Moum 2003). Numerical simulations show that dynamic processes related to internal waves in the waters adjacent to estuaries would contribute a large amount of energy to the mixing of the pycnocline (Pan 2009). Xie (2017) observed the mooring in a stratified estuary, pointing out that internal waves can cause huge vertical displacement of the water body and affect turbulent mixing characteristics and the ecological environment in this region.

Observations have also shown the existence of internal waves in the East China Sea (ECS) (Lozovatsky 2012). It is found that two internal wave hotspots exist in the ECS, one located southeast of the Changjiang Estuary and the other around Jeju Island. The internal wave distribution observed by satellites is shown in Figure 1. Hsu (2000) found the large number of internal waves distributed around Jeju Island by using synthetic aperture radar (SAR). Subsequently, the large number of internal waves distributed around Jeju Island has been proved by several studies, and it is found that the appearance of internal waves is related to the phase of periodic tides (Alpers 2005; He 2006). Li (2008) found the existence of internal waves near the Changjiang Estuary based on satellite images and analyzed the possible locations of internal waves in this region.

This study aims to explore the spatial characteristics of internal waves in the ECS using observations of MODIS. This paper is organized as follows. The data processing is presented in Section 2;

---

*Corresponding Authors: zhubaisu@cccltd.cn and lichen11@cccltd.cn

the spatial distribution of internal waves is revealed in Section 3; related conclusions are presented in Section 4.

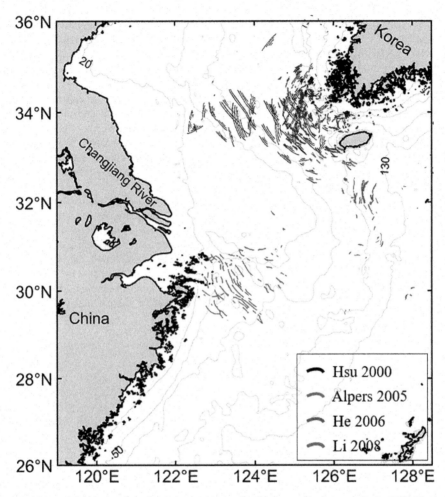

Figure 1. Map of the observed nonlinear internal wave distribution and bathymetry in the ECS. Black (Hsu 2000), purple (Alpers 2005), blue (He 2006), and red (Li 2008) curves are signatures of internal solitary waves, which are shown on satellite images published in previous studies.

2 DATA AND METHOD

This paper uses MODIS images to detect internal wave activity, which was an important method in the observation of internal waves. In recent years, due to the advantages of SAR, such as high accuracy and not being affected by weather factors, the feasibility of the study of ocean internal waves has been greatly improved. A series of studies have been carried out in the ECS (Alpers 2005; Hsu 2000; He 2006; Li 2008). In addition, the development of optical remote sensing technology has further promoted the study of nonlinear internal waves in the global ocean. MODIS is a medium-resolution imaging light spectrometer. Although the sensor is affected by clouds, its wide image coverage (global coverage), strong data availability (free download), and high temporal resolution (one to two images per day) have become indispensable auxiliary means for contemporary internal wave research.

The satellite images used in this article were taken from MODIS observations aboard the Terra and Aqua satellites. The entire earth's surface can be observed repeatedly with the coordination of two stars in about one or two days. There are three resolutions of MODIS, which are 250 m (band 1 to 2), 500 m (band 3 to 7), and 1,000 m (band 8 to 36), respectively. In this paper, the true-color images are created from the calibrated, corrected and geolocated radiance (level-1B) data by MODIS, with a spatial resolution of 250 m (bands 1 and 2).

MODIS acquisition mainly relies on the mirror reflection of sunlight from the sea surface to the sensor, and the intensity of reflection depends on the roughness of the sea surface (Wald 1983). The appearance of internal waves can be captured by MODIS true color images in the solar flare area. Since MODIS true color images are affected by night and cloud and fail to overcome the defect of visible light photography, we generally choose the cloudless MODIS true color images located in the solar flare area for analysis. In this paper, two valid satellite images were collected to analyze the characteristics of wave distribution. Satellite images are available on the LAADS website of the National Aeronautics and Space Administration (NASA) (https://ladsweb.modaps.eosdis.nasa.gov/search/).

The study area is in the coastal area of Zhejiang Province and southwest of Jeju Island. The coastal area of Zhejiang Province locates southeast of the Changjiang Estuary, the area is very shallow and the water depth is less than 80 m. Figure 2a is a part of all MODIS images acquired near the Zhejiang coast. This image shows that there are coherent internal wave packets propagating southwestward toward the Zhejiang coast. For the same propagating direction, the adjacent internal wave groups were generally evenly separated by 18 km. This suggests that these internal waves are periodicity generated through the interaction between tidal currents and bottom topography. This area is dominated by M_2 tidal with a period of 12.42 h. Therefore, the calculated phase speed of the internal wave is 0.3 to 0.4 m/s.

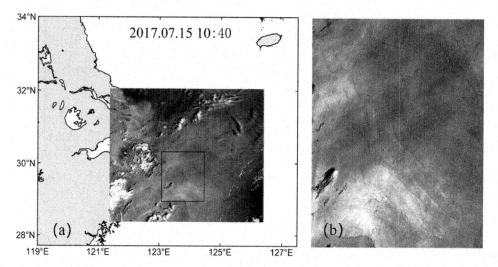

Figure 2. (a) MODIS image over ECS taken at 10: 40 on July 2017 and (b) a full 'resolution zoomed image' (black box in Figure 2a) showing many internal wave packets propagating toward China's coast.

3 SPATIAL DISTRIBUTION OF INTERNAL WAVE

Previous studies have shown that there are two hotspots of internal waves in the ECS, one is adjacent to the Changjiang Estuary and the other around Jeju Island (Hsu 2000; Li 2008). Figure 3 shows the MODIS true-color images taken at 10:45, August 04, 2015. The internal waves are mainly distributed on the southeast side of the Changjiang Estuary, which covers an area of 29.5–31.5°N and 122–125°E in summer. As can be seen from Figure 3, the internal wave mainly propagates to the southwest. The adjacent ISW groups were generally evenly separated by –16 km. However, the internal waves in this study are not generated from the shelf break. It most probably originates from generation sites located in the northeast direction, where the bottom slope changes abruptly.

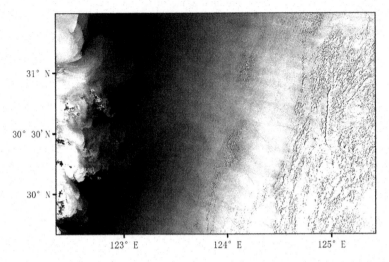

Figure 3. MODIS true-color image acquired on 04 August 2015 adjacent to Changjiang Estuary.

In the same period, many internal waves also appeared around Jeju Island (Figure 4). The internal waves were generated at different sites and propagated in different directions. Based on previous research, the wave packets were generated near the shelf break and Jeju Island where around some submarine mounts. Multiple generation sites of internal waves were discovered. In the fact, Lozovatsky (2015) also observed intensified turbulence within the pycnocline base field observation. They suggested that turbulence in a sharp pycnocline may be induced by the internal-wave breaking. The region surrounding Jeju Island has been identified as one of the hot spots for the occurrence of internal waves. Many internal waves in this region are tracked from MODIS images.

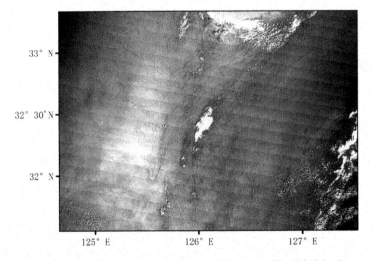

Figure 4. MODIS true color image acquired on 04 August 2015 surrounding Jeju Island.

4 CONCLUSIONS

MODIS has the comprehensive properties of high resolution, global coverage, and available images, which enables solar glint to be used for the first time to investigate the occurrence of internal waves on a near-global scale. A survey of true-color MODIS imagery acquired on 04 August 2015 found a lot of internal wave occurrences in the area adjacent to the Changjiang Estuary and regions around Jeju Island. The survey identified significant amounts of internal wave activity in ECS. The internal waves are mainly generated from the shelf break, where the bottom slope changes, and the interaction between topography and tidal current induced internal waves. The other is around Jeju Island, where internal waves are generated and spread towards the southwest, which is consistent with our satellite images. In addition, internal waves may also occur in shallow water where local topography changes, such as in the southeast of the Changjiang Estuary, where the topography changes greatly. Internal waves are generated and propagated to the southeast. In conclusion, there are a lot of internal waves in the ECS and the internal wave propagates in different directions emitting from their generation sites.

The presented results have strong implications showing that there are a lot of internal waves in the ECS. Internal waves can be induced by the interaction between strong tidal currents and topographic features. As is known to all, the internal waves can induce large vertical displacements and generate strong intense turbulence in the water column. In addition to the dynamic characteristics, the potential ecological importance of the internal waves is also important. Strong turbulent mixing can increase the nutrient supply in the upper layer by the increase in eddy diffusivity. Evidence shows that the internal wave processes in this area play a very strong regional modulation role, which can exchange Changjiang diluted water with seawater, further affecting the ecological environment of the region. The internal wave process in the plume may be a common phenomenon under the interaction of tide and topography. These findings also provide a reference for the dynamic process in the pycnocline of other continental shelf seas.

The vertical exchange of matter is influenced by internal waves, which largely depends on the probability of occurrence of the internal wave in the different parts of the ECS. In this study, many internal waves are found around Jeju Island and Changjiang Estuary. Remote sensing observation or further comprehensive observations are needed to answer this question. Nevertheless, in this study, we illustrate that in addition to the recently identified area adjacent to the Changjiang Estuary, the prevailing internal waves in regions southwest of Jeju Island also exist. This may provide further implications for understanding the dynamic characteristics and biogeochemical cycles in the ECS.

REFERENCES

Alford, M. H. Mickett, J. B. Zhang, S. (2012). Internal waves on the Washington continental shelf. *Oceanography*. 25: 66–79.

Alpers, W. He, M. X. Zeng, K. (2005). *The distribution of internal waves in the East China Sea and the Yellow Sea studied by multi-sensor satellite images. International Geoscience and Remote Sensing Symposium*, Seoul, Korea. 7, 4784–4787.

Bourgault, D. Janes, D. C. (2011). Galbraith P S. Observations of a large-amplitude internal wave train and its reflection off a steep slope. *Journal of Physical Oceanography*. 41, 586–600.

He, M. X. Chen, H. Wang, B. (2008). *A new internal wave activity sea area discovered in the Yellow Sea near Qingdao*. Paper presented at Dragon 1 Program Final Report 2004–2007, Beijing, China.

Holloway, P. E. (1987). Internal hydraulic jumps and solitons at a shelf break region on the Australian North West Shelf. *Journal of Geophysical Research: Oceans*. 92, 5405–5416.

Hsu, M. K. Liu, A. K. Liu, C. (2000), A study of internal waves in the China Seas and Yellow Sea using SAR. *Continental Shelf Research*. 20 (4-5), 389–410.

Jackson, C. da Silva, J. Jeans, G. (2012). The generation of nonlinear internal waves. *Oceanography*. 25 (2), 108–123.

Lee, J. H. Lozovatsky, I. Jang, S. T. Jang, C. J. Hong, C. S. Fernando, H. J. S. (2006). Episodes of nonlinear internal waves in the northern East China Sea. *Geophysical Research Letters*. 33 (18), L18601.

Li, X. F. Zhao, Z. X. Han, Z. (2008). Internal solitary waves in the East China Sea. *Acta Oceanological Sinica.* 27 (3), 51–59.

Lozovatsky, I. Lee, J. H. Fernando, H. J. S. Kang, S. K. Jinadasa, S. U. P. (2015). Turbulence in the East China Sea: The summertime stratification. *Journal of Geophysical Research: Oceans.* 120 (3), 1856–1871. https://doi.org/10.1007/s10236-015-0858-2.

Lozovatsky, I. Liu, Z. Y. Fernando, H. (2012). Shallow water tidal currents in close proximity to the seafloor and boundary-induced turbulence. *Ocean Dynamics.* 62 (2), 177–191.

Moum, J. N. Farmer, D. M. Smyth, W. D. (2003). Structure and generation of turbulence at interfaces strained by internal solitary waves propagating shoreward over the continental shelf. *Journal of Physical Oceanography.* 33 (10), 2093–2112.

Nash, J. & Moum J. (2005). River plumes as a source of large-amplitude internal waves in the coastal ocean. *Nature.* 437, 400–404.

Pan, J. & Jay, D. A. (2009). Dynamic characteristics and horizontal transports of internal solitons generated at the Columbia River plume front. *Continental Shelf Research.* 29, 252–262.

Wald, L. & Monget, J. M. (1983). Sea Surface Winds from Sun Glitter Observations. *Journal of Geophysical Research: Oceans.* 88, 2547–2555.

Xie, X. H. Cuypers, Y. Bouruet-Aubertot, P. (2015). Generation and propagation of internal tides and solitary waves at the shelf edge of the Bay of Biscay. *Journal of Geophysical Research: Oceans.* 120, 6603–6621.

Xie, X. Li, M. Scully, M. (2017). Generation of internal solitary waves by lateral circulation in a stratified estuary. *Journal of Physical Oceanography.* 47 (7), 1789–1797.

Application study of digital twin seawall based on GIS-BIM

Yi Hou*, Kaiyun Jiang*, Yadong Yu*, Hengyan Huo* & Andong Wang*
Zhejiang Design Institute of Water Conservancy & Hydro-electric Power Co., Ltd., Hangzhou, China

ABSTRACT: To promote the digitalization of seawall construction, this paper investigates digital twin seawall applications based on Geographic Information System (GIS) and Building Information Modeling (BIM). According to the structural characteristics of seawalls, we establish a BIM parametric modeling method by the conjunctive use of multiple software, significantly improving the intelligence and automation levels of seawall modeling. The method can be applied to similar projects. After integrating the lightweight BIM model with surrounding GIS data and tilt photography in the graphics engine, bind actual archives information with the model components by database method to form a GIS-BIM database plate. On this basis, a multi-source Internet of Things (IoT) such as video monitoring, tide-level monitoring, and panoramic images can be inserted, forging the combination of virtual and reality, moreover, achieving information mapping. The above research puts digital-twin seawall into practice and improves the digital level of construction management of seawall projects.

1 INTRODUCTION

As an essential barrier in the southeast coastal zone of China, the seawall is known as the "Marine Great Wall" with a history of more than 2,000 years. According to the Fifth Plenary Session of the 19th CPC Central Committee, a safe, reliable, green, and ecological seawall engineering system should be established with comprehensive functions and efficient operation. Given the practical problems during the seawall projects construction such as wide coverage, poor construction environment, complex management, and low level of information (Fan et al. 2020), the *One-hundred Billion Construction Plan of Zhejiang Seawall Project* points out that "based on Geographic Information System-Building Information Modeling (GIS-BIM) technology, build a 3D simulation model of key seawall projects to realize all-round, visual, and full-cycle management". Hence, new requirements have been put forward for the breadth and depth of new technologies application in seawall construction.

The digital twin is a science of multi-disciplinary attributes that integrates the physical world and information to interact with virtual reality. In recent years, the digital twin has received extensive and high attention. Thanks to the development of new-generation information technologies such as IoT, big data, cloud computing, and artificial intelligence, the digital twin application has gradually become possible. Referring to existing studies, the digital twin adopts GIS-BIM in the transportation industry (Zheng et al. 2020). We believe that GIS-BIM technology is also applicable to digital twin projects in the water conservancy industry.

GIS is a technical system for collecting, storing, analyzing, and managing spatial geographic information. BIM means a technology to dynamically manage the building data during a project's life cycle. (Cao et al. 2020) It typically uses the 3D model as the information carrier and visualization and parameterization as core functions to integrate relevant data of the project. Therefore,

---

*Corresponding Authors: 601081728@qq.com, 315970357@qq.com, 179052032@qq.com, 504101205@qq.com and wonand1995@163.com

information redundancy can be reduced for efficient information sharing and transmission. GIS-BIM is the integration and exchange of GIS at the macro level and BIM at the micro level to build up a 3D virtual digital sand table embracing macro-and-micro, indoor-and-outdoor, aboveground-and-underground levels (Rao et al. 2022), providing a foundation for engineering simulation and auxiliary decision-making. Currently, GIS-BIM technology has been widely and deeply employed in many fields such as construction, transportation, energy, municipal administration, and so on (Wu et al. 2019), while the research on GIS-BIM in seawall engineering mostly focused on framework and theories rather than application examples.

Based on the digital twin theory and GIS-BIM technology, this paper studies the application of digital twin seawall. In this study, a parametric modeling method is established by conjoining Civil 3D with Revit and Dynamo to automate the modeling of long-distance engineering repetitive machinery, improving the efficiency and quality of seawall BIM modeling. Next, the BIM model, tilt photography model, vector, terrain, and other multi-source data are integrated into the engine to depict the physical entity and information of seawall in digital space with high fidelity. On this basis, the IoT information is associated with spatial geographic information, building geometric information to form all-element twin information, furthermore coupled with algorithms (e.g., seawall safety evaluation) to build a digital twin seawall.

2 PARAMETRIC BIM MODELING FOR SEAWALLS

BIM model is the basis of information and data transmission, sharing, and application during each stage of the project's life cycle. Aiming at the efficient BIM modeling of seawall projects, we should gradually complete the axis processing, contour drawing, entity creation, station segmentation, attribute writing, and model export. The single BIM software cannot easily achieve efficient processing of the above steps simultaneously. Considering the BIM modeling principle, this paper combines civil 3D with Revit and Dynamo to make use of various software functions in long-distance engineering repetitive machinery, thus eliminating human errors and enhancing efficiency and quality. Finally, this paper forms a complete set of parametric automatic BIM modeling methods, as shown in Figure 1, which can be replicated and extended as a reference for similar projects.

Civil 3D is a solution that supports BIM based on AutoCAD to offer 3D design and analysis for the infrastructure industry. It can directly open a DWG file, convert two-dimensional lines into three-dimensional lines of the seawall, and accurately define spatial changes of the axis point by point. This method has remarkable advantages for the complex situation of overlapping horizontal and vertical curves (with a change in elevation and plane turning simultaneously).

Dynamo, a visual programming software based on Revit, has outstanding performance in parametric modeling by utilizing the API of Revit (Zhang et al. 2021). In this paper, the automatic modeling node design of Dynamo includes the axis fitting, entity creation, station segmentation, and attribute writing. The 3D axis and the section profile family of the seawall were imported into the Revit, and the NurbsCurve (non-uniform rational base spline) node was used to fit the modeling centerline. ByLoft (family types) nodes assigns the specific axis and profiles to create entities. According to the construction and management requirements, we define the axis at the specified station number to segment the model and divide the whole into parts, convert the segmented entities to families and automatically name them in batches according to station number ranges.

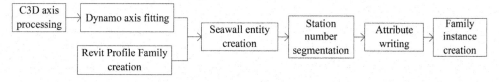

Figure 1. Modeling of seawall projects using parametric BIM.

The multi-software modeling method adopted in this paper can be summarized as follows. With Civil 3D, a 3D axis is created, Revit customizes section profiles, and Dynamo is used to create and edit entities. At its core, Dynamo programming is a positive design template that can be reused across multiple projects to quickly generate different schemes based on inputs of different axes and profiles.

3 GIS-BIM-BASED DIGITAL TWIN FOR SEAWALL CONSTRUCTION

Usually, BIM adopts an independent coordinate system, while the GIS data have different coordinate systems as there are various sources and collection methods (Qiao et al. 2021). As illustrated in Figure 2, the technical route of GIS-BIM integration is as follows. Firstly, carry out the coordinate conversion and data registration to align various information. Next, embed and flatten the data to realize the smooth fusion of multi-source data. Based on data fusion, the users can access GIS-BIM resources and services online through WebGIS development to complete spatial analysis, data query, and other tasks.

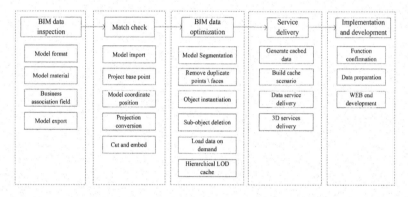

Figure 2. Technology route for GIS-BIM integration.

This paper applies BIM modeling through digital-analog separation. The seawall model is exported in FBX format for batch reduction. The lightweight model is imported into Cesium and Unity engines to fuse with the data of surrounding tilt photography, DEM, and DOM to build the GIS-BIM database plate. According to the project archives, the structural information of the seawall is sorted out to bind with model components on the web page through the JSON file, and it relates to multi-source IoT data such as video monitoring and tide-level monitoring to create a multi-dimensional and multi-temporal digital scenario.

Referring to the *Technical Guidelines for the Construction of Digital Twin Projects* issued by the Ministry of Water Resources (see Figure 3), the GIS-BIM-IOT technology constructs all-element twin information and couple algorithm models (e.g., seawall safety evaluation) to create digital twin seawall. There is an accurate mapping relationship existing between digital twin seawall and physical entity in spatial location, geometry, physics, behavior, and planning. To support the intelligent construction and management of engineering, the overall perception awareness, in-depth analysis, scientific decision-making, and accurate execution of seawall information should be enhanced (Huo et al. 2021).

4 PROJECT EXAMPLES

4.1 *Overview of projects*

The seawall project from the Yangtian Temple to the Tashan Dam section on the North Bank of the Qiantang River is a part of the standard pond. This part constitutes a flood control closed

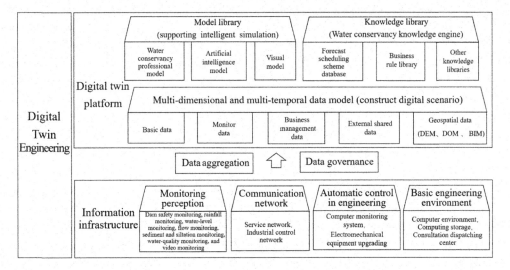

Figure 3. Overall framework of digital twin project construction.

line together with other seawalls in Hangzhou, Haiyan, Pinghu, and Haining, protecting nearly 6 million mu of cultivated land and the lives and property of over 10 million permanent residents in the Hangjia River Plain. The project aims at the progressive upgrading and reinforcement of pond sections that cannot meet the specifications of scouring prevention and overall stability safety factors. It mainly adopts measures like vertical scour prevention and suppression layers with a total reinforcement length of 16.5 km.

As suggested in Figure 4, the typical structural section of seawalls includes the embankment top, wave wall, slope protection, flood-control highway, flood-control vegetation blanket, ancient fish scale seawalls, pond water, fixed feet, and other parts. There are three types of fixed foot structures: reinforced concrete apron with sheet piles, precast block with sheet piles, and Accropode. Their structural modeling follows a similar logic. Taking the most complex ancient fish scale seawall as an example, the modeling method is further explained.

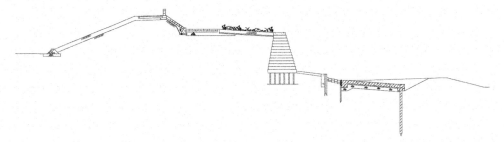

Figure 4. Typical structural section of seawall.

4.2 *Parametric modeling*

First, we open the DWG file of the seawall plane figure in Civil 3D and grasp the seawall axis to convert it into a route. According to the actual elevation, the seawall design profile is defined, and the elevation editor is used to modify the station number and elevation point by point. The section profile is created with Revit's "metric general model" family template. Considering the application requirements of the lightweight model, the backwater structure of the ancient seawall is simplified.

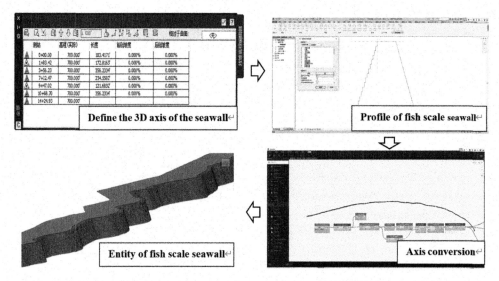

Figure 5. Key parts of seawall parametric modeling.

The seawall design profile is converted to a 3D polyline and introduced into Revit. Dynamo is used to convert PloyCurve-Civil 3D into NurbsCurve through the 3D polyline processing node group. NurbsCurve is a kind of mathematical representation which can simulate any form from simple 2D lines, circles, arcs, and rectangles to complicated 3D free curves. The process of fitting curves with PloyCurve is known as curve fitting. A curve is extracted from a polyline, points are read from the beginning to the end of each curve to sort them, and finally, NurbsCurve is applied to the curves. ByPoints are used to create NurbsCurve from points.

Seawall entities can be created through various approaches, among which structural framing beam by curve is the quickest by converting the axis into beams. According to the test, the essence of this method is the sweep method, and the section is perpendicular to the axis rather than plumb. If the height difference between the head and tail of the axis is large, the deviation from the actual value cannot be ignored; and the type of model component is a beam with too many useless parameters. After comparison, we found that using Solid.ByLoft to create a profile family was better as it can place a specified number of profiles along the axis and multiple profile lofts generate entities. In this paper, the lofting mode is changed from by cross sections to by cross sections plus guide curve to ensure smooth lofting along the axis.

We create a new Revit family file, set subcategories (e.g., fish scale seawall) and corresponding materials with the same name in the object style, and save the file as an RFT family template. The above template settings are the basis for automatic batch material assignment of family instances.

In regards to 97 groyne structures along the project, this paper takes "length," "width," and "number of stations" as control parameters to carry out automatic layout and structural adjustment along the specified station number.

4.3 *Model attribute writing*

According to the application requirements, this paper segments and names the batch of seawall model entities. Curve.PlaneAtSegmentLength node places the normal plane at the specified station segment of the axis and uses the plane group to segment. Since there is no node available for face cutting volume, it writes code through Python. What is more, this paper employs Dynamo to create an array of station number for each section from beginning to end, uses String from object to convert the station number into a string with a prefix, and automatically write the family name in batch in the form of "seawall K104240-K104340".

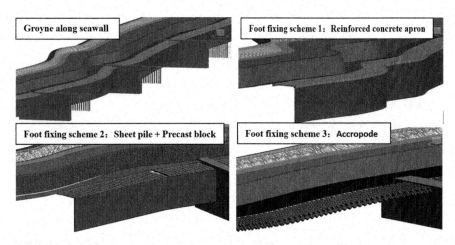

Figure 6. Detailed structure of model parts.

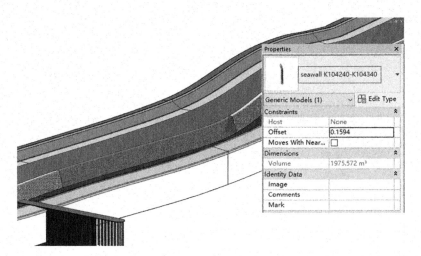

Figure 7. Model family name setting.

Following the classification and hierarchical structure of the *Building Information Model Classification and Coding Standard* (GB/T 51269), this paper sets the code of each model component to generate a model tree structure and realize the unified management and convenient search of the model.

4.4 *GIS-BIM application*

To make the loading and operation of the BIM model more efficient, this paper develops a data conversion tool for lightweight processing to reduce the number of model patches and improve the display efficiency, as shown in Figure 8.

Due to the length of seawall models, this paper sets a unified project base point, which will be exported in segments and assembled in the GIS engine. The BIM model inherits the Beijing 54 Coordinate System of the engineering drawing and converts the projection into the CGCS2000 coordinate system, which accurately matches the water system SHP, topographic DEM, and remote sensing images (You et al. 2021). The BIM model and DEM terrain, sketched through 3D drawing in the GIS engine, are respectively connected to both sides of the slope behind the embankment with set material and mapping.

Figure 8. Lightweight seawall model.

Figure 9. GIS-BIM visual window.

4.5 *Digital twin seawall*

Applying the method of digital-analog separation, the structural information of the seawall can be summarized into a JSON file following the rank of "name", where each row of JSON information is connected to the model components.

This paper establishes the data connection between the virtual digital world and the real physical world in the digital twin seawall scenario created by GIS and BIM. The digital twin scenario provides an immersive experience of the project with 360° images, and achieves the pre-construction with a comprehensive display of the project after the completion; the connection to video monitoring in the scenario can realize the real-time inspection of dynamics; the connection to tide-level and other IoT data helps display the real-time monitoring information; the structural information can also be queried with one click, and the design information can circulate throughout the whole life cycle. Thus, digital twin seawall information is available on one simple screen to extend the new working model of "space-time extension.

5 CONCLUSION AND PROSPECTS

This paper carries out an in-depth investigation of BIM parametric modeling and digital twin application of seawall projects and establishes a complete set of automatic parametric modeling methods for the seawall. On this basis, it employs digital-analog separation for lightweight modeling

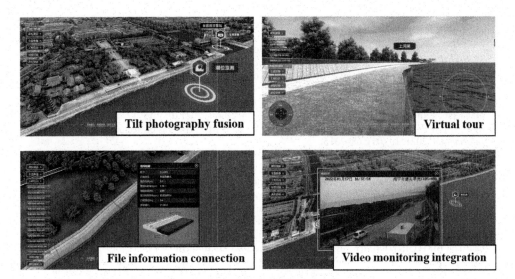

Figure 10. Digital twin applications.

and attributes connection. With the GIS-BIM technology, this paper creates a virtual reality scenario and integrates IoT information to explore digital twin seawall applications. After practical research, the following main conclusions are obtained.

1. Considering the long distance and relatively simple structure, seawalls are very suitable for parametric automatic modeling. Owing to the flexibility of Dynamo visual programming, it can improve the modeling efficiency by about 35%, guaranteeing the extensive application of seawall BIM.
2. GIS and BIM provide the database plate for visual management in engineering, creating broad application prospects. At present, the key technical issues in GIS + BIM application, such as multi-source data fusion and lightweight modeling can be solved manually. Furthermore, the standardization degree of solutions will be improved with increasingly mature technologies.
3. This paper innovatively proposed applying digital twin technology to the construction and management of seawall projects, which helps realize the multi-source panoramic monitoring and promotes the reform of construction management mode.

Based on the exploration carried out by this paper on digital twin seawall, the following areas require further research in the future: (1) developing the modeling method of multi-software application into software to form general tools; (2) both digital twins and physical seawalls require accurate mapping on all sides. Although "reflecting virtuality with reality" (Shi & Cai et al. 2019) has been realized, there is still a large gap between "controlling reality with virtuality." By integrating the sensing end and control end, we are expected to realize the integration of virtuality-reality and iterative optimization in the future.

ACKNOWLEDGMENTS

This work was supported by the Research on Key Technology and Application of BIM-based Pumping Station Design and Construction (Grant No. RA1804); the Research on Design and Deformation Monitoring Method of Steel Formwork for Flow Channel in Pumping Stations (Grant No. B2013); and the BIM+GIS-based Digital Asset Management and Application in Reservoir Engineering (Grant No. RC2149).

REFERENCES

Cao J C, Wang J Y, Chen M Q. Research and application of key technologies of intelligent site system based on BIM+GIS+IOT technology [J]. *Construction Science and Technology*. 2020 (Z1): 74–77.

Fan J J, Meng C C, Pan G H, Song Y Q. Application of BIM technology in project management of seawall engineering [J]. *China Harbour Engineering*. 2020, 40 (05): 75–78.

Huo J W, Li Y S, Zhang J H, Chen J Z, Guo D D. Application of digital twins technology in operation management of water diversion project [J]. *Small Hydro Power*, 2021 (05): 15–17.

Qiao T R, Liu P L, Liu J J, Ye P. Application analysis of BIM + GIS fusion technology [J]. *Geospatial Information*, 2021, 19 (01): 68–70+5.

Rao X K, Ma R, Zhang L, Xu Z M. Study and design of dike engineering safety management system based on GIS+BIM+IOT digital twin [J/OL]. *China Rural Water and Hydropower*: 1–16 [2022-01-8].

Shi Y W, Cai Z Y. Construction of water conservancy project operation management system based on digital twin technology [C]. *China Academic Journal Electronic Publishing House*, 2019: 185–190.

Wu P F, Liu Y S, Tan Y, Li J F. Advances and trends of integration between GIS and BIM [J]. *Geomatics & Spatial Information Technology*, 2019, 42 (01): 1–6.

You L Q, Wang N, Tao Y B, Zhang J R. Multisource data fusion in hydropower engineering and its applications based on BIM+GIS [J]. *Water Resources and Power*, 2021, 39 (08): 169–173.

Zhang S C, Guo X H, Bao D X. Parametric modeling technology of prefabricated box girder BIM model based on Dynamo [C]. *China Academic Journal Electronic Publishing House*, 2021: 437–441.

Zheng W H, Zhou X Y, Wu H P, Li H M, Zhu X T, WEN L J. Digital twin system for highway traffic based on 3D GIS technology [J]. *Computer Integrated Manufacturing Systems*. 2020, 26 (01): 28–39.

Study on the protection strategy of Dong traditional dwellings from the perspective of rural revitalization

Haifeng Chu*, Dianqi Fang* & Xiaoling Zhang*

School of Art and Design, Guilin University of Electronic Technology, Guilin, China

ABSTRACT: The report of the 19th Party Congress put forward the major strategy of rural revitalization, which triggered people to pay attention to the protection and development of traditional villages. In recent years, under the impact of rapid urbanization, ethnic minority villages are facing problems such as the extinction of ethnic characteristic culture and the loss of traditional architectural style. To improve the inner vitality of ethnic villages and show the unique ethnic culture, taking the conservation of Dong ethnic dwellings in Chengyang Bazhai, Sanjiang, and Guangxi as an example, we summarize and analyze the current problems of dwellings and their causes, combine the existing research results at home and abroad, and explore new strategies for the architectural conservation of ethnic minority dwellings under the strategy of rural revitalization from the perspectives of architectural style, functional structure and cultural inheritance of ethnic minority dwellings to promote the protection of village appearance, ethnic culture inheritance and regional economic development in minority areas.

1 INTRODUCTION

As an important carrier of Chinese vernacular civilization, ethnic dwellings focus on the unique ethnic architectural culture. However, in the current construction, commercial development planned by enterprises and spontaneous transformation by villagers are commonplace. Many traditional dwellings have been replaced by new buildings, the ethnic architectural culture and rural regional characteristics are gradually separated, and the ethnic dwelling architectural culture is in urgent need of protection. The "rural revitalization strategy", as the general grasp of rural revitalization in the new era, needs to take the comprehensive concepts of new rural construction, beautiful countryside, and field complex as the theoretical basis, and build a more systematic, macro, and scientific strategic decision-making plan on this basis (Li & Wang 2019). In today's rapid economic and social development as well as under the leadership of national policies, the protection of ethnic minority dwellings should propose strategies and models that are more in line with the development of the times, which is an important issue to be solved at present.

2 CURRENT STATUS OF RESEARCH ON THE PRESERVATION OF MINORITY DWELLINGS

In recent years, China has gradually deepened its research on the protection of minority residential houses, and in December 2012, the State People's Committee and the Ministry of Finance formulated and issued the *Outline of the Plan for the Protection and Development of Villages with Minority Characteristics* (2010–2015), which has served as a strong guide in terms of policy (Li 2014). Xiong Mei believes that the content of traditional residential research is no longer

---

*Corresponding Authors: 12672142@qq.com, 1466938038@qq.com and 244897410@qq.com

isolated and static, not only fixated on single-disciplinary research but interdisciplinary cross-integrated research (Xiong 2017). Lingling Deng believes that the Dong traditional architectural style inheritance protection is guided by policy, and then the introduction of professionals to protect and strengthen the development of professional-level such as fire and corrosion protection (Deng 2008).

Foreign countries have more in-depth studies on the conservation of traditional houses. The promulgation of the Venice Charter in 1964 gave a great impetus to the conservation of traditional houses and vernacular architecture. Japan not only protects the building facade and structure of traditional residential houses but also focuses on the inheritance of its traditional design techniques and spatial interpretation. Through his research and analysis of the Japanese residential system, reuse, and cultural heritage, Yang found that Japanese residential artisans focused on material extraction, practicality, and environmental harmony (Yang 2021).

3 CHARACTERISTICS AND PROBLEMS OF DONG FOLK DWELLING RESOURCES IN CHENGYANG BAZHAI

3.1 *Overview of Chengyang Bazhai and analysis of dwelling form*

3.1.1 *Overview of Chengyang Bazhai*

Chengyang Bazhai is located in Sanjiang Dong Autonomous County, Liuzhou City, Guangxi Zhuang Autonomous Region, and is a large village of 1,000 households of the Dong people. The Dong villages are located near the mountains and water, with a reasonable and ingenious layout, the whole sitting north to south, making full use of water sources and terrain to build buildings, and the natural environment and architectural landscape are integrated, fully reflecting the harmony and unity between man and nature (Huang 2015).

3.1.2 *Architectural forms of wooden dwellings in Chengyang Bazhai*

The Dong countryside is rich in cedar wood, and the dwellings are built with cedar wood as the main building material, and the construction strategy is fully adapted to the local conditions to solve the problem of dampness and rain, and the dwellings generally follow the "dry bar construction" wooden building structure. Dong dwellings are generally divided into a two-room, three-story building, with farming tools and livestock kept downstairs the upstairs is inhabited, with a staircase built on the side, and the front half of the second floor is divided into an outer corridor for the family to rest and move around. There is a fire pit inside, which can be used for heating and cooking, but more importantly, it is the place where the "ancestors" sit. The third floor is generally used for bedrooms and barns, and the entire house is built with cedar wood except for the roof tiles, surrounded by "hanging foot pillars", which are now called hanging foot buildings (Pan 2005).

3.2 *Current problems and causes of Dong dwellings in Chengyang Bazhai*

3.2.1 *Traditional architectural style protection is unfavorable*

The architectural style of traditional dwellings is facing serious threats due to the aging of wooden buildings and neglect of management and other real problems. The damage to the building has the following three points. First, is the phenomenon of unreasonable additions to residential buildings. Under the impact of economic development and tourism, local B&Bs, and catering industries have emerged. Due to the need for housing, villagers have expanded and renovated their dwellings, and the phenomenon of private construction is serious, leading to new houses that do not fit in with the original traditional dwelling form (Figure 1). Second, residential buildings change the original building materials. During the transformation of the first floor of most houses, the use of masonry and concrete materials has replaced cedar wood due to age, decay, and fire hazards, and the transformed houses are heavier and lack the lightness of wooden houses (Figure 2). Third, the problem of passing on the skills of residential construction, the traditional wooden dwelling

Figure 1. Private residential building addition.   Figure 2. Brick and wood dwelling.

construction skills are increasingly faded under the impact of modern steel and concrete, how to inherit the traditional building construction skills so that the village architecture culture to carry forward the heritage has become the key.

3.2.2 The imperfection of the functional structure of residential houses

There is no doubt that the Dong dry bar-style dwellings have many advantages, but there are also certain drawbacks of the traditional construction mode. First, the construction standard of residential houses is low, and residential houses are shared by people and animals, with insufficient ventilation and light, damp and dark environment, and poor sanitary conditions. Secondly, the functional division of the interior of the dwelling is unreasonable, and the dwelling relies on traditional fire pits for cooking and heating, and there are no windows or partitions, resulting in smoke and fire, which is a safety hazard. Finally, with the development of society, many villagers have changed the traditional model of "living on the upper floor and raising livestock on the lower floor", but overall, there is still less space for contact with the outside world, which does not fundamentally solve the problems of unsatisfactory indoor light and ventilation, and no functional space.

3.2.3 Inadequate display of the local culture in residential houses

Due to geographical location and other factors, the economic development of the region is relatively slow. To boost economic development, the village is vigorously developing its tourism industry, converting traditional dwellings into bed and breakfasts and guest houses, and promoting local commercialization. However, the modern residential construction in the area lacks systematic protection and targeted planning programs, and the residential architecture has lost the flavor and culture of the characteristic traditional residential houses, which is incompatible with the architectural style of traditional residential houses. Under modernization, more and more traditional dwellings have been affected by the commercialization of construction, and the original local culture in the villages cannot be reflected, and the unique dwelling culture is gradually declining.

Nowadays, with China's strong support for villages, villages have received unprecedented development. Dealing with the relationship between the preservation and renewal of traditional residential buildings is an important issue in the current village construction. In view of the problems and causes of the Dong traditional dwellings, the basic principles of architectural restoration are applied to the conservation and renewal of the dwellings.

4 PRINCIPLES OF PROTECTING THE DONG HOUSES IN CHENGYANG BAZHAI

4.1 The principle of authenticity in the conservation of residential houses

In recent years, China has attached great importance to the protection of traditional village style, emphasizing the need to protect the originality, integrity, and authenticity of cultural heritage (Chen

2016). In the process of restoration, the residential buildings should make full use of the original geographical features and settlement patterns, respect the natural texture of the local composition, protect the integrity of the rural landscape, and ensure the integration of residential construction with the village landscape. Secondly, the traditional techniques of residential architecture should be fully borrowed and studied, and proper protection should be carried out based on not changing the original appearance, and the architectural details, architectural forms, and architectural decorations of the original residential houses should be protected and repaired to reflect the cultural essence contained in the traditional architecture. The drum tower and theatrical stage, for example, are reasonably protected and maintained according to the traditional craft techniques in the village. This allows them to be used by local people as well as a local landscape highlight to demonstrate the village culture, which plays a crucial role in preserving and transmitting the village's material and intangible cultural heritage.

4.2 *The principle of gradual preservation of residential houses*

The conservation and renewal of ethnic residential buildings is an adaptive and progressive transformation process, with each stage of transformation providing direction and guidance for the subsequent stages (Wang 2018). The conservation of residential buildings is a continuous process, which should fully consider and retain the morphological characteristics of the buildings and the original cultural characteristics of the buildings, add reasonable functional structures in the process of renewal combined with the current residential needs, and gradually improve the integrity and coordination of traditional residential buildings. For example, to conserve the dwellings, it is necessary to incorporate the topographic form and architectural culture of the region, improve the architectural details of the exterior, then combine the interior decoration with the traditional culture, and use the decorative culture to demonstrate the unique features of the dwellings in terms of style, and gradually improve the overall state of conservation and renewal of the dwellings.

5 CONSERVATION STRATEGY OF CHENGYANG BAZHAI DWELLINGS IN THE PERSPECTIVE OF RURAL REVITALIZATION

Under the promotion of the rural revitalization strategy, Sanjiang Chengyang Bazhai has carried out the conservation of dwellings and landscape enhancement, etc. With the continuous expansion of the village scale, the conservation and renewal of dwellings are facing numerous challenges. Given the current situation of the traditional dwellings in Chengyang Bazhai, we strategically propose measures for their preservation and renewal in terms of their architectural style, functional form, and cultural heritage. First, while preserving the traditional characteristics of the minority dwellings, we adopt the method of "repairing the old as the old" to protect the architectural style and texture of the traditional dwellings. Secondly, combining with the local lifestyle, optimizing, and upgrading the building materials and the existing internal layout of residential buildings, replacing, and upgrading the building functions of residential buildings without changing the traditional way of living to better adapt to the modern lifestyle and drive the development of related industries. Finally, by tapping the local cultural genes and integrating the local material and non-material cultural resources, it is applied to the construction of the characteristic residential houses, reflecting the cultural connotation of the Dong people in Chengyang Bazhai, and adding a cultural and ecological atmosphere.

5.1 *Protect the traditional appearance of residential buildings*

Under the guidance of relevant policies, we adopt a combination of top-down and bottom-up approaches to protection measures for organic renewal of village dwellings, form an autonomous conservation and renewal model, promote the metabolism of villages, and achieve the goal of sustainable and healthy development of traditional dwellings. The resources of Chengyang Bazhai dwellings are centrally integrated and divided into three categories: well-preserved dwellings, dwellings that do not conform to the traditional style and unauthorized dwellings, and targeted protection strategies are proposed.

5.1.1 *Landscape restoration*
The buildings of Chengyang Bazhai that are of good preservation quality and in harmony with the village style are undergoing protective repair. Adhering to the principle of minimizing damage to the village residential buildings, the traditional cedar wood construction materials are used to integrate and renovate the architectural facade and color of such residential buildings, and to protect and repair them to continue the regional style of residential buildings. In addition, changes can be made to the interior of the building, such as adding a fixed kitchen and bathroom, to improve the traditional living pattern and enhance the living conditions of the residents.

5.1.2 *Form modification*
The residential houses in Chengyang Bazhai that do not match the surrounding environment will be renovated to reduce the conflict between such buildings and the overall appearance. The dwellings in the villages that have changed their traditional architectural forms are repaired, and the newly built brick and stone combination houses are renovated to maintain the original materials and colors of the dwellings, and to improve the consistency and integrity of the architectural style while not changing the structure. For example, the traditional buildings in Chengyang Bazhai are mostly wooden buildings with wood color as the main color, for such buildings, traditional regional materials should be used to restore and renovate them.

5.1.3 *Demolition of unauthorized buildings*
The illegal construction and addition of residential houses in the village should be treated consistently and handled properly. First, relevant policies and laws, and regulations are formulated, and the abandoned and illegally built dwellings in the villages are demolished according to law based on consultation. In addition, buildings and structures that conflict with the traditional landscape style and residential texture pattern are demolished to protect the original residential and landscape structures. A residential building that does not comply with the rules and regulations can be properly handled by utilizing the policy guidance provided by relevant departments to monitor each other and adhere to the rules and regulations.

5.2 *Optimize the functional structure of residential buildings*
Based on the problem of the imperfect functional structure of the Dong dwellings in Chengyang Bazhai, we optimize the functional structure of the dwellings by replacing and integrating the traditional functions of the dwellings to create a better living environment based on keeping the architectural space and style of the dwellings unchanged and combining the living style and habits of the Dong dwellings. Firstly, to strengthen the safety of traditional building materials that have fallen into disrepair to enhance the safety of traditional ethnic minority dwellings and reduce safety hazards. Secondly, according to the topography and terrain of the residential area, we combine natural light to improve the lighting and ventilation of the residential houses and use glass materials in the renovation of windows and balconies to increase the light permeability and illumination, thus reducing the humidity of the living environment. Thirdly, in addition to the protection of traditional drum towers and other buildings, additional service spaces are provided in the public space of the village to provide a place for the village to gather, deliberate, relax and chat, increase the diversity of the traditional space of the village, and improve the connection between private homes and public space.

In addition to the improvement of the internal functions of ethnic dwellings and the creation of external public leisure space, the conservation of traditional dwellings should also be in line with the

Figure 3. Bamboo decoration for B&Bs.

Figure 4. The use of ethnic decorative motifs.

development of tourism. For example, rational planning or new tourism areas to carry out cultural experience activities with ethnic minority characteristics and create comprehensive characteristic centers integrating handicraft making, cultural experience, and ethnic products purchase, without affecting the original spatial layout and way of living of local villagers, it optimizes the functional structure of residential houses, improves the tourism environment, and boosts the local economy. Through the functional improvement of the internal and external linkage of ethnic dwellings, the original living environment of local villagers is protected, which can effectively activate the original vitality of the village, promote the culture of ethnic characteristics, and help revitalize the development of the village.

5.3 *Innovative characteristic residential development*

Sanjiang Chengyang Bazhai, restricted by its geographical location, has long been less influenced by the outside world and has formed numerous material, non-traditional, and ethnic festival cultures with ethnic characteristics (Huang 2019). Using taxonomy, semiotics, and iconography, we examine the form of ethnic culture, excavate, and extract ethnic characteristics in minority villages, and through the extraction and reconstruction of such components, we integrate and summarize these cultural genes with local historical and cultural veins, and apply them to the process of protecting and renewing ethnic dwellings.

The conservation and renewal of Chengyang Bazhai dwellings cannot be separated from the innovative development of the characteristic B&B, for example, with the help of local fire pits facilities, modern electric fireplaces are implanted in the design of the living room of the B&B, which can not only give the effect of warming the room, preventing dampness, and repelling cold but also reflect the traditional fire pit culture of the Dong people and play a certain decorative effect. Furthermore, the local bamboo weaving technology is combined with Dong painting, and the Dong painting is drawn on bamboo and rattan weaving crafts to show the local customs and people and play a decorative role (Figure 3). As an important embodiment of intangible cultural heritage, the Dong weaving and embroidery craft concentrates on the ethnic-cultural characteristics, and the Dong traditional patterns are symbolically extracted and applied to the decoration of pillows, bedding, and curtains, adding to the ethnic-cultural atmosphere of the B&B. In addition to integrating local customs and modern lifestyles, it meets the psychological needs of tourists for a return to nature and the experience of ethnic and cultural styles (Figure 4).

6 CONCLUSION

Ethnic dwellings are a pivotal part of minority culture. With the development of modernization, the architectural style of traditional villages has been damaged to different degrees. For the protection of residential houses, we should fully respect the local historical style and architectural and cultural authenticity, and adopt the principle of gradual renewal to protect and repair the residential buildings of villages and inherit the culture of ethnic characteristics. At the same time, combined with the development of the cultural tourism industry, show the regional characteristics of culture, customs, and local conditions, fundamentally enhance the villagers' consciousness to protect the culture of residential houses, improve the cultural self-confidence and cultural self-improvement of minority areas. Thus, a holistic residential preservation strategy is formed to promote the preservation of residential style, cultural development, and sustainable economic development in minority areas, and effectively contribute to rural revitalization.

ACKNOWLEDGMENTS

This work was financially supported by the 2018 Ministry of Education Humanities and Social Sciences Research Planning Fund General Project (Grant No. 18YJA760009); 2021 Guangxi Philosophy and Social Science Planning Research Project (Grant No. 21BSH001); 2022 Innovation Project of GUET Graduate Education (Grant No. 2022YCXS094); 2021 Guangxi Philosophy and Social Science Planning Research Project (Grant No. 21BMZ0191); and 2022 Guangxi Postgraduate Education Innovation Program Project (Grant No. YCSW2022294).

REFERENCES

Chen HY. (2016) Discussion on the development of beautiful new countryside from the perspective of traditional village protection. *J. Construction Science and Technology*. 78–79.

Deng LL. (2008). Inheritance and protection of traditional architectural style of Dong villages. *J. Guizhou Ethnic Studies*. 77–82.

Huang C. (2015). *Exploration on the Architecture and Regional Culture of the Eight Dwellings of Chengyang Village of Dong Nationality in Guangxi*. D. Harbin Normal University.

Huang ZQ. (2019). Research on the development path of Sanjiang Dong non-traditional cultural tourism in the context of "creating special" strategy. *J. New West*. 24–25+40.

Li AH. (2014). Exploration on the policy of protection and development of villages with ethnic minority characteristics. *J. Journal of Central South University for Nationalities*. 42–45.

Li CY. & Wang D. (2019). New thinking on rural environment design research from the perspective of cultural revitalization. *J. Art Design Research*. 69–73.

Pan SH. (2005). *Research on the Development and Utilization of Dong Culture Tourism*. D. Guangxi Normal University.

Wang XX. & Zhu R (2018). Research on the conservation and development of ancient villages guided by touchmedia theory–Wuxi Yanjiaqiao as an example. *J. Western Journal of Habitat Environment*. 111–115.

Xiong M. (2017). Research progress and disciplinary orientation of traditional residential houses in China. *J. Urban Planning*. 102–112.

Yang FQ. (2021). Research on the problems and countermeasures for the conservation and utilization of domestic and foreign residential houses. *J. Urban Architecture*. 62–64.

Load transfer mechanism during building rectification using jacked pile

Hao Chen
Key Laboratory of Coast Civil Structures and Safety of Ministry of Education, Tianjin University, Tianjin, China
Third Construction Company of China Construction Fifth Engineering Bureau, Changsha, China

Kai Li
China Construction Fifth Engineering Bureau Co., Ltd., Changsha, China

Changjie He
Third Construction Company of China Construction Fifth Engineering Bureau, Changsha, China

Jitao Bai *
Key Laboratory of Coast Civil Structures and Safety of Ministry of Education, Tianjin University, Tianjin, China

Weiqiang Pan
Shanghai Tunnel Engineering Construction Co., Ltd., Shanghai, China

Dongfan Shang
Hebei Academy of Building Research Co., Ltd., Shijiazhuang, China

ABSTRACT: In the rectification of tilt building, it is often accompanied by pile installation to provide necessary lifting force or prevent further settlement of the building. The static jacked pile is often used to reduce the disturbance to the building foundation and soil during pile installation. However, research on the load transfer mechanism of the pile during building rectification is not insufficient. In this study, a coupled finite-difference and discrete-element method (FDM-DEM) was adopted to simulate both the jacked pile installation and the rectification of a building. A typical building with a reinforced concrete frame and a raft of 8 m×8 m×0.5 m was modeled. The jacked pile had a square section of 0.5 m×0.5 m and the soil of the ground was dry fine sand with D_{50}=0.4 mm. The development of the pile axial force and the raft contact pressure during the whole piling and rectification process was focused on and analyzed to reveal the load transfer mechanism. The settlements of the pile and the deformation of the raft were also monitored and discussed. Furthermore, the influence of pile length on the performance of rectification was analyzed. The results have a guiding significance for the buildings involving foundation repair and building rectification using jacked piles.

1 INTRODUCTION

The tilt of a building is one of the most common problems of existing buildings. If the rectification is not well performed, it is very likely to cause further damage to the building. A commonly used method for tilt correction is the lifting method. The jacking method is to raise the foundation with a jacking system or grouting beneath the side with a larger settlement. Piles are often installed

---
*Corresponding Author: jitaobai_123@tju.edu.cn

before the rectification to supply reaction forces to lift the building and prevent settlement after rectification. Many studies have been conducted on the piles enhancing buildings, especially on the micro piles. Alnuaim and El Naggar (2015) studied the influence of raft flexibility on the bearing capacity and settlement of the combined pile-soil model. Sadek et al. (2006) obtained the influence of the inclination angle of micro piles on the bearing capacity of micro piles. Misra and Chen (2004) obtained the analytical solution of micro piles under the action of tension and pressure. Alnuaim and El Naggar (2016) studied the performance of micro-piled rafts in the sand by combining centrifuge tests and finite element models. A total of 78 different cases were investigated to analyze the influence of factors such as the number of piles, pile spacing, raft thickness, and soil density on the performance of piled raft foundations.

However, there is still a lack of research on the load transfer mechanism of piles during the tilt correction process. In this study, a coupled finite-difference and discrete-element method (FDM-DEM) was adopted to simulate both the jacked pile installation and the rectification of a building, and the deformation characteristics, as well as load transfer mechanism of jacked pile during building rectification, were analyzed.

2 METHOD AND MATERIAL

2.1 Numerical model

As shown in Figure 1, a typical frame structure building on the sand is simulated. A coupled finite-difference and discrete-element method were adopted. The major of the model was generated by FDM, except that the soil surrounding the pile to be installed was modeled by DEM. The interaction between the zones of FDM and DEM is realized by wall elements covered on each surface of FDM zones contacting the discrete elements. The wall elements are normally rigid to the discrete elements and sever as boundaries, while the wall elements move together with its covered FDM zone. Therefore, the wall elements can be regarded as a medium to transfer the interaction between FDM and DEM zones.

The scale of the model size to the prototype size is 1:100 and accordingly, the gravity acceleration is 980 m/s^2. Therefore, this model simulated a centrifuge test, which is a common approach to reduce the calculation time of DEM, especially using real particle size. Furthermore, due to the symmetry, only a "slice" of the building and soil is modeled. The width of the model is 20 mm. The building has three storeys. The height of each storey is 30 mm, and the total height of the building is 110 mm. The wall, floor, and roof of the building are all 5 mm. The size of the raft is 10 mm × 80 mm × 20 mm (thickness × length × width).

Then model the pile and its potion. The pile has a section of 5 mm × 5 mm. Only half the pile is modeled and the pile center is on the boundary of the model. It means that a row of piles beneath the building is simulated and the pile spacing is twice the model width (40 mm). The pile length is 50 mm, 60 mm, and 70 mm in parametric studies. The soil depth is always twice the pile length to eliminate the boundary effect.

The base of the model soil is supported by pins and the four sides of the soil are supported by rollers, as shown in Figure 1. In addition, since the symmetry plane of the half pile overlaps the side boundary of the model, the pile side on the side boundary is also supported by rollers.

2.2 Materials

For the FDM part of the model, the materials of the building, raft, and piles are assumed to be linearly elastic. Toyoura Silica Sand (Japan) was chosen to model the soil. Toyoura sand is a kind of fine quartz sand from angular to sub-angular, containing about 90% quartz and 4% flint, with a d50 of 0.2 mm and strong granularity (Oda and Kazama, 1998). An elastoplastic model with the Mohr-Coulomb criterion was adopted to simulate the soil in the FDM zone. The parameters of FDM materials are listed in Table1.

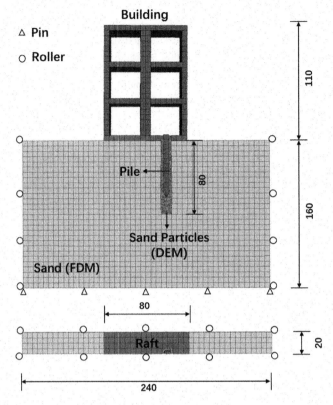

Figure 1. Model geometry and boundary conditions (unit: mm).

For the DEM part of the model, particle size enlargement was employed to reduce the calculation time. The particle size of Toyoura sand was enlarged twice so that the number of ball units in the final DEM model was controlled below 80,000. The gradations of the Toyoura sand and the model sand were shown in Figure 2. The void ratio of the modeled sand was 0.7. The parameters of the DEM materials were after the research conducted by Tu et al. (2017) and were listed in Table 2.

A numerical direct shear test on the modeled sand was conducted to verify the parameters of the model sand. Figure 3 shows that the results of the numerical results match the experimental results very well.

Table 1. Parameters of FDM material.

Model	Density (kg/m^3)	Poisson's ratio	Young's modulus (MPa)	Cohesion (kPa)	Friction angle (°)
Building	2500	0.2	24000	–	–
Raft	2500	0.2	24000	–	–
Pile	2500	0.2	30000	–	–
Soil	1553	0.3	60	0	31

2.3 Simulation procedure

The tilt of the building was set to be 4.5‰ as an initial state in each model, and the final state was 4.0‰, which meets the requirement of the building technical code in China. To achieve the aim of 4.0‰, the following two steps were carried out in the simulation.

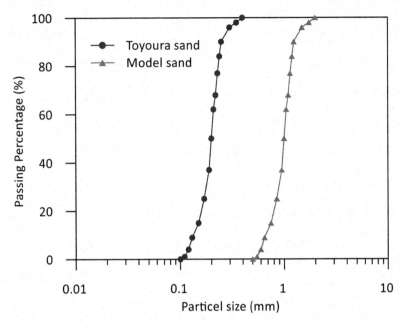

Figure 2. Gradations of the Toyoura sand and the model sand.

Table 2. Parameters of DEM material.

Properties	Toyoura sand	Model sand	Unit
Particle density	2640	2640	kg/m^3
Average particle size	0.2 mm	0.4 mm	mm
Maximum particle size	0.4 mm	0.8 mm	mm
Minimum particle size	0.1 mm	0.2 mm	mm
Coefficient of friction	0.7	0.7	–
Tangential stiffness	1	2	GN/m
Normal stiffness	1	2	GN/m

(1) Pile installation. The model pile was inserted into the soil through the hole (10 mm × 5 mm) on the raft, as shown in Figure 1.

(2) Rectification of building. The building was lifted from 4.5‰ to 4.0‰ by applying a displacement boundary around the hole on the raft. The reaction force of the displacement boundary was monitored and applied to the pile head. Thus, the jack between raft and pile in the lifting process was simulated through the above method.

3 RESULTS AND DISCUSSION

3.1 *Displacement of the model*

Figure 4 shows the vertical displacement of the building, the pile, and the soil after building rectification. The left roof and right raft have the maximum upwards and downwards displacement, respectively. The displacement changes gradually over the building, which indicates that the building has been rotated counterclockwise and rectified. The pile head also has a significant settlement but the settlement of the pile toe is relatively small. It means that the pile shaft is compressed and axial force is compressive force. The pile also drags down the surrounding soil, especially the soil near the pile toe. It can be seen that the influencing range of down drag extends over the whole

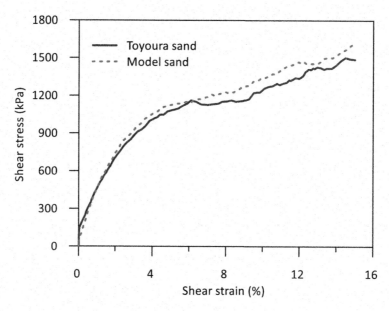

Figure 3. Experimental and numerical results of direct shear test.

length of the raft, causing the settlement of all the soil beneath the raft, which is unfavorable to the lifting of the building.

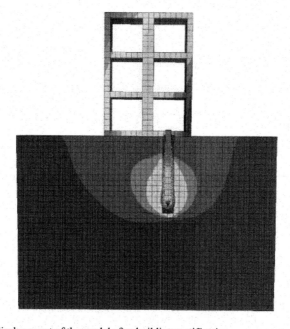

Figure 4. Vertical displacement of the model after building rectification.

Figure 5 shows the displacement development of the soil particles surrounding the piles during the model pile insertion. The DEM can capture the large local and discontinuous deformation of soil during pile installation. The soil particles at the interface between pile and soil have much larger vertical displacement than others. The maximum movement of soil particles is up to 3.38 cm, which is approximately half of the pile length.

Figure 5 also presents the displacement of soil particles after rectification. The modes of displacement in the two situations show few differences. The movements are all in the range of 1.25 cm to 2.25 cm. It indicates that during the rectification process the pile did not increase the soil settlement. The settlement of soil was mainly caused by pile insertion.

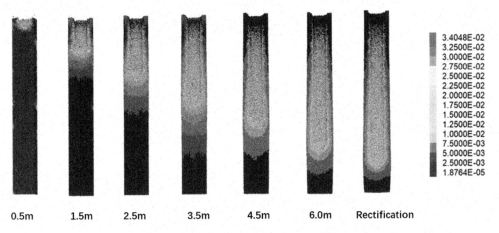

Figure 5. Displacement development of the soil particles surrounding the pile.

3.2 *Axial force along the pile shaft*

Figure 6 shows the axial force along the pile (5 m, 6 m and 7 m) after the insertion of the pile into the sand. The results are interpreted in the prototype unless stated otherwise. There is a very low compressive force along the upper part of the pile, while along the lower part, there is significantly increasing compressive force. This residual stress along piles was also found by Poulos (1987), who conducted a numerical investigation on driven piles. It should be noted that the axial force distribution along the upper part indicates that there is negative skin friction in this range. After the pile was compressed into the soil and the load on the pile head was removed, the pile tends to stretch due to the internal compressive axial force. The soil surrounding the pile resisted this tendency and therefore lead to negative friction along the upper part and positive friction along the lower part.

Figure 7 shows the axial force along the pile after the rectification of the building. The compressive force along the pile decreases nonlinearly with the increasing depth. The axial force after rectification becomes significantly larger than that after insertion. The final reaction load on the pile is approximately 150 kN, 200 kN and 200 kN for the pile of 5 m, 6 m and 7 m.

Since the weight of the building and rectification aim are the same for each model, the load on the pile head should be the same if the pile has enough bearing capacity. The results show that the 5 m-pile cannot supply sufficient reaction due to its low bearing capacity of 150 kN. Both the 6m pile and 7m pile have a reaction force of 200 kN, which can be regarded as the lifting force.

3.3 *Lifting load on the pile head*

Figure 8 presents the increase of lifting load on the head of piles during the building rectification. The final lifting loads on the 5m pile, 6m pile and 7m pile are 150 kN, 200 kN and 200 kN, respectively, which are consistent with the axial force shown in Figure 8.

3.4 *Settlement of pile head*

Figure 9 shows the settlement of the pile head during rectification. The 5-m pile has a larger settlement than the 6-m pile and 7-m pile. As shown in Figure 8, the 5-m pile has insufficient

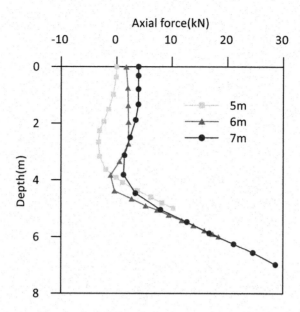

Figure 6. Axial force along the pile after pile installation.

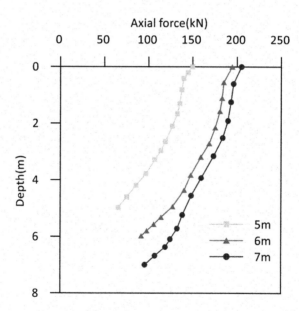

Figure 7. Axial force along the pile after building rectification.

bearing capacity to sustain the lifting load of 200 kN. Therefore, the bearing capacity had been fully mobilized during rectification and the settlement pile head became very large, although the maximum reaction load on the pile head was only 150 kN. In contrast, the 6-m pile and 7-m pile have smaller settlements of pile head under a maximum lifting load of 200 kN. The 7-m pile shows higher stiffness than 6-m pile because of its long length.

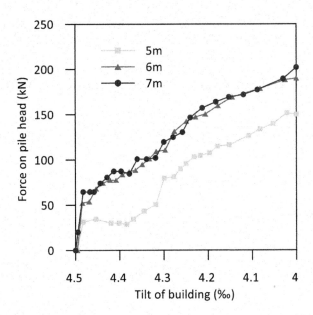

Figure 8. Lifting load on the pile head.

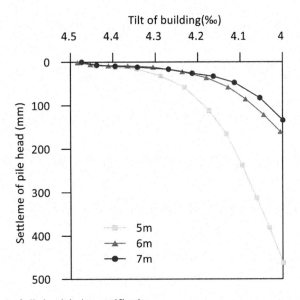

Figure 9. Settlement of pile head during rectification.

4 CONCLUSIONS

The deformation characteristics and load transfer mechanism of the jacked pile during building rectification were investigated using a coupled finite-difference and discrete-element method. And the influence of pile length was also analyzed. The conclusions can be drawn as follows.

(1) During the pile installation and building rectification, the pile drags down the surrounding soil, especially the soil near the pile toe. The influencing range of down drag extends over

the whole length of the raft, causing the settlement of all the soil beneath the raft, which is unfavorable to the lifting of the building.
(2) The soil particles at the interface between pile and soil have much larger vertical displacement than others. The movement of soil was mainly caused by the pile insertion and can be up to half of the pile length. During the rectification process, the pile did not increase the soil settlement compared to pile insertion.
(3) After the jacked pile installation, there is an obvious residual compressive force along the lower part of the pile.
(4) As long as the pile has sufficient bearing capacity to lift the building, the reaction forces of the piles are the same regardless of pile length. The pile length can only reduce the settlement of the pile head.

ACKNOWLEDGEMENTS

The authors are very grateful for the support of the National Natural Science Foundation of China (Grant No. 52178342), Tianjin Science and Technology Project (Grant No. 21JCZDJC00590), and Shanghai Excellent Academic/Technical Leader Program (Grant No. 20XD1432500).

REFERENCES

Alnuaim, A. M. & El Naggar, M. H. 2015. Performance of micropiled raft in sand subjected to vertical concentrated load: centrifuge modeling. *Canadian Geotechnical Journal* 52 (1): 33–45.
Alnuaim, A. M. & El Naggar, M. H. 2018. Performance of micropiled rafts in clay: Numerical investigation. *Computers and Geotechnics* 99: 42–54.
Misra A & Chen, C. H. 2004. Analytical solution for micropile design under tension and compression. *Geotechnical and Geological Engineering* 22 (2): 199–225.
Oda, M. & Kazama, H. 1998. Microstructure of shear bands and its relation to the mechanisms of dilatancy and failure of dense granular soils. *Géotechnique* 48 (4): 465–481.
Poulos, H. G. 1987. Analysis of residual stress effects in piles. *Journal of Geotechnical Engineering* 113 (3): 216–229.
Sadek, M., Shahrour, I. & Mroueh, H. 2006. Influence of micropile inclination on the performance of a micropile network. *Proceedings of the Institution of Civil Engineers-Ground Improvement* 10 (4): 165–172.
Tu, F., Ling, D., Hu, C. & Zhang, R. 2017. DEM-FEM analysis of soil failure process via the separate edge coupling method. *International Journal for Numerical and Analytical Methods in Geomechanics* 41 (9): 1157–1181.
Yan, G., Yu, H. & McDowell, G. 2009. Simulation of granular material behaviour using DEM. *Procedia Earth and Planetary Science* 1 (1): 598–605.

Protection and repair technology of ancient building walls based on big data

Sha Tao*

Shandong Jianzhu University, Jinan City, Shandong Province, China

ABSTRACT: In the process of restoration of cultural relics, due to the fragility of ancient buildings and cultural relics, a certain degree of uncertainty is provided for the restoration of the cultural relics. It is necessary to organize the design and development of a simulation system. This paper studies the protection and restoration technology of ancient building walls based on big data. First, it uses the literature research method to summarize the main existing problems in the protection and restoration process of ancient building walls and the significance of ancient building wall protection and restoration. This paper uses a questionnaire survey method to investigate the application status of ancient building wall protection and repair technology based on big data, and put forward relevant suggestions on ancient building wall protection and repair technology through analysis of the results. According to the survey results, the main problem of ancient building walls is corrosion, which accounts for about 45%, and deformation problems account for about 30%. For corrosion problems, anti-corrosion materials can be added when repairing, and drying can be added to the ancient building environment in consideration of weather problems. The holographic photography technology is widely used, about 45%, and the establishment of the database and the application of 3D printing are not thorough, which may be related to the lack of matching by the relevant technical personnel.

1 INTRODUCTION

Since the early 90s, China has made significant progress in the protection of ancient buildings (Huang 2017; Jie 2021). And the theory of building protection has also made significant progress. The research mainly focuses on three aspects. The first is the protection of western historical buildings (Fu 2021; Wang 2018). The second is the research on the protection laws and regulations of typical western historical sites and historical buildings (Yan 2018; Zuo 2019), and the third is the research on the protection and planning of historical and cultural cities in China (Ge 2020; Liao 2017).

In the research on the protection and restoration technology of ancient building walls based on big data, many scholars have conducted research on it and achieved good results. For example, the Daxiong Palace in Xiamen Nanputuo is used as a virtual modeling object, and many figures are measured and photographed on the spot. Camera photos are used as the main data foundation to study the mechanism of combining three-dimensional modeling and MultiGen Creator for the space reconstruction of ancient buildings (Liao 2021). The Indian National Software Technology Center uses 3D modeling software to perform detailed spatial simulation reconstruction of the ancient palace ruins of Fatehpur Sikri, "Victory City" in Agra, according to plan, topographical, cross-sectional views of buildings and photographic portraits, and perform detailed spatial simulation reconstruction on the mobile terminal or the Internet. The virtual roaming system of ancient buildings was mentioned in the study of Wei (2021).

---

*Corresponding Author: 30536761@qq.com

This paper studies the protection and restoration technology of ancient building walls based on big data. First, it uses the literature research method to summarize the main problems existing in the protection and restoration process of ancient building walls and the significance of ancient building wall protection and restoration. This paper uses a questionnaire survey method to investigate the application status of ancient building wall protection and repair technology based on big data, and put forward relevant suggestions on ancient building wall protection and repair technology through the result analysis.

2 RESEARCH ON PROTECTION AND RESTORATION TECHNOLOGY OF ANCIENT BUILDING WALLS BASED ON BIG DATA

2.1 Planning and design of ancient building protection

Protected areas are designated according to the safety and integrity requirements of historic buildings. Ancient buildings in key protected areas have the highest cultural relics value, requiring ancient buildings to maintain the status quo, not to rebuild or build new buildings, verification of dilapidated ancient buildings should be restored based on full observation and verification. To ensure the integrity of the ancient architecture, the construction and reconstruction of its affiliated cultural relics should be coordinated with the ancient architecture itself. The construction of the control zone is the division of the surrounding environment of the ancient buildings for the integrity and harmony of the packaging environment, which is a continuation of the multi-protection area. Building control zones are classified according to the intensity and content of the control.

Figure 1. Dilapidated walls of old buildings.

2.2 The Main existing problems in the protection and restoration of ancient building walls

(1) The nature of the wall maintenance project was improperly placed, blindly complying with the requirements of the people who benefited the most.
(2) The evaluation of the historical era of the ancient building walls is vague, even artificial.
(3) In the process of protection and restoration, freely understand the national guidelines for the protection of cultural relics.
(4) The nature of the problems related to the protection and repair of ancient building walls is inconsistent with the actual operation of the repair process: the problem is large, the repair is small; the problem is small, and the repair is not.
(5) Reference materials for the recovery plan are insufficient and unscientific. The design and construction are based on the subjective creation of the restoration staff and based on certain graphics, which caused some losses and consequences. Completely modern materials were

also used in the wall restoration of some ancient buildings, which led to differences in materials. There are also some problems, such as drilling holes in ancient walls. Restoring the ancient city wall is a long-term process. One fix cannot solve all problems. Some problems will continue to occur during the restoration process, including wall material information, historical information, and building information.

2.3 *Issues that we need to pay attention to in the restoration of ancient building walls*

(1) The problem of materials used for wall repair and protection in ancient buildings, and the new and traditional materials used in the wall repair process must be used reasonably.
(2) Technical construction issues in the process of restoration of ancient buildings: construction and protection technology do not meet the requirements, take shortcuts, waste materials, waste workforce, and material resources, and cause gradual damage to ancient buildings.
(3) For management issues in the construction process, such as bidding issues, detailed rules for bidding requirements must be clearly defined and human factors must be eliminated.
(4) From the beginning to the present, the archive restoration work has carried out a detailed record of the restoration work of the ancient city wall, so that future generations can have a comprehensive understanding of the history of the ancient city wall.

2.4 *Significance of protection and restoration of ancient building walls*

(1) Protecting ancient buildings is the carrier of protecting history and culture
Ancient architecture is an important carrier for inheriting the cultural and artistic spirit. We can learn the rich and colorful cultural tone from ancient architecture.
(2) Ancient architecture is an important reference for new architectural design and new artistic creation
Chinese ancient architecture has reached a very high level of artistic and technological achievement and has made great contributions to the history of world architecture. Scholars have studied a wide range of subjects from ancient times to the present, including building types, materials, structures, art decoration, and traditional styles.
(3) Ancient buildings are an important material basis for the development of tourism
With the progress of China's economic productivity and the continuous improvement of people's material level, citizens' needs for culture will also become more urgent. In the new era, ancient buildings have undertaken the historical tasks of the new era of people's leisure, entertainment, and cultural activities.

Figure 2. The restored appearance of the ancient building.

2.5 Big data algorithm

(1) Min count algorithm

The probability density function sets X as a machine random variable. If, for any real number a < b, P {a ≤ X < b} = f(x)dx, then X is a continuous random variable, and f(x) is its probability density function. The Min Count algorithm is proposed in the literature. The algorithm performs cardinality estimation based on the statistical information of the hash result. As the name implies, it is based on the minimum value of the sequence to estimate the cardinality. According to the algorithm, assuming that the minimum hash result of all elements in a multiset is x, the estimate of set cardinality n is approximately one. In mathematical terms, the algorithm is described as follows: [0, 1]. The minimum probability density f(x) of n random X-machine uniform variables is $n(1-x)^{n-1}$, so the mathematical expectation of this value is expressed by the equation below.

$$E(M) = \int_0^1 x \cdot n(n-1)^{n-1} dx = \frac{1}{n+1} \tag{1}$$

According to the calculation result of the minimum mathematical expectation of the interval [0, 1], it is easy to think of: when one is expected, its value is approximately equal to M. When the count-min sketch is analyzed and studied mathematically, it is found that x is equal to one. In the mathematical expectation integral equation, a divergence point is defined by the formula below.

$$E\left(\frac{1}{M}\right) = \int_0^1 \frac{1}{x} \cdot n(1-x)^{n-1} dx = +\infty \tag{2}$$

The network data collected this time is the text data reflecting tourists' evaluation of ancient buildings and tourists' spatial points of interest (POI) data carrying spatial geographic coordinates.

POI data are generally presented as point data. Point data generally refers to the data set with geographic coordinate information. The processing process is as follows. By writing the rules of locomotive collector or using Python to write the connection code, the data set of coordinate information contained in the web page can be collected in large quantities, including the data of public comments and Weibo. After removing some vacant information and useless information, the data set dominated by coordinates can be obtained. The text data collected in this paper is processed by writing locomotive collection rules and using the JiebaR package loading function in the Python platform after obtaining the text data.

The first step is to load the JiebaR language toolkit on the Python platform. Manually load the dictionary by loading the dictionary in the Jieba word segmentation kit. According to the requirements of this study, 10 words such as dragon ancient architecture and architectural protection are input for recognition in word segmentation.

The second step is the particle. Word segmentation is to break a sentence into recognizable phrases and read them. The table is used to write the collected travel notes into the R language platform, and Jieba is used to divide the comments and travel notes, ranking the phrases from high frequency to low frequency.

The last step is to remove the relevant words. Exclude words that are broader or have no obvious reference, such as "we", and "some", and the frequency of the remaining terms is calculated.

3 INVESTIGATIONS ON THE APPLICATION STATUS OF ANCIENT BUILDING WALL PROTECTION AND RESTORATION TECHNOLOGY BASED ON BIG DATA

3.1 *Purpose of the investigation*

This paper uses a questionnaire survey to investigate the current situation of the application of big data-based protection and repair technology of ancient building walls, and investigates the problems of the wall at this stage and the application of repair technology. Through the analysis of the results, corresponding opinions on the application of wall protection and repair technology are put forward.

3.2 Questionnaire survey

(1) Number of questionnaires

According to the minimum sample size formula in statistics, the author sets the confidence level of the questionnaire to 80%, and the allowable error does not exceed 8%. Calculate the minimum sample size as

$$n_0 = \left(\frac{t_a}{2\Delta p}\right)^2 = \left(\frac{1.645}{2 X 0.075}\right)^2 = 120 \quad (3)$$

That is, the minimum sample size of this questionnaire is 120 copies.

(2) Source of the questionnaire

This article is a survey of ancient building wall protection and restoration technology based on big data. The field is specified. Therefore, a field distribution questionnaire is used to randomly select 3 ancient building wall protection and restoration research institutes in this city, using a research institute and B research institute respectively. Research institutes and C institutes will conduct questionnaire surveys on them. According to the minimum sample size, the number of questionnaires distributed by the three research institutes are: 40, 50, and 60, and the number of questionnaires returned are: 39, 48, and 60.

Table 1. Distribution of questionnaires.

	Research institute A	Research institute B	Research institute C
Questionnaire distributed	40	50	60
Questionnaire recovery	39	48	60

4 DATA ANALYSIS

(1) Investigation of problems in the walls of ancient buildings

This paper uses a questionnaire design to investigate the problems that occurred in the ancient building walls during the restoration of the 3 Ancient Building Wall Protection and Restoration Institute.

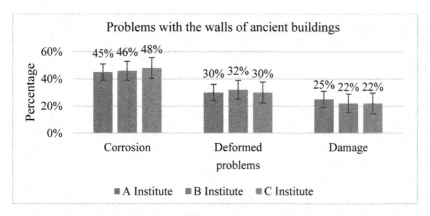

Figure 3. Problems with the walls of ancient buildings.

It can be seen from Figure 3 that the main problem of the ancient building wall is corrosion, which accounts for about 45%, and the deformation problem accounts for about 30%. For corrosion problems, anti-corrosion materials can be added when repairing, and weather problems can be used in ancient buildings.

(2) Investigation of application of ancient building wall restoration technology

This article uses questionnaires to investigate the three ancient building wall protection and restoration research institutes through questionnaire design, and researches the application status of the institute's restoration technology.

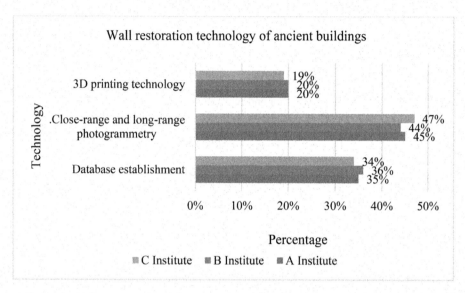

Figure 4. Wall restoration technology of ancient buildings.

It can be seen from Figure 4 that the holographic photography technology is widely used, about 45%, and the establishment of the database and the application of 3D printing have not been thoroughly applied, which may be related to the lack of matching by the relevant technical personnel.

(3) Word frequency analysis of big data

Table 2. Word frequency statistics of ancient buildings.

Ranking	Entry	Frequency	Ranking	Entry	Frequency
1	Scenery	638	6	Wood carvings	391
2	Food	579	7	Stone carvings	325
3	Park	514	8	Former residences	254
4	Ancestral halls	472	9	Folk houses	217
5	Memorial archways	459	10	Bookstores	198

As shown in Table 2, through data collection and word segmentation statistics, in the information on the protection of ancient buildings, the vocabulary of scenery is the largest, followed by food and parks. On the contrary, there are few words related to ancient architecture. It shows that the publicity for the protection and restoration of ancient buildings is still not in place.

5 CONCLUSIONS

The protection and renewal of traditional buildings should take protection as the primary premise. However, the development of architectural protection in China started late, and villages are facing the trend of decline and "hollowing out". The urgent renewal and development of traditional buildings are mainly manifested in the renewal of the village's intangible environment, which involves social, cultural, economic, and other factors. This paper analyzes the non-material environment of traditional buildings through Internet data and mobile phone platform data, which can help us better grasp social activities and provide direction for the protection and renewal of ancient buildings from the perspective of tourists and residents.

REFERENCES

Fu M, Wang F, Lin G. Design and research of bone repair scaffold based on two-way fluid-structure interaction [J]. *Computer Methods and Programs in Biomedicine*, 2021, 204 (8): 106055.

Ge L, She Y, Jia Y, et al. Research on the identification of college students' mental health problems based on campus big data [J]. *Journal of Physics: Conference Series*, 2020, 1486 (5): 052029 (8pp).

Huang J, Ma K, Huang J. Species diversity distribution patterns of chinese endemic seed plants based on geographical regions [J]. *Plos One*, 2017, 12 (1): e0170276.

Jie X, Ping L. Research on parametric modeling and digital reproduction of ancient buildings on the southern silk road [J]. *Journal of Physics: Conference Series*, 2021, 1802 (4): 042019 (6pp).

Liao J. Research on "Precise Translation" of commercial advertising based on big data [J]. *Journal of Physics Conference Series*, 2021, 1744 (3): 032121.

Liao S, Xie Y, F Xiao. Research on the integration of architecture and interior design in the era of big data [J]. *Agro Food Industry Hi Tech*, 2017, 28 (1): 95–97.

Wang Y. Research on internet application of big data in traditional Chinese medicine based on ancient Chinese medicine books [J]. *Boletin Tecnico/Technical Bulletin*, 2017, 55 (10): 114–119.

Wei Y. Research on the improvement of students' intercultural communication competence through electronic english newspapers based on big data analysis under the computer internet [J]. *Journal of Physics Conference Series*, 2021, 1744 (4): 042059.

Yan W. Research on the protection of women's rights and the countermeasures of social support based on big data network background [J]. *International Journal for Engineering Modelling*, 2018, 31 (1): 252–257.

Zuo Y. Research and implementation of human-autonomous devices for sports training management decision making based on wavelet neural network [J]. *Journal of Ambient Intelligence and Humanized Computing*, 2019 (11): 1–7.

Exploring the design of public space renovation in old city communities in the post-epidemic era

Ning Xian* & Yuqing Zhao*
College of Design and Art, Shenyang Jianzhu University, Shenyang, China

ABSTRACT: Considering the new crown epidemic that affected all aspects in people's lives, this article aims to improve the environmental quality of public spaces in old urban communities and to prevent and reduce the threat to public safety from small-scale outbreaks of the new crown epidemic in communities. By analyzing the current situation and problems of community public space in the old city, the authors explore the transformation design of community public space levels, community transportation, public service facilities, and community landscape. By exploring the problems existing during community prevention and control and combining the policy requirements in the post-epidemic era, the article proposes a three-tier community risk prevention and control system based on the problems faced by community residents in the low-, medium- and high-risk prevention and control stages, providing new ideas and methods for community disaster response. The study points out that the renewal of old communities in the post-epidemic era should balance the transformation of traditional community problems with the transformation of community response and post-disaster spatial environmental restoration.

1 INTRODUCTION

The outbreak of the new crown epidemic is an unprecedented challenge to the world's public health security. With the gradual control of the epidemic in China, epidemic prevention and control has entered a normalized phase in the post-epidemic era. However, several small-scale outbreaks in some areas have also revealed problems such as poor prevention and control facilities in communities and single community prevention and control policy. From the perspective of epidemic prevention and control, the authors take the response strategy under the epidemic as the entry point and use the public space of the old city community as the carrier to explore this issue at the level of design transformation.

2 CORE ELEMENTS OF COMMUNITY SPACE AND RELATED THEORIES

2.1 Old town concept definition

A community is a complex that integrates residential, commercial, educational, medical, and administrative functions. The spatial hierarchy can be divided into neighborhoods, residential communities, and residential units from large to small, with a hierarchical relationship of inclusion (Zhang et al. 2021). The core elements of community space are roughly the same, including community entrance, spatial boundaries, public facilities, and road traffic.

Old city communities have a unique functional position in the city-building process and are important players in the urbanization process. After the reform and opening, to meet the basic

---

*Corresponding Authors: 378932850@sjzu.edu.cn and 995484305@qq.com

material needs of people's lives, the government built many residential communities in areas close to urban centers. Due to the national financial situation at that time, these communities were characterized by smaller spatial scale, lower spatial enclosure, and less planned public areas, but could meet the daily needs of community residents. In March 2021, the *Outline of the Fourteenth Five-Year Plan of the National Economic and Social Development of the People's Republic of China and the Vision 2035* pointed out in the eighth chapter that urban development should be transformed, urban renewal should be accelerated, the functions of stock areas such as old neighborhoods, old factories, old blocks, and urban villages should be renovated and upgraded, and public facilities and emergency shelter functions of buildings should be improved. In this paper, we take the old city after the reform and opening as the research object and explore its public space renovation design.

2.2 Urban renewal theory

The theory of urban renewal is the necessary and planned transformation of areas in cities that have become unsuitable for a modern urbanized urban social life due to the expansion of urban development. Since the theory of urban renewal was proposed in 1958, it has matured over 60 years of development. Community renewal theory is an extension of urban renewal theory, an exploration of the middle and micro levels, and a planning and practice process of urban renewal back to grassroots communities. From urban renewal to community renewal, it is not only the change of spatial scope and scale from macro-city to micro-community but also represents the return of urban planning from urban development to people-oriented values (Li 2014).

3 THE CURRENT SITUATION AND PROBLEMS OF EXISTING COMMUNITY PUBLIC SPACE IN THE OLD CITY

3.1 Status of public space in old city communities

Due to the phenomenon of urban expansion and urban contraction triggered by rapid urbanization, there is a significant population loss, decline in vitality, and community decline in older urban areas. Many communities that have been built for a long time lack the necessary renewal and maintenance, and it is difficult to keep up with the development of changes in the times, gradually presenting a scene of decay and obsolescence, which is the community decline. Community decline is one of the major problems in old urban communities, and scholars have classified "community decline" into three types: physical community aging, functional community decline, and structural community decline (Sun 2020).

In the late 1990s, with the emergence and development of commercial housing, to cope with the disconnect between the old neighborhoods and the surrounding environment, government-led efforts were made to make full use of the old city space, improve infrastructure conditions, brighten the environment, and fill in the gaps. However, the scale of community renewal at this stage is relatively small, and the overall transformation concept is not clear enough. In the 14th Five-Year Plan, urban renewal will be incorporated into the national policy level, and the transformation of community public space in old urban areas has become an important part of urban development and renewal at this stage.

3.2 Existing problems of community public space in the old city

Old urban community public spaces have many problems due to their early age and poor maintenance. Since the emergence of the epidemic in September 2019, the epidemic has been effectively prevented and controlled in China, but small-scale outbreaks have occurred from time to time. Entering the post-epidemic era, the regular prevention and control of the epidemic are key areas of national work in China. Therefore, at this stage, the public space renovation strategy in old urban communities should consider the element of epidemic prevention and control. The existing problems of public spaces in old urban communities are divided into two major aspects: common problems and epidemic prevention and control problems. The two aspects of the problem contain and influence each other, and the transformation of one side will also promote the strengthening of the other.

3.2.1 *Common problems*

The three main problems of community public space in the old city are the decline of community public space infrastructure, the weakening of neighborhood relations in the community, and the hidden danger to community public safety.

a. Decline of community public space infrastructure: The old city community is built for a long time, and the planning was not comprehensive when it was built, which led to a variety of internal streets and alleys, chaotic community space levels, and overly narrow passage widths. Older urban communities are also more prone to fires due to aging building materials and pipelines, and the width of access roads in many existing older urban communities often cannot meet the requirements for large emergency vehicle traffic.

b. Weakening of neighborhood relations in the community: Due to the disorder of community public space levels, some communities lack dedicated areas for the elderly to communicate with each other, resulting in many elderly people gathering on the roadside to communicate with each other, which cannot meet the communication needs of community residents and poses a hidden danger to the personal safety of the elderly. In the old city communities, there are many haphazard plantings, which affect public transportation and destroy the aesthetics of public space, while generating many land enclosures and land-grabbing conflicts, further intensifying the conflicts among community residents.

c. Hidden danger of community public safety: Public safety hazards in the community are mainly in the areas of personal safety and health safety. Some communities have poor lighting conditions and no monitoring facilities, and most old urban communities lack monitoring facilities, affecting the safety of community residents' lives. Some of the garbage in the old city is piled up in the open and there is no garbage classification, which is easy to breed germs and produce odor, and the garbage is soaked with dirt and wastewater in rainy and snowy weather, plus most of the ground in the old city community is uneven and easy to accumulate water and breed bacteria, which affects the quality of community space and community public health and safety. The status of public space in old city communities is shown in Figure 1.

Figure 1. Status of public space in old city communities.

3.2.2 *Epidemic prevention and control problems*

China has achieved great results in epidemic prevention and control, and the epidemic has been effectively prevented and controlled, but small outbreaks also occur from time to time, and a series of problems have surfaced in some communities during epidemic prevention that deserves our summary.

During the epidemic prevention and control, some communities have the problem of passive epidemic prevention and control. The emergency facilities for community prevention and control are relatively simple, the working conditions of epidemic prevention personnel are poor, the application of new technologies is low, the isolation method after a small-scale epidemic outbreak is simple, and the prevention and control requirements do not match the epidemic situation. Specific performance in the community boundary and entrance control are mostly temporary tents, kiosks, and in some communities only a table. Most communities are manually verified, which is inefficient and increases the risk of infection for epidemic prevention staff. In addition, the community entrance and boundary of the form of closure on the use of steel plates, blocking mesh directly blocked. The planning of closed gates and roads is not conducive to the life of residents, and at the same time, people and vehicles are concentrated at the same entrance and exit, and outsiders are also mixed in, easily causing congestion at the entrance and exit, increasing the risk of cross-infection of community residents. The selection of materials for public spaces in the community does not consider disease resistance and antimicrobial properties, increasing the risk of compartmentalized infection. The express take-out receiving area is haphazardly stacked, and the process of taking food also increases the possibility of cross-contamination. In summary, it is urgent to strengthen the construction of public health and safety facilities in the community.

4 STRATEGIES FOR RENOVATING PUBLIC SPACE IN OLD URBAN COMMUNITIES

4.1 Retrofitting strategies for common problems

The renovation strategies for common problems include upgrading the ground conditions of the community, putting the creation of space aesthetics in second place, introducing aerial photography of the community area in the old city community, having the statistical analysis of pedestrian flow at each entrance and exit, re-coordinated planning of each road traffic in the space, strengthening slow traffic, separating pedestrian and vehicular traffic, and setting primary and secondary channels, emergency channels, and widening channels; these channels do not meet the requirements of emergency vehicle rescue and elderly's protection. It is appropriate to use paving materials with large friction coefficients such as permeable concrete and permeable bricks for sidewalks and add ramps and handicapped access and booster facilities to the terrace area.

Most of the problems of haphazardly being built and placed in the public space of the old city community are because some community residents have the demand for planting, and this demand is often not only for the acquisition of planting results but as a way of recreation. It is possible to re-plan the location of flower beds and greenery in the old city and build part of the public pocket planting area to meet the demand of residents for recreation according to the needs and quotas, and to reduce the demand in the community while increasing neighborhood relations, Including the problem of space clutter. Through the reorganization of community space, according to the results of the questionnaire survey and the spatial environment needs of the user group, each communication space is added, and for communities without unused space, residents' planting activity areas are set up around the public planting areas.

For security issues in community public spaces, increase the number of smart light poles and increase the coverage of monitoring and timely alarm devices in the community. In terms of community health and safety, we will improve the community garbage disposal methods, set up a unified garbage disposal area, and set up a separate epidemic-proof garbage disposal station based on the separation of wet and dry garbage. Adding sewage tanks and rain shelters to the garbage disposal area to prevent the secondary pollution of the community environment, leveling the road to prevent the flow of garbage and sewage, and eliminating the breeding of mosquitoes and germs to provide a place to reduce the risk of spreading germs.

4.2 Retrofitting strategies for community preparedness problems

Today, it has been recognized that despite the high level of technological advancement, humans are still unable to fully conquer and control nature, especially the occurrence of epidemics and disasters (Qian et al. 2020). Therefore, in the context of habitat construction, "prevention-adaptation-use" reflects the strategic evolution of security response: from instinctive "prevention and avoidance" to conscious "adaptation" and then to active "smart use" (Qian et al. 2020). Since the problems caused by large-scale outbreaks cannot be solved independently with the volume of the community, community public space renovation for epidemic prevention and control should focus on the low- to medium-risk prevention and control stage of the outbreak.

4.2.1 Low-risk prevention and control stage

The low-risk prevention and control stage in the text means no confirmed cases, no new confirmed cases for 14 days, or no indigenous infection cases in the county (district) where the community is located. Usually, during this phase, the daily life of the community residents is not affected, the community residents do not need to be isolated, the entrance and boundaries of the community are not restricted, and the community residents only maintain normal outbreak prevention and control behaviors. The focus of community outbreak prevention and control at this stage is on preventing the inflow of infected persons and planning for small-scale outbreaks. Initiatives at the low-risk prevention and control stage are focused on controlling the movement of people, reducing the transmission of the virus, and preparing for community outbreak emergencies.

(1) Disperse traffic: According to the planning of the pedestrian and vehicular traffic flow after the transformation of the community, emergency vehicle access is reserved. The reserved channel should meet the requirements of large emergency vehicles, and the community residents commonly used entrances and exits to maintain a certain distance, close to the main roads outside the community, to save time for emergency rescue; and to avoid the rescue process of infected people on the residents of the daily passage, reduce the flow of cross, interference, and reduce the chances of secondary transmission of the virus.

(2) Enclosure method: As the regional boundary was relatively open when the old city community was built, more secondary entrances and exits were not conducive to the construction of the main line of defense during the epidemic period, and the use of blocking nets, steel nets, steel plates, and other various materials to complete the blocking had an impact on the environmental aesthetics of the community and later recovery. By adding a metal slide on the ground of the secondary entrance and placing movable flower pools and tree pools above, combined with the communication area along the street at the boundary of the space, it meets the aesthetics while opening and closing flexibly according to the requirements of epidemic prevention and control, meeting the needs of aesthetics, communication, and closure during the daily and prevention and control periods. The community secondary entrance communication area model is shown in Figure 2.

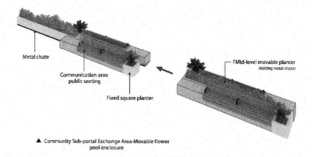

Figure 2. Community secondary entrance communication area model.

(3) Spatial reorganization: Government and related departments should also provide clear entrances and exits for all areas within the community and unused public spaces, and reserve buffer

areas at the community's entrances and exits as areas to facilitate prevention and control both inside and outside the community. In the low-risk prevention and control stage, both community residents and epidemic prevention staff are prone to burnout, and the severe winter makes the outdoor working environment of epidemic prevention staff harsh. Therefore, exclusive areas should be set up for community epidemic prevention staff and emergencies, and technologies such as infrared temperature measurement, automatic code registration, and ultraviolet disinfection should be used to reduce the work intensity of epidemic prevention staff, improve the working environment of community epidemic prevention staff, and ensure their health and safety. The community main entrance buffer model is shown in Figure 3.

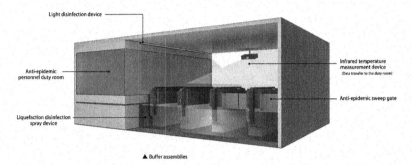

Figure 3. Model for the community main entrance.

(4) Improving facilities: We should increase the use of antimicrobial materials in community public spaces, especially in spaces that meet the daily interactions of community residents. As reported in Chemical Engineering Journal (CEJ), the team led by Professor Wong Ming-yan in the Department of Mechanical Engineering, Faculty of Engineering, University of Hong Kong, adjusted the chemical composition and microstructure of stainless steel. In a paper entitled *Anti-pathogen stainless steel combating COVID-19*, it was stated that the studied pathogen-resistant stainless steel (Cu; 20%wt) could significantly reduce 99.75 % and 99.99 % of live SARS-CoV-2 on its surface within 3 h and 6 h, respectively. In addition, the present anti-pathogen stainless steel showed excellent ability against the influenza A (H1N1) virus (H1N1), and Escherichia coli (E. coli) (Liu et al. 2020). The widespread availability of this material will substantially reduce the risk of personal contact transmission. Specific data on this material is shown in Figure 4.

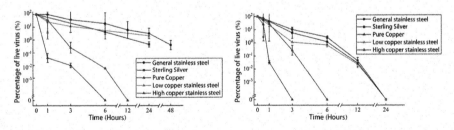

Figure 4. Novel coronaviruses are active on different metal surfaces (left). The activity of influenza A virus on different metal surfaces (right).

(5) Technology application: Adding intelligent environmental protection facilities, intelligent lighting, intelligent environmental monitoring, intelligent seating, and comprehensive message panels can be set at the entrance of community units and major public areas, which can meet part of the lighting needs in the community daily. The content of the panel includes date and weather, social hotspots, advertisements and notifications placed in the community, etc. During the epidemic period, the panel will be changed to include the development of the epidemic and its prevention

and control, the popularization of epidemic prevention measures, and the inquiry into medium and high-risk areas. After the epidemic has passed, the panel can also be retained to continue playing its message delivery and lighting functions.

4.2.2 Mid-risk prevention and control stage

The risk prevention and control phase in this paper refers to the period when the community is in a county (district) with no confirmed cases or a small number of controllable confirmed cases and no concentrated outbreaks. Emergency preparedness for epidemics in the low-risk phase period was made effective, and strict control of the mobile population in the community, relying on the identification role of entrance and border control to prevent the epidemic from worsening, was the main task in the medium-risk prevention and control phase.

For pedestrian flow control, the community should implement nucleic acid testing and emergency quarantine stations at the emergency access points and buffer zones in the low-risk prevention and control phase, as well as disinfection spraying facilities at the entrances and exits of the emergency access points to prevent the secondary spread of the epidemic by foreign emergency vehicles.

The following steps should be taken to control the spread of the disease: new prevention and control amenities and help-aid facilities should be added for home isolators, electronic isolation monitoring facilities should be put in place for infected households and single households, and new material collection and distribution areas and express disinfection cabinets should be added in the community to centralize the disinfection of foreign materials.

4.2.3 High-risk prevention and control stage

The strategy of the high-risk prevention and control phase has shifted from prevention to control, with a large outbreak in the district (county) where the community is located, the presence of infected persons in the community, and the restriction of the daily life of community residents and their isolation. The strategy in this phase lies in internal isolation and external support and should focus on the support of prevention and control personnel in the community. Moreover, one should effectively use the results of preparation during the low- and medium-risk prevention and control period to make small and smart renovations to public spaces in the community.

(1) Internal isolation: First, the health service stations in the community should be converted into light treatment stations, closing the entrances and exits for residents and keeping only emergency vehicle access. Most communities in old urban areas do not have elevators, and additional material handling aids should be installed in public spaces to facilitate efficient prevention and control by epidemic prevention personnel.

(2) External support: Emergencies are provided for medical personnel and patients, and the borders and entrances pay corresponding attention to the inspection and disinfection of emergency personnel entering and leaving. The centralized point for the diversion of external materials and internal waste, "time-sharing, zoning and centralized" intelligent control, effective use and transformation of existing epidemic prevention and control facilities. Three-level community risk prevention and control systems are shown in Figure 5.

4.3 Community spatial environment restoration in the post-epidemic era

In the post-epidemic era, the epidemic forms a delicate balance with people's lives. The prevention and control strategy in the normalized phase of prevention and control should be kept loose on the outside and tighter on the inside compared to the outbreak, and the impact on the lives of community residents should be appropriately reduced, in addition to other safe prevention and control facilities in the epidemic time should be modified to play their hidden role. For example, the entrance buffer assembly can be used to stockpile emergency supplies and facilities in case of disasters, the access control system can increase community security, and the use of antimicrobial materials can reduce the risk of germs spreading in the community. The design of a movable barricade system and community notification panel can meet the requirements of prevention and control at the time of the epidemic, and can further perform its secondary function in the process of

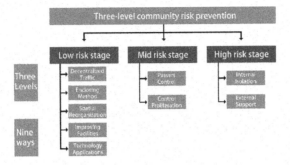

Figure 5. Three-level community risk prevention and control system analysis diagram.

community spatial environment restoration after the epidemic. The design of community retrofitting is multidisciplinary and needs to be further refined.

5 CONCLUSION

In general, China has made greater achievements in epidemic prevention and control, but in the process, we are also warned that community renewal in the post-epidemic era should consider community public space reconstruction, community transportation improvement, community public service facility renewal, community environment, landscape optimization and enhancement, community disaster response, and other aspects of transformation. This is not only conducive to the improvement of the quality of the living environment of community residents, but also social development and urban outlook, and more conducive to meeting the new challenges facing social development in the new era. Because the research involves multidisciplinary fields, the parts in material science and planning content are not deep enough, and the community disaster response transformation strategies only stay in epidemic prevention and control, involving other manufactured or natural disaster response strategies, which are yet to be further improved in all subsequent research processes.

REFERENCES

Li, S, J. (2014). *D. Research on residential community renewal based on the perspective of urban new immigrant community resource demand*. Xi'an: Xi'an International Studies University.

Liu, L. T. & Chin, A. & Yu, P. & Poon, L. & Huang, M. X. (2022). Anti-pathogen stainless steel combating COVID-19. *J. Chemical Engineering Journal*, Volume 433, Part 3.

Qian, Z. L. & Wang, Z. & Qiu, Z. & Zheng, Y. (2020). Urban and rural "safety and health unit" construction system and coping strategies—Based on the reflection on the "prevention-apply-apply" response mechanism of epidemics and disasters. *J. City Planning Review*, 2020,44 (03): 25–30.

Sun, Y. (2020). M. *Community renewal planning and design*. Beijing: China Construction Industry Press.

Zhang, Y. & Wang, Z. & Qian, Z. L. & Zheng, J. C. & Guo, R. (2021) Research on the space suitability update of existing urban communities under the concept of safety and health in the post-epidemic era. *J. Architecture and Culture*, 2021 (12): 106–108.

Research on risk assessment and control of BIM application in prefabricated medical building projects

Lili Jiao*

Yunnan University of Business Management, Yunnan, Kunming, China

ABSTRACT: At present, the application of BIM technology in prefabricated building projects has become a hot spot in the industry. However, in the actual development process, due to the lack of BIM talents and the disproportion of input and output, the application of BIM in prefabricated medical building projects has potential risks, which restricts the use of BIM technology as a digital carrier in prefabricated medical building projects. In this regard, construction enterprises should take risk management and control measures, train, and reserve more professional and technical personnel, improve technical equipment, and update construction equipment promptly to provide basic guarantees for improving construction efficiency. This paper uses the TOPSIS comprehensive evaluation method to construct a BIM application risk assessment model for prefabricated medical building projects and conducts an empirical analysis of the risk assessment of BIM application in prefabricated medical building projects. The article concludes with a discussion of risk control measures for BIM applications in prefabricated medical building projects, intending to provide some useful references for the orderly construction of prefabricated medical building projects based on BIM.

1 INTRODUCTION

The *Guiding Opinions on Vigorously Developing Prefabricated Buildings* points out that the development of prefabricated buildings is a major change in the construction method and an important measure to promote the supply-side structural reform of the construction industry, which is conducive to saving resources and energy, reducing construction pollution, and improving labor. Production efficiency and quality safety level. At the same time, to promote the development of the construction industry, the provincial and municipal governments have successively issued documents on the promotion and application of BIM, laying a solid foundation for the rapid development of BIM. The application of BIM technology in the construction of prefabricated medical building projects can improve the efficiency of architectural collaborative design, reduce design errors, optimize production processes, and improve construction efficiency, but there are also some potential risks in the application of BIM in prefabricated medical building projects. Therefore, to reduce the risk occurrence rate of BIM application and ensure the quality of prefabricated medical construction projects, it is of great significance to carry out risk assessment research and control of BIM application in prefabricated medical building projects to promote the in-depth application of BIM in prefabricated medical buildings and promote prefabricated medical buildings development of architecture.

2 CONSTRUCTION OF BIM APPLICATION RISK ASSESSMENT MODEL FOR PREFABRICATED MEDICAL BUILDING PROJECTS

The application of BIM technology in the construction of prefabricated medical building projects is a new direction of innovation and development in the construction industry (Han 2020), which

*Corresponding Author: 85562212@qq.com

helps to optimize the construction process, reduce architectural collaborative design errors, improve design efficiency and construction efficiency, and ensure the construction quality of prefabricated medical building projects (Hu 2021). Therefore, to promote the in-depth application of BIM in prefabricated medical buildings, by adopting the TOPSIS comprehensive evaluation method, from the aspects of technology, economy, personnel, management, and law, a risk assessment model for BIM application in prefabricated medical building projects is constructed. Provide some useful references for the better application of BIM technology in prefabricated buildings.

2.1 Construction of BIM application risk evaluation index system for prefabricated medical building projects

According to the principle of risk evaluation index of BIM application in prefabricated medical building projects, first-level indicators and second-level indicators are constructed (Jin 2021). The first-level indicators mainly include technical risks, economic risks, personnel risks, management risks, and legal risks. Second-level indicators include insufficient data security, insufficient model integrity, insufficient data interaction, and insufficient software compatibility. Uncertain additional expenditures, high software and hardware costs, and increased design costs for prefabricated buildings are also present (Liao 2021). There is insufficient interaction between disciplines, and there is an insufficient number of technical personnel. BIM application goals and positioning are unclear, and workflow changes are difficult. It is difficult to change the management process, and the cooperation of all participants is passive; there is a lack of dispute resolution mechanisms, a lack of standard format contracts for BIM applications, and a lack of insurance suitable for BIM applications.

2.2 Determination of weights of risk assessment indicators for BIM application in prefabricated medical building projects

Here, the linear proportional processing method is used to carry out dimensionless processing of each index, and then the subjective weight is determined by the analytic hierarchy process.

(1) Constructing a judgment matrix

When calculating the risk evaluation index of BIM application in prefabricated medical building projects (Sun 2021), the analytic hierarchy process is generally used, through the judgment matrix, and judged and scored by experts. The constructed judgment matrix A is expressed as:

$$A = \begin{bmatrix} a_{11} & a_{12} & \cdots & a_{1n} \\ a_{21} & a_{22} & \cdots & a_{2n} \\ \vdots & \vdots & \ddots & \vdots \\ a_{n1} & a_{n2} & \cdots & a_{nn} \end{bmatrix} \quad (1)$$

In the judgment matrix A, n represents the number of rating indicators, and the i-th row and the i-th column correspond to the same evaluation indicator; $a_{ij} > 0, a_{ij} = 1/a_{ij}, a_{ii} = 1$, and $i, j = 1, 2, \ldots, n$.

(2) Hierarchical single ordering and consistency check

First, the weight vector is obtained by using the AHP eigenvector method, which is divided into five steps ($Q = (q_{ij})_{n \times n}$).

$$q_{ij} = a_{ij} / \sum_{k=1}^{n} a_{kj} \quad (2)$$

Second, normalize the elements of the constructed judgment matrix A by column to obtain a normalized matrix α; $\alpha = (\alpha_1, \alpha_2, \cdots, \alpha_n)^T$.

$$a_{ij} = \sum_{j=1}^{n} q_{ij} \quad (3)$$

Third, normalize the vector α to obtain the judgment matrix eigenvector.

$$w_i = \alpha_i / \sum_{k=1}^{m} \alpha_k \tag{4}$$

Fourth, calculate the maximum characteristic root λ_{max} of the judgment matrix.

$$\lambda_{max} = \sum_{i=1}^{n} \frac{(AW)_i}{mW_i} = \frac{1}{n} \sum_{i=1}^{n} \frac{\sum_{j=1}^{n} \alpha_{ij} w_j}{w_j} \tag{5}$$

Fifth, calculate the consistency index CI:

$$CI = \frac{\lambda_{max} - n}{n - 1} \tag{6}$$

(3) Hierarchical total ordering and consistency check

Suppose the construction matrix of A_j, B_j, C_j, D_j, and E_j related factors in the criterion layer (P) is checked for consistency in the single ordering, and the single ordering consistency index CI_j is obtained ($j = 1, 2, \ldots, 5$), the corresponding average random consistency index is CR_j, then the total sorting random consistency ratio of the target layer (O) is:

$$CR = \frac{\sum_{j=1}^{5} CI_j a_j}{\sum_{j=1}^{5} RI_j a_j} \tag{7}$$

2.3 BIM application risk assessment model for prefabricated medical building projects

First, based on establishing the normalized matrix, the normalized weighting matrix is further constructed. By using the analytic hierarchy process to calculate the weight ω_{ij} of each evaluation index, and weighting Y_{ij} according to the formula, the weighted standardized matrix is obtained.

$$Z = \begin{bmatrix} \omega_1 y_{11} & \omega_2 y_{12} & \cdots & \omega_n y_{1n} \\ \omega_2 y_{21} & \omega_2 y_{22} & \cdots & \omega_n y_{2n} \\ \vdots & \vdots & \ddots & \vdots \\ \omega_1 y_{m1} & \omega_2 y_{m2} & \cdots & \omega_n y_{mn} \end{bmatrix} \tag{8}$$

Second, determine the positive and negative ideal solutions for each item.
The correct solution is: $Z^+ = (Z_1^+, Z_2^+, \cdots, Z_n^+)$
The negative ideal solution is: $Z^- = (Z_1^-, Z_2^-, \cdots, Z_n^-)$
Third, divide the extreme value interval. Calculate the closeness of each index and each comment interval, divide the extreme value interval of each column element composed of negative ideal solution and positive ideal solution into N layers, and the interval of each layer is $H_n = (h_n^1, h_n^2)$, $i = 1, 2, \cdots, n, t = 1, 2, \cdots, N$.

The closeness of each index of the standardized decision matrix to each comment interval is:

$$E(N_i) = \left| x_{ij} - \frac{h_{ij}^1 + h_{ij}^2}{2} \right| \tag{9}$$

Based on the calculated closeness of each index, calculate the weighted closeness of each evaluation scheme.

$$Q_j(N_i) = 1 - \sum_{j=1}^{n} w_j E(N_i) \tag{10}$$

Fourth, the eigenvalues are calculated and each evaluation scheme is graded. The level at which the maximum value of the weighted closeness is located is the comment level described by the evaluation object (Wang 2022). In the actual evaluation process, there may be multiple schemes belonging to the same evaluation level. To determine the pros and cons of the two schemes, it is necessary to distinguish them by calculating the eigenvalues.

$$\overline{Q_j}(N_i) = \frac{Q_j(N_i) - \min Q_j(N_i)}{\max_j Q_j(N_i) - \min Q_j(N_i)} \quad (11)$$

$$\lambda_i = \frac{\sum_{j=1}^{m} h \overline{Q_j}(N_i)}{\sum_{j=1}^{m} \overline{Q_j}(N_i)} \quad (12)$$

3 EMPIRICAL ANALYSIS OF RISK ASSESSMENT OF BIM APPLICATION IN PREFABRICATED MEDICAL BUILDING PROJECTS

Collect data related to the BIM application risk of prefabricated medical building projects through investigation (Wang 2021), and use the specific process of the above model construction to carry out an empirical analysis of the BIM application risk assessment of prefabricated medical building projects (Wang 2020), determine the weight of each indicator, calculate the eigenvalues of the project, and then compare with other The project calculation results are compared, as shown in Table 1 and Table 2 below.

Table 1. Weight of each indicator.

Criterion layer	Criterion layer weights	Indicator layer	Indicator layer weights	Weights
Technical risk	0.1941	Insufficient data security	0.5501	0.0113
		Insufficient model integrity	0.1438	0.0279
		Insufficient data interactivity	0.2478	0.0481
		Insufficient software compatibility	0.5501	0.1068
Economic risk	0.1941	Economic benefits are unclear	0.0280	0.0055
		Uncertain additional expenses	0.0433	0.0084
		High cost of hardware and software	0.4385	0.0851
		The cost of prefabricated building design increases	0.0868	0.0168
Personnel risk	0.2846	Insufficient experience in BIM application in prefabricated building projects	0.1209	0.0344
		Lack of interaction between disciplines	0.0418	0.0217
		Insufficient existing technical staff	0.4981	0.1417
Manage risk	0.1680	BIM application goals and positioning are unclear	0.2199	0.0369
		Difficulty in changing workflows	0.1432	0.0241
		Difficulty managing process changes	0.0320	0.0054
		Negative cooperation among the parties	0.0516	0.0087
Legal risks	0.1593	Lack of dispute resolution mechanism	0.5902	0.0940
		Lack of standard form contracts for BIM application	0.1023	0.0163
		Lack of insurance for BIM applications	0.2583	0.0411

Based on the above calculation results, the index weights such as lack of dispute resolution mechanism (Yao 2020), unclear application target and positioning of BIM, insufficient existing technical personnel, high cost of software and hardware, and insufficient software compatibility are the highest among the corresponding five types of risk factors. Explain that they are the key

Table 2. Calculation results.

Project	Eigenvalues	Weighted post progress	Risk statement
P1	3.32971	0.99587	Smaller
P2	2.52324	0.99531	Normal
P3	2.16667	0.99563	Normal

risk factors; the risk of project 1 is relatively small and can be ignored, and the risks of project 2 and project 3 are both moderate, but compared with the two, the risk of project 3 is relatively higher.

To effectively reduce the risk of BIM application, it is necessary to take corresponding risk control measures: First, construction enterprises should strengthen the training of professional and technical personnel, improve the personnel training system, establish cooperative relations with universities, integrate the existing resources of both parties, and establish a talent training practice base, to provide students with more practical opportunities, let students learn to apply theoretical knowledge to practice and improve students' professional skills. Furthermore, construction enterprises should continuously update technical equipment and improve system functionality; improve management processes and strengthen collaborative management (Yin 2020); clarify the application goals and positioning of BIM as well as understand its specific application scope, and then combine it with the actual situation of construction projects. It is applied to construction to give full play to its due value.

4 CONCLUSION

To sum up, the application of BIM technology in prefabricated medical building projects will generate certain risks, among which the lack of technical personnel and the high cost of software and hardware are the key risk factors. Therefore, to reduce the risk occurrence rate of BIM application, construction enterprises should take risk control measures, train, and reserve more professional and technical personnel, improve technical equipment, and update construction equipment in time to provide basic guarantees for more efficient construction. In this paper, the research on risk assessment and control of BIM application in prefabricated medical building projects is not perfect. In the future stage, we should continue to pay attention to the relevant research trends of BIM application risk assessment and control in prefabricated medical building projects, and enrich our research experience to make up for the research in this paper.

REFERENCES

Cheng Lianhua, He Chen. (2021). Construction and application of safety risk assessment system for construction projects [J]. *Science, Technology and Engineering* 21 (27): 11882–11889.

Han Liehuilou. (2020). Research on BIM technology application risk assessment method based on improved AHP [J]. *Railway Construction Technology* (05): 165–170.

Hu Zhudan, Tang Shuang, Yang Minjie. (2021). Risk assessment of BIM technology application in EPC projects [J]. *Engineering Economics* 31 (04): 68–73.

Jin Changhong, Zhan Neng. (2021). Research on risk assessment of "BIM+VR" technology application based on TOPSIS and grey correlation [J]. *Journal of Anyang Institute of Technology* 20 (04): 69–73.

Liao Haochen. (2021). Research on the risk evaluation index system of industrial construction projects under the fast path method [J]. *Operation and Management* (05): 60–63.

Sun Yufeng, Dai Xia, Guo Shuo. (2021). Analysis on the risk assessment method of green building project life cycle [J]. *Journal of Shandong University of Technology and Business* 35 (05): 52–60.

Wang Haizi, Li Yuan. (2020). Risk assessment of green building projects from the perspective of investors based on AHP-FCE [J]. *Brick and Tile* (07): 134.

Wang Qingshan. (2022). Research on risk assessment of construction project cost control during construction stage based on AHP-cloud model [J]. *Railway Construction Technology* (03): 197–202.

Wang Zhenshuang, Sun Jianshu, Zhou Yanxin, Zhao Ning. (2021). Research on risk assessment index system of construction waste recycling PPP project [J]. *Journal of Engineering Management* 35 (03): 58–63.

Yao Liangyun, Li Lulu, Li Xiaojuan. (2020). Risk analysis and response of BIM application in green construction projects [J]. *Shanghai Energy Conservation* (08): 878–886.

Yin Xiaowei, Lu Yufen. (2020). Application of BIM technology in construction project risk management target system [J]. *Anhui Architecture* 27 (08): 210–212.

Quasi-static seismic tests and damage evaluation of high-strength reinforced concrete columns

Huang-bin Lin*
Jimei University, Xiamen, China

Qi-fang Zeng*
Huaqiao University, Xiamen, China

ABSTRACT: The PEER-based structural quasi-static column test database is built. Through the quasi-static test of ten specimens SP01 to SP10, the influence of the main configuration parameters of test components (shear span ratio λ, concrete strength grade f_c, axial compressive ratio n_0, longitudinal reinforcement ratio ρ_l, and stirrup reinforcement ratio ρ_w) on ductility performance and the evaluation of their relationship are studied, the influence of changes in main parameters on the force-displacement response and energy consumption and ductility response and the evaluation of relationship are studied, and the evaluation of the influence of control factors in the restoring force model on test energy consumption and ductility index is studied, and the main index variables for describing the rules of stiffness degradation, strength degradation, pinching degradation and energy consumption damage of test components are studied. This paper obtains seismic performance and damage evaluation of high-strength RC columns and builds the database of test columns used for energy principle-based analysis of quasi-static tests.

1 INTRODUCTION

In recent years, the tests and studies of high-strength concrete have gradually increased. The seismic performance and constitutive relationship of the frame column, which is the most important component in structures, have become hot topics of research for high-strength RC structures. Currently, the study of column seismic tests and compression components is an important part of this field. The damage process of RC columns is a process of energy dissipation, release, and transformation. Different damage modes correspond to different energy transformation rules. The energy principle may be the hope for conquering the limitation in the force and deformation evaluation system. For new type structures, comprehensive consideration should be given to the deformation of structural components and hysteretic energy consumption to evaluate the seismic performance of structural components. Therefore, it is necessary to study the column seismic tests that match the new type of high-strength reinforcement and high-strength concrete. Through analysis of the tests, the relationships between structural deformation and energy consumption, between energy consumption and ductility, and between ductility and damage are comprehensively analyzed, the quasi-static tests and damage performance of high-strength reinforced concrete columns are studied, and the influence of shear span ratio λ, concrete strength grade f_c, axial compressive ratio n_0, longitudinal reinforcement ratio ρ_l and stirrup reinforcement ratio ρ_w on the ultimate bearing force, skeleton curve, restoring force curve, ductility performance, and damage mode is analyzed. Because the quantity of test columns for individual study teams is very limited, this paper finally

---

*Corresponding Authors: linhuangbin@jmu.edu.cn and qfzeng@hqu.edu.cn

builds the database of PEER-based quasi-static test columns, which provides reliable and sufficient data sources for subsequent more extensive establishment of high-strength column damage evaluation models.

2 QUASI-STATIC TEST DESIGN AND LOADING PROGRAM OF HIGH-STRENGTH RC COLUMNS

Summary of quasi-static test components. The specimens are taken from the bottom column model of conventional frame structures, with a scale of the model and prototype of 1:3. The geometric dimensions of the specimens and the test loading device are shown in Figure 1. The concrete strength grade f_c, stirrup reinforcement ratio ρ_w, axial compressive ratio n_0, longitudinal reinforcement ratio ρ_l and shear span ratio λ are shown in Table 1. The material mixing ratio and strength design and mechanical properties of specimens are shown in Table 2. The mechanical properties of reinforcement materials are shown in Table 3. A total of ten specimens are manufactured in two batches for the tests. The specimens in the first batch are numbered SP01 to SP04, and those in the second batch SP05 to SP10. The "⊥" type loading is adopted. A projection of 25 mm at either side of the ⊥ type column head is used for fixing the horizontal x-axis loading actuator, and the vertical y-axis loading actuator acts on the ⊥ type column top. The loading contact face column top is embedded with B8@50 mm reinforcing meshes and 10 mm thick steel plates, which are used for preventing the column top concrete from being damaged due to local compression when the y-axis is loaded with relatively high axial compression. The ⊥ type component bottom beam is designed as 400 × 950 mm (longitudinal reinforcement 10B16 stirrup 8B60), playing the function of fixing the pedestal and test columns and meeting the rigid coupling design at the bottom during the loading process. The test measuring devices and data acquisition system are shown in Table 1. The flow of the load-displacement double-mixing control method loading program is shown in Table 2.

Table 1. Summary table of test measuring devices and data acquisition system.

Measuring system	Measuring device layout and data acquisition system description
Load measuring system	The horizontal load and vertical load are measured through the pressure sensor. The electro-hydraulic servo program controlled structural tester is adopted for automatic acquisition of horizontal load and displacement of the loading column head.
Displacement measuring system	Measure the displacement of specimen pedestal and loading points (electronic displacement gauge). The displacement gauge is used for measuring the lateral displacement of column top horizontal force action points and possible slippage at the column bottom. The displacement gauges are mounted symmetrically at both sides of the middle part of the bottom beam to measure possible slippage at the bottom beam. The torsion of column heads at both sides is measured to eliminate the influence of torsion.
Strain measuring system	Measure longitudinal reinforcement and stirrup strain at the specimen force bearing area (resistance strain gauge). With its layout range at the column bottom plastic hinge area, the longitudinal strain gauge (5 mm × 3 mm, 120Ω±0.2%) is used for monitoring the strain condition in this area and measuring the yield range at the cross-section effective height h_0. The stirrup strain gauge (2 mm × 3 mm) acquires shearing deformation and lateral strain. The detailed strain gauge layout is shown in Figure 1 (a total of 20 single-column strain gauges). The force, displacement, and strain signals are acquired by the DH3816 data acquisition device. The electronic extensometer acquires and measures bending deformation and shearing deformation at the plastic hinge area and reinforcement slippage deformation at the node area.

Table 2. Flow table of load-displacement double-mixing control method loading program.

Test stage	Loading control	Description of mixing control load main process
Stage one	Axial force trial loading	Exert 40% of the test axial load. Through the monitoring of reinforcement strain at the same cross-section in RC columns, judge if this test load meets the axle center force bearing condition. Adjust continuously and start formal loading when the loading condition meets the requirement.
Stage two	Preloading	Preload repetitive load (20% crack load Q_{cr}) twice. Check if the loading device and each data acquisition system work normally.
Stage three	Horizontal preloading	The horizontal load and column lateral displacement show linear changes. The load control and step loading are adopted. The load increment at each step is 1/5 of the calculated ultimate load. When cracking is approached, the increment step differential load is reduced until the tensile reinforcement of the specimen reaches the yield condition.
Stage four	Load control loading	After the yield condition is reached, the displacement control is adopted. Load at an increment of Δ_y. Reciprocating repetitive loading is carried out twice at each step of control displacement.
Stage five	Displacement control loading	When the specimen bearing force is lowered to 85% of the maximum peak load Q_{max}, determine if the critical damage stage is reached and gradually reduce the cycle times until the test is terminated.

Note: Loading is carried out under the test stipulations in the load-displacement double-mixing control loading method.

3 ANALYSIS OF QUASI-STATIC RESTORING FORCE HYSTERETIC CURVE AND TEST PHENOMENA

After quasi-static tests, the summary of test results of main feature points in the restoring force curve of SP01 to SP10 are shown in Table 2, the summary of the quasi-static test loading program and restoring force stage evaluation is shown in Table 3, and the damage evaluation during the test process of quasi-static loading program is shown in Table 4.

3.1 Loading program and restoring force stage evaluation

Table 3. Summary table of quasi-static test loading program and restoring force stage evaluation.

Loading stage	Quasi-static test loading and restoring force curve rules	Restoring force stage evaluation
Load control cycle	20% of the ultimate load Q_u control. No visible crack is seen in the appearance of the component column. The component restoring the force cycle course is in a linear status. After unloading, the residual deformation of the component column is relatively small and there is no hysteretic E_{cyc} energy loop.	Elastic stage
Load control cycle	40% of the ultimate load Q_u control. There is a tiny horizontal bending crack at the root of the tension side of the component column. The unloading curve and loading curve coincide. The restoring force curve stiffness change is relatively small, and no obvious hysteretic E_{cyc} energy loop is formed.	Elastic stage
Displacement control cycle	The oblique cracks of the specimen continuously expand and connect to form the main oblique crack. The small crack in the component column develops evenly and slowly. With the increase of displacement δ and the increase of cycle time n, the restoring force curve continuously degrades. This trend is more obvious after the component yields. The horizontal displacement increases, the crack develops, oblique cracks of 45° to 60° appear at both sides of the column, and relatively obvious hysteretic E_{cyc} energy loops are formed.	Yield stage

(continued)

Table 3. Continued.

Displacement control cycle	The component reaches Q_{max}. The main oblique crack develops and widens, and expands to the full height range of the component column to form X type main cracks and obvious hysteretic E_{cyc} energy loops.	Elastic-plastic stage
Displacement control cycle	When the component is close to the bearing force limit, Q_u decreases. Small oblique cracks with roughly the same direction expand and connect, the restoring force stiffness rapidly degrades, and the column concrete is crushed with breaking sound and drops. The hysteretic E_{cyc} loop envelope energy rapidly decreases.	Limit failure stage

3.2 Test process and damage analysis and evaluation

Table 4. Table of damage evaluation during the test process of quasi-static loading program.

Test stage	The main description of the process damage condition of test components	Test stage	Repairability	Damage evaluation
1	The loading load is lower than the cracking load Q_{cr}. The hysteretic curve gradient change is small, the hysteretic loop energy formed by loading and unloading at positive and negative directions is not obvious, the specimen hysteretic loop energy is relatively low, and the component stiffness is unchanged. During loading, the $Q\delta$ curve rises along the straight line and after unloading, the residual deformation δ_{rd} is relatively small. The specimen is at the elastic stage.	Intact	Reparable	to 0.20
2	The specimen cracks. With the increase of displacement δ and cycle time n, the loading curve gradient decreases continuously and this trend is more obvious after yielding. $Q\delta$ deviates from the original straight line. After unloading, the residual deformation δ_{rd} increases. Before the specimen yields, there is no obvious change in the loading and unloading stiffness.	Slight damage	Reparable	0.20 to 0.60
3	When the load reaches the yield load Q_y, the loading and unloading stiffness gradually decreases and changes with the increase of cycle time n. The displacement amplitude δ and cycle time n increase. At the relatively large displacement amplitude, the loading stiffness shows obvious degradation, and the outer RC protective layer is continuously crushed and drops. The component stiffness continuously decreases and starts showing elastoplastic performance.	Medium damage	Irreparable	0.60 to 0.80
4	After Q_{max} is reached, at the displacement amplitude of each stage, when unloading is just started, the displacement changes lags, and such a trend is more obvious with the increase of the axial compressive ratio n_0. With the increase of axial compressive ratio, the $P - \Delta$ effect of the component increases. During unloading, the horizontal force gradually accelerates its lowering, but the change in the bending moment at the column root is relatively small, and the displacement change lags the reduction of horizontal force.	Serious damage	Irreparable	0.80 to 1.00
5	When the load is close to the ultimate load Q_u, the load decreases, and the displacement further degrades. The X type main cracks expand and connect. The stiffness rapidly decreases, and most of the column bottom RC is crushed and dropped. Irreparable damage occurs at the specimen.	Collapsed	Irreparable	> 1.00

Note: The specimen damage stage evaluation grade is determined according to the damage evaluation rule in the literature (Reinhorn et al. 2009).

Table 5. Evaluation of the influence of main influencing parameters in the quasi-static test on ductility.

Influencing factor	Analysis of the main influence of control parameters on ductility performance	Ductility evaluation
Shear span ratio λ	For SP09, the total energy consumption is large, but the hysteretic curve is narrow, after the maximum bearing force is reached, the bearing force rapidly decreases, and brittle failure occurs. For SP05 to SP10, with the increase of λ, the hysteretic curve becomes fuller and the ductility better. The ductility of SP10 ($\lambda= 2.4$) is superior to that of SP05 ($\lambda= 1.5$), the ductility coefficient is increased by 9.3%, and after the bearing force is reached, the loading of the next stage can be carried out, with better seismic performance displayed. SP01 to SP04 have the same shear span ratio. With the change in RC strength (f_c) and longitudinal reinforcement ratio (ρ_l), the ductility changes accordingly. As the main parameter for determining short columns, λ plays its main role in test hysteretic ductility analysis.	☆ ☆ ☆
Axial compressive ratio n_0	The hysteretic curve of SP06 is long and narrow than that of SP05, and the hysteretic loop envelope energy is smaller. With the increase of n_0, the total energy consumption of the component gradually decreases to up to 19.8%, which indicates that the higher the loading axial compressive ratio (n_0) is, the more unfavorable the seismic performance of the component is. But when n_0 increases to a certain extent, the influence is not obvious. SP01 to SP04 have the same axial compressive ratio, but with the change of f_c and ρ_l, the ductility performance will change n_0 has a relatively great influence on column hysteretic characteristics. A higher axial compressive ratio may cause the component to show obvious strength degradation at relatively low displacement ductility μ_Δ and unstable hysteretic loops at relatively high displacement ductility μ_Δ, and there is the possibility of a sudden loss of vertical bearing capacity. The ductility coefficient change is 1.3% and the maximum envelope energy ductility coefficient change is 32.1%, which indicates that n_0 has a more obvious influence on the energy parameter ductility index. When the axial compressive ratio n_0 is relatively low, the hysteretic loop performance is good and pinching is not obvious.	☆ ☆ ☆
Concrete strength f_c	For SP01, SP02, and SP03, the bearing force increases with the increase of RC strength. When the RC strength increases from C60 to C80, the bearing force increases from 261.3 kN to 364.2 kN, with an increase of 39.4%. Yield displacement δ_y increases by 7.9%, but δ_u decreases by 1.6%, the ductility coefficient decreases overall, which indicates that with the increase of f_c, the ductility coefficient decreases. The RC strength grade has a direct influence on component strength degradation. With the increase of displacement, the bearing force of components of different RC strengths will degrade and show gradual and stable degradation. In later stages, the bearing force degradation will accelerate, but the rate of increase is not high. With the increase of f_c, the maximum load increases, and the bearing force degrades.	☆ ☆
Longitudinal reinforcement ratio ρ_l	For SP01 and SP02, when the longitudinal reinforcement ratio is higher and the reinforcement form is more reasonable, the larger the hysteretic curve is and the gentler the reduction section is after the maximum horizontal load, the specimen deformation capacity increases, and the energy consumption capacity increases. The longitudinal reinforcement ratio (ρ_l) has a relatively great influence on column cracking displacement. The longitudinal reinforcement ratio (ρ_l) increases, the cracking displacement decreases by 25.4%, and the initial stiffness increases by 15.6%, but the change in the ductility coefficient based on displacement ($\mu_\Delta^\pm$) is not great, and the ductility coefficient based on envelope energy increases by 17.7%, showing prominent influence. With the increase in longitudinal reinforcement ratio, the hysteretic characteristics and ductility increase accordingly. The hysteretic envelope loop energy increases and pinching decreases, the energy consumption capacity increases, and the stiffness increases. With the increase of ρ_l, the change in the component's ultimate bearing capacity is not great, but after the component reaches the maximum load (Q_{max}), the ultimate deformation capacity increases, and the ultimate bearing force decrease in a relatively slow manner.	☆ ☆
Stirrup reinforcement ratio ρ_w	Under repetitive load, the cycle times of SP08 with a higher stirrup reinforcement ratio are more than those of SP06. Although the difference in the hysteretic curve fullness is relatively small, the total energy consumption of SP08 is superior to that of SP06. The energy consumption increases by 47.4%. After the maximum bearing force (Q_{max}) is reached, in each cycle the rate of decrease of bearing force of SP08 is less than that of SP06, which indicates that the component with higher ρ_w has better energy consumption ductility capacity.	☆ ☆

Note: "☆☆☆" means prominent influence on ductility; "☆☆" means medium influence on ductility; "☆" means slight influence on ductility.

3.3 *Test process and damage analysis and evaluation*

Different parameters are set for the components in the test. After comparison, the influence of each parameter on the hysteretic performance of components is obtained. The analysis of the influence of the shear span ratio λ, concrete strength grade f_c, axial compressive ratio n_0, longitudinal reinforcement ratio ρ_l and stirrup reinforcement ratio ρ_w on the ultimate bearing force, skeleton curve, restoring force curve, ductility performance and damage mode is shown in Tables 5 to 7.

Table 6. Evaluation of the influence of changes in main parameters in the test on force-displacement response.

Influencing factor	δ_{cr} (mm)	Q_{cr} (kN)	δ_y (mm)	Q_y (kN)	δ_{max} (mm)	Q_{max} (kN)	δ_u (mm)	Q_u (kN)	$K^+_{initial}$ (kN/mm)
Shear span ratio λ	↓	→	↑↑	↓↓	↑↑↑	↓↓↓	↑↑↑	↓↓↓	↓↓
Axial compressive ratio n_0	→	↑↑	→	↑	↓	↑	↓	↑	↓
RC strength f_c	↑↑	↑↑	↑↑	↑↑	↓	↑	↑	↑↑	↑↑
Longitudinal reinforcement ratio ρ_l	↓	↑	↓↓	↑↑	↓	↑	↓	↑	↑↑
Stirrup reinforcement ratio ρ_w	↑	↓	↑↑	↑	↑	↑	↑	↑	↑

Note: ↑↑↑: prominent increase; ↑↑: obvious increase; ↑: slight increase →: tiny change; ↓↓↓: prominent decrease; ↓↓: obvious decrease; ↓: slight decrease; ∼: tiny fluctuation. δ_{cr} is cracking displacement; Q_{cr} is component cracking load; δ_y is yield displacement; Q_y is yield load; δ_{max} is maximum displacement; Q_{max} is maximum load; δ_u is ultimate displacement; Q_u is ultimate load; $K^+_{initial}$ is restoring force initial stiffness.

Table 7. Evaluation of the influence of changes in main parameters in the test on energy consumption and ductility index response.

Influencing factor	$E^\pm_{cyc\cdot total}$ (kN·mm)	$E^\pm_{cyc\cdot ela\cdot total}$ (kN·mm)	$E^\pm_{envelope}$ (kN·mm)	$\varphi^\pm_{cyc\cdot cum}$	$\mu^\pm_E$	$\mu^\pm_{E\cdot ep}$
Shear span ratio λ	↓	↓	↓	↑↑	↑↑	↑↑
Axial compressive ratio n_0	↓↓	↑↑↑	↑↑	↓↓	↓↓	↓↓
RC strength f_c	↑↑	↑↑	↑↑	→	↓	↓
Longitudinal reinforcement ratio ρ_l	↓	↓	↓	↓	↓	↑
Stirrup reinforcement ratio ρ_w	↑↑	↑↑	↑	↓	↑	↑↑

Note: $E^\pm_{cyc\cdot total}$ is the sum of hysteretic energy consumption in all loops; $E^\pm_{cyc\cdot ela\cdot total}$ is the sum of hysteric elastic energy in all loops; $\varphi^\pm_{cyc\cdot cum}$ is the damping ratio of hysteretic cumulative energy consumption in positive and negative directions in each loop; $\mu^\pm_E$ is the ductility index based on the double-parameter energy method; $\mu^\pm_{E\cdot ep}$ is the ductility index based on the maximum envelope energy. Other symbols are the same as the above.

3.4 Analysis of main control parameters and structural damage

The analysis of the test damage process of components SP01 to SP10 and the influencing factors and describing parameters of the restoring force model is shown in Table 8. The summary of main indexes for test damage analysis is shown in Table 9. The evaluation of the influence of control factors in the restoring force model on test energy consumption and ductility index is shown in Table 10.

4 BUILDING OF PEER-BASED QUASI-STATIC TEST COLUMN DATABASE

The building of a structural damage analysis and evaluation system based on the energy principle should be supported by a sufficient real test column database. PEER (2010) (Pacific Earthquake Engineering Research Center) establishes the Tall Buildings Initiative (TBI) research plan 2010, suggests the improvement of performance-based seismic design methods and standards and pushes forward practical application of performance-based seismic design methods for tall buildings. Based on the tests of the topic, this paper collects measured data from PEER and relevant test references (Lin & Wang 2008a, b ; Taylor & Stone 1993; Taylor et al. 1997; to build a test database,

Table 8. Analysis of the test damage process and the influencing factors and describing parameters of the restoring force model.

Influencing factor	Analysis of the test damage process and the influencing factors and describing parameters of the restoring force model	Describing parameter
Stiffness degradation rule	Each time the specimen is subject to loading, the restoring force gradient decreases with the increase of the load. After comparison of the loading curves in the same direction each time, the gradient gradually decreases, which indicates that stiffness degradation occurs under repetitive load. Secant stiffness is adopted to analyze the stiffness degradation rule of each specimen under repetitive load. Before the component cracks, stiffness degradation of each specimen is relatively small, but with the increase of displacement amplitude, stiffness continuously decreases. RC strength grade has a relatively great influence on the initial stiffness. With the increase of RC strength grade, the initial stiffness increases, and stiffness degradation of the specimen with a relatively high RC strength grade is faster after cracking. The longitudinal reinforcement ratio has a relatively small influence on the initial stiffness of each specimen, but after cracking the stiffness degradation of the specimen with a high longitudinal reinforcement ratio and relatively reasonable reinforcement form is relatively slow.	Stiffness degradation parameter (α)
Strength degradation rule	When the high-strength RC column is under repetitive load, at the displacement amplitude of a certain stage, the phenomenon that its peak load decreases with the increase of cycle time is called strength degradation. The strength degradation of the component has a relatively great influence on its force-bearing capacity. The faster the strength degradation is, the faster the reduction of its capacity to resist the load is. For the column with a relatively high longitudinal reinforcement ratio and relatively reasonable reinforcement form, with the increase of displacement amplitude, the strength degradation is relatively stable, but when the longitudinal reinforcement ratio is relatively low, the strength degradation is relatively fast. If the RC grade remains the same, the higher the longitudinal reinforcement ratio and the more reasonable the reinforcement form, the stronger the hysteretic curve of the component, and the gentler the reduction section after the maximum horizontal load, the better the ductility performance and the higher the energy consumption capacity.	Ductility strength degradation (β_d) Energy strength degradation (β_e)
Pinching degradation rule	After several times of repetitive loads, inapparent contra flexure points appear in the loading curves, initial pinching is formed, and the pinching degree gradually increases with repetitive load. In the beginning, the unloading curve is relatively steep, and the restoring force deformation is small, after the load decreases, the curve tends to be gentle, the restoring force deformation gradually accelerates (restoring force deformation hysteresis), and the curve gradient decreases with the increase of repetitive loading and unloading times, and there is residual deformation of the component δ_{rd}, which increases with the continuous accumulation of repetitive loading and unloading times, and the pinching type restoring force curve is displayed. Pinching degradation depends on such factors as tensile crack development width, tensile reinforcement elongation strain, reinforcement, concrete relative slippage, change in the RC compressive plastic deformation accumulation neutral axis, etc.	Pinching degradation parameter (γ)
Energy consumption and ductility rule	Energy consumption capacity is an important index for evaluating the seismic performance of high-strength RC columns. The hysteretic envelope energy represents energy consumption at each cycle. The component energy consumption is closely associated with ductility performance and other relevant indexes. After the component enters the elastic-plastic stage, it is known from the relationship between energy consumption and ductility that energy consumption has a certain influence on the ductility index. Hysteretic curve envelope energy under positive load is a little different from that under negative load, which relates to the initial condition of the column and construction quality.	Energy influencing parameter (β)

which can be used as the data for damage evaluation in subsequent topic studies and the training data samples of test components for prediction and evaluation of ductility coefficient under ultimate load through the optimized BP algorithm. These data include the test data from study teams in the USA, Canada, New Zealand and Japan. The summary table gives a brief introduction to all test items and summarizes the main characteristics of each column specimen such as $\Delta_y M_{max}, V_{max} M_{max}/M_{ACI}$ and

Table 9. Summary table of main indexes for test damage analysis of components SP01 to SP10.

Influencing factor	$E^{\pm}_{cyc\cdot total}$ (kN·mm)	$E^{\pm}_{cyc\cdot ela\cdot total}$ (kN·mm)	$E^{\pm}_{envelope}$ (kN·mm)	$\varphi^{\pm}_{cyc\cdot cum}$	δ_y (mm)	Q_y (kN)	δ_{max} (mm)	Q_{max} (kN)	δ_u (mm)	Q_u (kN)	$\mu^{\pm}_E$
SP01	11666	27268	3628	0.068	3.80	261	7.66	338	8.39	255	2.21
SP02	9256	23732	2442	0.062	3.50	290	7.07	379	7.09	267	2.02
SP03	14361	36667	4175	0.062	4.10	364	6.96	426	8.26	302	2.01
SP04	6614	16708	2461	0.063	3.60	316	6.98	376	7.06	283	1.96
SP05	7288	9562	4904	0.121	8.10	186	12.80	238	13.26	167	1.64
SP06	4968	9276	2227	0.085	5.80	190	9.40	229	9.46	192	1.63
SP07	5835	12230	2768	0.076	6.10	208	9.38	255	9.88	199	1.62
SP08	10891	22899	2957	0.076	6.40	211	10.39	259	10.53	204	1.65
SP09	12343	30690	3800	0.064	6.70	270	9.94	333	10.02	286	1.50
SP10	6530	12860	2717	0.081	8.10	179	13.16	222	13.26	166	1.64

Note: $E^{\pm}_{cyc\cdot total}$ is the sum of hysteretic energy consumption in all loops; $E^{\pm}_{cyc\cdot ela\cdot total}$ is the sum of hysteric elastic energy in all loops; $E^{\pm}_{envelope}$ is the sum of maximum envelope energy in all loops; $\phi^{\pm}_{cyc\cdot cum}$ is the damping ratio of hysteretic cumulative energy consumption in positive and negative directions in each loop; δ_y is yield load; Q_y is yield load; δ_{max} is maximum displacement; Q_{max} is maximum load; δ_u is ultimate displacement; Q_u is ultimate load; $\mu^{\pm}_E$ is ductility index based on the double-parameter energy method.

Table 10. Evaluation of the influence of control factors in the restoring force model on test energy consumption and ductility index.

Control and influencing factors in the restoring force model	$E^{\pm}_{cyc\cdot total}$ (kN·mm)	δ_y (mm)	δ_u (mm)	Q_u (kN)	$E^{\pm}_{cyc\cdot ela\cdot total}$ (kN·mm)	$E^{\pm}_{envelope}$ (kN·mm)	$D^{\pm}_\Delta$
Stiffness degradation factor	★	★★★	★★★	★★	★	★	★
Slip or fracture closure factor	★★	★★	★★	★★	★★	★★	★★
Energy degradation factor	★★★	★★	★★	★	★★	★★	★★★
The energy-based strength degradation factor	★★	★	★★	★★★	★★	★★	★★
The ductility-based strength degradation factor	★★	★★	★★	★	★★	★★	★★

Note: "★★★": prominent influence; "★★": medium influence; "★": slight influence; "☆": little influence. $E^{\pm}_{cyc\cdot total}$ is total energy consumption; δ_y is yield displacement; δ_u is ultimate displacement; Q_u is ultimate load; $E^{\pm}_{cyc\cdot ela\cdot total}$ is total elastic energy; $E^{\pm}_{envelope}$ is total envelope energy; $D^{\pm}_\Delta$ is damage value.

damage mode and the horizontal load-displacement travel records of the specimens as well as the restoring force curves are saved in digital format. Due to limitations in space, this paper randomly selects 38 quasi-static columns (including those for the test in this paper), and lists them in table 11, which only shows the basic information of the components and the complete test data of restoring force curves $Q(x) \delta(x)$ of collected test components.

5 CONCLUSIONS

Based on the analysis of data in the PEER test, the PEER-based structural quasi-static column test database is built, the data of a total of 279 real quasi-static test columns are collected, the main parameters and damage modes in the test are summarized, and these data are provided for hysteretic curve energy calculation and damage evaluation in subsequent studies and used as training and prediction data samples for prediction and evaluation of ductility index under ultimate load through the optimized BP algorithm. After a detailed introduction to the quasi-static test of SP01 to SP10 specimens, this paper reaches the following conclusion. (1) After analysis of the quasi-static

Table 11. Data parameters in the training set and test set of quasi-static RC column specimens.

No.	Specimen No.	f_c/ MPa	n_0	λ	ρ_l/ %	ρ_w/ %	f_{yk}^l/ MPa	f_{yk}^w/ MPa	μ_Δ^e	δ_{yield}/ mm	δ_{ult}/ mm
1	1006040 (Légeron & Paultre 2000)	98.2	0.39	6.99	2.15	4.26	457	404	3.12	40.72	127.00
2	10013040 (Légeron & Paultre 2000)	104.3	0.37	6.99	2.15	1.96	457	418	1.15	40.43	46.60
3	806040 (Paultre & Mongeau 2001)	78.7	0.41	6.99	2.15	4.26	467	438	4.82	36.07	173.96
4	1206040 (Paultre & Mongeau 2001)	109.2	0.41	6.99	2.15	4.26	467	438	3.18	38.35	122.13
5	1005540 (Paultre & Mongeau 2001)	109.5	0.41	6.99	2.15	3.30	467	825	6.46	20.70	133.77
6	1008040 (Paultre & Mongeau 2001)	104.2	0.37	6.99	2.15	2.27	467	825	3.55	30.41	108.01
7	1005552 (Paultre & Mongeau 2001)	104.5	0.53	6.99	2.15	3.30	481	744	3.28	28.01	91.84
8	1006052 (Paultre & Mongeau 2001)	109.4	0.51	6.99	2.15	4.26	481	744	2.46	36.87	90.86
9	1006015 (Légeron & Paultre 2000)	92.4	0.14	6.99	2.15	4.26	469	391	6.70	27.24	182.38
10	1006025 (Légeron & Paultre 2000)	93.3	0.28	6.99	2.15	4.26	456	404	4.73	36.87	174.52
11	10013015 (Légeron & Paultre 2000)	94.8	0.14	6.99	2.15	1.96	469	391	3.95	30.91	122.10
12	10013025 (Légeron & Paultre 2000)	97.7	0.26	6.99	2.15	1.96	456	404	3.05	30.36	92.47
13	BG1 (Saatcioglu & Grira 1999)	34.0	0.43	5.12	1.95	1.01	571	262	3.32	14.91	49.51
14	BG2 (Saatcioglu & Grira 1999)	34.0	0.43	5.12	1.95	2.01	571	262	3.67	22.78	83.51
15	BG3 (Saatcioglu & Grira 1999)	34.0	0.20	5.12	1.95	2.01	571	262	6.54	17.75	116.00
16	BG4 (Saatcioglu & Grira 1999)	34.0	0.46	5.12	2.93	1.31	571	262	4.15	20.11	83.51
17	BG5 (Saatcioglu & Grira 1999)	34.0	0.46	5.12	2.93	2.70	571	262	6.04	19.20	116.00
18	BG6 (Saatcioglu & Grira 1999)	34.0	0.46	5.12	2.93	2.70	580	262	8.21	14.13	116.00
19	BG7 (Saatcioglu & Grira 1999)	34.0	0.46	5.12	2.93	1.31	580	262	6.49	17.87	116.00
20	BG8 (Saatcioglu & Grira 1999)	34.0	0.23	5.12	2.93	1.31	580	262	5.76	20.48	118.00
21	BG9 (Saatcioglu & Grira 1999)	34.0	0.46	5.12	3.28	1.31	580	262	5.62	21.01	118.00
22	BG10 (Saatcioglu & Grira 1999)	34.0	0.46	5.12	3.28	2.71	570	262	6.81	17.33	118.00
23	C1005N (Matamoros 2000)	69.6	0.05	3.74	1.93	1.01	381	357	3.88	11.52	44.70
24	C1010N (Matamoros 2000)	67.8	0.10	3.44	1.93	1.01	381	357	3.75	11.85	44.45
25	C1020N (Matamoros 2000)	65.5	0.21	3.37	1.93	1.01	381	357	3.42	11.14	38.10
26	C50N (Matamoros 2000)	37.9	0.05	3.48	1.93	1.01	381	357	4.09	10.82	44.20
27	C520N (Matamoros 2000)	48.3	0.14	3.72	1.93	1.01	381	357	2.67	14.36	38.40
28	C540N (Matamoros 2000)	38.1	0.36	3.35	1.93	1.01	381	357	1.73	14.89	25.70
29	SP01	67.1	0.20	1.90	1.608	0.451	451	435	1.86	4.51	8.39
30	SP02	67.1	0.20	1.90	3.928	0.451	484	435	1.22	5.80	7.09
31	SP03	75.9	0.20	1.90	1.608	0.451	451	435	1.11	7.43	8.26
32	SP04	70.7	0.20	1.90	1.608	0.451	451	435	1.27	5.54	7.06
33	SP05	57.3	0.20	1.90	3.35	0.451	515	497	1.31	10.11	13.26
34	SP06	57.3	0.35	1.90	3.35	0.451	515	497	1.67	5.65	9.46
35	SP07	5.73	0.50	1.90	3.35	0.451	515	497	1.51	6.53	9.88
36	SP08	57.3	0.35	1.90	3.35	0.671	515	497	1.39	7.56	10.53
37	SP09	57.3	0.20	1.50	3.35	0.451	515	497	1.40	7.16	10.02
38	SP10	57.3	0.20	2.40	3.35	0.451	515	497	1.52	8.75	13.26

Note: The test data are stored in digital format in the database. The table lists a total of 38 groups of real test data (from the PEER database and preliminary topic tests), where λ is the shear span ratio; f_c is the concrete strength grade; n_0 is the axial compressive ratio; ρ_l is the longitudinal reinforcement ratio; ρ_w is the stirrup reinforcement ratio; f_{yk}^l is the longitudinal reinforcement strength; f_{yk}^w is the stirrup reinforcement strength; δ_{yield} is the specimen yield displacement; δ_{ult} is the specimen ultimate displacement.

restoring force hysteretic curve and test phenomena, the relationship between the loading program and the restoring force stage evaluation and damage evaluation is obtained. (2) After analysis of main configuration parameters and structural performance, the influence of main configuration parameters of test components (shear span ratio λ, concrete strength grade f_c, axial compressive ratio n_0, longitudinal reinforcement ratio ρ_l and stirrup reinforcement ratio ρ_w) on ductility performance and the evaluation of their relationship are obtained. (3) After analysis of main control parameters and structural damage, the relationship between the test damage process and the influencing factors and describing parameters of the restoring force model is obtained, the main indexes for test process damage analysis of SP01 to SP10 are obtained, and the evaluation of the influence of control factors in the restoring force model on test energy consumption and ductility index is obtained. (4) The rules of stiffness degradation, strength degradation, pinching degradation, and energy consumption damage of test components can be described by adopting the index variables ($\alpha\beta_d-\beta_e\gamma-\beta$). For high-strength structures with complex restoring force energy consumption damage, it is more reasonable and practical to use ($\alpha\beta_d-\beta_e\gamma-\beta$) to describe the restoring force model.

ACKNOWLEDGEMENTS

This work is supported by the Natural Science Foundation of Fujian Province China (Grant No. 2019J01711), the Demonstration Course Foundation 2022 of Huaqiao University (Grant No. 612-50122021), the Education & Scientific Foundation of Fujian Province of China (Grant No. JAT200257), and the Ph.D. Scientific Research Fund of Jimei University (Grant No. ZQ2017009). We are very grateful for their financial support.

CONFLICT OF INTERESTS

The authors of the paper declare that there is no conflict of interests regarding the publican. The authors do not have a direct financial relationship with the commercial identity which might lead to a conflict of interests for any of the authors.

REFERENCES

Légeron, F. & P. Paultre. (2000). Behavior of high-strength concrete columns under cyclic flexure and constant axial load. *ACI Struct. J.* 97 (4), 591–601.

Lin, H. B. & Q. F. Wang. (2008a). Damage evaluation of high-strength reinforced concrete structure based on IDRAC. *J. Build. Structures* (China) 29 (S1), 255–259.

Lin, H. B. & Q. F. Wang. (2008b). Seismic behavior on HRB400 high-strength reinforced concrete columns. *J. Build. Structures* (China) 29 (S1), 36–41.

Matamoros, A. B. (2000). *Study of drift limits for high-strength concrete columns*. Illinois: Universtiy of Illinois at Urbana-Champaign.

Paultre, P., F. Légeron, & D. Mongeau. (2001). Influence of concrete strength and transverse reinforcement yield strength on behavior of high strength concrete columns. *ACI Struct. J.* 98 (4), 490–501.

Peer. (2010). *Guidelines for performance-based seismic design of tall buildings* (TBI 2010). Berkeley, CA: Pacific Earthquake Engineering Research Center, University of California.

Reinhorn, A. M., H. Roh, & M. V. Sivaselvan, et al. (2009). IDARC2D Version 7.0: *A program for the inelastic damage analysis of structures*. Buffalo: University at Buffalo, State University of New York.

Saatcioglu, M. & M. Grira. (1999). Confinement of reinforced concrete colummns with welded reinforcement grids. *ACI Struct. J.* 96 (1), 29–39.

Taylor, A. W. & W. C. Stone. (1993). *A summary of cyclic lateral load tests on spiral reinforced concrete columns*. Gaithersburg, USA: Building and Fire Research Laboratory, National Institute of Standards and Technology.

Taylor, A. W., C. Kuo, & K. Wellenius, et al. (1997). *A summary of cyclic lateral load tests on rectangular reinforced concrete columns*. Gaithesburg, USA: Building and Fire Research Laboratory, National Institute of Standards and Technology.

Research on renovation design of modern office space

Chi Sun* & Long Cheng*
Institute of Design and Art, Shenyang Jianzhu University, Shenyang, China

ABSTRACT: With the development of society, the traditional office space has been unable to adapt to modern people's office mode, so people put forward a new demand for modern office mode. Because the construction of new space needs to consume huge workforce, material resources, and financial resources, the rational transformation of the old building's interior space will become a more economical and sustainable choice. In the context of national resource constraints, transforming the modern office space design is the main problem. Based on the study of space layout, material use, and space structure, we provide three methods of transformation and reuse, namely, using the movable partition, recycling waste materials, and dividing and expanding space. In terms of energy saving, the paper puts forward two methods, namely, space adjustment based on the original point of the equipment in the smallpox concealment project and application of Low-e film coated doors and Windows.

1 INTRODUCTION

With the development of urbanization, urban architectural space tends to be saturated. Most of the functions and environment in the building space have been unable to meet the requirements of today's social development. Therefore, spatial transformation design gradually replaces initial design and becomes the main means of social improvement in urban growth and urban renewal.

At present our country is faced with a more and more serious energy crisis, the Ministry of Housing and Urban-Rural Development posted a *Circular of the Ministry of Housing and Urban-Rural Development on Further Reserving, Utilizing, and Renovating Existing Urban Buildings* in September 2018, which requires to keep attaches great importance to the city of existing buildings and upgrading, establish and improve the existing urban buildings reserve utilization and update the modification mechanism. In the past, the reconstruction method of "large demolition and large construction" in space reconstruction design not only consumes time and energy but also wastes resources and destroys the ecological environment. Rational organization of functional space and renovation design based on the concept of renovation and reuse and environmental protection and energy saving can prolong the renovation period, improve the generation of construction waste in the renovation process to a great extent, and realize the sustainable development of ecological environment.

2 PURPOSE AND SIGNIFICANCE OF STUDY

2.1 Research objective

The development of enterprises in cities is an inevitable factor of social progress. Under the background of national resource shortage, in the process of modern office space transformation, the

---

*Corresponding Authors: 645163536@qq.com and 1023839557@qq.com

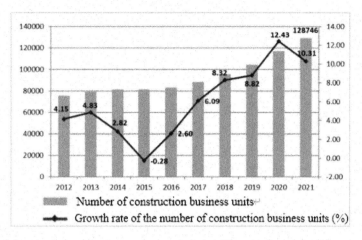

Figure 1. Total output value and Growth rate of China's construction industry from 2012 to 2021.

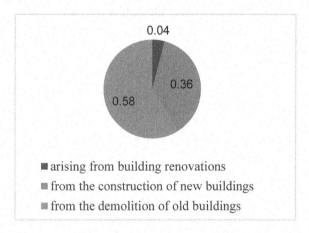

Figure 2. Main links of Construction waste generation in China.

combination of transformation and reuse technology and energy-saving transformation can greatly save transformation resources, save transformation funds, and reduce the emission of construction waste and energy wave. In this paper, effective methods are summarized to alleviate the pollution and social and economic loss caused by the transformation of modern office space in the process of the urban environment to accelerate the pace of urban development.

2.2 *Significance of the study*

The cost of the internal space structure is about 1/3 of the total cost. Under the condition that the original infrastructure design remains unchanged, the internal renovation can save a lot of money. Compared with the initial design, the initial investment, such as demolition cost, can be reduced. Compared with new construction, reconstruction embodies the advantages of a short construction period, cost savings, and high efficiency. The maintenance and demolition work during the construction will certainly have a certain impact on the natural environment and the urban environment. Therefore, adopting the mode of "innovation, transformation and reuse" will prolong the service life of old buildings and ensure their use value.

3 MODERN OFFICE SPACE TRANSFORMATION AND REUSE METHODS

3.1 *Keep the layout of the original space as much as possible*

In the transformation of modern office space, reallocating space layout is the primary task of space transformation. The main purpose is to meet the functional needs of the new, modern office. The transformation of the space is not to completely abandon the functional layout of the old building space and rearrange it, but to meet the new requirements of the users. Based on the previous spatial layout, try to retain the part that can be used, overthrow the part that is not needed, and then re-plan the functional area (Sun 2019). As shown in Figure 3, movable or detachable partitions are used in modern office space to achieve the purpose of changing space anytime and anywhere. In this way, the layout of the original space is not only used but also transformed and utilized, saving the transformation cost fundamentally.

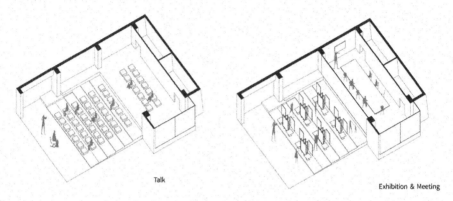

Figure 3. Gad · Line plus Studio office space stair meeting room mobile partition.

3.2 *Reuse of materials*

In the demolition of old building space, many users and valuable old materials will be generated. In addition to renewable resources, these discarded construction wastes also include some non-renewable items in building production (Liang 2018). "The transformation and redesign of previously ignored old materials can have a special humanistic concern, making the space interesting and innovative." The reuse of old materials reduces resource consumption and environmental damage. It also broadens the range of applications and promotes the combination of simple technologies and high technologies to minimize negative impacts. At the present stage when resources are gradually exhausted, all design studies without considering environmental issues are worthless. The whole process of interior design should use a lot of energy and consumables, and then the construction can save raw materials as far as possible, the use of old materials is an effective way to save environmental protection and maximize the energy consumption of resources (Li 2017).

3.3 *Reuse of spatial structure*

During the demolition and transformation of the internal space, the original structure of the internal space can be retained, repaired, and reused to achieve the purpose of saving resources. Moreover, the architectural structure in most of the space is of certain preservation value, which is an epitome of urban culture. In the design of modern office space transformation, flexible use of the original building space structure is also the key to the design of modern office space transformation. The structure of the old building space may also limit the scale and visual experience of the new space to some extent. At the same time, it is necessary to make use of the spatial structure of the old building and plan the spatial scale reasonably from the perspective of the spatial function (Peng 1998).

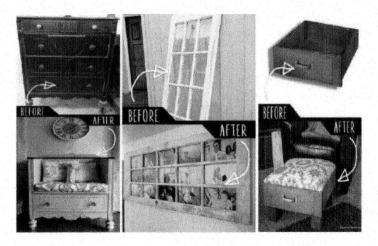

Figure 4. Reuse of materials.

3.3.1 *Space segmentation*
Space segmentation refers to the division in the horizontal direction or vertical direction, the larger space is divided into smaller space or combined space to be used.

In the horizontal direction to the space to break up the method also called the horizontal break up method usually with some partition wall, partition, furniture, landscape, and so on means, the original inner space of those larger spaces is divided into a few smaller spaces. Through the transformation and reuse of the planning of the plane layout.

Vertical segmentation is also known as the vertical segmentation method, for this method is usually used for reconstruction, the requirements are more complex, the internal space area is limited, and the lifting of high space. By adding some mezzanine space in the vertical space, the vertical dimension of the space is improved. This transformation method not only expands the use area of the space but also brings new possibilities and innovations for the planning of space functions. For example, the loft form is a typical concrete application of this style. The application of the horizontal partition method and vertical partition method is usually inseparable, which needs to be combined to form a relatively stable and complete spatial free combination form.

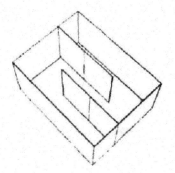 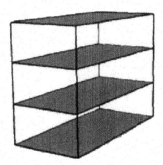

Figure 5. Horizontal and vertical segmentation.

3.3.2 *Space merging*
As the name implies, space consolidation refers to the way that some partition walls in the space are dismantled and broken through, and several relatively independent spaces are united to become a larger and more continuous space. This kind of space merges way, in fact, also can be divided into horizontal merges and vertical merges in a broad sense.

Horizontal consolidation involves the horizontal removal of some non-structural walls. Vertical integration is breaking the height limit by removing partial floor slabs to create spaces suitable for the function. For example, the atrium, vestibule, and other Spaces are mostly made in this way. In the process of a vertical merger, the stress of the building structure needs to be considered. If necessary, some stress components can be added to balance the stress of the whole building (Hou 2017).

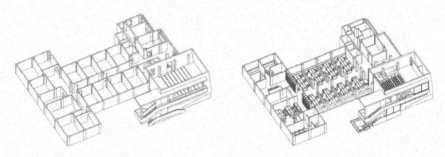

Figure 6. Space merge.

3.3.3 *Space expansion*

Space expansion is appropriately expanded within the scope of the original building space relationship to become a whole. This kind of space transformation method is called space expansion. It can also be divided into horizontal expansion and vertical expansion.

The horizontal extension has the highest technical feasibility. It refers to an additional mode that meets the needs of scale expansion and functional increase by adding new parts attached to the original space around or in a certain direction under the conditions of the existing building.

Vertical extension refers to the use of the existing building vertical space, to expand the building scale and increase the use area. Common practices include addition, basement extension, and mezzanine extension. Story extension can be divided into two methods, one is to build on the original structure, and the other is not related to the original structure, that is, the load of the added part is directly transferred to the ground.

Sandwich extension imposes the load force of the added part on the original structure, which has high requirements on the original structure and is suitable for structures and some relatively complete frame space structures. Therefore, not all space reconstruction can be adopted in this way. Only very few specific circumstances can use this way to increase the use of space area (Zhang 2013).

4 MODERN OFFICE SPACE ENERGY-SAVING RENOVATION METHOD

4.1 *Concealed works energy-saving renovation*

In recent years, in response to the energy crisis and the need for environmental protection, the energy-efficient design of spaces has been a well-thought-out and common choice in the global design community. Based on safety, if displacement and additions are made, they must be recovered and demolished, resulting in a certain degree of material waste. Therefore, in the process of modern office space renovation, the reasonable transformation of hidden works can effectively reduce energy, reduce energy loss, and improve the efficiency of energy use in the space (Hu 2006).

Smallpox concealment engineering is generally the most important one in the process of office space renovation. The incomplete renovation will affect the appearance of the space and even the operation of the enterprise to a certain extent. In the renovation of concealed works, the biggest one is the transformation of water and electricity ventilation. Usually, the pipelines of water and electricity and equipment in modern office space "do not go to the ground", so most of the design of the ceiling is usually used to hide the materials that can be removed and are easy to maintain. In the process of concealed engineering transformation, in addition to energy saving in decorative materials, we can also achieve energy saving through design techniques, and at the same time, we can make the space innovative (Liu 2006).

a. Cover engineering of the pipeline is the modern office space and office equipment, space function is closely linked. At the beginning of the design for its design center, through their location, planning space, the location of the device will affect the power consumption, reasonably planning the location of the electrical equipment and according to the original point of the space for repair, can be in the process of transformation can largely save resources.

b. In the treatment of pipelines, the use of materials can be reduced through the treatment of finishes, and the bare pipelines can be treated with simple finishes, which not only saves costs but also increases a sense of memory for the original space.

c. With the rapid development of science and technology today, intelligent technology has stepped onto the social stage. In the transformation process of concealed works, intelligence and reconstruction can be combined, and intelligent facilities and intelligent means can be used to achieve the purpose of energy saving.

4.2 Energy-saving renovation of external window glass

Doors and Windows are one of the most important parts of energy loss in construction engineering, so in the process of modern office space renovation, the focus is to strengthen the energy-saving transformation of doors and Windows, one of the effective solutions is to use new energy-saving glass doors and Windows, as far as possible to reduce the rate of solar radiation. The thermal energy parameters of different types of glass are given in Table 1. In the simulation of building energy consumption, by comparing the envelope load formed by the glass with Low-e reflection film and ordinary white glass, the thermal conductivity load of window glass is reduced by 11.66%, the radiation load is reduced by 25.17%, and the overall external window load is reduced by 19.18%. In addition, the comprehensive heat transfer coefficient K value of this kind of glass is lower than the external window heat coefficient, not more than 2.8W/(m-K) stipulated in relevant standards, which is required by relevant load regulations (Wang 2020).

Table 1. Thermal parameters of different types of glass.

Types of glass	The visible light passing rate	Solar power passing rate	Heat transfer coefficient K	Solar heat conduction coefficient	Shading coefficient
Single standard glass	90%	90%	6	0.84	1
Ordinary insulating glass	63%	51%	3.1	0.58	0.67
Standard vacuum glass	74%	62%	1.4	0.66	0.76
Low-e film coated hollow (low permeability)	51%	33%	2.1	0.43	0.49
Low-e film coated hollow (high permeability)	58%	38%	2.4	0.49	0.56

Because Low-e glass has an appropriate visible light passing rate, it can shield indoor and outdoor strong light to a certain extent and has a Low solar transmittance, which can effectively prevent solar heat radiation from entering the room. Not only does it limit most of the solar heat entering the house in winter, but it also limits more solar energy entering the house in summer. Because the solar energy intensity in winter is only about 1/3 of that in summer, the thermal insulation performance is not affected.

5 CONCLUSIONS

This paper summarizes the following conclusions based on the research on the design of modern office space renovation based on relevant cases at home and abroad.

a. Reuse of functional layout of space. Based on the original functional layout, purposefully retain the parts that can be used and re-plan and add new functional areas, which can fundamentally save the cost of reconstruction.

b. Reuse of old materials: Reasonable use of old material design in the renovation process is a sustainable and innovative energy-saving renovation method.

c. Reuse of space structure: according to the size of space, three methods of space segmentation, space combination, and space expansion are used to transform and design and use the structures in the interior space of old buildings to achieve the purpose of saving space.

d. Replan the space through the equipment point of the ceiling concealment project and selectively expose part of the pipeline to achieve energy-saving transformation.

e. The adoption of new low-E membrane doors and Windows can effectively reduce the passing rate of solar radiation and achieve the purpose of energy saving in the selection of materials.

At present, the renovation of modern office space in China is still in the initial stage. The continuous development of China's economy will eventually push the construction market to saturation, and then spatial renovation will become the main means of urban renewal, and the waste of resources and pollution of the environment during the renovation process will become the main problems we have to face. This paper can effectively solve the problem of resource waste and environmental pollution in the process of transformation by studying the methods of transformation and reuse, which has sustainable significance. In western developed countries, space reconstruction projects have been systematic and procedural. In China, the topic of type transformation has just begun. Compared with foreign countries, the government's policy support, the public's awareness of participation, and the concept of transformation occupation are still insufficient, so further research is needed.

REFERENCES

Hou, S. (2017). *Research on Renovation of Administrative Office Building*. D. Anhui Jianzhu University.

Hu, J. (2006). *Research on Interior Space Renovation Design in Environmental Optimization*. M. Beijing: Guangming Daily Press. 8.

Li, Y. (2017). *Research on Reuse of Old Materials in Interior Design*. D. Dalian University of Technology. 66.

Liang, J.H. (2018). Research on Reuse Value of Old Materials in Interior Design. *J. Residence*. 15.

Liu, G.Y. & G. Liu. (2006). *Transformation and Regeneration of Old Building Space*. M. Beijing: China Architecture and Building Press. 1, 22.

Peng, Y.G. (1998). *Architectural Space Combination*. M. Beijing: China Architecture and Building Press.

Sun, M.X. & T. Geng. (2019). From "old" to "new" – A study on Interior Renovation Design of Old Buildings– Taking Office Space as an Example. *J. Furniture and Interior Decoration*. 6, 2.

Wang, X.L. & S. K. Wang. (2020). Energy conservation. *J. Xinyang Vocational and Technology College*. 39, 7–8.

Zang, J.H. (2013). *Research on Interior Space Renovation Design of Old Industrial Buildings*. D. Southwest Forestry University. 15–26.

Research on the influencing factors of residential satisfaction in the renovation of old communities

Xueting Huang* & Guanghua Li*

Chengdu University of Technology, Chengdu, Sichuan, China

ABSTRACT: The reconstruction of old residential areas is an important measure to improve residents' life happiness and living satisfaction in the era of stock planning. To further understand the relationship between residential satisfaction and various transformation work, and to find out the key factors affecting residential satisfaction. Taking the renovation of five old residential areas in Chengdu as an example, this paper uses descriptive statistics, correlation analysis, and CATREG to study the influencing factors of residential satisfaction. The results show that the overall satisfaction of residents is not very satisfactory; public activity space, social environment, and community infrastructure are key factors affecting residential satisfaction, and respondents' age and monthly income also have a significant impact on overall satisfaction.

1 INTRODUCTION

In recent years, with the advancement of urbanization, most urban housing has changed from an incremental model to a stock model. Therefore, the renovation of old communities is an important measure for China to deal with the era of stock development. Due to the differences in the location, construction time, and characteristics of residents of the old community, the renovation plan for the old community should be formulated according to local guidelines and opinions. There are many renovation projects in old communities, and they are closely related to residents. Therefore, it is necessary to grasp the specific renovation content and clarify what to change and how to change it. Residents, as the experiences of community renovation, can truly reflect their feelings about the community. By analyzing the residents' satisfaction with the community's residence to study the content of the renovation of the old community, the needs of the residents can be better met.

At present, relevant scholars mainly focus on the content and strategies of the renovation of old residential areas, and there are few studies on the factors affecting residents' satisfaction. Cai et al. (2017) explored the content and countermeasures of the renovation of old communities from the perspective of micro-renovation. Li (2021) used the analytic hierarchy process to sort the renovation content of old communities and determine the key renovation content. Zhao et al. (2017) started with the current situation of Beijing's aging population and proposed suitable aging countermeasures for the renovation of old residential areas in the future from three aspects: the vertical auxiliary transportation system of residential units, the public service facilities for community home-based elderly care, and the relationship between parking spaces and activity venues.

The research on resident satisfaction mainly focuses on two aspects. On the one hand, it is to study the key factors affecting residents' satisfaction, and the other is to study the evaluation system of residents' satisfaction. Taking Suining City as an example, Li (2020) used the Pearson correlation method to explore the key influencing factors of satisfaction with the renovation of old urban areas and believed that environmental sanitation was an influencing factor of residents'

---

*Corresponding Authors: 942404372@qq.com and liguanghua13@cdut.cn

satisfaction. Gao et al. (2020) used factor analysis to find that infrastructure and environmental improvement is the most important for residential satisfaction. Mohit (2012) found through research on public rental housing in the Maldives that residential satisfaction is affected by housing physical characteristics, service provision, community public facilities, and community social environment. Fried (1982) found that housing quality is the most direct and most important factor affecting residential satisfaction. Azimi and Esmaeilzadeh (2017) found through regression analysis that different housing types have different key factors affecting residential satisfaction, neighborhood characteristics are a key factor for all housing types, but architectural characteristics only affect the satisfaction of apartments residents. Etminani et al. (2017) used factor analysis and regression analysis to find that the physical characteristics of buildings are the main factors affecting residential satisfaction, and the socioeconomic characteristics have little effect on residential satisfaction. Ibem and Aduwo (2013) found that the three main factors affecting residential satisfaction are comfort and safety, the size of the living and sleeping areas of the residence, and the management of the residential area. Riazi and Emami (2018) used structural equation modeling to find that planning policy, design principles and relationships are the influencing factors of residential satisfaction, and race is a moderator of neighborhood relationship and residential satisfaction. Xue et al. (2016) surveyed high-rise residential residents and found that air quality and thermal comfort have the greatest impact on residential satisfaction. Xiao et al. (2019) built an evaluation index system for the implementation effect of the renovation and improvement of old communities from three aspects: residential function improvement project, facility improvement project, basic property management, and long-term management mechanism, and builds an evaluation model based on hesitant fuzzy sets of interval values.

From previous studies, it is found that there are very few studies on the influencing factors of residential satisfaction in old communities. Therefore, this paper uses the survey data of Chengdu to study the key factors affecting the satisfaction of residents in old communities through descriptive statistics, correlation analysis, and regression analysis. The research conclusions can enrich the relevant theories of residential satisfaction, provide reference and basis for the renovation of old communities, and have important practical significance for guiding urban renewal.

2 RESEARCH DATA AND METHOD

2.1 *Study area and sample description*

As the capital city of Sichuan Province, Chengdu is one of the first pilot cities for urban renewal in China. According to the Chengdu Housing and Urban-Rural Development Bureau, by the end of 2021, Chengdu had renovated 4,945 old residential areas with a construction area of more than 35 million square meters, benefiting about 480,000 households. In this study, five typical old communities, namely Xinhong Community, Xinhua Community, Sanjiefang Community, Wansheng Community, and Shuangqiao North Road Community were selected as sample units.

The data source of this article is from the field investigation and in-depth interviews conducted by the author from 2021.12-2022.1 in five typical old communities in Chengdu. Based on consulting literature and soliciting expert opinions, the questionnaire is designed in two parts: the first part is the basic information about the households and the second part is the evaluation of the residential satisfaction index. At the same time, the overall satisfaction of the respondents was also collected. A total of 250 questionnaires were distributed in this survey, 228 questionnaires were recovered, of which 205 were valid questionnaires, and the effective rate of questionnaire recovery was 82%. The questionnaire is mainly conducted by a household survey. To interview young residents who have jobs, the survey time is mainly concentrated on rest days.

2.2 *Variables and research methods*

The purpose of this study is to evaluate the key factors affecting residential satisfaction in old residential areas. This paper uses SPSS 23.0 software to analyze the influencing factors of residential satisfaction by using correlation analysis and CATREG. The explained variable of regression analysis is the overall satisfaction of residents, which is divided into 1-5 grades. The higher the grade, the higher the satisfaction. The respondent's socioeconomic attributes, housing conditions, public activity space, outdoor environment, community infrastructure, community support facilities, and social environment were introduced into the optimal scale regression model as explanatory variables. The variables used in this paper and their definitions are shown in Table 1.

Table 1. Main variables and definitions of measuring residential satisfaction.

Variable	Variable definitions
Gender	Respondent's gender
Age	Respondent's age, an ordinal variable ranging from 1-4.
Education	Respondent's education, an ordinal variable ranging from 1-4.
Profession	The respondent's occupation is a nominal variable with values ranging from 1-6.
Monthly income	Respondent's monthly income, an ordinal variable ranging from 1-5.
Residence time	Respondent's residence time, an ordinal variable ranging from 1-4.
Homeownership	Own/rent housing.
Housing conditions	Respondents' mean evaluation scores for housing quality, ventilation, and lighting building energy efficiency, privacy, building façade, and vertical traffic.
Public activity space	Respondents' mean evaluation score for illegal construction, stairwells and public corridors, barrier-free facilities, pipeline regulation, and residents' activity places.
Outdoor environment	Respondents' mean evaluation score for green landscape, noise, parking space, resident quality, environmental hygiene, neighborhood relationship, building density, and road traffic design.
Community infrastructure	Respondents' mean evaluation score for sanitation facilities, lighting facilities, security facilities, fire protection facilities, water, electricity and heating pipe network facilities and communication pipe network facilities.
Community supporting facilities	Respondents' mean evaluation score for basic services, leisure and entertainment, social services, courier services and transportation.
Social environment	Respondents' mean evaluation score for property services, community cultural activities, and maintenance of public facilities.
Overall satisfaction	Respondents' evaluation of overall residential satisfaction in the community, an ordinal variable ranging from 1-5.

Source: Compiled by the Author

3 DATA ANALYSIS AND RESULTS

3.1 Respondent's residence satisfaction

This paper divides residents' satisfaction into six categories, the statistical results of the mean values of various indicators are shown in Table 2. Residents have the highest satisfaction with housing conditions (3.12), and the lowest satisfaction with the social environment (2.94), community infrastructure (2.90), and community support facilities (2.80). In terms of overall satisfaction indicators, the average resident satisfaction is 2.62, less than 3, indicating that residents have a low level of satisfaction with the community, and the scores of all indicators are less than 4. This also reflects that residential satisfaction has not reached an ideal level.

3.2 Correlation analysis

The main purpose of correlation analysis is to study the closeness of the relationship between variables. In statistical analysis, the correlation coefficient is often used to quantitatively describe the closeness of the linear relationship between two or more variables. According to different data characteristics, different correlation coefficients are usually used. There are three kinds of correlation coefficients commonly used in statistics, including the Pearson correlation coefficient,

Table 2. Average of 6 types of resident satisfaction variables.

Variable category	Mean	Standard deviation
Housing conditions	3.12	0.63974
Public activity space	3.08	0.71106
Outdoor environment	2.98	0.59886
Community infrastructure	2.90	0.70332
Community supporting facilities	2.80	0.73404
Social environment	2.94	0.6995
Overall satisfaction	2.62	0.722

Source: Compiled by the authors.

Kendall's rank correlation coefficient, and Spearman's rank correlation coefficient. Among them, the Pearson correlation coefficient is suitable for continuous data, but not suitable for the analysis in this paper, and the Spearman rank correlation coefficient is suitable for the case where the variable has a rank attribute. Therefore, it can be used to explore the correlation between each variable in this paper and the overall satisfaction, that is, the closeness of each variable and the overall satisfaction.

The results are shown in Table 3. The data analysis results show that the overall satisfaction of residents is significantly positively correlated with the six types of influencing factors, among which the outdoor environment has the most significant correlation with the overall satisfaction of residents, and the Spearman correlation coefficient is 0.489. Followed by community supporting facilities, community infrastructure, and public activity space, the Spearman correlation coefficients were 0.463, 0.451, and 0.412, respectively. Finally, there are Housing conditions and social environment, and the Spearman correlation coefficients are 0.397 and 0.381, respectively.

Table 3. Correlation coefficients between resident satisfaction variables and overall satisfaction.

		Housing conditions	Public activity space	Outdoor environment	Community infrastructure	Community supporting facilities	Social environment
Overall satisfaction	Spearman Rho	0.397**	0.412**	0.489**	0.451**	0.463**	0.381**
	Sig.	0.000	0.000	0.000	0.000	0.000	0.000

**Correlation is significant at the 0.01 level (two-tailed).

3.3 Key factors affecting resident satisfaction

In order to test and analyze the influence of different categories of factors on residential satisfaction, further optimal scale regression analysis is needed, that is, the overall satisfaction of residents is taken as the explained variable, and housing conditions, public activity space, outdoor environment, community infrastructure, community support facilities, and social environment were set as explanatory variables, and the socioeconomic characteristics were added, including gender, age, education, occupation, monthly income, residence time, and housing ownership. As shown in Table 4, the R square and the adjusted R square of the optimal scale regression equation in the model summary table are both greater than 0.9, indicating that the regression model can explain more than 90% of the total variation, and the fitting effect is good.

As shown in Table 5, the results of parameter estimation are given in the coefficient table. Since the variables are standardized by scale regression, the obtained coefficients are also standardized. From the significant value of the F test, among the socioeconomic characteristics of residents, the age and monthly income of the respondents have a significant impact on residents' overall satisfaction, with regression coefficients of 0.108 and -0.043, respectively. Among them, age has a significant positive impact on resident satisfaction, indicating that the older the age, the higher

Table 4. Model summary.

	Multiple R	R square	Adjusted R square	Apparent prediction error
Standardized data	0.983	0.967	0.956	0.033

Source: Compiled by the authors.

the resident satisfaction; the monthly income has a significant negative impact on the resident satisfaction, indicating that the higher the monthly income, the lower the resident satisfaction. Among the six types of influencing factors of resident satisfaction, each type of influencing factor has a significant positive impact on the overall satisfaction of residents, and the public activity space has the most significant impact on residents' satisfaction, with a regression coefficient of 0.26. Followed by the social environment, community infrastructure, and community support facilities, the regression coefficients were 0.245, 0.221, and 0.203 respectively. The outdoor environment and housing conditions have the least impact on residents' satisfaction, with regression coefficients of 0.173 and 0.146, respectively.

Table 5. Coefficients of the regression analysis to identify the variable that predicts the overall satisfaction in the housing estates.

Variables	Beta	Bootstrap (1000) estimate of standard error	Df	F	Sig.
Gender	0.012	0.013	1	0.771	0.381
Age	0.108	0.034	3	10.256	0.000**
Education	0.045	0.027	1	2.717	0.101
Profession	0.066	0.021	5	9.628	0.388
Monthly income	-0.043	0.019	2	5.353	0.006**
Residence time	-0.024	0.019	1	1.716	0.192
Homeownership	0.017	0.015	1	1.425	0.234
Housing conditions	0.146	0.025	6	33.3	0.000**
Public activity space	0.26	0.03	6	77.329	0.000**
Outdoor environment	0.173	0.029	6	35.228	0.000**
Community infrastructure	0.221	0.029	5	58.414	0.000**
Community supporting facilities	0.203	0.031	6	44.16	0.001**
Social environment	0.245	0.025	6	97.709	0.000**

Note: Dependent variable represents the overall satisfaction; "**" represents the significance at the 0.01 level.

4 CONCLUSIONS

This paper conducts a questionnaire survey on five typical old communities in Chengdu, and studies the residential satisfaction and influencing factors of residents in old communities through statistical analysis methods. From the above research analysis, the following conclusions can be drawn:

(1) Residents are not satisfied with the overall satisfaction evaluation of the old community, among which the satisfaction of housing conditions is relatively high, and the satisfaction of community supporting facilities and community infrastructure is relatively low. This shows that although the old community is dilapidated, the quality of the houses meets the design standards, and the residents have lived for a long time and have become accustomed to various housing conditions, so the residents are relatively satisfied with the housing conditions; the old community has been built for a long time, the phenomenon of equipment aging, functional

degradation, the material loss has occurred in the old community, and the lack of sanitation facilities in the old community, poor sanitation conditions, and the general lack of entertainment facilities and elderly care facilities have led to residents' low satisfaction with the community's supporting facilities and infrastructure.

(2) The outdoor environment has the most significant correlation with the overall satisfaction of residents, the housing conditions and the social environment have a low degree of correlation with residential satisfaction. Residents are more concerned about the outdoor environment. During the survey, it was found that the parking spaces in the old community were not properly planned, the parking in the community was chaotic, the roadside road was occupied, and the residents threw garbage at will, resulting in a poor sanitary environment in the community. Therefore, the subsequent renovation of old communities should pay more attention to the outdoor environment to improve residents' satisfaction.

(3) In terms of the significance of the influencing factors, the most significant influences on overall satisfaction are public activity space, social environment, and community infrastructure, the least significant is the outdoor environment and housing conditions. In the early stage of the construction of old communities, there was no reasonable planning, resulting in no activity venues in the community, and many communities did not have property management, and various facilities were lack of maintenance, resulting in a decline in residents' satisfaction. The age and monthly income of the respondents have a significant impact on the overall satisfaction, the housing satisfaction of socially disadvantaged groups such as the elderly and low-income groups is more worrying, and more attention should be paid to the housing satisfaction of these groups.

5 LIMITATIONS AND FUTURE RESEARCH

The research conclusions obtained in this paper are based on the actual residential satisfaction data of old residential areas in Chengdu, and the analysis results are consistent with the facts, but this research still has certain limitations. Due to the limitation of time, workforce, and other conditions, the number of samples collected in this study is small, resulting in errors between the data obtained and the actual situation. With time, residents' attention to each variable of satisfaction and the evaluation results will change accordingly. Future research will expand sample collection and select more old communities for research; due to the regional nature of real estate itself, there will be differences in the influencing factors of residents' satisfaction in different cities, so it is hoped to increase the influencing factors of different cities to evaluate differences in the key influencing factors of urban residents' satisfaction and establish a database of residents' satisfaction in the renovation of old communities in different periods, which can reflect the needs of residents and the changes in their satisfaction.

REFERENCES

Azimi, N. & Esmaeilzadeh, Y. (2017). Assessing the relationship between house types and residential satisfaction in Tabriz, Iran. *Urban Sciences*. 21 (2), 185–203.

Cai Yunnan. (2017). Research on the content and countermeasures of the old urban district-micro-renovation. *Urban Development Studies*. 24 (4), 29–34.

Etminani, R. (2017). Assessment of residential satisfaction in Mehr Housing Scheme: a case study of Sadra New Town, Iran. *Housing Theory and Society*. 34 (3), 323–342.

Fried, M. (1982). Residential attachment: sources of residential and community satisfaction. *Social Issues*. 38 (3), 107–119.

Gao Hui. (2020). A case study on the renovation of old residential areas in Hangzhou based on residents' satisfaction. *Architecture and Culture*. (5), 119–121.

Ibem, E. O. & Aduwo, E. B. (2013). *Assessment of residential satisfaction in public housing in Ogun State, Nigeria*. Habitat International. 40, 163–175.

Li Jiang. (2021). Research on the renewal strategy of old residential area in Beijing from the view of level analysis method. *Industrial architecture*. 51 (10): 66–74.

Li Qin. (2020). Research on the influencing factors of residents' satisfaction in the renovation of old urban areas-Taking the renovation of old urban areas in Suining as an example. *Journal of Beijing University of Architecture and Technology*. 36 (1): 18–23.

Mohit, M. A. & Azim, M. (2012). 'Assessment of residential satisfaction with public housing in Hulhumale', Maldives. *Procedia – Social and Behavioral Sciences*. 50, 756–770.

Riazi, M. & Emami, A. (2018). Residential satisfaction in affordable housing: A mixed method study. *Cities*. 82, 1–9.

Xiao Yi. (2019). Study on the implementation effect evaluation method of updating and improving the old residential areas. *Construction Economy*. 40 (1), 102–106.

Xue, P. (2016). A structured approach to overall environmental satisfaction in high-rise residential buildings. *Energy and Buildings*. 116, 181–189.

Zhao Lizhi. (2017). Countermeasures for the transformation of old residential areas in Beijing under the background of aging. *Urban Development Studies*. 24 (7), 11–14.

Application of concrete pouring construction technology in construction engineering construction

Nan Zhao*

China Energy Railway Equipment Co., Ltd., Beijing, China

ABSTRACT: In construction engineering, concrete is a very important material, which directly affects the overall quality of construction engineering. In the process of the rapid development of society, people have put forward higher requirements for the comfort of buildings. In this case, concrete will be increasingly widely used. In the actual construction process, the relevant personnel should understand the characteristics of concrete pouring in detail, combined with the actual situation of the construction site, and control each link in the construction, so that the whole process reaches the prescribed standards. At the same time, appropriate measures should be taken to control the focus of the project quality, rationally allocate resources, promote the smooth implementation of the project, and achieve good economic and social benefits. This paper describes the problems existing in the construction of concrete pouring construction technology and then analyzes the application of concrete pouring construction technology for the exchange and reference of relevant people.

1 INTRODUCTION

Concrete plays a very important position in modern building construction, and has a key impact on the robustness and stability of the building structure. In the process of construction, the hydrology, climate, and terrain of the construction site should be analyzed according to the actual situation, and targeted countermeasures should be formulated on this basis to ensure that each link of the concrete pouring process is effectively implemented. This paper analyzes the technology of concrete pouring construction and its existing problems in detail, and shows its concrete application in construction engineering, which has certain practical and reference significance.

2 THE CONCRETE POURING CONSTRUCTION TECHNOLOGY IN THE CONSTRUCTION OF CONSTRUCTION ENGINEERING PROBLEMS

2.1 *Prone to cracks*

Concrete strength and strong growth rate, are directed by the temperature, humidity, and time control and influence. Therefore, in the process of concrete production, to ensure that each link does not exceed the prescribed temperature limit, especially the negative temperature construction in the cold and cold areas, pay great attention to the temperature limit and anti-freezing insulation measures. When the outdoor daily average temperature for 5 consecutive days is lower than 5°C, that is, the winter construction temperature, to enter the winter construction, the concrete engineering should be carried out according to the requirements of the winter construction. The freezing point of concrete is -3°C, the concrete starts to freeze at -3°C, and the freezing expansion value is 8% to 9%,

---

*Corresponding Author: 850562811@qq.com

when the freezing speed is greater than the cement condensation speed, the concrete structure will be destroyed. Cement hydration shall stop at a temperature of 0°C to 3°C, so as for cement hydration, heat preservation, heat preservation, and antifreeze measures must be taken. Theoretically, the stagnation of cement hydration is-15°C, but hydration below-3°C is extremely slow. According to the characteristics of concrete pouring, pouring cracks are often encountered in the actual concrete pouring. The concrete pouring, the concrete formwork support is not strong, leading to the local deformation and settlement of the formwork, and eventually leading to the concrete cracks. The second is that when the removal of the mold is unreasonable, it will increase the possibility of concrete cracks. The third is because the mass concrete in the actual construction management, due to the lack of hydration and cause the temperature difference between inside and outside, and eventually the concrete cracks, which requires the relevant staff to regularly water the concrete (as shown in Figure 1). Finally, after the completion of the concrete pouring, if not the crack curing, it will affect the bearing capacity of the concrete structure, and the concrete cracks will be formed for a long time.

Figure 1. Concrete watering.

2.2 *Easy to appear dew tendon phenomenon*

In the process of concrete pouring, often encountered column, shear wall, and other concrete local loose problems. This phenomenon is related to less mortar and more gravel. In the actual concrete pouring process, we will encounter honeycomb holes, local exposed reinforcement, and other problems. There are four reasons for exposing steel bars. The first one is insufficient concrete mixing. Second, the concrete mixing uniformity and the vibration are insufficient. Third, the concrete workability is not strong. Fourth, if in the process of concrete pouring and vibration, too much concrete is added, or if there is a problem of no segmented perfusion. This phenomenon is mainly caused by the false vibrations of the concrete. This ultimately reduces the vibrational effect of the material, and cannot improve the quality of concrete pouring. Fifth, during the concrete pouring and vibration process, if the vibrator bar is placed between the trench walls, it would fail to improve the compactness of the concrete vibration, leading to template displacement or severe water seepage.

2.3 *Easy to appear hemp surface problems*

Through the analysis of concrete pouring construction, the reasons reduce the ease of concrete and increase the isolation of the concrete, and the problem of concrete mixing density; third, the concrete mixing time is relatively short. In the case of inadequate water control, it will affect the distribution state of mortar and stone, and eventually lead to concrete segregation, which may lead to hemp points on the surface of concrete pouring. Therefore, under the background of the stable operation and development of the construction industry to improve the quality of concrete, managers should make a concrete pouring management plan to maximize the role of concrete pouring and promote the sustainable development of the industry.

3 CONCRETE POURING AND CONSTRUCTION TECHNOLOGY IN CONSTRUCTION ENGINEERING CONSTRUCTION

3.1 *Comprehensive and layered pouring technology*

At present, China's construction technology is constantly reformed. As the most common pouring technology in site construction, the comprehensive layered pouring technology has been widely used in high-rise buildings. However, as the number of applications increases, many problems arise during the run. For example, in the construction process, some staff will carry out the construction according to their own operation experience, rather than according to the professional theory, which makes their work lack theoretical guidance, and threaten the future application of the building. Therefore, in the pouring process, the relevant personnel should effectively control each link, to ensure that the quality of technical operation meets the requirements, and further improve the construction level. Comprehensive layered pouring technology is a kind of commonly used technology in concrete pouring construction in China, which is generally suitable for projects with low technical content and small construction scale (Su et al. 2021). When concrete pouring, the order from bottom to top is generally used. In the process of applying the comprehensive layered pouring technology, the relevant construction personnel need to pour the second layer of concrete after completing the first layer of concrete. If the initial setting conditions of the first layer of concrete are not perfect, the construction personnel need to carry out continuous concrete pouring. To improve the level of concrete pouring, the construction personnel need to ensure that the plane scale of the building structure is not greater than the prescribed scope, and should firmly adhere to the basic principle. If the pouring interval is large, the two ends need to be poured separately and then in the middle. This can effectively improve the stability of the concrete pouring structure.

3.2 *Shear force wall pouring technology*

Shear wall pouring technology is a more common concrete pouring construction technology in construction engineering construction. In the process of applying this technology, the form of a long pipe is usually used. Specifically, first, a layer of concrete formwork with a thickness of about five cm was poured in a relatively symmetrical way in the specified direction, and then the template was used as the cornerstone to pour the shear wall (Li 2020). In addition, in the process of pouring the shear wall, there will be many construction cracks; therefore, the construction personnel need to pay special attention to the direction of the crack, and carefully determine whether the crack is on the door hole or the curtain hole. Secondly, when pouring the shear wall, we should also ensure the continuity of its operation, and try not to suspend the operation. Third, in the vibration process of the shear wall interface, the construction personnel need to control the strength to ensure that it can meet the corresponding vibration standards. In this way, the tightness of the concrete can be effectively improved, so that it can be tightly connected. Fourth, the relevant construction personnel also need to ensure the unity of the location of the hole and the concrete standard around the hole, to ensure that the pouring of the wall and internal and external wall columns can be completed uniformly. When vibration, the construction personnel must ensure that the distance between the vibrating rod and the hole is more than 30 cm and evenly vibrate around the hole to reduce the frequency of deformation in the hole (as shown in Figure 2). In addition, to reasonably control the total thickness of the steel protective layer and reduce the adverse impact of the pouring link on the shear wall structure, the construction personnel need to improve the accuracy and stability coefficient of the steel fixation operation in the actual operation, which is also conducive to the smooth development of the subsequent links.

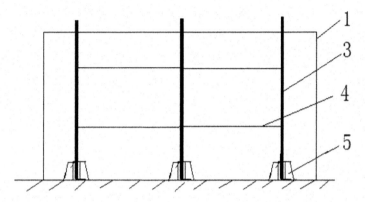

Figure 2. Vibration method.

3.3 Level layered pouring technology

The inclined plane layered pouring technology is an upgraded version of the integrated layered pouring technology. Generally, inclined casting technology is suitable for construction projects with a slope of one-third (Yang 2020). The construction personnel shall ensure that the thickness of the structure of the project is more than three times to improve the level of inclined casting. In the process of applying this technology, the construction personnel first need to vibrate from the inclined end of the concrete pouring layer, and then move slowly upward after the completion of the vibration technology to effectively improve the concrete pouring level.

3.4 Beam and plate pouring technology

In the process of applying this technology, the relevant construction personnel must adopt a professional concrete pouring scheme according to the beam and plate in the actual construction project, and clarify the beam and column nodes (as shown in Figure 3. During this period, if the builder wants to place the ribbed floor, the usual pouring method includes the mud penetration approach. Specifically, according to the stepped layout, the beam and plate should be layered pouring. During this time, the actual beam and slab pouring work shall be done after the established pouring direction is reached. Moreover, in the process of pouring the floor, the construction personnel need to ensure that the thickness of the beam and plate does not exceed the total thickness of the virtual paving, but also need to ensure that the vibration direction is consistent with the pouring direction. In the vibration link, the mark should be moved in real-time according to the actual situation to effectively control the thickness of concrete. After vibration, a scraper shall also be used to ensure the strong flatness of the surface after concrete pouring (Wang 2016). Finally, if the beam plate or beam body of the wall column, the relevant personnel need to ensure the pouring of the column or wall to improve the quality of the concrete.

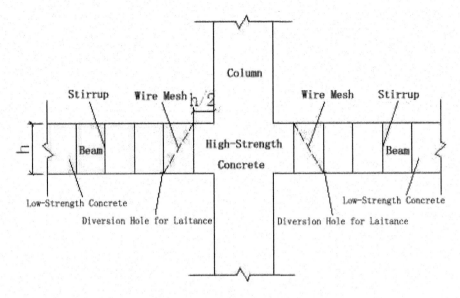

Figure 3. Elevation diagram of the beam and column nodes.

4 THE APPLICATION OF CONCRETE POURING CONSTRUCTION TECHNOLOGY IN THE CONSTRUCTION ENGINEERING CONSTRUCTION KEY POINTS

4.1 Strictly control the construction quality

In the process of modern construction engineering construction, it is necessary to strictly control the quality of concrete construction, and its construction quality control can be divided into four parts. The first is to control the pouring time. The key to cast-in-place concrete construction is to strictly grasp the pouring time. For projects that need secondary pouring, the interval between the two pouring should be controlled within 1:5 hours. To prevent cracks, the entire pouring work needs to be completed within five hours. The second is the concrete height control. In the concrete formwork stage of construction, the dumping of steel skeleton or impact formwork is not concentrated. The rolling method is adopted at the low concrete height of two meters, and the free-falling height of the discharge pipe outlet to the pouring layer is controlled below 1.5 meters. The third one is vibration control. In the concrete beam and plate pouring stage, to ensure that the treatment and vibration have a good compact, the beam and column nodes. Concrete pouring has a certain construction quality. First, pour high-grade building concrete, and then pour low-grade concrete. To effectively avoid quality problems such as honeycomb concrete, the height of pouring high-grade concrete should always be higher than the height of the surrounding low-grade concrete. The fourth is maintenance and control. To ensure the maintenance quality, concrete pouring construction, after the completion of two, or three plastering curing, if necessary, with film cover seal.

4.2 Strengthen the degree of control of materials

Concrete material is an important factor affecting the application level of concrete pouring technology. Relevant construction personnel to give full play to the application effect of concrete pouring technology must carefully check the quality level of concrete pouring materials. Specifically, in the process of selecting concrete pouring materials, it is necessary to arrange professional procurement personnel to choose concrete materials and to choose the most cost-effective materials according to the actual needs of the construction project. Before the materials officially enter the site, the relevant procurement personnel should carefully check the qualification certificate of the concrete materials, carefully compare the corresponding batches, and verify the materials through sampling inspection. Ensure that the quality of concrete materials is qualified before officially entering the site (Zhang 2020).

4.3 Ensure the quality of concrete

In the process of construction to effectively ensure the quality of concrete, we must improve the scientific nature of concrete, using a professional way to carry out the production of concrete. In the process of concrete mixing, the construction personnel are required to strictly mix cement, strictly follow the strength, and design standards of the project, professional mixing cement, water, sand, and other admixtures, and follow the relevant specifications and regulations of the construction injection sequence, to ensure the rationalization of the process. When the concrete material is reasonably matched, the construction personnel need to strictly control the concrete mixing time and the corresponding temperature, so that the concrete reaches a higher compactness and uniformity standard. In addition, the relevant construction personnel also require careful detection and verification of the concrete mix ratio and the corresponding quality grade. If the deviation value is greater than the specified specification scope, the relevant construction personnel need to deal with it immediately. The transportation of concrete is also an important factor affecting the quality of concrete to ensure the overall quality of concrete, we must choose the appropriate transportation mode, and try to reduce the loss caused by the concrete in the process of transportation. There is a certain distance between the actual concrete mixing station and the project site. First, before the formal transportation of concrete, the transport personnel should systematically understand the transportation equipment and the designated transportation route to provide the most scientific and efficient transportation scheme and improve concrete transportation efficiency. Secondly, when the assembled concrete is transported to the conveying pump, the relevant construction personnel need to verify the condition of the concrete in real-time to avoid cement, sand, and gravel mixed into the concrete, to ensure the use of the concrete effect. Third, in the process of connecting the concrete pump, it is also necessary to verify the reliability of the pump and place it in the designated position to avoid dangerous accidents. In addition, some lubricant is applied to the conveying pump to ensure that the air in the conveying pump is kept open and avoids adhesion problems between the concrete and the conveying pump.

4.4 Make good preparations

During the construction process, the preparation work is mainly divided into three parts. First, do a good job of construction organization and technical safety disclosure to emphasize and explain the problems that need to pay attention to in the construction process, especially the problems that may be encountered in the pouring process. Second, check the template and its support to ensure that the elevation, position, and size are correct, strength, stiffness, and tightness meet the requirements, and the garbage in the template should be removed. Third, check whether the grade, diameter, quantity, discharge position, and protective layer thickness of the reinforcement and embedded parts meet the requirements of the design and specification, and make the acceptance record of concealed works. At the same time, by adjusting the beam plate and shear wall, column and beam, vibration time, spacing, and other key construction points, focus on the control of the concrete mark. In addition, in the concrete pouring equipment to ensure that there are no construction problems in the concrete pouring process, the construction personnel should prepare another spare concrete pouring equipment. The equipment shall be checked and tested before the equipment starts work. If a problem or fault is found, it should be repaired timely to ensure the proper operation of the equipment. Weather conditions shall also be considered before pouring the concrete (Xu & Wang 2020). When it rains, the concrete should be protected with plastic film in advance to ensure smooth pouring.

5   CONCLUSION

In the construction of construction engineering, concrete pouring is a very key link, which has a crucial impact on the overall quality of construction engineering. Relevant personnel should understand the characteristics of the technology in detail, and on this basis, make the preparation work before the construction. At the same time, the relevant personnel should do a good job of foundation pouring, shear wall pouring, positioning pouring, beam, and plate pouring and a series of work, control the whole process of construction, improve the quality of construction projects, to achieve good economic and social benefits. Relevant units should also conduct training for construction personnel to constantly improve their overall level.

ABOUT THE AUTHOR

Zhao Nan (1985.8-), male, Han nationality, was born in Yulin City, Shaanxi Province. He is an engineer with a bachelor's degree. His research directions include engineering project bidding management and engineering project implementation of the whole process of management.

REFERENCES

Li Qi. Explore the application of concrete pouring construction technology in construction engineering construction [J]. *Architecture and Decoration*, 2020 (4): 2.

Su Yichao, Li Baojun, Wang Daoxia, et al. Explore the application of concrete pouring construction technology in construction engineering construction [J]. *Modern Property: China Modern Journal*, 2021 (1): 1.

Wang Strengthen. *Application standard of concrete pouring technology in construction Engineering* [J]. 2021(2016–12):75–76.

Xu Yanjiao, Wang Zhenzhen. Application of concrete pouring construction technology in construction Engineering [J]. *Scenic spots*, 2020 (6): 1.

Yang Ming. Application of concrete pouring technology in construction [J]. *Sichuan Cement*, 2020 (11): 2.

Numerical simulation of corrosion of steel liner based on meso-structure of containment

Zhimin Li
School of Civil Architecture, University of Jinan, Jinan, Shandong, China

Shenggang Chen
School of Mechanics and Civil Engineering, China University of Mining and Technology, Xuzhou, Jiangsu, China

Kun Liu
Shandong Jianyan Metrology Testing Limited Company, Jinan, Shandong, China

Xianda Feng*
College of Civil Architecture, University of Jinan, Jinan, Shandong, China

ABSTRACT: Corrosion of steel liner is an important problem in the durability design of containment structures. Chloride ions from containment structure to steel liner surface change alkaline environment, resulting in corrosion of steel liner. According to the Fuller grading curve, a two-dimensional mesoscale model of containment was generated. Based on Fick's second law and Butler-Volmer's law, a two-dimensional mesoscale steel liner corrosion model of containment was established, and the influence of coarse aggregate on chloride ion transmission and surface corrosion of steel liner was analyzed. The results show that the surface of the steel liner can be divided into three stages: non-corrosion, corrosion expansion, and total corrosion. With the expansion of the corrosion area, the corrosion potential is becoming increasingly negative, and the average corrosion current density is gradually reduced. The coarse aggregate can change the diffusion path of chloride ions, and the surface of the steel liner shows an uneven corrosion state. Increasing the volume fraction of coarse aggregate can delay the expansion of chloride ions in the containment and the start time of corrosion on the surface of the steel liner.

1 INTRODUCTION

The containment is the last barrier to preventing accidents in nuclear reactors (Gong 2017). Corrosion of containment steel liner is the main form of aging. Corrosion of steel liner will affect its overall tightness and bring hidden dangers to the safe operation of nuclear power plants (Li 2021). Due to the large volume of containment concrete structure and the internal spread of reactor pressure vessels, the existing corrosion detection equipment is difficult to detect and has low applicability, which cannot better reflect the corrosion state of containment steel liner. It is very necessary to simulate the whole process of corrosion caused by chloride ion corrosion of containment structure to find out the corrosion location and corrosion state of containment steel liner earlier and make countermeasures.

---

*Corresponding Author: cea_fengxd@ujn.edu.cn

2 BASIC THEORIES OF INTERNAL CORROSION OF CONCRETE

2.1 Diffusion of erosion ions in concrete

Assuming that the containment concrete structure is a saturated concrete material with a uniform internal structure, chloride ions do not react with the internal material, and the boundary concentration is not affected by the external environment. At this time, the diffusion process of chloride ions in the concrete structure follows Fick's second law (Ventura 2020), as shown in Eq. (1).

$$\frac{\partial C_{cl}}{\partial t} = D_0 \frac{\partial C_{cl}^2}{\partial x^2} \tag{1}$$

where C_{cl} is the chloride ion concentration (mol/m^3), t is the chloride ion erosion time (d), D_0 is the chloride ion diffusion coefficient (m^2/s), and x is the distance of the chloride ion concentration boundary (mm).

2.2 Electrochemical corrosion calculation

The potential distribution follows the Laplace equation (Warkus 2008):

$$\nabla \cdot \left(\frac{1}{\rho} \nabla \phi\right) = 0 \tag{2}$$

where ϕ is potential (V), and ρ is concrete resistivity (Ω·m).

According to Ohm's law, the current density in concrete is (CAO 2013):

$$i = -\frac{1}{\rho} \nabla \phi \tag{3}$$

where i is current density (A/m^2).

The expression of anodic corrosion current density and cathodic corrosion current density is (Fang 2017):

$$i_a = i_{oa} \cdot 10^{\eta/\beta_a} \tag{4}$$

$$i_c = i_{oc} \cdot 10^{\eta/\beta_c} \tag{5}$$

where i_a is anodic corrosion current density (A/m^2), i_c is cathodic corrosion current density (A/m^2), and β_c is cathodic Tafel slope (V).

To quantify the influence of chloride ion concentration on the corrosion zone position of steel liner surface, the piecewise function is used to represent (Zhu 2021), and the formula is Eq. (6) and Eq. (7).

$$g_a(Cl) \begin{cases} 0; C_{cl} < C_{Cl}^{crit} \\ 1; C_{cl} > C_{Cl}^{crit} \end{cases} \tag{6}$$

$$g_c(Cl) \begin{cases} 1; C_{Cl} < C_{Cl}^{crit} \\ 0; C_{Cl} > C_{Cl}^{crit} \end{cases} \tag{7}$$

where C_{cl}^{crit} is the critical chloride ion concentration; C_{cl}^{crit} =0.2%wt.

3 ESTABLISHMENT OF CORROSION MODEL

3.1 Basic size

The model size is designed as 100 mm × 100 mm. The aggregate volume fraction is 0.5.

3.2 Formation of concrete meso-aggregate

According to the continuous gradation curve of coarse aggregate proposed by Fuller (Wu 2006), the distribution of coarse aggregate in concrete is determined as follows:

$$P = 100\sqrt{\frac{D_0}{D_{max}}} \qquad (8)$$

Where D_0 is the sieve size, P represents the mass percentage of coarse aggregate that can pass through the sieve size D_0, and D_{max} is the maximum coarse aggregate particle size.

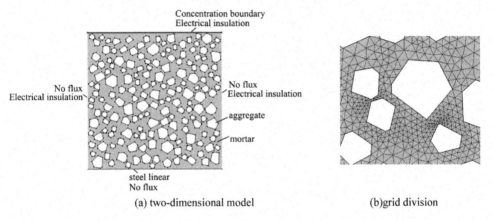

(a) two-dimensional model (b) grid division

Figure 1. Two-dimensional Meso-model and meshing of concrete.

3.3 Initial and boundary conditions

3.3.1 Chloride diffusion boundary

Chloride ions diffuse from the upper surface of containment to the internal structure, and the upper surface is the boundary of chloride ion erosion concentration. At the initial moment, the chloride ion content in concrete is 0, and the erosion boundary and the initial boundary conditions of internal chloride ion are determined by Eq. (9). The flux-free boundary is determined by Eq. (10).

$$C|_{x=0mm} = C^s_{Cl}, Cl|_{t=0,x>0mm} = C^0_{Cl}, Cl|_{x=100mm} = C^0_{Cl} \qquad (9)$$

where C^s_{Cl} is chloride ion erosion concentration boundary; Cl^0_{Cl} is the initial concentration of chloride in the structure.

$$J_{Cl}|_{x=0mm, x=100mm, y=100mm} = 0 \qquad (10)$$

where J_{Cl} is chloride diffusion flux.

3.3.2 Electrode boundary

The electrode reaction expression of the steel liner surface is shown in Eq. (11) and Eq. (12).

$$i^a_{oa} = i_{oa} \times ga(C_{Cl}) \qquad (11)$$

$$i^p_{oc} = i_{oc} \times gc(C_{Cl}) \qquad (12)$$

where i^a_{oa} is the expression of anode electrode reaction, and i^p_{oc} the expression of cathode electrode reaction.

The steel liner is an electric insulation boundary, which is described in Eq. (13).

$$i|_{x=0, x=100, y=0, y=100} = 0 \qquad (13)$$

3.4 Model reliability verification

To verify the accuracy and reliability of the model, based on the classical diffusion theory, the numerical simulation results are compared with the experimental data of 28 d chloride ion diffusion in reference (Tang 2015). The model adopts a two-dimensional model of 100 mm × 100 mm. The parameters used in the model are shown in Table 1 and the comparison results are shown in Figure 3. It can be seen from the figure that the simulation results are in good agreement with the experimental results, which proves that the model has good reliability. The following electrochemical corrosion numerical simulation using this model has a certain practical reference value.

Table 1. Parameters required for model verification.

Time (d)	Surface chloride content (%wt.)	Internal initial concentration (%wt.)	Diffusion coefficient ($10^{-12} m^2/s$)
28	0.572	0	7.26

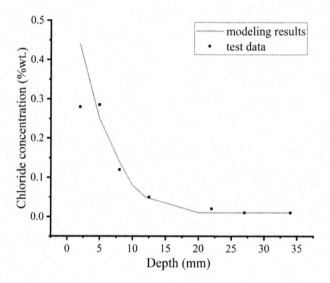

Figure 2. Comparison of chloride diffusion simulation results with experimental data.

4 CALCULATION AND ANALYSIS OF STEEL LINER CORROSION MODEL

4.1 Results and analysis

The numerical simulation period is 30 a. When the steel liner is corroded by chloride ion for 16.7 a, the right side of the steel liner boundary first reaches the critical chloride ion concentration, and the surface of the steel liner is corroded. The simulation results are reflected in three aspects: chloride ion concentration, corrosion potential, and corrosion current density.

4.1.1 Analysis of corrosion time

Figure 4 shows the distribution nephogram of chloride ion concentration in 16.7 years, 16.9 years, and 17 years of chloride ion erosion, and gives the critical chloride ion concentration of 0.2% wt. isoline. It can be seen from Figure 4 that the chloride ion concentration is 0.2% wt. isoline intersects with the right side of the steel liner in 16.7 years of chloride ion erosion. At 16.9 years of erosion, half of the steel liner reached the critical chloride ion concentration, and the corrosion area accounted for about 0.54. After 17 years of erosion, only a small fraction of the steel liner in the area with very dense aggregates has not yet reached the critical chloride ion concentration, and the corrosion area accounts for about 0.9. When the chloride ion erosion reaches 17.1 years, the entire steel liner surface reaches the critical chloride ion concentration, and the entire steel liner is completely depressive.

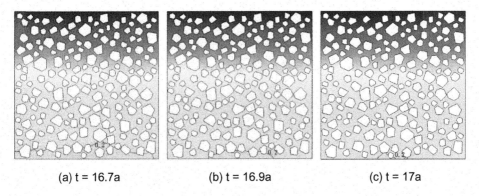

(a) t = 16.7a   (b) t = 16.9a   (c) t = 17a

Figure 3.   Distribution nephogram of chloride concentration.

4.1.2 Corrosion potential

Figure 4 shows the corrosion potential cloud chart of the steel liner surface. Figure 5 shows the corrosion potential curve of the steel liner surface. It can be seen from the two figures that the corrosion zone (anode) of steel bars has higher negative corrosion potential, and the passivation zone (cathode) has lower negative corrosion potential. With the expansion of the corrosion area, the corrosion potential of both anode and cathode moves in the negative direction, and the corrosion potential difference between anode and cathode gradually decreases.

4.1.3 Corrosion current density

Figure 6 shows the influence curve of corrosion area change on corrosion current density. It can be seen from the figure that when corrosion occurs, the corrosion current density increases rapidly, and then decreases rapidly. The corrosion current density gradually stabilizes with the expansion of the corrosion area.

4.2 Effect of concrete coarse aggregate on steel liner corrosion

To study the influence of the shape and content of coarse aggregate on chloride ion diffusion, different shape models of circular, quadrilateral, hexagonal and octagonal coarse aggregate were established, respectively. A two-dimensional random hexagonal aggregate model with 0, 0.25, 0.5, and 0.75 coarse aggregate content was established. The aggregate ratio was 0.5, the surface chloride ion concentration was 0.572 %wt., and the diffusion coefficient Dcl was $7.26 \times 10^{-12} m^2/s$. It can be seen from Figure 8 that under certain conditions such as aggregate ratio and surface chloride ion concentration, the difference in chloride ion concentration at the same depth of aggregates with different shapes is small. Therefore, the influence of coarse aggregate shape on chloride ion diffusion is small. With the increase of coarse aggregate content, the concrete structure is denser and the chloride diffusion is more difficult. At the same depth, the chloride content is smaller.

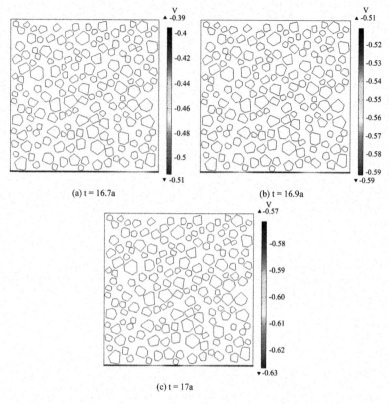

Figure 4. Corrosion potential distribution nephogram of the steel liner surface.

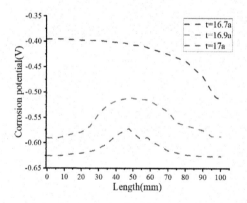

Figure 5. Corrosion potential curve of steel liner surface.

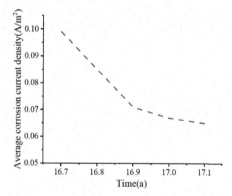

Figure 6. Changes in corrosion current density.

5 CONCLUSION

In this paper, the corrosion law of containment steel liner in a chlorine salt environment was explored from a mesoscopic perspective, and the following conclusions were drawn: The numerical simulation method can better simulate the corrosion development process of containment steel liner in a chloride environment, which can be applied to the anti-corrosion design of actual nuclear power

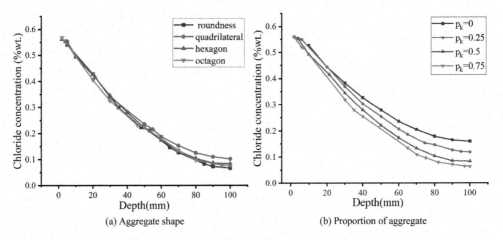

Figure 7.   Effect of coarse aggregate on corrosion of steel liner.

plants. With the increase of coarse aggregate content, chloride diffusion is more difficult, which can effectively delay the corrosion start time of steel liner; the corrosion current density gradually decreases with the increase of chloride ion erosion time.

ACKNOWLEDGMENT

This work was supported by the National Key Research and Development Program (Grant No. 2019YFB1900903).

REFERENCES

Cao C, Cheung M M S, Chan B Y B. Modelling of interaction between corrosion-induced concrete cover crack and steel corrosion rate[J]. *Corrosion Science*, 2013, 69: 97–109.
Fang Jiuxin, Ma Yuefeng, Jin Shijie, et al. Simulation of steel corrosion in concrete under chloride environment [J]. *Low temperature building technology*, 2017, 39 (11) : 1–3 + 15.
Gong Jinxin, Wan Guangze, Guo Junying, et al. Research status and progress of containment aging in nuclear power plants [J]. *Industrial buildings*, 2017, 47 (01): 1–9+32.
Li Wenxu. *Experimental study on mechanical properties of nuclear power plant containment steel liner after corrosion* [D]. Dalian University of Technology, 2021.
Tang Zhijie, Liao Kaixing, Kong Xianglong, et al. Study on chloride ion erosion law of coastal environmental containment concrete [J]. *Concrete*, 2015, 05: 66–69.
Ventura A, Amiri O. Analysis of corrosion risk due to chloride diffusion for concrete structures in marine environment[J]. *Marine Structures*, 2020, 73: 112.
Warkus J, Raupach M. Numerical modelling of macrocells occurring during corrosion of steel in concrete[J]. *Materials and Corrosion*, 2008, 59(02): 122–130.
Wu Junyong. *Automatic generation of concrete meso-structure* [D]. Dalian University of Technology, 2006.
Zhu Wanghua. *Numerical simulation of non-uniform corrosion of steel bars based on concrete microstructure* [D]. Dalian University of Technology, 2021.

Research on the repair measures of the destabilized embankment of blasting and squeezing

Xiao Jianbo*
Zhuhai Dahengqin City New Center Development Co., Ltd., China

Huang Weihong*
Zhuhai Construction Engineering Holding Group, China

Fang Yuhang*
Tianjin Port Engineering Institute Co., Ltd. of CCCC, China

ABSTRACT: Given the geological conditions and design requirements of the east breakwater in a coastal city, the breakwater adopts the blasting and extrusion silt for foundation treatment, and the problem of instability occurs during the treatment of blasting and extruding the silt foundation, and the restoration measures are studied. Combined with the construction process, the blasting and extruding dredging embankment is introduced due to construction problems, which leads to the failure of the bottom, the instability of the embankment, and the displacement accident, the causes of the accident are analyzed, and the main repair measures taken after the destabilization of the blasting and extrusion dredging embankment are introduced in detail, which provides a reference method for similar projects in the future.

1 INTRODUCTION

With the rapid development of the economy, the contradiction between the supply and demand of land resources in China's coastal areas has become increasingly prominent. Building embankments around the sea and using dredged spoil to make the land for supporting construction behind the wharf has become an effective way to increase construction land and alleviate land tension (Hu 2014). Large construction machinery and complex construction technology are not required for the blasting silt squeezing dike, which has the advantages of fast construction speed, low investment, and quick effect. Its application scope is becoming wider and wider, and it has played an important role in the construction of railways, expressways, ports, airports, and nuclear power plants (Pang 2014; Yu 2009, 2011). In 1992, the breakwater of Shengsi central fishing port adopted the blasting silt squeezing technology to treat the silt under the breakwater with a thickness of 6 to 10 m. In 1996, the project was rated as a high-quality project (Ye 2008). Subsequently, the blasting compaction technology was used in dozens of projects, such as Miaoling of Lianyungang port, Gaoqi shelter in Xiamen, and Zhuhai Dahe breakwater (Hu 2012; Tong 2012; Wang 2010), and the thickness of the treated soft foundation was developed from 10 m to 25 m. However, the bottom falling effect of the blasting compaction dike is easily affected by the blasting parameters and dumping parameters. When the reclamation in the dike reaches a certain elevation and the blasting compaction dike fails to fall in place, the dike is prone to instability and displacement accidents, which will bring certain risks to the project construction. Based on the engineering design and construction monitoring data

---

*Corresponding Authors: 1602188531@qq.com, 155087178@qq.com and fangyuhang@tpei.com.cn

of the East breakwater in a coastal city, this paper analyzes the causes of the displacement of the main breakwater, puts forward effective repair measures, and verifies them.

2 PROJECT OVERVIEW

The East Breakwater Project of a coastal city is an important part of its port construction project and an important link in the layout of port construction. Its main breakwater, as a permanent land boundary breakwater, is extremely important for its stability. The total length of the embankment of the project is 2,460 m, including 1,120 m for the main embankment and 1,340 m for the West embankment, forming an enclosed area of 1.50 km² (2,256 mu). The reclamation elevation of the enclosed area is considered 9.0 m, and the reclamation capacity is 12.52 million m³, meeting the needs of channel dredging soil reclamation. The location plan is shown in Figure 1.

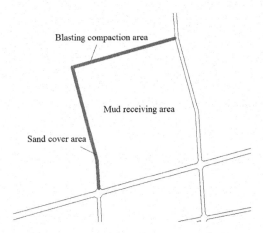

Figure 1. The plan of the project.

The exposed soil layer within the embankment foundation can be divided into 6 soil layers. Silt II 1 has high compressibility and poor geological properties. The exposed thickness of this layer is 3.90 to 7.10 m. Il1 muddy silty clay layer is sandwiched with a layer of silty sand layer, which is thin and should not be used as a bearing layer. Silty clay is distributed below, with uniform soil quality, containing a small number of calcareous nodules, with a particle size of 2 to 20 mm. Most holes are exposed, local sections are missing, and the bearing capacity is good, so it can be used as a bearing layer. The clay exposed in the site area is marine sediment with soft soil characteristics, stable distribution, and large thickness. It is proposed to use blasting to squeeze silt for foundation treatment.

3 DISPLACEMENTS OF THE MAIN EMBANKMENT

After the main embankment is closed by blasting, the elevation of the embankment top is 8.5 m, and the mud surface in the reservoir is dredged to 6.7 m. During the loading process, it is found that the embankment body within a total of 40m around zk1+030 has a large outward displacement, the maximum displacement is 7 to 10 cm/d, and the horizontal displacement during the reclamation period is 35 cm to 55 cm. The loading is stopped at the inner and outer sides as soon as problems are found, and the possible causes of embankment displacement in this section are analyzed.

Two days after stopping the internal and external loading, it is found that the embankment body tends to be stable, and there is no outward sliding trend, which proves that the embankment body is in a critical equilibrium state in this case. It is found by drilling at the front edge of zk1+030 that the bottom fall at this position is less than 2.6 m.

4 CAUSE ANALYSIS OF MAIN EMBANKMENT DISPLACEMENT

(1) The main embankment was originally planned to be closed before the Spring Festival. As the blasting was stopped in advance before the mountain Festival, the construction plan shall not be adjusted. There are not enough materials within and outside the main embankment for protection. After two large storm surges before and after the Spring Festival, the stones at the head of the embankment were overturned, the stones at the head of the embankment slipped, and the end blasting could not distribute the explosive, resulting in the over footage of this section.

(2) Based on the treatment experience of similar projects in the past, the construction unit, after consultation, determined to carry out remediation according to the construction scheme of side blasting with double charge and multiple side blasting once, which was also strictly implemented during construction.

(3) After the closure of the embankment, although the borehole was drilled in the zk1+000 section with similar chainage, which showed that the bottom fell well, the borehole inspection was not carried out in the zk1+030 section. After it was determined to be qualified, subsequent construction such as block installation, widening of the inner side of the embankment, internal hydraulic filling and loading, and external dredging and unloading were carried out. As a result, displacement was found after loading, which caused great difficulty in treatment.

5 MAIN EMBANKMENT DISPLACEMENT REPAIR SCHEME

According to the drilling results and cause analysis, the repair scheme for the displacement of the main embankment is to strengthen by side blasting. The specific scheme is as follows.

(1) Remove the Accropode of zk0+950~zk1+095 section;

(2) Excavate the bottom protection block stone at the slope toe, and throw the excavated bottom protection block stone to the root of the secondary platform to serve as land throwing and falling. The 5 m section widened inside shall be unloaded and excavated, and the excavated stones shall be directly transferred to the outside for dumping and filling (Figure 2).

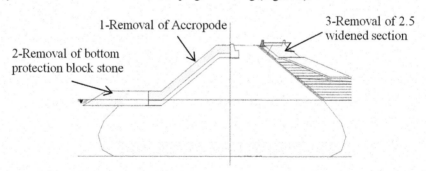

Figure 2. Schematic diagram of component removal and stone excavation.

(3) The blasting cycle of small charge and small footage shall be adopted to advance from the dumping and filling of stones on land to the stone tongue on the outer edge of the embankment. The side blasting footage is 2 m, and the treatment width is 15 m to 17 m. The section length of the first round of side blasting is 20 m. The construction is from zk1+075 to zk0+970. The blasting charge per 20 m is 400 kg, the charge spacing is 1.5 m, the charge insertion depth is 8 m, the embankment top elevation is +6.5 m, and it is loaded to 8.5 m before blasting. After the completion of the first

round of side blasting, the section length of subsequent side blasting is 50 m, the charge per meter is 30 kg, and the footage is 5 m (see Figures 3 and 4).

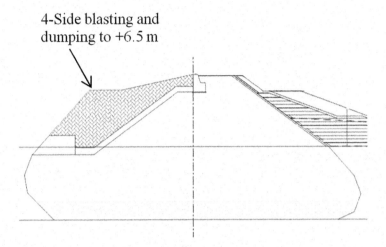

Figure 3.   Side blasting construction after dumping and filling to +6.5 m.

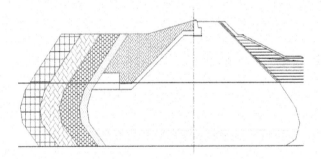

Figure 4.   Cyclic footage advance.

(4) The construction of side blasting is from zk1+075 to zk0+970. The first round of 1 to 5 blasts is 20 m in length and 2 m in the footage. The section length of 6 to 11 shots is 50 m and the footage is 5 m (Figure 5).

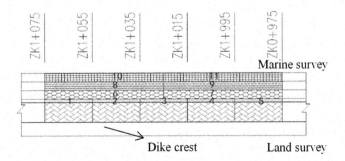

Figure 5.   Schematic diagram of blasting propulsion.

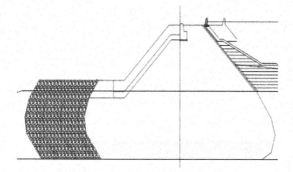

Figure 6. Accropode armor.

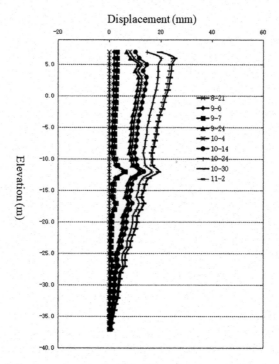

Figure 7. Horizontal displacement curve in the ZK0+970 section.

(5) The dumping and filling shall be carried out at high tide. Bamboo poles shall be inserted into the dumping and filling range and sidelines for benchmarking, and the dumping and filling footage shall be strictly controlled. Within the scope of blasting implementation, riprap ballast shall be carried out before blasting construction. High tide blasting shall be selected for blasting to balance the side pressure of sludge inside as much as possible.

(6) After the side blasting reinforcement is completed, the excess stones shall be excavated according to the design section to restore the Accropode armor, as shown in Figure 6.

The total amount of replacement stone materials in this blasting is 30,250 m^3, which is calculated according to the platform excavation to be +3.5 m after blasting. According to the volume balance method, the embankment reinforcement implemented in this blasting scheme has been bottomed.

6 DETECTION OF DISPLACEMENT REPAIR EFFECT OF MAIN EMBANKMENT

Through volume balance and drilling, the ground elevation of the levee reaches the design section elevation. the design requirements are met. Inclinometers are buried at zk0+970 and zk1+030, and close attention pay to the displacement change of the embankment body in this section, as shown in Figures 7 and 8.

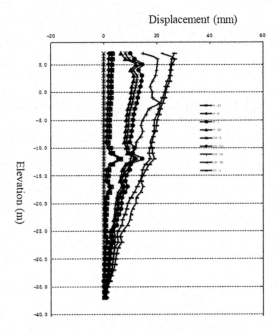

Figure 8. Horizontal displacement curve in the ZK1+030 section.

According to zk0+970 inclinometer data, the daily maximum horizontal displacement is 1.2 mm and the weekly maximum horizontal displacement is 4.6 mm. According to zk1+030 inclinometer data, the daily maximum horizontal displacement is 1.4 mm and the weekly maximum horizontal displacement is 4.4 mm, meeting the design requirements. The horizontal displacement of the main embankment tends to be stable.

7 CONCLUSIONS

(1) The construction plan should be strictly controlled implementation, minimize the impact of storm and tide on the stones at the embankment head, and strictly control the blasting footage.
(2) The side blasting shall be strengthened by sections and the footage shall be strictly controlled. A small charge and small footage blasting cycle are adopted.
(3) After the dike is repaired, the elevation of the mud receiving area is dredged to +8.0 m. After half a year of drying observation, it is shown that the displacement and settlement of the dike are within the allowable range, indicating that the blasting compaction dike is not in place, so the side blasting strengthening scheme is feasible and effective.

REFERENCES

Hu Xiaojun, Construction technology of inverted filter layer of blasting extrusion silt embankment. *Port Section*, 2014(9): 10–13.

Hu Yunchu, Wang Jian. Several problems in the construction of explosion and siltation in the east revetment of Gaoqi Haven in Xiamen. *Journal of Zhejiang Water Conservancy and Hydropower College*, 2012(12).

Pang Liang, Li Wu, Selection of wharf and barge structure in Xuwei Port Area, Lianyungang. *Journal of Water Conservancy and Water Transport Engineering*, 2014, (2):60–65.

SL435-2008 *Design Code for Seawall Engineering*.

Tong Qihua. Treatment of deep silt layer blasting and extrusion of coastal embankment engineering. *Shanghai Land and Resources*, 2012, 33(4):48.51.

Wang Weidong, Cheng Qi. Construction of embankment project in Miaoling Phase III Experimental Area of Lianyungang Port. *China Harbor Construction*, 2010(12):45–48.

Ye Dongying. Application of explosion dredging method in breakwater engineering of fishing port in the outer sea. *Water Transport Engineering*, 2008(6):37–41.

Yu Haizhong, Hu Ronghua, Research and application status of blasting and extrusion technology. *Construction Technology*, 2009, 38: 1–4.

Yu Haizhong, *Research on the mechanism and detection method of rock-throwing blasting and extruding silt embankment*. Beijing: China Academy of Railway Sciences, 2011.

Application of incremental launching technology in prestressed concrete box girder construction

Xue Fan* & Wu Rui*
CCCC Wuhan Harbour Engineering Design and Research Co., Ltd., Wuhan, Hubei, China
Hubei Key Laboratory of Advanced Materials and Reinforcement Technology Research for Marine Environment Structures, Hubei, China
Research and Development Center of Transport Industry of Intelligent Manufacturing Technologies of Transport Infrastructure, Hubei, China

Lu Tao* & Yang Tianliang*
CCCC Wuhan Harbour Engineering Design and Research Co., Ltd., Wuhan, Hubei

ABSTRACT: Taking the box girder jacking of the approach bridge of Fuyimen Bridge in Zhoushan as an example, this paper introduces the walking jacking construction technology of prestressed concrete box girder, analyzes the influence of adjacent cushion pier height difference, segment overweight, internal and external surface temperature difference and pre-stress loss of finishing rolled screw steel on box girder stress under the most unfavorable stress state, the research shows that the height difference of adjacent buttress and the temperature difference between the inner and outer surface of box girder are the main factors leading to stress increase of box girder during launching. On this basis, puts forward the control points of prestressed concrete box girder jacking construction that the height difference between adjacent cushion piers should be under 10mm and the temperature difference between the inner and outer surface of the box girder should be under 5°C, which provides a reference for the walking jacking construction of other prestressed concrete box girders.

1 INTRODUCTION

Walking incremental launching construction technology has many advantages, such as small horizontal force, less temporary engineer- ing quantity, good adjustability, high degree of auto-animation, and visualization (Zhang 2015). Since it was successfully applied to Jiubao Bridge in Hangzhou, it has gradually replaced the traditional dragging method and has been used in the construction of steel structure bridges such as deep valleys and crossing lines in China (Zhao 2016). However, for the concrete box girder, the walking incremental launching also has a very high lifting and falling frequency, which makes the box girder easy to crack and becomes the key and difficult point of the incremental launching construction control. Liu Dianyuan (Liu 2018) and Yan Dingyu (Yan 2020) analyzed the incremental launching construction of the prestressed concrete bridge by simulation and showed the structural safety of the prestressed concrete bridge in the launching process. However, they did not analyze the impact of factor changes on construction safety. Zhou Fei This paper qualitatively analyzed the influencing factors on the safety of prestressed concrete beam launching structure and gives the correspond- ing improvement measures, but he did not make a quantitative analysis on the corresponding factors (Zhou 2020). Huang Dukang selected

---

*Corresponding Authors: 276754187@qq.com, 990335563@qq.com, China434345225@qq.com and 8080053@qq.com

many factors such as material characteristics, and load action to roughly judge the sensitivity of the horizontal displacement of the pier-top in jacking construction and bending moment (Huang 2020), but the influence of corresponding factor changes on the main beam structure was not analyzed.

In this paper, the Fuchimen Bridge approach bridge prestressed concrete box girder incremental launching construction as the background, for prestressed concrete box girder walking incremental launching construction process sensitivity factors were analyzed in detail for the future of the same type of bridge construction provides a technical reference.

2 ENGINEERING OVERVIEW

The approach box girder of Fuchimen Bridge is a prestressed concrete continuous box girder with a span arrangement of 30 m+6×50 m and a total length of 330 m. The main beam of the superstructure adopts a single-box single-chamber section with equal height and is arranged in left and right widths. The top width of the main beam of a single box girder is 12.35 m. the thickness of the roof is 27 cm, the thickness near the fulcrum is 70 cm; the base plate is 27 cm thick, and up to 80 cm thick near the supports. The beam height at the center line of the box girder is 3.3 m, and the height-span ratio is 1/15.2. According to the design drawings, the beam body is divided into 14 sections of 17 m+11×25 m+11.5 m +26.5 m, and each section is pushed after pouring and curing.

3 CONSTRUCTION TECHNOLOGY OF WALKING PUSHING

According to the layout characteristics of the approach bridge span of Fuyimen Bridge, the jacking process of the box girder is designed. The general layout of the temporary structure of the jacking process is shown in Figure 1.

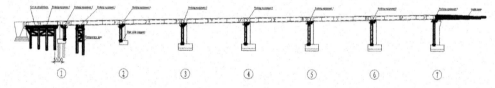

Figure 1. Overall process layout of box girder jacking of Fuchimen Bridge approach bridge.

The temporary jacking project of prestressed concrete beam mainly includes a cast-in-situ platform and formwork system, pier support, temporary pier, and guide beam. The cast-in-situ platform is arranged between 0 # pier and 1 # pier, and the length of the cast-in-situ platform is 25.6 m. The formwork system is arranged on it. According to the characteristics of a box girder, the formwork system is mainly composed of bottom formwork and corresponding support system, side formwork and support system, internal formwork and support, end formwork, and other parts. To reduce the negative cantilever bending moment of the initial jacking section, the temporary pier is arranged between the 1 # pier and the 2 # pier. The temporary pier is mainly composed of a steel pipe column, transverse distribution beam, and longitudinal distribution beam. Each permanent pier is arranged by the pier side bracket, the bottom of the pier side bracket steel pipe is connected with the cap by the embedded parts, and the pier side bracket beam is connected with the pier body through the wall support to overcome the horizontal force in the process of concrete box girder jacking. The steel guide beam is designed at the head of the box girder to reduce the maximum cantilever of the box girder in the jacking construction. The steel guide beam is 38.6 m in length and 80 t in weight and is welded by a Q345B steel plate. Pedestrian jacking equipment with a three-way motion function is arranged on temporary pier and pier side support.

The specific jacking construction technology is as follows. (1) After the installation of cast-in-situ support and template system is completed, the reinforcement is bound. (2) Install the guide beam and adjust the guide beam line type. (3) Concrete pouring and maintenance. (4) The crawler jacking equipment is enabled to lift the box girder synchronously. After the box girder is completely separated from the cushion pier, the crawler jacking equipment pushes a stroke forward. (5) The walking pushing equipment drops synchronously until the pushing equipment is separated from the box girder, the box girder is placed on the temporary cushion pier, and the pushing equipment is pulled back. (6) Repeat steps 4 and 5, pushing a box girder in place and adjusting the position. (7) Repeat steps 3, 4, 5 and 6 to complete the jacking construction of steel box girder. (8) Adjustment of box girder line type, completion of the falling beam, pouring the last box girder concrete approach bridge construction is completed.

4 ANALYSIS OF KEY CONTROL FACTORS OF JACKING CONSTRUCTION

Walking incremental launching construction, the box girder needs to keep lifting and lowering (Zhang 2015), and in the process of pushing forward, due to the change of fulcrum position, the box girder needs to constantly bear the positive and negative bending moment. To prevent the box girder from cracking during jacking, the sensitivity of the box girder needs to be analyzed. The following four variables are selected to calculate and analyze the jacking process of the box girder: (1) consider the height difference between two adjacent fulcrums in the longitudinal direction of 1cm; (2) according to the relevant specifications, considering the temperature difference between the inner and outer cavity of the box girder is 5°C; (3) consider box girder concrete overweight 3%; (4) according to the relevant specifications, consider the loss of prestressing 10%.

The spatial finite element model of the box girder is established by using finite element software MIDAS/Civil, and the main beam is simulated by the spatial beam element. The boundary constraint conditions are as follows: vertical and horizontal constraints are set at each pushing equipment, and vertical constraints are set at pier 2. We analyze the initial stage and intermediate stage of pushing respectively.

4.1 Initial segment pushing

The stress diagram of the box girder under the ideal state is shown in Figure 2.

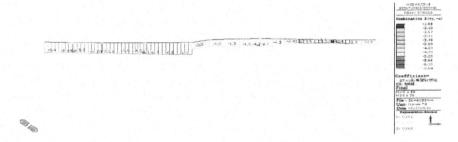

Figure 2. Box girder stress diagram under ideal state (MPa).

During the jacking process, when the equipment is pulled back, the box girder needs to be supported on the temporary support pier. Due to the high sensitivity of concrete materials to displacement, and during the pouring process of the box girder, the deformation of the bottom template will affect the flatness of the box girder floor, and the adjacent temporary pier will produce an unbalanced cushion height difference in the jacking construction. The stress changes of box girder when the height difference of adjacent temporary cushion pier is –2 mm, –6 mm, –10 mm, –14 mm, and –22 mm is analyzed. The calculation results are shown in Table 1. The stress nephogram of 10 mm and 20 mm height difference is shown in Figures 3 and 4.

Table 1. Stress statement of box girder under different height differences of piers.

Factor condition	Stress (MPa)	Cumulative increment (MPa)
The benchmark	−3.8	−
−5 mm	−1.6	1.4
−10 mm	−0.2	1.4
−15 mm	1.4	1.6
−20 mm	2.8	1.4

Figure 3. Stress diagram of the main beam when height difference of fulcrum pier is 10 mm (MPa).

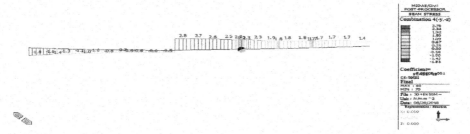

Figure 4. Main beam stress diagram when height difference of pier is 18 mm (MPa).

When the box girder is poured, there is compression deformation of the template. The actual pouring amount of concrete is generally greater than the theoretical amount, and the influence of excessive concrete pouring on the stress of the box girder is considered. Box girder overweight calculated by 3%, box girder stress diagram as shown in Figure 5.

Figure 5. Stress diagram of overweight 3% box girder.

Since the box girder needs to be pushed in summer, there will be a large temperature difference between the inner surface and outer surface of the box girder, and the stress of the box girder is allowed when the temperature difference between the inner and outer surface of the box girder is 5°C. The model is loaded according to the +5°C temperature gradient, and the box girder stress diagram is obtained as shown in Figure 6.

Figure 6. + 5°C stress diagram of box girder under problem gradient.

In the construction process of a box girder, the prestress loss caused by shrinkage and creep of concrete, relaxation of prestressed reinforcement, elastic compression of concrete and other factors will reduce the prestress in the jacking construction of the box girder. Considering the prestress loss of finishing screw thread steel by 10%, the stress diagram of the box girder is calculated as shown in Figure 7.

Figure 7. Stress diagram of box girder with 10% prestress loss.

According to the above analysis, in the ideal state, the lower flange of the main beam is compressed, and the minimum compressive stress is −3.8 MPa, which is located at the junction of 2 # and 3 # segments. In an ideal state, the main beam structure is safe when jacking.

When the height difference of the adjacent temporary cushion pier is 10 mm, the lower flange of the main beam is compressed, the minimum compressive stress is −0.2 MPa, and the ideal state increases by 3.6 MPa; when the height difference of adjacent temporary cushion pier is 20 mm, the lower flange of the main beam is pulled, the minimum tensile stress of the main beam is 2.8 MPa, which is 6.4 MPa higher than the ideal state.

When the box girder concrete segment is overweight 3%, the lower flange of the main beam is compressed, the minimum compressive stress is −3.8 MPa, and there is almost no change in the ideal state.

When the temperature difference between the inner surface and the outer surface of the box girder reaches 5°C, the lower flange of the main girder is compressed, and the minimum compressive stress is −2.3 MPa, which is 1.5 MPa higher than the ideal state.

When the prestress loss of finishing rolling rebar is 10%, the lower flange connecting the guide beam and the main beam is compressed, and the maximum compressive stress is −3.4 MPa, which is 0.4 MPa higher than that in the ideal state.

Based on the above factors, the stress of the box girder under various unfavorable factors is shown in Table 2.

Table 2. Summary of stress analysis at bottom of girder segment connection.

Factor conditions	Stress (MPa)	Segmental overweight (3%)	The temperature gradient (+5C)	Loss of prestress (10%)	Summation
The benchmark	−3.8	0	1.5	0.4	−1.9
−5	−1.6				0.3
−10	−0.2				1.7
−15	1.4				3.3
−20	2.8				4.7

According to Table 2, it can be seen that the height difference of the adjacent cushion pier and the temperature difference inside and outside the box girder have a great influence on the overall stress of the box girder in the jacking construction. When the height difference of the adjacent cushion pier reaches 10mm, under the superposition of various unfavorable factors, the tensile stress of the box girder bottom plate is 1.7 MPa, which reaches the tensile limit of concrete material, and the box girder has a great risk of cracking.

4.2 Push middle segment

When pushing the middle segment, the box girder is in a large span position as a whole, and the segment of the box girder is in the position of the maximum bending moment in the middle span. The influence of different change factors on the stress of the box girder under this working condition is analyzed. The stress of the box girder under different influence factors is shown in Table 3.

Table 3. Summary table of stress analysis of main girder floor in mid-span state.

Factor conditions	Stress (MPa)	Segmental overweight (3%)	The temperature gradient (+5°C)	Loss of prestress (10%)	Summation
The benchmark	−1.5	0.1	1.2	0.6	0.4
10	−0.9				1.0
15	−0.6				1.3
20	−0.3				1.6

Through Table 3, we can conclude that under the ideal state, the minimum compressive stress of the box girder bottom plate is −1.5 MPa; when the height difference of the adjacent cushion pier is 10 mm, 15 mm, and 20 mm. The stress of the box girder bottom plate increases by 0.6 MPa, 0.9 MPa, and 1.2 MPa. When the box girder segment is 3% overweight, the stress of the box girder bottom plate increases by 0.1 MPa; when the temperature difference between the inner surface and the outer surface of the box girder is 5°C, the stress of the box girder bottom plate increases by 1.5 MPa, and when the prestress loss of the box girder is 10 %, the stress of the box girder bottom plate increases by 0.6 MPa.

It can be seen that in the mid-span state, the main factors affecting the stress of the box girder are the height difference of adjacent support cushion piers and the temperature difference between the inner and outer surfaces of the box girder. When the height difference of the adjacent cushion pier reaches 10mm, under the superposition of various unfavorable factors, the tensile stress of the box girder bottom plate is 1 MPa, which is close to the tensile limit of concrete material, and the box girder has the risk of cracking.

By comprehensively comparing the jacking stage and the mid-span stage in the initial stage, it can be found that the factors that have a great influence on the stress of the box girder are the height difference of the adjacent temporary support pier and the temperature difference between the inner and outer surfaces of the box girder. When the height difference of the adjacent temporary support pier is 10 mm and the temperature difference between the inner and outer surfaces is 5°C, the stress of the bottom plate of the box girder is close to the tensile limit of the material, and the box girder has a large cracking risk.

5 CONCLUSIONS

In this paper, the factors that lead to the increase of box girder stress in the process of jacking construction are analyzed in detail in combination with the jacking construction of the prestressed concrete bridge of Fuyimen Bridge in Zhoushan. The stress of the main beam of the box girder under the influence of the height difference of the adjacent cushion pier, the overweight of the segment, the temperature difference of the internal and external surface and the prestress loss of the finishing rolled screw steel under the two most unfavorable conditions are calculated, respectively. The main conclusions are as follows.

(1) Different factors have different effects on the increase of box girder stress, among which the height difference of the adjacent buttress and the temperature difference between the inner and outer surface of the box girder are the main factors.
(2) When the height difference between adjacent cushion piers is 10mm and the temperature difference between the inner and outer surface of the box girder is 5°C, the tensile stress of the box girder increases sharply, which is close to the tensile limit of concrete materials. These two indicators should be strictly controlled in the process of jacking construction.

The analysis results of this paper provide the basis for the jacking construction of prestressed concrete bridges in the future and have a certain reference value.

REFERENCES

Huang Dukang(2020). *Sensitivity Analysis for Construction Parameters and Finiteelement Model Modification in Closure Jacking Stage of Continuous Rigid Frame Bridge.*

Liu Dianyuan, Sun Yuenan, Zhang Xingzhi, Qi Tiedong(2018). Simulation and analysis of construction control of prestressed Concrete Continuous Beam with walking Type [J]. *Journal of Highway And Transportation Technology.*

Xie Daoping, Liu Yiping, Wu Mingwei, Liu Dongdong(2017). Research and application of jacking technology of long-span steel truss girder [J]. *Sino-foreign Highway.*

Yan Dingyu (2020). Simulation analysis of launching construction process of prestressed concrete continuous beam bridge[J]. *Journal Of Shijiazhuang Institute Of Railway Technology.*

Zhang Hong, Zhang Xiaoping, Guo Qiang, Xue Zhiwu. Launching trajectory planning for the variable cross-section steel box girder[J]. *Int. Conf. Adv. Manuf. Ind.* 2015:31–37.

Zhang Hong, Zhang Yongtao, Zhou Renzhong(2012). Research and application of walking automatic push equipment system [J]. *Sino-foreign Highway.*

Zhao Renda, Zhang Shuangyang(2016). Research status and development trend of bridge jacking method [J]. *China Journal of Highway and Transport.*

Zhou Fei(2010). Research on construction technology of step-type pushing for prestressed concrete box girde[J]. *Building and Traffic.*

Application and guiding value of BIM technology in road engineering design

Lingmei Zhang*
Linyi University, Linyi, Shandong, China

ABSTRACT: According to the development trend of road engineering projects, improving the efficiency of road engineering design and changing the concept of road engineering planning and design are the necessary paths to meet the requirements of road engineering construction in the new period. The emergence of BIM technology will put forward comprehensive application solutions to the shortcomings of traditional CAD graphic drawing in the design stage of road engineerings construction projects, such as high error rate, frequent changes, and difficult communication between design and construction. With the application advantages of three-dimensional visualization, structured data, and collaborative work, BIM can comprehensively improve the decision-making accuracy of the conceptual design of road engineering, speed up the drawing speed, realize the transmission of data information, further strengthen the close connection between design and construction, optimize the overall process, improve the management mode of road engineering, and promote road engineering. Based on this, this paper will face the actual road design stage, with the help of BIM technology and Autodesk Civil 3D platform, comprehensively realize the construction of the road BIM data model from multiple angles, and prove the significance of the application and popularization of BIM technology in road engineering design by case analysis.

1 INTRODUCTION

Since the reform and opening up, China's development has been based on the basic national conditions, insisting on economic construction as the center and vigorously promoting urbanization and urban construction, which has greatly changed the face of China's urban and rural development and significantly improved people's living standards and quality of life. At this stage, China has entered a new period of development, and the promotion of China's urbanization process and the proposal of a rural revitalization strategy have become the necessary guarantee for the development of the national economy and socialist modernization with Chinese characteristics. Urbanization and rural revitalization are closely related to road engineering. Road engineering is not only related to the construction of transportation networks, but also directly affects the development of regional industry and has positive significance for the development of the local economy. According to statistics, in 2021, the investment scale of China's transportation infrastructure reached 3.6 trillion yuan, of which the investment scale of expressways and highways at all levels was increasing year by year, accounting for more than 80%. All kinds of new construction, renovation, expansion, and restoration projects will continue to expand. In addition, a series of new technologies, new materials, and new facilities put forward new requirements for road engineering construction.

Road construction projects usually go through three stages: decision-making, implementation, and operation. The implementation stage is an important link for the project to achieve its goal, which is divided into the design stage and the construction stage (Ye, 2022). In the design stage of

---

*Corresponding Author: 24674079@qq.com

road engineering, designers not only need to consider the influence of various factors comprehensively, but also need to meet the relevant building standards and practical requirements, such as road functional requirements, regional planning requirements, beautiful appearance requirements, material and technical requirements, and cost economy requirements. Therefore, the quality of survey and design of road engineering projects plays a decisive role in the overall road engineering quality. However, under the traditional management mode and production mode, the road engineering design stage is limited by the performance of the tool system, resource sharing and coordination, data information transmission, etc., which leads to the obvious weakness of the organic combination of road engineering design and construction, and the design defects and errors can't be corrected in time. The secondary adjustment in the subsequent construction stage will cause a lot of resource waste, seriously affecting the production efficiency of road engineering. Given this, the "2016–2020 Construction Informatization Development Outline" issued by the Ministry of Housing and Construction puts forward the requirements of promoting the deep integration of information technology and enterprise management, actively exploring the new mode of engineering management and production under the situation of "internet plus," deeply studying the innovative application of BIM, Internet of Things and other technologies, accelerating the popularization and application of BIM, and realizing the upgrading of survey and design technology (Yang 2020).

Therefore, this paper will focus on the comprehensive solution of introducing BIM technology in road engineering design to complete the forward design and realize the informatization of construction engineering. It shows the comprehensive application of BIM technology in the road engineering design stage in the form of case analysis, effectively improves various difficulties faced by the current road engineering design stage, and further confirms the important significance of BIM technology in road engineering design.

2 ROAD ENGINEERING DESIGN AND BIM TECHNOLOGY

2.1 Road engineering design

Road engineering refers to the planning, design, construction, maintenance, and management of roads, and their engineering entity, which is a branch of civil engineering. Roads can be divided into municipal roads, factories, mine roads, forest highways, etc., according to their location, traffic characteristics, and usage requirements. Among them, highway engineering includes national roads (expressways and main trunk lines), provincial roads, county roads or township roads, etc. Its purpose is to connect cities and villages and improve the social transportation system. The municipal road engineering belongs to the city's internal service system and is divided into trunk roads, secondary roads, branch roads, etc., according to the traffic function, to adapt to the urban traffic as the benchmark requirement (Yu 2020). There is no obvious distinction between the highway and municipal roads by virtue of a single appearance, but there are obvious differences in prescribed standards, management authority, and service functions. For example, the service object of highways is mainly cars, emphasizing traffic flow, driving experience, driving safety, and comfort. The service objects of municipal roads are people and vehicles, emphasizing smoothness and accessibility, as well as a large number of surrounding constructions such as sidewalks, green belts, underground pipe networks, humanistic signs, and decorations, and the overall complexity is higher. In the actual design process, road engineering designers should distinguish the differences between the two to grasp the design concepts of the two and complete the road design well.

The main contents of road engineering design include road network planning and route survey design, subgrade engineering design, pavement engineering design, road drainage engineering design, and many other links. Municipal road design will show different characteristics according to design codes and standards. For example, in the phase of road network planning and route survey and design, the design of municipal roads should conform to the basic planning of the city, and the choice of route type is strictly restricted and relatively simple. However, highway design needs more consideration of the influence of topography and hydrological environment on the route, and it also needs to complete the final selection of the route from the perspective of overall highway network planning. In the process of pavement design, there are many intersections on municipal roads, and vehicles start and stop frequently, so special attention should be paid to the shear resistance design of the pavement near the intersections. By strengthening the surface hardness of pavement and adopting comprehensive measures such as rigid subgrade, the appearance of rutting can be reduced. The highway design can ignore this part of the design content.

Road engineering design is different from other architectural engineering designs. The process is complex and long, involving many departments and specialties, and characterized by systematicness, complexity, and subjectivity. Figure 1 shows the key flow chart of a road design link, which can intuitively reflect the relationship between various departments and units designed in the road engineering design stage and is the most indispensable key link in the whole road engineering construction.

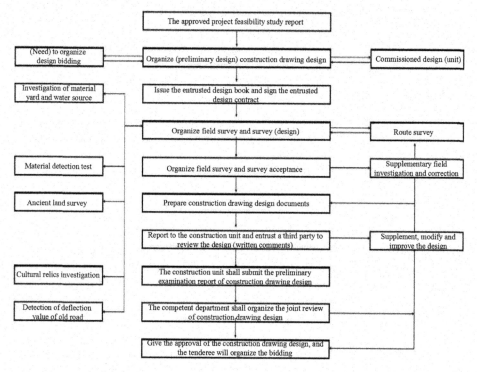

Figure 1. Key flow diagram of highway design.

2.2 BIM technology

Building Information Modeling (BIM) originated in the United States, and it is a brand-new concept or idea emerging in engineering construction. It realizes the visualization and quantitative analysis of the construction project by an informative description of the architectural and functional attributes of the project to achieve the purpose of replacing design with computers (Wan 2022). With the development of computer application science and technology and network information technology, BIM has gradually formed a standardized and systematic comprehensive digital solution for the whole life cycle of construction projects. That is to say, by constructing a parametric 3D data model, the project information among different jobs and departments is highly aggregated, and the digital features of various elements and functions of the project are expressed to realize the digitalization, informationization, and virtualization transformation of the construction project and form an integrated system environment that can support the design, construction, and management of the construction project. It can be seen that the BIM concept has been gradually upgraded and iterated into an applied technical means, a method and tool for creating and utilizing 3D models to manage and optimize the whole process of design, construction, and operation of construction projects, and a complete narration and expression of relevant information of construction projects (Wei 2022).

There are obvious differences between BIM technology and traditional architectural engineering design and management methods in the practical application process, especially in the architectural engineering design stage, which shows many advantages such as parameterization, visualization, relevance, and synergy. Among them, parameterization, as the primary feature of BIM technology in practical application, is not only reflected in the construction of a 3D data model, but also supports the on-demand output of various types of data. Visualization is mainly embodied in the visualization of design results and the visualization of the design process. That is to say, replacing the traditional two-dimensional plane drawings with three-dimensional models can improve the intuitiveness and fineness of the design results and support the real-time display of the whole design process, which greatly facilitates designers to preview and modify the design results and improves the design efficiency. Relevance is reflected in the fact that all design objects in the model are interrelated, and the change of one element or one data will update and modify all objects in the model, which greatly improves design work efficiency. Collaboration refers to the unified BIM data platform, which will coordinate the participating professions and departments, realize the integration of work content, share data resources and further improve the design quality and efficiency.

The application of BIM technology can't be separated from the support of computer science and software engineering, especially in the face of complex architectural engineering design. Single software or platform can't meet the actual needs, and more software is needed to cooperate for modeling and analysis. The common BIM software platforms include Autodesk, Bentley, Nernetschek Graphisoft, and Gery Technology Dassault. The modeling software and related functional modules of the four companies are shown in Figure 2.

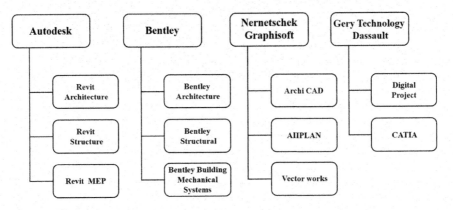

Figure 2. BIM platform and commonly used software.

For the road engineering designed in this paper, the author mainly studies and applies Civil 3D of Autodesk platform, and its interface is shown in Figure 3. Civil 3D, as a relatively mature BIM software for road engineering design at present, has realized the object packaging of route design. The design method used in designing road planes, longitudinal sections, and cross sections are similar to the traditional plane design, so it is easy to operate. Civil 3D has a collision checking function, analysis function based on road model (sight distance checking, driving simulation), component editor, and special visual programming software, which help lower the secondary development threshold of some functions and improve design efficiency (Zhao 2020).

3 APPLICATION OF BIM TECHNOLOGY IN ROAD ENGINEERING DESIGN

Road projects are mostly key construction projects related to urban construction and transportation, and often have the obvious characteristics of large scale, long lines, large quantities, high complexity, and strong professionalism. The emergence of three-dimensional digital design technology and collaborative design mode with BIM as the core concept can gather a variety of auxiliary functional components, design all the links in the design process separately, and finally complete the assembly, which can greatly reduce human labor, improve design efficiency, and also provide great help for the subsequent construction and construction stage, and complete the balanced transition from design period to construction period and even operation period. Therefore, this paper will illustrate the comprehensive application of BIM technology in the 3D model establishment in the design stage with an actual case of a highway construction project, so as to prove the significance of the application and popularization of BIM technology in road engineering design.

3.1 Create a digital terrain model

After knowing the basic situation of this highway project, combined with the basic technical indicators, the digital 3D ground model is completed by obtaining the key contents such as the address, hydrology, and topography along the highway to realize the digital virtual of the real environment and clearly and intuitively reflect the address hierarchy structure. It is convenient for designers to analyze the actual geological problems accurately, determine a reasonable design scheme, communicate between design and construction, formulate a scientific construction scheme, and reduce project risks. Table 1 shows the technical indexes of highway engineering projects (Tang 2016).

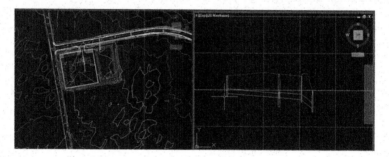

Figure 3. The Civil 3D operation interface.

Table 1. Technical indicators of a highway engineering project.

Technical index of a highway	
Highway classification	Class A
Design speed	Road section design speed 100km/h
Pavement and subgrade	Two-way four lanes, wide subgrade 26.0m
Automobile load grade	Highway-Class I
Peak acceleration of ground motion	0.10g
Construction bid section	SI section 3.96km and SII section 7.61km

Digital Terrain Models (DTM) are established to define highly irregular terrain. As the foundation and key of highway 3D design, it is related to the final determination of the highway design scheme. Under the Civil 3D software, by extracting and importing the data information of contour lines and elevation points in the original DWG topographic map and using a series of disjoint three-level idol grids to show the scattered topographic points, the digital topographic surface is formed to more intuitively reflect the ups and downs of the terrain, as shown in Figure 4 for the process of making topographic surface. After the digital terrain surface is generated, it will continue to preview, view, adjust and modify, and finally complete the construction of the terrain surface model.

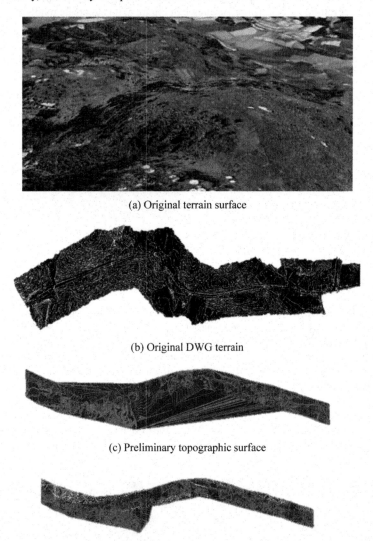

(a) Original terrain surface

(b) Original DWG terrain

(c) Preliminary topographic surface

(d) Final terrain surface model

Figure 4. Making process of terrain surface.

3.2 *Plane line design*

The significance of highway line design lies in considering the overall design capacity of highways and the layout of highway routes according to highway technical standards. Highway alignment generally consists of a straight line, circular curve, and transition curve. The selection of alignment and parameter setting should conform to the vehicle's driving trajectory, and meet the coordination requirements of driving safety, comfort, sight distance control, environment along the line, and other details. Under the Civil 3D software, the intersection method is used to complete the plane line design, which includes the following steps: line design data analysis, route object creation, focus line creation, graph element addition, design display, and so on (Ren 2018). At the same time, the software also supports importing design specifications to check the scientificity and rationality of each parameter setting automatically. As shown in Figure 5, it is to create renderings (partial) of the route.

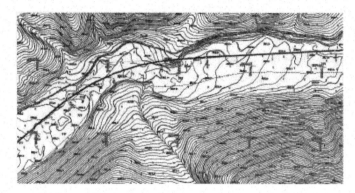

Figure 5. Renderings of creating routes (partial).

3.3 *Profile design*

The main task of the profile design is to study the size and length of the geometric composition of the undulating space line according to the dynamic characteristics of the vehicle, the road grade, the local natural geographical conditions, and the engineering economy to achieve the effects of safe and rapid driving, economical and reasonable transportation and comfortable passengers. After the plane line design is completed, Civil 3D software will automatically draw a profile line according to any selected base point, as shown in Figure 6. This profile is a surface profile, which can display the elevation change of the original terrain and surface of the route with intuitive parameters. The design profile can be created manually according to slope length, gradient, and control elevation conditions. (Xiao 2019) Under the Civil 3D software, the design profile is drawn through the profile layout tool, and parameters such as slope length, slope, and radius are set. As shown in Figure 7, the profile design results.

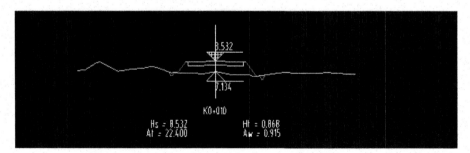

Figure 6. Surface profile.

In the actual design process, the designer can tile the vertical section window and the plane line window, so that the adjusted vertical section can be seen while adjusting the line plane, and the line plane can be conveniently adjusted to an ideal position. In addition, the designer can also adjust

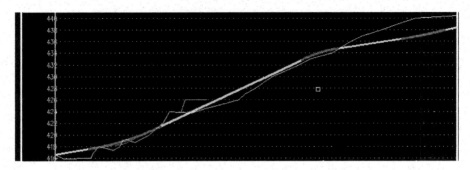

Figure 7. Profile section design results.

the plane line according to the profile design line, so that the curved profile line is as close as possible to the designed profile line to enhance the similarity and reduce the amount of excavation and filling in the highway construction stage, which reflects the application advantages of Civil 3D in this stage.

3.4 *Cross-sectional design*

Cross-section design refers to the design and determination of the form of highway cross-section, the position and size of each component, according to the technical design index, combined with various natural factors such as geology, topography, hydrology, and climate. The purpose is to ensure enough section size, strength, and stability, make it economical and reasonable, and simultaneously provide the basis for the quantity calculation of subgrade earthwork and highway construction and maintenance (Lu 2021).

A highway cross-section is a vertical section along the route direction at a certain point on the highway centerline. The cross-sectional design results in a cross-sectional design line including lanes, shoulders, partitions, side ditch slopes, intercepting ditches, berms, speed-changing lanes, environmental protection, and other facilities. Cross-section design is similar to vertical section design, but the overall complexity is large, reflecting the advantages of Civil 3D software from the side. In the actual design process, it is known from the highway design index that this section is a two-way four-lane first-class highway standard, and some detailed data are that the middle bandwidth is 3.5m, the width of a single lane is 2*3.75 m, the width of the hard shoulder is 3.0m, and the shoulder width of dirt road is 0.75 m. The pavement structure includes 4cm SMA-13+8cm AC-20C+36cm cement stabilized macadam +20 cm low-strength cement stabilized macadam (Zhao 2016). Therefore, the cross-section design will be divided into three major parts, namely the middle belt and the carriageway, as shown in Figure 8. After half of the design is completed, the other half of the highway design can be quickly realized through mirror operation. When all components are designed, the component assembly command can be executed to form a complete highway cross-section design, as shown in Figure 9, which is the cross-section assembly effect diagram.

3.5 *Road model creation*

Under the Civil 3D software, it is more standard. The designed road centerline, profile design line, and cross-section are assembled using the Create Road command, and the road model is automatically generated. The data model and behavior model of each basic road unit is fused to ensure that the road information model can respond in time according to the changes in road planning and design requirements at any time. At the same time, the visualization of the road information model is realized by using 3D simulation technology. Figure 10 shows the final road model.

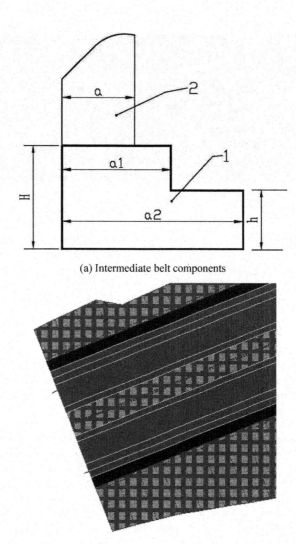

(a) Intermediate belt components

(b) Carriageway components

Figure 8. Cross-section design of highway.

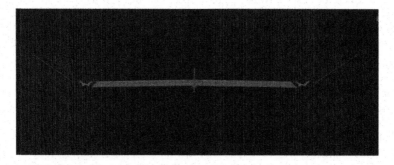

Figure 9. Cross-sectional assembly effect drawing.

392

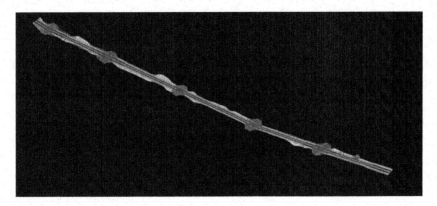

Figure 10. Road model drawing (partial).

4 CONCLUSION

The emergence of 3D digital design technology and collaborative design mode with BIM as the core has brought a qualitative leap to the design efficiency of road engineering construction projects. Compared with traditional graphic design, advanced 3D design technology can control and allocate the whole survey and design process more accurately and efficiently. At the same time, the visual simulation and simulation of the running state, basic performance, and appearance of road engineering are also realized. With the characteristics of covering the whole life cycle of road engineering, the quality of road engineering construction is greatly optimized, the project cycle is shortened, and the cost is reduced. Based on the understanding of the connotation of the BIM technology concept, this paper selects Civil 3D as the support of a software platform and combines design practice with actual engineering projects to prove the positive application of BIM technology in road engineering design and modeling.

REFERENCES

Lu Biao, Wang Xiaoxing (2021). Applicability Analysis of Highway Cross-section Design. *Transpo World*.07.
Ren Kangwei (2018). Research on Route Design Trend and Principle of First-class Highway. *Transpo World*.05.
Tang Tao, Qu Guoqing (2016). Digital Elevation Model and Its Application in Highway Survey and Design. *Sichuan Cement*.04.
Wan Haixia (2022). Application and Development Trend Analysis of BIM Technology in Construction. *Popular standardization*.01.
Wei Jiayi (2022). Application of BIM Technology in Architectural Engineering Design. *Real Estate World*.02.
Xiao Bonan (2019). *Research on Supporting Model of Highway Profile Design Process under BIM Environment*. Chang'an University.04.
Yang Long (2020). *Research on the Application of BIM in Road Engineering Design*. Jilin Jianzhu University.04.
Ye Guoping (2022). Application Analysis of BIM Technology in Road Engineering Design. *Sichuan Cement*.01.
Yu Ruihua (2020). Analysis on Measures of Municipal Engineering Construction Management. *Intelligent City*.12.
Zhao Wei (2020). Characteristic Application of Road Design and Modeling Function in Autodesk Civil 3D Software. *Green Environmental Protection Building Materials*.09.
Zhao Yurong (2016). Analysis of the Whole Process Supervision of First-class Highway Construction. *Technology and Enterprise*.01.

Development and testing of remote monitoring system for roadbed construction quality

Zhongke Tian*
Tianjin Port Engineering Institute Co., Ltd. of CCCC First Harbor Engineering Co., Ltd. Tianjin, China

Lu Yang
China Harbour Engineering Co., Ltd., Tianjin, China

Bin Li
Tianjin Port Engineering Institute Co., Ltd. of CCCC First Harbor Engineering Co., Ltd. Tianjin, China

ABSTRACT: To prevent over-pressure and leakage of roadbed rolling equipment in the working area, improve the quality of roadbed rolling construction and increase efficiency. This study used a remote monitoring system based on the WEB page management method, based on 3D simulation technology, focusing on the control of roadbed compaction and pavement paving compaction process, and developed a set of high-precision roadbed rolling construction influence factors automatic collection device, and developed a corresponding roadbed construction quality monitoring system according to the functional requirements. Through two tests and adjustments, the vibration acceleration variator worked well. According to the actual measurement on-site, the range of digital display at strong vibration was 50–60 m/s, which was equivalent to about 5–6 g of gravitational acceleration. This showed that the equipment and platform data collection was accurate, the platform was running smoothly, met the needs of on-site construction quality control, and was able to carry out on-site construction.

1 INTRODUCTION

The traditional construction quality control of roadbeds and pavement mainly relies on the staff's experience, which can easily lead to over-pressure and leakage, resulting in inconsistency in the degree of compaction in each construction area, which makes the quality inspection more difficult and reduces the construction efficiency. (Xue et al. 2022)

The intelligence of compaction machinery is a major direction of future development in the engineering field. (Ma et al. 2008) Ma Xueliang et al. established the intelligent control optimization objective of the compaction process based on energy balance and the corresponding objective function to promote the development of an intelligent control system of oscillating roller (Ma et al. 2008) Xgma (Sanming) Heavy Machinery Co., Ltd. has developed an intelligent tandem vibratory roller control system, which combines electronic control technology and hydraulic transmission technology to achieve stepless automatic amplitude change by adjusting the phase angle of eccentric block, but still cannot complete the fast and accurate acquisition of working parameters such as amplitude, frequency and driving speed of target compaction effect.

Therefore, we intend to develop and test the "remote monitoring platform for roadbed pavement construction quality" in order to prevent over-pressure and leakage during rolling, enhance the mechanization of construction, and improve the quality and efficiency of construction. At the same time, the platform can provide more comprehensive compaction information for all units involved

*Corresponding Author: tianzhongke@tju.edu.cn

in the project, which can be used as evidence for process improvement and construction acceptance to guarantee the consistency of construction quality. (Chen et al. 2019)

Through the design and development of the "Roadbed Pavement Compaction Remote Monitoring Platform," the following construction objectives were expected to be achieved:

- Develop a remote monitoring system based on WEB page management mode, realize the remote monitoring of the rolling construction process of multiple projects, and provide managers with the technical means of remote supervision of the construction process.
- Formulate unified and standardized data interface standards, fully compatible with the site equipment of each project, ensure data consistency, and achieve the management goal of remote data collection and real-time monitoring.
- Based on the 3D simulation technology and the subgrade structure data, the 3D simulation and emulation interaction of the roadbed structure are realized, and the main parameters of the operation of the field compaction equipment are reflected in multiple dimensions.

2 SOFTWARE FUNCTION DESIGN OF THE REMOTE MONITORING PLATFORM

The platform consists of 9 subsystems: data driving warehouse, map comprehensive application, construction quality management, construction progress management, data collection management, data early warning management, roadbed compaction report analysis, basic data management, and system data management. The functional structure of the platform is shown in Figure 1 below:

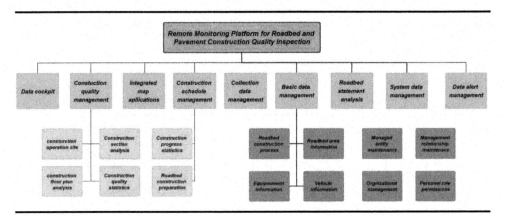

Figure 1. Functional structure diagram of the platform.

Through the data display of the remote monitoring platform, the prominent problems in the construction site could be found and corrected in time to ensure that the whole construction process will be under control, so as to achieve high efficiency and high-quality management of the expressway construction process.

3 SYSTEM TEST SCHEME

3.1 Overall working route

In order to realize the real-time monitoring of the compaction quality of the roller during the construction process, the existing compaction equipment needed to be modified. (Liu et al. 2018) Therefore, this study adopted the ECV algorithm as the construction vibration information output value of the roller; based on the differential positioning technology of BeiDou and GPS, we obtained the high-precision rolling trajectory algorithm and rolling traverse algorithm of the roller to realize the real-time acquisition of compaction speed, compaction traverse, and ECV value.

The specific working ideas were as follows:

- Pre-installation preparation: mainly to determine information such as data information entry, listed of stake coordinates, personnel, and user lists.
- Hardware equipment installation: roller control hardware installation and implementation.
- Run debugging: After installing the hardware, debug the working status of each hardware. Running the system to see if there were any problems.
- Equipment improvement: analyze and summarize the problems during the testing process and proposed improvement measures.

3.2 Hardware and equipment installation

The intelligent compaction system integrated a high-performance GNSS receiver, supporting GPS, BD, and GLONASS, and achieved centimeter-level positioning accuracy through carrier phase difference technology (RTK while integrating LTE high-speed wireless data transmission unit and high-speed processor to ensure real-time data acquisition, processing, and transmission. (Cao et al. 2021)

It can be combined with the peripheral infrared temperature sensor, intelligent compaction sensor, and a series of means to collect the accurate position of the roller and rolling information, and display the compaction degree, the number of passes, rolling areas, rolling weak areas, etc. in the form of graphics and numerical values.

Through the flat panel display installed in the cab to guide the roller operator to strengthen the rolling of weak areas promptly, managers could also use the mobile terminal APP to view the problems in construction in a timely and effectively and could conduct accurate testing of weak areas during routine inspection to reduce hidden quality problems and improve construction efficiency.

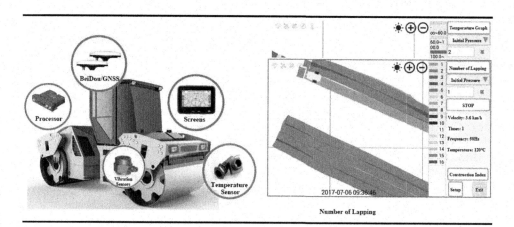

Figure 2. Installation of each hardware equipment.

Table 1. Intelligent compaction of data monitoring.

power	positioning accuracy	installation site
5 W	2cm	road roller

4 FIELD TEST RESULTS

In order to ensure the operation effect of the platform and hardware equipment and be suitable for the construction site application scenario to a greater extent, the site test was conducted twice. The site test situation, encountered problems, and solutions were summarized as follows:

4.1 *Advantages of the equipment and platform*

The platform currently developed in this topic used sensing technology and mobile Internet transmission technology under the condition of hardware and software combination to realize real-time collection, analysis, evaluation, and early warning of key data in the construction process, which made up for the shortage of traditional engineering quality management. Specifically, it has the following advantages:

- Centimeter-level positioning (horizontal accuracy of 2–3 cm, elevation accuracy of 4–6 cm).
- Intelligent warning and real-time correction of abnormal data are found.
- Based on a rasterization algorithm and supported by a spatial database, it realizes accurate calculation of crushing area and forms a statistical report of work area quality to achieve the goal of query ability and traceability.
- Based on the development of a 3D geographic information engine, it can view the topography, features, and geomorphological information in and around the roadbed compaction area through a 3D perspective, and can extend the overlay of tilt photography and BIM model data to form more accurate topography and work area information.
- The CMV algorithm based on the Fourier transform could calculate the roadbed compaction in real-time.
- Realize playback of historical data to view the construction quality at that time.
- Based on the construction zone, the construction quality and progress of the cross-section can be viewed graphically.

4.2 *Main problems existing in the construction process*

- The rolling coverage rollers were prone to leakage, under-pressure, and partial pressure during normal operation.
- When making up for the missed pressure area or completing the rolling to exit the site, the roller had gone out an extra distance in the site because of inertia, and the overlapping part would cause the red image of the central console to be overwritten, and the overwriting would cause the original image of the rolling traverse to be lost.
- Before rolling construction, the constructor needed to provide the field roadbed width and number of layers and adjust the coordinate system and other relevant test parameters. After providing the average roadbed width and number of layers, the roadbed range in the cloud image could be set as a rectangle, and if it encountered a longitudinal slope with a large filling section, the roadbed width varied at each location in the same horizontal plane. In the construction process, when the average roadbed width had been set unreasonably, the intelligent device could not provide error alerts.
- The intelligent rolling technology system in this project was only for the construction application and research of single soil, single construction environment, and specific models of equipment. The test data, parameters, and correlations accumulated from project construction were no longer general after changes in the nature of the fill soil material, construction environment, or construction equipment.
- Currently, the system platform is not perfect, and the common performance of each equipment component is not strong. Moreover, the equipment needed to be maintained by professional manufacturers, and the frequency of installation, disassembly, and damage was high.
- The rolling speed control was not precise enough and could not be accurately controlled within 4 km/h.

4.3 *Improvement measures*

- Using the rolling number cloud map (Figure 3) provided by the intelligent rolling system terminal can monitor whether there were any phenomena, including leakage pressure, dead corner, or over-pressure, in each rolling area of each layer in real-time, so as to facilitate the rectification and implementation, that is, to ensure the construction quality and improve the construction effect. (Zhao et al. 2018)
- The installation of the intelligent rolling system provided construction personnel with timely construction data and corrected the operation process that did not meet the requirements. And under the guidance of test and inspection data, it saved construction resources and improved the one-time inspection pass rate by preventing leakage and over-compaction. The areas with unqualified compaction were handled in time to improve the acceptance rate and avoid repeated testing, thus improving work efficiency. (Wu et al. 2017) Through information-based monitoring and data analysis, we could save the costs of machinery, fuel consumption, and labor to gain some economic benefits.

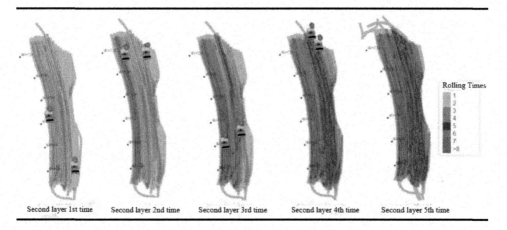

Figure 3. Intelligent rolling times count figure.

- The installation of an intelligent compaction system could restore the construction status of a specific location at that time to a certain extent, which helped to trace and analyze the causes of the problems, timely found the area where compaction was not in place, and prevented over-compaction or under-compaction. The compaction process achieved continuous quality control and promptly output the compaction report, facilitating timely investigation and remediation to ensure construction quality.
- It was necessary to analyze and summarize the test data for different conditions to improve the construction efficiency of roadbed filling in a complex environment. In addition, the compaction degree fitted by this system did not fully reflect the actual situation of roadbed filling, so it needed a lot of sampling work by inspectors and comparative correlation with the data of this system to ensure that the final roadbed quality met the design requirements.
- It was recommended to build a roadbed intelligent rolling system platform, which could be tested for different soil and construction environments. Furthermore, a complete set of self-testing standards should have been summarized to facilitate the application of the system in construction.
- The LED screen outside the car could monitor the speed of the roller in real-time. At the same time, according to the rolling speed map provided by the intelligent rolling system, it could accurately determine the speeding rolling driving area, which helped timely rectification and implementation. In this test, the roller driver drove on previous experience in the first layer of

static rolling. But speed control was inaccurate beyond 4 km/h, and the beyond part displayed red. After being corrected, the results improved significantly.

5 CONCLUSIONS

- In the study, a set of high-precision roadbed rolling construction influence factors automatic collection device was developed, a 3D network visualization integration method based on key factors of roadbed construction was proposed, and a corresponding roadbed construction quality monitoring system was developed based on this basis according to the functional requirements.
- The system could provide feedback to all parties of the project with real-time construction information, and it also could alarm the area of substandard rolling quality, which can visually indicate the location of substandard quality and facilitate timely remediation, thus providing advanced technical means for all parties involved in the construction to carry out integrated management.
- Through two tests, the results showed that the equipment and platform data collection was accurate, the platform ran smoothly, and the multi-machine operation was stable to meet the needs of on-site construction quality control.

6 LIMITATIONS AND NEXT RESEARCH PLAN

The limitation of this study is that only the applicability of the equipment and platform to highways has been studied, and later it will be devoted to the application and promotion of all types of road construction projects.

REFERENCES

Cao Y., Liu Q.B., Xiao Z.W., Wang R.W., Shi L.X., Li Z.M., Yang Y.H. and Mao Y.J. 2021, *Highway*, **2**, 57–63.
Chen Z.Y., Zhao Y.F., Zou B., Jiang L. and Zhao H.M. 2019. *Water Resources and Hydropower Engineering*, **8**, 1–7.
Liu D.H, Gao L., Lin M. and Li Z.L. 2018. *Journal of Hohai University (Natural Sciences)*, **46**, 307–313.
Ma X.L., Sun Z.W. and Long S.G. 2008. *Chinese Journal of Construction Machinery*, **6**, 299–305.
Ma X.L., Sun Z.W., and Long S.G. 2008. *Equipment Management & Maintenance Technology*, **11**, 81–84.
Wu C.Y., Zhang L. and Zhao P. 2017. *Journal of China & Foreign Highway*, **37**, 42–45.
Xue H., Sun M.X., Chen G.L., and Tang Q. 2022. *Communications Science and Technology Heilongjiang*. **335**, 36–38.
Zhao Y., Chen N. and Fan W.S. 2018. *Modern Transportation Technology.* **15**, 1–4.

Application research of BIM technology in outdoor engineering of a data center project

Hang Zou*, Zhanqiang Liu*, Jianchao Wang* & Lin Xue*
China Construction First Group Corporation Limited, Beijing, China

ABSTRACT: The construction of a data center is highly professional and needs a strong ability to integrate the resources of the project. This paper takes a data center outdoor project as the background, which has a narrow, wide distribution of surface, a large quantity, complicated pipeline, construction process, the characteristics of the tight, more use of BIM technology. A three-dimensional model of a professional, comprehensive network of outdoor collision checks is established, which can efficiently organize resources, shorten the construction period, and improve the efficiency of comprehensive outdoor pipeline construction.

1 INTRODUCTION

The data center uses the existing Internet communication lines and bandwidth resources to establish a standardized professional telecom room environment and provide enterprises and governments with server hosting, renting and related value-added services (Yan et al. 2015). As the center of data storage and circulation, it has high requirements for all aspects of construction.

A data center project in Tianjin covers an area of about 30,000 square meters with a total construction area of 57,996 square meters. The outdoor pipe network of the project includes intelligent communication, fire control, and other electrical pipelines, rain sewage, water supply, middle water, spray, fire hydrant, other water supply, drainage pipelines, and outside thermal lines. Outdoor pipeline supporting works include main road, wall, cable trench, etc. The project site is narrow, wide distribution, large and complex pipeline, construction procedures, tight time limit, outdoor engineering adopts the combination of the permanent and temporary technical scheme (Zhang 2018), the main structure of the construction at the same time, and all kinds of outdoor pipelines interlaced, part of the pipeline near the structure foundation, through the field road, construction is challenging.

Given the above problems, BIM technology is used to establish a professional 3D model, to deepen the design of outdoor pipe network, overall arrangement, unified excavation of the same path, to meet all professional outdoor construction, reduce the impact on structural construction, mechanical and electrical equipment transportation (Mei 2021). Clarifying the route and elevation of all kinds of pipelines, especially solving the collision problem of key parts, can not only meet the requirements of one-time optimization, but also provide favorable technical support for the overall construction scheme of outdoor pipe network, reasonably arrange the process, shorten the construction period and guarantee the schedule, which plays a crucial role in cost control.

---

*Corresponding Authors: zouhang0601@163.com, 251504062@qq.com, 330445249@qq.com and 915494915@qq.com

2 OUTDOOR COMPREHENSIVE PIPELINE DEEPENING DESIGN

2.1 Problem analysis

The outdoor pipe network of the project includes intelligent communication, fire control, and other electrical pipelines, rain sewage, water supply, middle water, spray, fire hydrant, other water supply, drainage pipelines, and outside thermal lines. Outdoor pipeline supporting works include main road, wall, cable trench, etc. According to the original construction drawings, the site, building structure, and outdoor pipe network is modeled by BIM technology. The analysis shows that the project site is small, the amount of pipelines is large and complex, and all outdoor pipelines interlaced. Some of the pipelines are near the structural foundation, and the pipelines cross the road at the site, so the construction is tough. In the outdoor pipe network of the data center, the electric pipeline has the requirement of covering depth, and the transverse width and longitudinal depth can reach more than 1 meter, which requires a great space. However, the sewage pipe and storm water pipe are limited by the elevation of the municipal storm sewage well entrance, so there is less space for optimization. The original design drawing did not comprehensively consider the electrical pipeline, water supply, and drainage pipeline, so the collision situation is very serious. Suppose the construction is carried out according to the original plan. In that case, the rework rate of the project will be huge, which will increase the project cost, significantly affect the project quality and duration, and there are certain hidden dangers (Chen 2017).

2.2 Deepening the design of the comprehensive outdoor pipeline

2.2.1 Principles of deepening design of outdoor pipe network

The comprehensive and deepening design of the outdoor pipe network should follow the following principles:

1) Underground pipelines are laid from the building to the center of the road;
2) In the vertical position of all kinds of pipelines, the elevation of rainwater and sewage pipelines is reduced and changed due to the limitation of the elevation of the municipal rainwater sewage pipeline interface; In principle, the electrical pipeline is located at the top layer, and the rest of the water pipes should be laid as flat as possible.
3) All pipelines should be laid parallel or vertically with the road as far as possible. When pipeline cross, should follow the principle of avoidance: small tube let big tube, pressure tube let gravity tube, give conduit let drainpipe, fittings less tube let fittings many tubes, etc.
4) The minimum horizontal and vertical distance between all kinds of pipelines and buildings and facilities shall conform to the requirements of the minimum vertical and horizontal net distance of pipelines.

2.2.2 Determine the location and specifications of pipeline structures

Outdoor pipeline structures mainly include rainwater wells, sewage inspection wells, valve wells, etc. In the process of deepening the design, it is necessary to consider the location of the structures on the pipeline, the size, depth, and spacing of the structures, the size of the access, the collision between the structures and the structure, and other issues.

3 APPLICATION OF BIM TECHNOLOGY IN OUTDOOR ENGINEERING

Through the comprehensive analysis of the original design scheme, we ensure the construction quality, meet the requirements of the construction period, and seek a better solution. Considering outdoor engineering is more, more scientific and practical management control is needed. We must make an overall arrangement, unified arrangement, unified excavation, pipeline ditch different slot, meet all outdoor professional construction, reduce the influence of the structure construction, electrical and mechanical equipment transportation work, and guarantee time limit for a project schedule.

3.1 *Modeling of outdoor pipe network and supporting projects*

Modeling of outdoor pipe networks and supporting projects is based on design and construction drawings, which mainly include civil engineering data such as general plot plans, detailed drawings of ground structures, construction drawings of outdoor professional pipelines, and outdoor landscape design data (terrain, vegetation, and greening, etc.).

The civil engineering data include the general plot plan and detailed structure drawing. The data includes the plot red line, exterior wall line of the main building, exterior wall line of the basement, cap, driveway, landscape, road surface and terrain elevation, roof elevation of basement structure, etc.

Construction drawings of outdoor professional pipelines include intelligent, communication, fire control, and other electrical pipelines, rainwater pipes, sewage pipes, water supply pipes, middle water pipes, spray pipes, fire hydrant pipes and other water supply pipes, and outside thermal lines, including pipe diameter and soil covering depth.

Outdoor landscape design data mainly include green space, vegetation, road, etc. The buried depth of the pipeline laying under green space or driveway should be paid attention to, and reinforcement and protection measures should be taken for laying under the driveway (Gui et al. 2015).

3.2 *Collision check*

After modeling according to the original construction drawings, we check the collision of mechanical and electrical pipelines, find the main collision points, analyze the collision causes, and organize the owner and the designer to discuss the design scheme in depth for the disputed collision points.

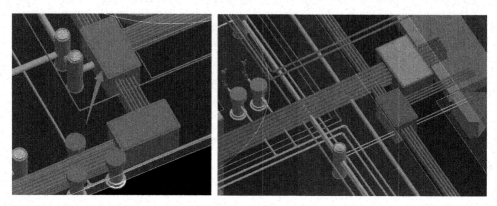

Figure 1. Collision points of the original design scheme.

3.3 *Optimization scheme*

Optimization scheme 1: weak-current pipeline, electric well, rainwater pipeline, and rainwater well collide. There are 40 weak-current pipelines in this position, with seven pipes φ 100 for each of the six layers. The weak current pipeline will be moved to the road below. The optimization scheme is convenient for construction and increases the amount of concrete encapsulation of the electrical pipeline.

Optimization scheme 2: weak current pipelines and electric Wells coincide with sewage pipelines and sewage Wells. There are 30 weak current pipelines in this position, and each layer has six pipes

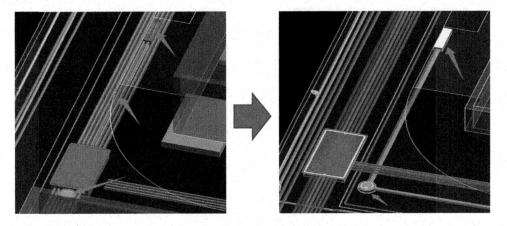

Figure 2. Comparison of outdoor pipe network deepening design scheme before and after (1).

φ 100. The weak current pipeline will be moved to the road below. The optimization scheme is convenient for construction and increases the amount of concrete encapsulation of the electrical pipeline.

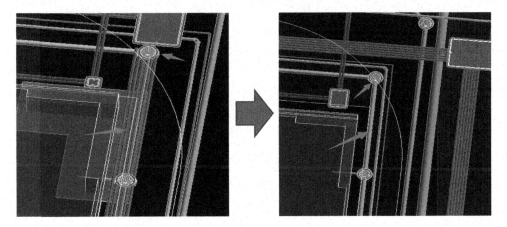

Figure 3. Comparison of outdoor pipe network deepening design scheme before and after (2).

Optimization scheme 3: storm water pipes collide seriously with weak current pipelines and electric Wells. There are 30 weak current pipelines in this position, including DN300 and DN600 stormwater pipes. Each layer of five layers has six pipes φ 100, and this position should be connected to a new plot. The solution is to optimize the rainwater storage pool, optimize the number of weak electric pipelines, reduce the elevation of rainwater pipes, avoid collision and facilitate construction.

Optimization scheme 4: there are 28 strong electric pipelines in this position (five pipes φ 200 for each layer of four layers, eight pipes φ 100 for each layer of 1 layer). The diameter of storm sewage pipes is DN150 and DN300, respectively. Due to the influence of municipal storm sewage well elevation, there is not much room for optimization of storm sewage elevation. The solution was to add a cable trench between the two buildings, move the strong electric line down, and increase the size of the strong electric well.

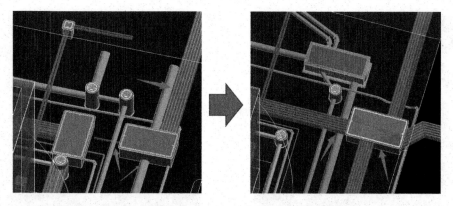

Figure 4. Comparison of outdoor pipe network deepening design scheme before and after (3).

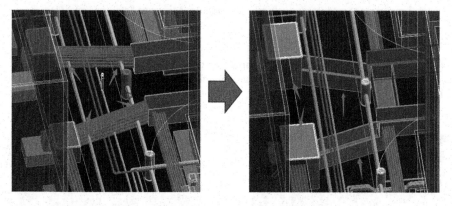

Figure 5. Comparison of outdoor pipe network deepening design scheme before and after (4).

4 OVERALL IMPLEMENTATION OF OUTDOOR PROJECTS

4.1 *Determine the construction of the building and outdoor pipe network*

According to the requirements of the owner, the construction of the data center will be guaranteed first. After the main body of the data center is completed, the construction of the power building and operation and maintenance building will be supplemented. In this project, the excavation and construction of the outdoor pipe network are carried out in the stage of the foundation pit, and the outdoor pipe network is constructed from south to north.

4.2 *Construction survey wiring*

According to the provided measurement reference points, we organize the plane coordinates and elevation transfer, carry out the construction site plane, road, trees, and terrain elevation measurement, and finally carry out the design control acceptance of the plane coordinates and elevation.

4.3 *Preparation for earthwork construction*

We level the site according to the design or construction requirements, scope, and elevation, dump the earthwork to the specified dumping area, and strip and preserve valuable topsoil. In the construction area, all the silt and garbage that affect the quality of the project should be removed, and the filling stone should be thrown into the proper disposal. Drainage measures shall be taken to drain water from the ground or low-lying areas in the construction area.

4.4 Earth excavation

Earthwork excavation is carried out following the principle of "stratification, block, symmetry and balance" and in strict accordance with the excavation process of each partition required by the design working condition.

4.5 Pipe network laying

This project has many kinds of outdoor pipelines and strong and weak electric pipelines, which cross with other majors. The operation and maintenance building provides formal water for the power building and data center building, and the formal electricity routing of each building also needs to pass through the outdoor area. The strong and weak electric pipelines require the concrete encapsulation scheme, which can be prefabricated on the ground at the same time as the earthwork excavation and be directly lifted when the installation conditions are met. Each section of the construction process is arranged reasonably from bottom to top to reduce the number of secondary excavations as far as possible.

4.6 Earth backfill

Before earth filling, the supervision, construction, landscape, civil engineering, and other units shall organize concealed inspection and acceptance and ensure that each process meets the design and specification requirements before the construction can be carried out.

5 CONCLUSION

Data center engineering comprises large and complex pipelines, multiple construction procedures, and a tight construction period. BIM technology can be used to realize construction simulation and visual management, and an accurate model can guarantee future operation and maintenance.

Based on a data center project in Tianjin, this paper analyzes the problems in the original design drawing and construction difficulties and clarifies the principle of deepening the design. BIM technology is used for modeling outdoor pipe networks and supporting projects, and the optimization scheme is analyzed and explained. Based on the principle of technology first, the implementation plan of outdoor engineering of the data center project is determined, which has guiding significance to the implementation of outdoor engineering.

REFERENCES

Chen Xinlun. (2017). Discussion on key points of outdoor engineering quality supervision [J]. *Henan Building Materials*, (6):3.

Gui Xueming, Yang Min. (2015). Application of BIM technology in overall outdoor design of Shanghai Tower [J]. *Water & Wastewater Treatment*, 41(4):6.

Mei Yi. (2021). Application of road combination technology in housing construction engineering [J]. *Construction Machinery and Maintenance*, (5):4.

Yan Li, Liang Weiqi, and Jia Liang. (2015). Special research and summary of IDC room outdoor engineering construction management [J]. *Jiangxi Building Materials*, (6):1.

Zhang Tao. (2018). Discussion on the application of Yonglin combination in building engineering construction [J]. *Building Technology Development*, 45(20):3.

Risk assessment of tunnels using 3S technology: A case study of the Atal Tunnel

Yu Bian, Hao Chen*, YongPeng Yang, Meng Li, Ya Guo & Ling Chen
China Aero Geophysical Survey & Remote Sensing Center for Natural Resources, Haidian, Beijing, China

Xin He & Hao Tang
The 10th Geological Brigade of Liaoning Province Co., Ltd., Dongzhou, Fushun, China

ABSTRACT: The Atal Tunnel linking Manali and Leh is an important infrastructure that can ensure all-weather connectivity and movement of residents in these valleys. Considering its important transportation value, the main objective of this study was to delineate risk assessments of the tunnel to guarantee safety. Geotechnical and mechanical characteristics, fault-like features, and geological disasters are significant factors when conducting a risk assessment of the tunnel. These data along the tunnel and nearby highways delineate potential risk areas. This study applied multiple survey methods, including integrated geological surveys and remote sensing (RS) approaches. The 3S technology (geographic information systems, RS, and global positioning system [GPS]) was accurately and efficiently applied to monitor the external environment of the tunnel, especially in areas of mountainous topography, high altitude, and inaccessibility. Based on the comprehensive findings, 37 geological disasters were interpreted, and two concentrated risk assessment areas were delineated along the tunnel. Thus, the results of this study maybe can provide a reference for risk assessment in areas similar to where the Atal Tunnel is located, such as the Qinghai–Tibet Plateau, and contribute to tunnel construction safety.

1 INTRODUCTION

Risk assessment of tunnels is important for security management, as tunnel construction can damage neighboring structures and endanger human life. Most tunnels are constructed in areas with challenging natural conditions, such as complex terrains (including mountains and large canyons). Conducting conventional ground investigations, particularly in remote areas with complex terrain, is extremely challenging. Remote sensing (RS) techniques, which enable a remote analysis of the Earth's surface, can be effective in areas with limited accessibility (Akram et al. 2019; Pour & Hashim 2015; Rezaei et al. 2020). Over the last 20 years, satellite-based monitoring techniques have been successfully used to study phenomena on the Earth's surface, revealing considerable details about ground surface deformations (Ba et al. 2020). Satellite images obtained by sensors with high spatial and spectral resolutions have played important roles in geological surveys, fault mapping, environmental monitoring, and climate change studies. Previous studies have revealed the effectiveness of RS, satellite imagery, and geographical information system (GIS) in controlling natural hazards, as well as for natural space management during engineering and construction projects (Baghdadi et al. 2005; Cetin & Sevik 2016; Pour & Hashim 2015).

The Atal Tunnel in India is the world's longest high-altitude highway tunnel (9.02 km). It passes through the Pir Panjal Range, linking Manali and Leh. Before the tunnel's construction, heavy

---

*Corresponding Author: 1076057045@qq.com

snowfall could cut off Lahaul for months at a time. Therefore, the tunnel has strategic importance and monumental significance for the people of the Lahaul Valley, as it provides all-weather connectivity. Moreover, its construction reduced the distance between Manali and Leh by 46 km. According to reports in the Indian media (The Times of India, Indian Defense News), the journey to Lahaul and Spiti Valley from Manali, which required approximately 5 hours before the tunnel's construction, now only takes 10 minutes. Thus, the Atal Tunnel, which ensures the connectivity and movement of residents in these valleys, is an important infrastructure with transportation value.

The Atal Tunnel was opened in 2020. To date, only a few relevant investigations have been conducted. Construction of the 9.02-km-long tunnel took ten years and cost 400 million dollars. Some parts of the tunnel are located in a fault fracture zone, and others feature high water pressure or are only buried to a shallow depth. These factors increase the possibility of disasters involving the inrush of karst water and mud. Herein, historical data were collected from news sources and recorded relevant locations and dates. The main objective of this study was to investigate the available geological information in the Atal Tunnel area, particularly in high-risk areas, to analyze and prepare for these threats. Considering the geological conditions of the study area (mountainous topography, high altitude, and inaccessibility), RS technology represents an appropriate approach for achieving these objectives. Therefore, in this study, the ability of RS to provide credible results that can aid the management of tunnel security was investigated. Herein, we summarize existing knowledge regarding events associated with engineering breaches during tunnel construction. The results were integrated to explore the advantages of 3S (GIS, RS, and global positioning system [GPS]) in external environment safety monitoring, disaster prevention, and investigation. In conjunction with our findings, problems encountered during tunnel construction can offer an important reference for subsequent tunnel construction in areas such as the Qinghai–Tibet Plateau.

2 METHODS

The analysis conducted in this study was based on archived data from the Satellite Pour l' Observation de la Terre (SPOT) satellite, which has four bands and records 6-m multispectral data that are georeferenced under the China Geodetic Coordinate System 2000 (CGCS2000). Its data meet the requirements of basic topographic and thematic maps. Google Maps were also used, as this platform includes vector maps of global city administrations, traffic data, and business information provided by Google Inc. It can also provide satellite photos at different resolutions and help visualize contours and terrains. Information fusion technology was used in this study. Through the integrated usage of multiple-source information, data fusion can help achieve more objectives and reveal intrinsic knowledge regarding certain objects or targets. RS spatial analysis is important in ore-forming predictions using multi-informational synthetic analysis. We summarized existing knowledge regarding events associated with engineering breaches during tunnel construction. Suitable data were selected, validated, and revised, following which integrated information was produced. In summary, a method of RS image mining was adopted based on object-oriented image analysis; visual interpretations were combined with computer information-aided extraction to conduct a thematic interpretation (Figure 1).

Through GIS, the spatial characteristics of information associated with fundamental states can be acquired, and this information can be manipulated. This indicates that a comprehensive approach is required to reflect the specific operating conditions of a given task. One of the key steps in RS image fusion is band integration; this process can utilize fusion technology to achieve the best fusion image; thus, this method was considered appropriate for the present study area. Disaster recognition was further explored using a comprehensive interpretation method based on optical RS and Google Earth images. The approach developed in this study for integrating various causal factors to delineate risk assessment areas and especially exploring the advantages of Google Earth images will help formulate appropriate strategies for tunnel engineering surveys.

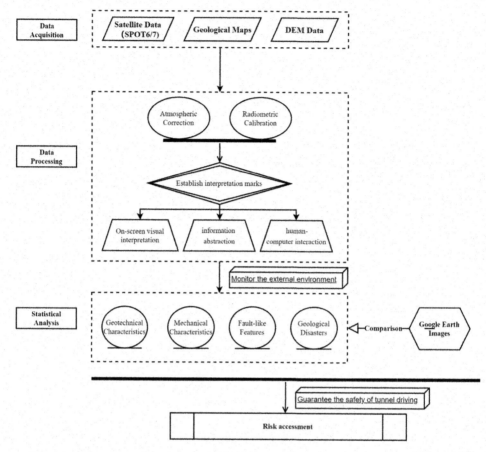

Figure 1. Technology road mapping.

3 RESULTS

3.1 Regional geological data

The study area is located in the Inner Himalayas across the Pir Panjal Range, rising as a result of movements along the faults of the MCT zone (Ahmad & Bhat 2012; Agarwal et al. 2018); the area is highly mountainous and features a mixture of high ranges, flat or gently sloping meadows, deep and narrow gorges, and steep slopes. The topography is highly rugged, and the elevation varies greatly from 1,200 to 6,000 m. Rock exposures in the area's ridges are gneisses and granite gneisses, with migmatites and thin bands of schists in the eastern portion of the Rohtang gneissic complex. A large fold dominates the structural geology of the Pir Panjal Range, comprising the southwestern slope of the Great Himalayan Range (Burbank & Johnson 1982, 1983; Bhatt 1989; Basavaiah et al. 2010; Mukherjee 2015). This forms the root zone for the Jutogh thrust sheet of the Kulu–Mandi–Narkanda area, such that these rocks occupy the southern limb of a regional anticlinal fold that varies from 25° to 35° in the area (Figure 2). The cumulative effects of more than four phases of folding accompanied by granitic intrusions and a deep burial depth have led to meso-to-hypo-grade metamorphic rocks having incredibly intricate disharmonic, recumbent, and superposed minor folding. The region experiences frequent seismic activity and geological hazards, posing great challenges to the maintenance of operational safety.

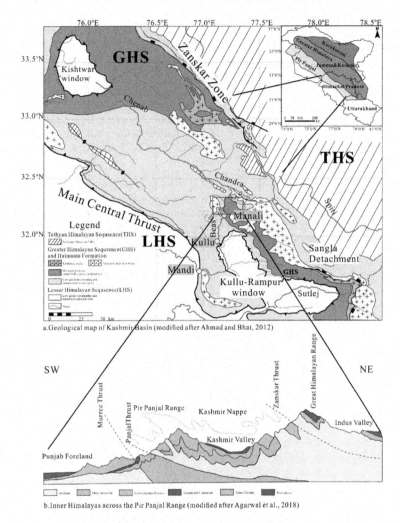

Figure 2. Study area: (a) Geological map of Kashmir Basin (modified after Ahmad & Bhat 2012). and (b) Inner Himalayas across the Pir Panjal Range (modified after Agarwal et al. 2018).

3.2 *Engineering geological*

Engineering geology is essential for heterogeneous rock conditions of the tunnel excavation. A joint aquifer ensures continuous water inflow to the tunnel in areas with hard rock types; less seepage water is encountered in areas featuring shale. To increase the safety of re-profiling works in challenging ground conditions, the Atal tunnel is designed and built as a drained tunnel that is completely straight, with the north portal being located at a high altitude in a region with a high rock hardness and small ridges (i.e., a stable region). The first blast took place at the south portal through Quartzitic Schist, highly jointed and crossed by numerous shear zones, parallel or sub-parallel to the axis. The rock surrounding the south portal is soft, with high levels of water ingress in fault zones; these conditions resulted in mud inrush disasters during excavation. From the assessed rock mass behavior and control water inflow, the tunnel progressed according to the actual geotechnical conditions. Using remote sensing in mapping and recognition studies of rocks on the satellites images, combined with the petrophysical parameters collected as detailed above, the identified rocks were classified into seven levels (Table 1, Figure 3).

Table 1. Classification of hardness.

Hardness Level	Lithological Characteristics
I	The rock is fresh, with slight structural influence, undeveloped or slightly developed joint fractures, closed and short extension, no or few weak structural planes, and a fault bandwidth of <0.1 m; it has a whole block masonry structure.
II	The rock is fresh or relatively fresh and has been subjected to little tectonic influence. Joints or fissures are slightly developed, and there are a few weak structural planes with poor interlayer bonding. The fracture bandwidths of faults are <0.5 m, and the rock structure comprises block or layered masonry.
III	The rock is relatively fresh or weakly weathered and is affected by geological structures. Cracks have developed, and some are opened and filled with mud. There are several soft structural planes, and fault fracture zones are <1 m.
IV	Similar to III. There are many faults and weak structural planes. Fault fracture zones are <2 m, and the local structure is crushed, similar to gravel.
V	Sand, landslides, debris, pebbles, gravel, and soil.
VI	Soil, soft plastic clay, wet saturated fine sand, and soft soil.
VII	Similar to VI, but more flexible.

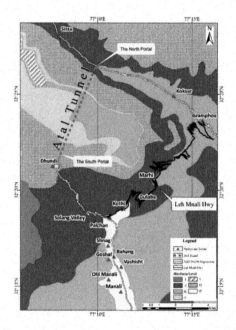

Figure 3. Hardness classification.

3.3 *Risk assessment*

Risk assessment is characterized by comprehensiveness, complex geological conditions, and considerable buried depth, especially in areas where the conventional survey is difficult to implement. Disaster recognition using the 3S technology plays an important role in safety monitoring. The GIS framework provides a suitable environment for spatially integrating several layers, all of which can contribute to the susceptibility of a given area to disasters (Abraham et al. 2020; Dhakal et al. 2000; Liu et al. 2019; Saraf 1999). When developing a model to predict landslide susceptibility, a digital elevation model (DEM) plays a significant role in deriving the elevation, slope aspect, and slope angle (Lee et al. 2001; Kahal et al. 2021). Remote sensing interpretation of geological disasters is characterized by professionality, pertinence, and empiricism. According to previous investigation results of geological hazards, we have discussed SPOT and Google images; 37 geological disasters were interpreted using the comprehensive interpretation method, including 28 collapses and nine landslides. These disasters were concentrated in two regions along the tunnel and roads, particularly along the Leh–Manali highway.

Considering the geotechnical conditions, especially the rock structure and disaster location offers an important reference for risk assessment. Different types of rocks have different uniaxial compressive, tensile, and shear strengths. Here, we considered the geotechnical conditions and different rock mass types, rock structure (strength, types and properties of discontinuities, and fault zones), hydraulic properties and conditions, and the size and location of the tunnel. The identified rocks were classified into seven levels using remote sensing in mapping and recognition studies of rocks on the satellite images, combined with the petrophysical parameters collected as detailed above. The rocks in border regions are relatively soft and are affected by geological structures, and the petrography characteristics are easily deformed. The abovementioned coincident sites with geological disasters can be analyzed. Based on this approach, ten hazards were identified in the study area; these hazards were classified into three levels and were primarily concentrated in and around two regions (in or near the tunnel's north and south portals; Table 2, Figure 4).

Table 2. Characteristics of three hazard levels.

Hazard Rating	Characteristics	Numbers
I	These hazards are strongly affected by the development of geological disasters or other large-scale vibrations, which will induce damage and fragmentation of the covering rock mass in the tunnel. A difficult situation might cause tunnel collapse.	1–4
II	These hazards are affected by the development of geological disasters; they will influence the tunnel and its road traffic capacity.	5–8
III	These hazards have a small effect on traffic safety but should be considered.	9

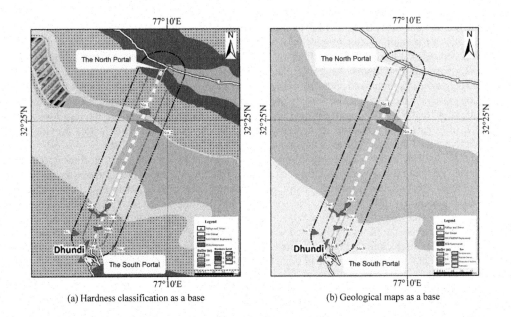

(a) Hardness classification as a base   (b) Geological maps as a base

Figure 4. Risk assessment results.

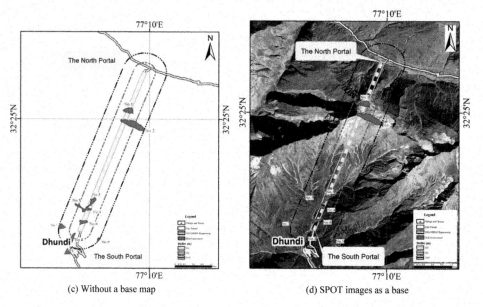

(c) Without a base map (d) SPOT images as a base

Figure 4. Continued.

4 DISCUSSION

Geotechnical design, in addition to the consideration of economic considerations, safety during construction, stability, and environmental aspects, involves the rapid installation of support measures and simple changes (adaptations) to excavation methods and adoption of support measures based on actual geotechnical conditions. In this study, land cover information and fault fractures were extracted from satellite images in a clear, concise, and targeted manner. Existing geological maps in the study area exhibit several similarities with this extracted information, implying that it is possible to use the 3S technology to aid in site selection and guarantee the safety of tunnels, especially in mountainous topography areas with high altitudes and inaccessibility.

The geological linkages between fundamental data and risk assessment information revealed that RS, particularly principal component analysis and the directional filtering of satellite images, could deliver an important and interesting risk assessment map of the Atal Tunnel. Both engineering geology analysis and geological disaster recognition were necessary to delineate risk areas. These results show that RS-based multi-informational synthetic analysis can estimate the locations and trends of targets. The outcomes of applying this approach to the Atal Tunnel area provided a predictive model that could be used to conduct a susceptibility risk assessment.

The geological model for the Atal Tunnel was developed in several steps, according to the project's different stages. When lacking geological and drilling surveys, several important geological problems that affect design and construction cannot be identified in advance; these geological uncertainties can result in casualties, increase costs, and prolong the construction period. Similar to the Atal Tunnel area, the Inner Himalayas feature complex geological conditions, such as a large burial depth, active faults, and high altitudes. Increasing numbers of tunnels will be constructed in this area in the future, and therefore, the method used in this study offers an approach to delineate risk assessment areas and contribute to tunnel construction safety in the Himalayas. Based on our results, we suggest that 3S can play an important role in the comprehensive comparison of site selection as well as guaranteeing the safety of tunnels.

However, the materials used in this study are still limited, and the tunnel is also targeted. We hope the methods we used will contribute to the tunnel construction safety in areas similar to where the Atal Tunnel is located, and it does not apply to all aspects. Tunnel construction is affected by various factors, and it is unlikely that any stand-alone method based on a single causal factor would be able to ensure tunnel safety. The influencing degrees of different factors differ between regions, and economic factors must sometimes be considered. These issues will be studied in the future.

FUNDINGS

This study was supported by the Key Laboratory of Airborne Geophysics and Remote Sensing Geology Foundation projects (2020YFL29) and the Programs of the China Geological Survey

ACKNOWLEDGMENTS

We thank Jianxin Zhou and Wenzhi Zhang for their assistance with data collection and study conceptualization, particularly for their valuable discussion. We also would like to acknowledge James Francis for editing this manuscript.

REFERENCES

Abraham, M. T., Satyam, N., Pradhan, B., Alamri, A. M. (2020). Forecasting of landslides using rainfall severity and soil wetness: A probabilistic approach for Darjeeling Himalayas. *Water.* 12, 804.

Agarwal, K. K., Shah, R. A., Achyuthan, H., Singh, D. S., Srivastava, S., Khan, I. (2018). Neotectonic activity from Karewa Sediments, Kashmir Himalaya, India. *Geotectonics.* 52, 88–99.

Ahmad, S., Bhat, M. I. (2012). Tectonic geomorphology of the Rambiara basin SW Kashmir Valley reveals an emergent out-of-sequence active fault system. *Himalayan Geol.* 33, 162–172.

Akram, M. S., Mirza, K., Zeeshan, M., Ali, I. (2019). Correlation of tectonics with geologic lineaments interpreted from remote sensing data for Kandiah Valley, Khyber-Pakhtunkhwa, Pakistan. *J. Geol. Soc. India.* 93, 607–613.

Ba, M. H., Ibouh, H., Lo, K., Youbi, N., Jaffal, M., Ernst, R. E., et al. (2020). Spatial and temporal distribution patterns of Precambrian mafic dyke swarms in northern Mauritania (West African craton): analysis and results from remote-sensing interpretation, geographical information systems (GIS), Google Earth ™images, and regional geology. *Arab. J. Geosci.* 13, 209.

Baghdadi, N., Grandjean, G., Lahondère, D., Paillou, P., Lasne, Y. (2005). Apport de l'imagerie satellitaire radar pour l'exploration géologique en zones arides. *C. R. Geosci.* 337, 719–728.

Basavaiah, N., Appel, E., Lakshmi, B. V., Deenadayalan, K., Satyanarayana, K. V. V., Misra, S., et al. (2010). Revised magnetostratigraphy and characteristics of the fluviolacustrine sedimentation of the Kashmir basin, India, during Pliocene–Pleistocene. *J. Geophys. Res.* 115, 17.

Bhatt, D. K. (1989). Lithostratigraphy of the Karewa Group, Kashmir valley, India and a critical review of its fossil record. Mem. *Geol. Surv. India.* 122, 1–85.

Burbank, D. W., Johnson, G. D. (1982). Intermontane-basin development in the past 4 Myr in the northwest Himalaya. *Nature.* 298, 432–436.

Burbank, D. W., Johnson, G. D. (1983). The Late Cenozoic chronologic and stratigraphic development of the Kashmir intermontane basin, Northwestern Himalaya. Palaeogeogr. Palaeoclimatol. *Palaeoecol.* 43, 205–235.

Cetin, M., Sevik, H. (2016). Evaluating the recreation potential of Ilgaz Mountain national park in turkey. environ. *Monit. Assess.* 188, 52.

Dhakal, A., Amada, T., Aniya, M. (2000). Landslide hazard mapping and its evaluation using GIS: an investigation of sampling schemes for a grid-cell based quantitative method. *Remote Sens.* 66, 981–989.

Kahal, A. Y., Abdelrahman, K., Alfaifi, H. J., Yahya, M. M. A. (2021). Landslide hazard assessment of the Neom promising city, Northwestern Saudi Arabia: an Integrated Approach. *J. King Saud Univ. Sci.* 33. 101279.

Lee, C. F., Li, J., Xu, Z. W., Dai, F. C. (2001). Assessment of landslide susceptibility on the natural terrain of Lantau Island, Hong Kong. *Environ. Geol.* 40, 381–391.

Liu, G. W., Wang, C. J., Li, G. H., Gao, W. F., Zhang, Z. G. (2019). Application research on the remote sensing technology in geological disaster prevention and control of the existing railway. *J. Railway Eng. Societ.* 249, 23–27.

Mukherjee, S. (2015). *A review on out-of-sequence deformation in the Himalaya*, in. (Lond.) Spec. Publ., eds. S. Mukherjee, R. Carosi, P. van der Beek, B. K. Mukherjee, and D. Robinson. 412, 67–109.

Pour, A. B., Hashim, M. (2015). Hydrothermal alteration mapping from Landsat-8 data, Sar Cheshmeh copper mining district, south-eastern Islamic Republic of Iran. *J. Taibah Univ. Sci.* 9, 155–166.

Pour, A. B., Hashim, M. (2015). Integrating PALSAR and ASTER data for mineral deposits exploration in tropical environments: a case study from Central Belt, Peninsular Malaysia. *Int. J. Image Data Fusion.* 6, 170–188.

Rezaei, A., Hassani, H., Moarefvand, P., Golmohammadi, A. (2020). Lithological mapping in the Sangan region in Northeast Iran using ASTER satellite data and image processing methods. *Geol. Ecol. Landscapes.* 4, 59–70.

Saraf, A. K. (1999). IRS-1C-LISS-III and PAN data fusion: an approach to improve remote sensing based mapping techniques. *Int. J. Remote Sens*. 20, 1929–1934.

Study of external FRP-angle combination reinforcement node method

Chen Qianqian*
Wanjiang University of Technology, Maanshan, China

Xu Ruiqing*
China Mcc17 Group Co., Ltd, Maanshan, China

ABSTRACT: In order to reduce the collapse of the whole building caused by the failure of the joints, the method of strengthening the beam-column joint with an external FRP-Angle combination is proposed. This paper draws the following conclusions through comparison and analysis of low-profile repeated loading experiment, and numerical simulation of externally attached FRP-Angle concrete T joint: (1) The shape and trend of the force-displacement curves of the beam end in the T-node test and the finite element simulation are roughly the same. The ultimate load of the numerical simulation is very close to the experimental value, and the beam end displacement in the numerical simulation is smaller than the experimental value. (2) The crack development of the finite element simulated specimen is consistent with that of the specimen in the test process. (3) With the increase of concrete deformation, the FRP stress increases gradually but does not reach the ultimate stress. FRP plays a certain role in bearing the tensile stress of concrete and restraining the deformation of concrete, which is consistent with the experiment. (4) When the specimens are destroyed, the stress of the upper and lower angle steel exceeds the yield strength, and the stress concentration phenomenon appears around the bolt hole. The angle steel undertook a partial shear force and bending moment in the joint combination reinforcement. Therefore, it is effective and feasible to use ANSYS to simulate the experiment of FRP- Angle combination strengthening beam-column joint, which lays a foundation for the subsequent use of numerical simulation techniques to study the influence of different strengthening methods on the mechanical properties of joint.

1 INTRODUCTION

Beam-column joint, as the force transmission hub of the frame structure, plays the role of connecting the beam-column, coordinating component deformation, and ensuring structural integrity. In recent years, multiple earthquake disasters have shown that it is also the weak and most vulnerable part of the frame structure. The failure of the joint usually leads to the overall collapse of the structure. In order to reduce such damage, it is urgent to carry out effective seismic reinforcement for the beam-column joint (Xu 2015). For the reinforcement of concrete frame joints, a lot of research has been done both at home and abroad. The reinforcement methods are to increase the section, paste steel plate, outsource steel, and so on. Due to the lightweight and soft material of FRP, which can be cut and bent, short construction period, and no wet operation, FRP reinforcement methods have been developing in the recent 25 years, attracted increasing attention from the engineering community, and a lot of research results have been published (Huang 2004; Lu 2004; Wu 2005; Xian 2007; Yu 2004). However, FRP is a brittle material with poor ductility, which is not conducive to stress redistribution, and it is easy to fall off at the negative angle of the beam column. Moreover, there is less research on using the nonlinear finite element method to simulate the reinforcement of

---

*Corresponding Authors: 1032602846@qq.com and 783450688@qq.com

frame joint with external FRP. Therefore, this paper puts forward the method of external FRP-Angle combination reinforcement, which is to paste FRP on the surface of the beam and column and paste Angle steel on the negative corner of the beam and column. The angle steel can not only prevent the fall off of FRP material, but also strengthen the node. At the same time, this paper also uses ANSYS software to conduct numerical simulation for the experiment of strengthening beam-column joint with external FRP-Angle combination, which lays a foundation for the subsequent use of numerical analysis techniques to study the mechanical properties of the unreinforced joint, only pasting FRP and external FRP-Angle combination method.

2 EXPERIMENT

2.1 Laboratory equipment and loading method

The experimental equipment for this test is shown in Figure 1. The axial loading force at the column end of the T joint specimen is 200 kN, which is applied by the hydraulic jack at the column end at one time, and remained constant in the test. The horizontal low cyclic load is applied to the beam end, which is controlled by displacement. Before the loading displacement of the beam end reaches 8 mm (equivalent to the beam end displacement when the unreinforced node yields), the load increases by 1 mm at each stage, and the cycle is repeated once. When the loading displacement of the beam end reaches 8 mm, the displacement of each loading actuator increases by 2mm, and the cycle is repeated three times. When the peak load of the specimen drops to 85% of the maximum peak load, it is considered to have reached the failure load (Wang 2008).

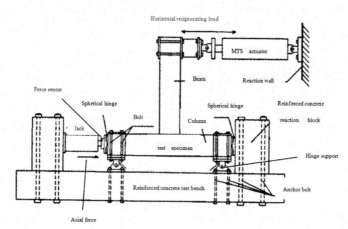

Figure 1. Experimental equipment.

2.2 Test model

The reinforcement diagram of the T joint test specimen is shown in Figure 2, and the compressive strength of concrete is 30.8MPa. T joint is externally reinforced with the FRP-Angle combination, as shown in Figure 3. The FRP is made of the unidirectional carbon fiber cloth, with an elastic modulus of 230 GPa, mass per unit area of 200 g/m^2, and tensile strength of 3650MPa. The angle steel is Q235 equilateral angle steel. Firstly, the node core area is wrapped with two layers of U-shaped FRP in the horizontal direction, and the horizontal fiber cloth is extended to the two sides of the beam end outside the core area to enhance the shear strength of the node core area. Secondly, at the negative angle formed by the beam end and the column end, two layers of L-shaped FRP are pasted, and the beam and column are extended along a certain length. The width of FRP is equal to that of the beam to enhance the flexural performance of the beam end. After completing the above operation, three layers of FRP are wound at the ends of the U-shaped and L-shaped cloth to enhance the anchoring effect and restrain the concrete of the beam and column end to a certain extent. Finally, two layers of vertical FRP are added to the side of the core area to enhance the shear performance of the joint further. In addition to FRP reinforcement, two additional Q-235 equilateral angle steel of L160mm×12mm type are added at the negative angle of the beam and column for combined reinforcement, and they are installed with epoxy adhesive and M16×190 bolt. The addition of angle steel will further strengthen the bending strength of the beam end of the joint point[7].

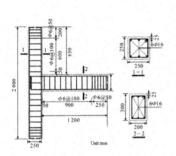
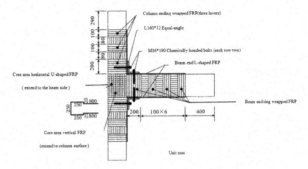

Figure 2. Reinforcement diagram of T node.

Figure 3. External FRP-Angle combination reinforcement node.

3 NUMERICAL SIMULATION

3.1 Finite element model

To establish a finite element model with ANSYS, it will be tedious to take the whole modeling because the specimen has symmetry in the Z direction, so only take half of the structure for modeling, which can not only greatly reduce the number of nodes and units of the model, but also save memory and improve the calculation speed. The finite element model, as shown in Figure 4 to Figure 10.

3.2 Selection of model element body

The steel distribution of the specimen model is relatively uniform, so the integral model can be adopted; that is, all the steel is dispersed into the solid concrete unit. The concrete unit adopts SOLID65, the steel unit adopts LINK8, and the FRP unit adopts Shell41. It is assumed that the bond between the concrete and steel and FRP and concrete is good without considering the bond slip. Angle steel and bolt units are SOLID45. In order to avoid the stress concentration phenomenon and make the calculation results easy to converge, this paper especially sets steel pad block at the loading place when the specimen is loaded. The pad block unit also adopts SOLID45. The contact pairs of the TARGE170 element and CONTA173 element are adopted to simulate the bond relationship between angle steel and FRP and bolt and concrete. The contact stiffness is defined as 0.1 and 0.15, respectively. The diffusion crack mode is selected, the transfer coefficient of closed crack is set as 0.9, and that of cracking load is set as 0.5.

3.3 Selection of material constitutive relation

The constitutive model proposed by E. Honested in the United States, namely the multi-linear follow-up strengthening material model KINH, is applied in concrete, and the failure criterion of concrete is the Willam-Warnke five-parameter failure criterion. Steel includes steel bar, angle steel, and bolt. It is assumed that they are ideal elastic-plastic materials. Bilinear follow-up strengthening model BKIN is adopted in the constitutive model. FRP is assumed to be an ideal linear elastic material with ultimate strength and only tensile strength. For specific content, please refer to the reference (Xu 2015).

3.4 *Loading method and boundary conditions*

Considering the complexity of the model used in this paper, it is difficult to achieve convergence of the results by low-cycle repeated loading, so the T-shaped frame node is subjected to monotonic displacement loading. The end of the column is hinged by a spherical joint, and a symmetric constraint is imposed on the symmetric surface. The load is applied in two steps: first, the axial pressure is applied at the column end, and 200 KN force is evenly dispersed on the node; Second, the displacement load is applied to the beam end, and the point of displacement load is coupled to a certain point, and then the displacement load is applied to the point. Finite element simulation constraint and loading of T-shaped node are shown in Figure 11.

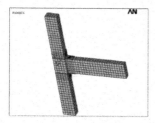

Figure 4. Finite element model.

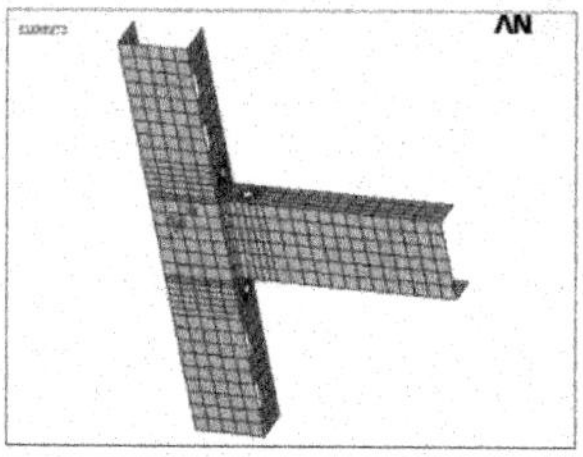

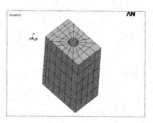

Figure 5. FRP finite element model around.

Figure 6. Concrete bolt element.

Figure 7. Loop wrapped FRP model.

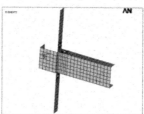

Figure 8. L, U FRP model.

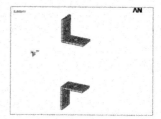

Figure 9. Angle steel model.

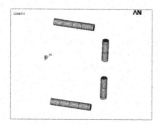

Figure 10. Bolt model.

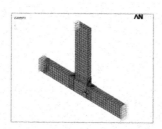

Figure 11. Constraints and loading diagram of T node.

4 COMPARATIVE ANALYSIS OF EXPERIMENT AND SIMULATION

4.1 Force-displacement curve of specimen beam end

Force-displacement curves of beam end of T-shaped joint test and finite element simulation are shown in Figure 12. As can be seen from the figure, the shape and trend of the two curves are roughly the same, and the numerical simulation ultimate load is very close to the experimental value. The numerical simulation ultimate load is 103.3kN, and the experimental ultimate load is 100.7kN, with a difference of 2.6%. The beam end displacement in the numerical simulation is much smaller than in the experiment. The beam end displacement in the numerical simulation is 24.8mm, and that in the experiment is 38mm, with a 34.7% difference. The reasons for the excessive displacement deviation are as follows: Firstly, the bond-slip phenomenon between steel bar and concrete, concrete and FRP, and FRP and FRP is not considered in the modeling of this paper. All of these will cause the stiffness of the specimen simulated by the finite element method to be slightly larger under the same load, resulting in smaller beam end displacement than the test value. Secondly, the specimens used in the test should be polished before reinforcement, which will weaken the specimen section to some extent and then affect the bearing capacity and stiffness of the specimen. Under the same load, the beam end displacement of the specimen with serious section weakening should be correspondingly larger. Thirdly, a low cyclic load is applied to the beam end in the test, while monotonous displacement is applied to the beam end in the numerical simulation, which also causes the displacement value of the finite element analysis to be less than the test value to some extent. In conclusion, under the same load, it is reasonable that the beam end displacement of the numerical simulation specimen is smaller than that of the test specimen.

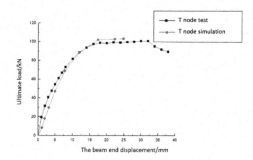

Figure 12. Comparison curve between T node test and finite element simulation.

4.2 Crack development and failure mode of specimens

The development process of cracks in the numerical simulation of a T-shaped node is shown in Figure 13. In the figure, red represents the micro-crack with small width, which is called the first crack; blue shows the final fracture with a larger width, known as the third fracture; green represents the width between the first crack and the third crack, called the second crack; bending crack is the short vertical line, while shear crack and cable-tension crack are inclined short straight lines (Wang 2009). At the initial stage of loading, slight bending cracks appear at the top edge of angle steel and beam, while no cracks appear in the node core area at the early stage of loading, as shown in Figure 4.13 (a). As the load increases, the cracks at the beam end gradually extend towards the direction of the beam compression zone and away from the node core zone, and a small number of cracks appear in the node core zone, as shown in Figure 4.13 (b). As the load continues to increase, the cracks at the beam end continue to increase rapidly in two directions: the compression zone at the bottom of the beam and the direction far from the node core zone, and the cracks at the node core zone also enter the stage of rapid development, with a large number of shear cracks occurring, as shown in Figure 4.13 (c) (d). With the further expansion of beam end displacement, cracks between beam end and node core area become dense, and many cracks also appear on the column, as shown in Figure 4.13 (e). The final morphology of fracture development is shown in Figure 4.13 (f). In general, the crack development of the finite element simulation specimen is the same as in the test process.

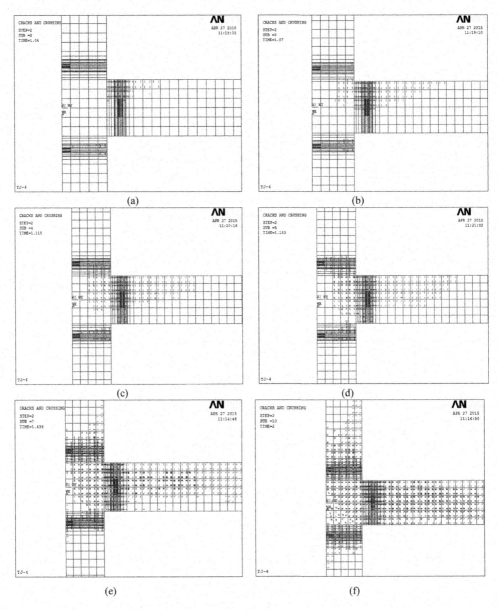

Figure 13. Crack development process of T-joint of specimen.

4.3 *Changes of FRP wrapped in specimens*

FRP is a new type of material with lightweight, high strength, tension, and no pressure. When the deformation of concrete in the core area only reaches a certain value, FRP can play a role and show superior performance. In this paper, the stress development process of L-type FRP in the y-direction is taken as an example. As can be seen from Figures 14–16, the stress on the FRP is very small at the initial loading stage. At the middle loading stage, the deformation of concrete increases, and the stress on FRP increases obviously. At the late loading stage, many third cracks appear, resulting in large deformation of concrete and a rapid increase of FRP stress. The stress is still increasing until the failure of the specimen. Finally, FRP does not reach the ultimate stress, and tensile failure occurs. The FRP wrapped in other parts is the same. In addition, although the FRP has not been destroyed, the stress of some parts of the FRP has reached a high value, such as the stress of u-type FRP in the core area and the stress of L-type FRP in the beam-column reaches about 1000MPa. These results indicate that FRP is important in indirectly participating in shear and bending resistance, directly bearing tensile stress, and restraining concrete in increasing concrete deformation. This is consistent with what is observed in the experiment.

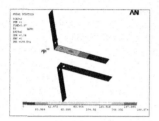

Figure 14. Y-direction stress of L FRP in early loading stage.

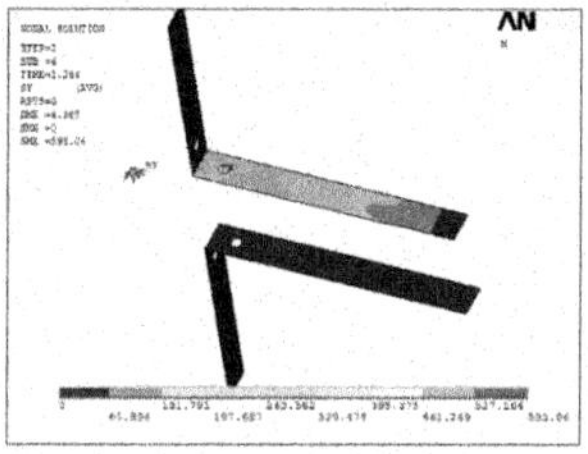

Figure 15. Y-direction stress of L FRP in middle loading stage.

Figure 16. 16 Y-direction stress of L FRP in destroy time.

4.4 Stress changes of Angle steel specimens

As can be seen from Figures 17–18, there is large tensile stress in the upper angle steel of the beam at the connection of the angle steel limbs and large compressive stress in the corresponding position of the angle steel at the lower part of the beam, and the maximum value is more than 300 MPa exceeding the yield stress of the steel. The stress level around the bolt hole is relatively high, reaching the yield stress of steel, and the stress concentration phenomenon appears around the bolt hole. The larger angle steel stress indicates that the angle steel bears part of the shear force and bending moment in the joint combination reinforcement. This is consistent with the experimental phenomenon.

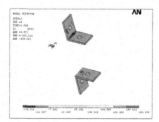

Figure 17. First principal strain diagram of angle steel.

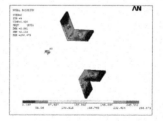

Figure 18. Angle steel MISES strain diagram.

5 CONCLUSION

This paper draws the following conclusions through comparison and analysis of low-profile repeated loading experiment, and numerical simulation of externally attached FRP-Angle concrete T joint:

(1) The shape and trend of the force-displacement curves of the beam end in the T-node test and the finite element simulation are roughly the same. The ultimate load of the numerical simulation is very close to the experimental value, and the beam end displacement in the numerical simulation is smaller than the experimental value. (2) The crack development of the finite element simulated specimen is basically consistent with that of the specimen in the test process. (3) With the increase of concrete deformation, the FRP stress increases gradually but does not reach the ultimate stress. FRP plays a certain role in bearing the tensile stress of concrete and restraining the deformation of concrete, which is consistent with the experiment. (4) When the specimens are destroyed, the stress of the upper and lower angle steel exceeds the yield strength, and the stress concentration phenomenon appears around the bolt hole. The angle steel undertook a partial shear force and bending moment in the joint combination reinforcement. Therefore, it is effective and feasible to use ANSYS to simulate the experiment of FRP-Angle combination strengthening beam-column joint, which lays a foundation for the subsequent use of numerical simulation techniques to study the influence of different strengthening methods on the mechanical properties of joint. However, it is assumed that the bond between steel bar and concrete and between concrete and FRP is good. There is no need to consider the bond-slip in this paper, which is not consistent with reality, so the analysis results have a certain gap with the real value; this problem needs to be further studied.

REFERENCES

Huang Xiaokui, Cui Kaicheng, Xiong Danan (2004). Experimental study on strengthening beam-column joints with carbon fiber cloth. *Journal of Wuhan University of Technology*. 26(2):30–33.

Lu Zhoudao, Song Yantao, Wang Liguo(2004). Experimental study on seismic resistance of carbon fiber reinforced concrete frame joints. *Structural Engineers*. 20(5):39–43.

Wang Bu, LIU Boquan, WANG Pu(2008). Test of T-joint of concrete reinforced with FRP. *Journal of Chang'an University*. 28(2): 69–74.

Wang Fengchao, LI Zhenbao, Lu Xiao, et al.(2009) Finite element analysis of crack width of reinforced concrete beams. *Journal of Disaster Prevention Science and Technology College*, 2011 (3): 01–04.

Wu Bo, Wang Weijun(2005). Experimental study on seismic behavior of reinforced concrete frame joints reinforced with carbon fiber cloth. *Journal of Civil Engineering*. 38(4):60–65.

Xian Qiaoling, Jiang Chuanliang, Zhou Fulin(2007). *Test and analysis of seismic strengthening of concrete frame joints with CFRP*. Earthquake Engineering and Engineering Vibration. 27(2):104–111.

Xu Ruiqing(2015). *Study of external FRP-Angle combination reinforcement node method* [D]. Xi'an: Chang'an University

Yu Qiong(2004). Discussion on reinforcement method of frame joints. *Structural Engineers*. 1(1):62–70.

Jacking construction technology of No.3 landscape bridge around Ma'an Island Road

Xu Qi* & Wen Dingxu*
CCCC WuHan Harbour Engineering Design And Research Co. Ltd, Wuhan, Hubei, China
Hubei Key Laboratory of Advanced Materials & Reinforcement Technology Research for Marine Environment Structures, Hubei, China
Research and Development Center of Transport Industry of Intelligent Manufacturing Technologies of Transport Infrastructure, Hubei, China

Yang Jun*
CCCC WuHan Harbour Engineering Design And Research Co. Ltd, Wuhan, Hubei, China

ABSTRACT: Maandao Huandao Road No.3 landscape bridge is a (50+50) m self-anchored suspension bridge, and the main arch tower is set along the bridge in the middle of the span. The main girder of steel box girder is 107m in length and 31.1m in width. The whole bridge adopts the construction technology of steel box girders and the main tower which is scattered on the shore and pushed on the top of the tower as a whole. Compared with the traditional drag method, the horizontal force is greatly reduced in the construction process, so the temporary pier structure is lighter and lighter. Multi-point hydraulic synchronous control technology can control the construction precision of jacking at the millimeter level. The new pier mounting device of the guide beam can solve the problem that the front end of the guide beam cannot be mounted due to too much deflection.

1 THE INTRODUCTION

Pusher construction technology is a kind of assembly construction method of the bridge that uses a multi-point propulsion device to move forward the beam structure, which is assembled or poured on the station section by section (Zhang 2003). There are some problems in traditional jacking construction, such as low synchronization of equipment, being prone to the "leapfrog" phenomenon, the uncontrollable reaction force of the supporting pier, and large damage to the main beam slip surface. The walking push construction technology creatively applies the self-leveling principle to bridge construction, solves the problems of large horizontal bearing capacity of piers, poor structural adaptability, and difficult linear control of construction, reduces the manufacturing cost of the equipment system, and greatly improves the efficiency and safety of bridge construction (Tan 2010). Western Express Highway and SV Road Santacruz are constructed by the Cantilever Incremental Launching method. It has been proved that bridge construction by this method results in lesser consumption in time and is economical for large projects (Manish 2020).

The walking jacking construction technology was first applied to the main girder construction of Hangzhou Jiubao Bridge in 2009. After nearly ten years of iteration and accumulation, its application scope has been expanded from the uniform section box girder jacking to the complex section bridge jacking, from the straight line jacking to the space curve jacking, and the jacking speed has also been increased from the initial less than 2m/h to 4m/h. The bridge assembly construction of a long-span beam arch composite system bridge, truss structure bridge, and minimal curvature

---

*Corresponding Authors: 719303393@qq.com, wendingxu@163.com and 413179891@qq.com

radius structure bridge across the main channel, canyon, railway, and highway is realized. Table 1 below lists several representative projects that adopt the walking push construction method.

Table 1. Representative projects constructed by the walking push method.

Time	Project name	Construction characters
2014	Wuhan Dongfeng Avenue Expressway (Ma 2019)	The idea of "bending instead of bending" is used to adapt to the variable height of the vertical curve, and the construction of adaptive fitting of steel box girder with variable height section is realized for the first time in the world.
2015	Beipanjiang Bridge of Bidu Expressway (Xie 2017)	The whole jacking construction of the truss structure bridge with the span layout of 80m+2×88m is realized for the first time by using the following jacking technology of steel truss beam joints.
2019	Exit ramp of Zhuhai Lotus Bridge (Huang 2020)	The construction of a steel box girder with a minimum curvature radius of 60m is realized for the first time in the world by using differential pushing technology.
2020	Jinan Fenghuang Yellow River Bridge	The total weight of a steel box girder is about 63,000 tons, realizing the largest weight, width and distance of a single steel box girder in the world.

2 ENGINEERING OVERVIEW

Ma 'an Island No. 3 Landscape Bridge is located in Zhongshan city, Guangdong Province. The length of the bridge is 107m, and the width of the deck is 31.1m. The hole span layout of the bridge is (50+50) m self-anchored suspension bridge. The cable auxiliary beam stress system is adopted in the design, and the main girder is a steel box girder with an equal section. The vertical curve adopts an arc line for transition, and the radius of the circular curve is 2000m.

The main girder adopts the form of a single box double chamber equal section steel box girder, the beam height is 2.0m, and the diaphragm connection is set between the two pieces. The width of the bottom plate of the steel box girder is 19m. A longitudinal baffle plate is set in the steel box girder to enhance its overall stiffness. The box body and the connection between sections are all welded.

The main tower adopts the "circular" structure, with the main beam as the dividing line, divided into the upper column and lower column, the upper column is steel structure, the section is trapezoidal isosection, the transverse width is 2m, the height is 1.4m, and the main beam is consolidated, the thickness of the roof, bottom plate, and web are 32mm. The lower tower is composed of a steel structure, concrete, and steel-concrete section. The cross-section of steel structure and concrete is 4m in standard transverse width, and the height is a variable section (see Figure 1).

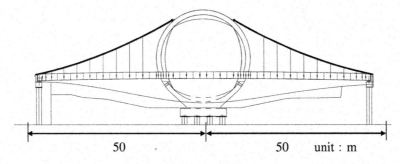

Figure 1. Elevation layout of Ma 'an Island No. 3 Landscape Bridge.

3 STEEL BOX GIRDER PUSH CONSTRUCTION SCHEME

Ma 'an Island No. 3 Landscape Bridge adopts the walking pushing method for construction. The overall construction scheme is as follows: after the steel box beams and the main tower are assembled, the whole tower is pushed to the top; after the pushing is in place, the beams are dropped, and the system is transformed, and then the bridge deck is paved. The whole bridge construction adopts 12 sets of 300 tons and eight sets of 1200 tons of walking pushing equipment.

Before pushing construction, set up the tire rack on the south bank assembly site for scattered box girders. The steel beam is processed in the factory and transported to the site for assembly. In order to reduce the workload of welding outside the factory and facilitate transportation, the main beam is divided into 30 sections, and the heaviest section is about 72.5 tons. After the beam section is transported to the assembly site, the steel box girder is hoisted and welded successively from the near shore side to the far shore side by using a 400-ton truck crane. After the completion of the main beam assembly, the main tower was assembled. The main tower was divided into seven sections, with the heaviest section being about 20.1 tons. First, we set up the main tower support bracket on the main beam, and then use 200 tons of truck crane for the main tower lifting. Each section of the arch rib is equipped with two lifting lugs, and 25 tons of hand-pulled gourds are set at the position of the lower lifting lugs to adjust the Angle of the tower. The general scheme of jacking construction is shown in Figure 2 below.

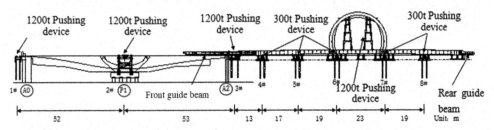

Figure 2. General scheme of jacking construction.

Before the top push, finish pouring the abutment of A0 and A2, and pour the retaining wall of the bridge pier after the completion of the falling beam. The design length of the jacking device is 116.89m, and the distance from the cross bridge to the center of the jacking device is 11.1m. The central span of the longitudinal design of the onshore push point is 25m, corresponding to the longitudinal web position of the steel box girder.

4 THE KEY TECHNOLOGY OF WALKING PUSHING CONSTRUCTION

4.1 Pushing facilities

4.1.1 Assembly frame

According to the position of the box girder joint, the assembled tire frame is set in the form of a steel cushion beam and low pier pile, as shown in Figure 3. In the construction of the tire frame, the longitudinal alignment and pre-camber of the bridge should be considered comprehensively, and the welding shrinkage allowance should be reserved. The transverse alignment should be constructed according to the designed transverse slope. In order to control the position and height of the beam section, longitudinal and transverse baselines and reference points are set on the tire frame in advance. An independent observation point is set outside the tire rack to monitor the tire rack at any time. A certain jacking space is reserved at the bottom and side of the tire frame to correct the linear changes of the steel beam caused by gravity, foundation settlement, and other factors.

The tread is supported by a steel foundation with a size of 1.5×1.5m and a height of 0.588m. In order to ensure that the maximum earth pressure of a single pile is less than 120KPa, it is

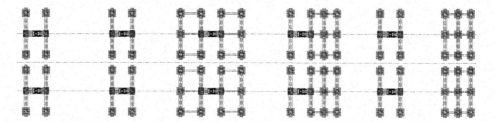

Figure 3. Flat layout of assembling tire rack.

necessary to conduct foundation treatment in advance for the position of the foundation. After completion of the treatment, construction of other structures on the ground. The elevation of the top surface of a single steel pipe pile is calculated according to the elevation of the top surface of the tire frame. The positioning accuracy and vertical accuracy of the steel pipe pile should be controlled during installation to avoid excessive errors. After the construction of each row of steel pipe piles is completed, the piles are connected to each other to increase their stability of the piles. The horizontal connection adopts φ 245*6 steel pipe connection. Pile cap construction shall be carried out after all steel pipe piles and connections are completed. Before construction, measure the elevation of the top of each pile, cut off the part of the steel pipe pile that is too high, and install the pile cap steel plate.

4.1.2 *Water temporary pier*

As a temporary bearing structure in construction, a temporary pier mainly bears the vertical force of a steel box girder and guide girder. The top of the temporary pier is a frame structure, the whole 3-piece HN800*300 beam is used for the transverse bridge, and the 5-piece HN800*300 box girder structure is used for the distribution beam to support the two 1200T pushing equipment. One supporting pier is arranged at 3m positions before and after each pushing device. The height of the pier is slightly higher than that of the bridge form about 80mm, and the top elevation is adjusted by adding and reducing pads and steel plates. The frame structure is φ 1000*10 steel pipe main column, the main column is connected with φ 630 * 8mm steel pipe as a whole, and the column and the cap are connected with an anchor structure.

4.1.3 *Guide beam*

The length of the guide beam is selected according to the maximum cantilever distance of the steel beam, and the maximum span of the jacking reaches 47.6m. In order to meet the requirements of the jacking while minimizing the weight of the guide beam, the design length of the lead beam is selected as about 0.7 times the maximum span. The guide beam is a plate beam with an I-shaped section, which is connected with a truss in the middle and is 35m long, as shown in Figure 4. In

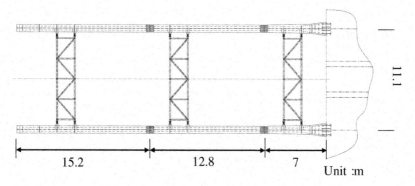

Figure 4. Plan of front guide beam structure.

order to facilitate transportation, the two main beams are divided into three sections, with a total weight of 58T. The root of the guide beam is connected by web and steel box girder mediastinum plate butt welding and external welding reinforcement plate. Corner using welding process hole, on both sides of the guide beam symmetrical arrangement.

In order to reduce the negative bending moment of the rear end cantilever of the jacking beam body and the support of the rear end when the beam falls, a set of rear guide beams is set. The guide beams are i-shaped plate beams with a length of 7m and a total weight of 11.3t.

4.1.4 Stepped pushing equipment

The whole bridge section uses 12 sets of 300T, and four sets of 1200T jacking system, each set of system consists of 1 jacking equipment and 1 hydraulic pump station. The jacking equipment has orthogonal independent vertical jacking, horizontal pushing and horizontal correction functions in space, which can realize the six-degree-of-freedom translation and rotation fine-tuning action of the beam body jacking, and can well complete the adjustment and forming of the linear jacking of the bridge.

In order to ensure the construction quality of jacking, the control system of the whole bridge adopts the principle of multi-point hydraulic synchronous control to ensure that the synchronous precision of horizontal jacking between piers is controlled within 5mm, and the synchronous precision of jacking and falling is controlled within 4mm. A pressure sensor is installed in the hydraulic system to monitor the load of each stress point, and the pressure difference on both sides of the pier is controlled within 10%. A horizontal Angle sensor is installed on the box girder, which can control the balance degree of the main girder. When the tilt Angle exceeds the set value, the system will stop and alarm, and start the horizontal Angle calibration program. After the calibration and adjustment is completed, the top push operation will continue.

During the construction, the maximum cantilever length of the guide beam is about 48m. In order to avoid that the front end of the guide beam is too large to bend down, leading to the failure of the pier, this project designed a guide beam pier mounting device. The device consists of a jack, an upper pier roller and an upper pier bracket. The pier mounting process of the guide beam is shown in Figure 5: a) Before the guide beam reaches the pier, install the upper pier roller on the pier; B) Jack up the end of the guide beam until the bottom surface of the guide beam is higher than the roller. The guide beam pier bracket down on the pier roller; C) Push forward the steel box

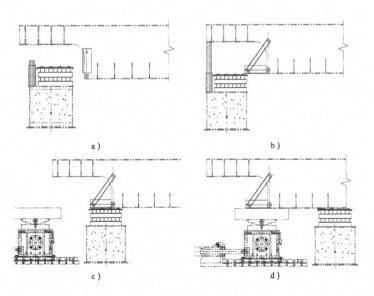

Figure 5. Diagram of upper pier of guide beam.

girder to the head of the guide beam beyond the support pier; D) Continue pushing forward the steel box girder to the next pushing equipment.

4.2 Steel box girder assembly and jacking

The steel box girder is lifted to the tire frame section by section by automobile crane for welding and assembly. The welding sequence is as follows: butt butt of bottom plate → butt butt of inner web of box girder → butt butt of stiffening rib → butt butt of roof → welding of auxiliary parts of bridge deck. In the welding process, the deformation of steel box girder should be measured in real time, mainly including the deformation of joints, the deviation of main beam axis, the length of segments after splicing (to avoid error accumulation) and the elevation difference of the bottom plate between two segments.

Due to the large span of steel box girder, it is necessary to add pre-arch amount when assembling. The elevation of final installation and positioning is superimposed with pre-arch amount curve of longitudinal section drawing design curve, and then the pre-arch value caused by uncertain factors such as temperature change and welding is comprehensively considered. After assembling the steel box girder and the main tower, the overall push shall be carried out. The specific construction steps are as follows:

(1) After assembling the front and rear guide beams on the ground, lift the whole to the front and rear ends of the box girder to complete docking with the box girder.
(2) Remove the arch rib assembling support, debug the pushing equipment, and start pushing after confirmation.
(3) The box girder is pushed forward 32.5m, and the front end of the guide beam reaches the position of 2# temporary pier. The guide beam pier mounting device is used to assist the pier mounting.
(4) Push the box girder forward, push the whole bridge in place, use 1#, 2#, 3# pushing equipment group to drop the box girder in place, after completing the system conversion, fix the box girder and bridge support, remove the front and rear guide beams and pushing equipment.

4.3 Pushing process equipment and pad height adjustment

The radius of the vertical curve of Maandao No. 3 landscape bridge is 2000m. Due to the difference between the construction vertical curve and the completed bridge vertical curve, in order to avoid the uneven deformation of the steel beam caused by the incomplete fitting of the jacking equipment and the bottom of the steel beam during the construction process, the height of the supporting piers should be adjusted according to the difference of the two vertical curves. When the elevation of the top of the pier is more than 10mm lower than the elevation of the bottom of the box girder, it indicates that the pier needs to copy the pad, 10mm thick steel plate can be used; If the support reaction force exceeds the theoretical calculation value by more than 10%, it means that the height of the backing plate should be reduced and the gravity of the steel box girder should be evenly distributed to other surrounding support piers.

4.4 Falling beam construction

After the jacking construction is completed, the steel box girder should be converted from temporary pier to permanent pier for fixing. In the process of girder falling, the monitoring unit should use the total station instrument to monitor the mileage, deflection and other parameters of the box girder to ensure that the bridge form of the box girder is consistent with the design form. In the process of beam falling, the relative elevation difference between two adjacent temporary piers does not exceed the theoretical calculation value. After completion of the girder fall, the steel box girder is fixed to the permanent pier, and then the front and rear guide beams and temporary piers are removed.

4.5 Construction monitoring

In each construction process, the jacking displacement, pushing displacement and deviation correction displacement of the box girder, and the deviation of the center line position of the box girder and the guide beam were monitored. The jacking, propelling and rectifying displacements are directly measured by the displacement sensors in the three directions of the equipment. They not only directly reflect the displacement of the box girder, but also reflect the synchronous error of each jacking point action. During the construction process, the sensor will transmit the measured value to the man-machine interaction interface of the main console in real time. The operator will judge the synchronization of each point according to the feedback data. If the displacement synchronization error of each point is large, it should stop immediately and find the cause of the problem.

Midline deviation monitoring of steel box girder and guide girder is mainly to measure the deviation of web position of box girder relative to temporary support point. The web of box girder is the function point of each pushing equipment. In order to prevent deformation caused by excessive local stress, it has been strengthened. If the offset of the box girder is too large, the operating point of the equipment deviates from the web position, which will affect the construction quality. During measurement, mark the web position on the bottom surface of the box girder directly. After each push, measure the offset of the mark. If the offset exceeds the specified value, correct the deviation.

4.6 Computational analysis

4.6.1 Overhead overall calculations

According to the structural characteristics of the project, ANSYS software is used to calculate and analyze the structural strength and fulcrum reaction force in the process of jacking. The main steel structure box girder, front and rear guide beam truss and support structure are simulated by BEAM188 element.

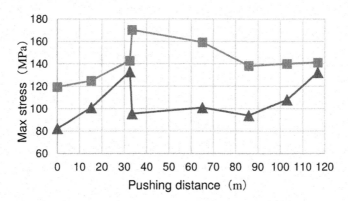

Figure 6. Stress variation curves of steel box girder and guide girder during pusher construction.

According to the calculation (as shown in Figure 6), when the jacking reaches 32.5m, the front end of the steel box girder is in the maximum cantilever state, and the overall maximum stress of the box girder is 133.1mpa, which appears at the contact position between the 3# jacking device and the steel box girder, which is less than the design value of steel tensile and bending strength 305MPa. The maximum displacement is −59.03mm, which appears at the connection position between the steel box girder and the guide girder. After pushing 1m forward, the stress of the guide beam suddenly increases from 142.8mpa to 170.2mpa. This is because after the front end of the guide beam is mounted, the guide beam and box beam between P1 and A2 piers form a simply supported beam structure, and the maximum stress is generated when the guide beam bends down under its own gravity. At this time, the maximum displacement of the guide beam is -54.4mm.

In the process of jacking construction, the maximum cantilever length at the tail of box girder is reduced from 16m to 9m due to the design of front and rear double guide beams, which improves construction safety.

4.6.2 Calculation of local structure

According to the overall calculation, the maximum reaction force of the towing fulcrum of the walking pushing equipment is 6350kN (considering 1.2 unbalance coefficient), and the contact surface of the pushing equipment is designed to be 1200mm in the direction of the bridge × 700mm in the direction of the bridge.

1) Calculation of zone between compression flange and longitudinal stiffener

When the steel beam is jacked up, the lower flange of the steel beam is pressed and the upper flange is pulled. When the slide block is between two adjacent diaphragmers of the box beam, the web is most dangerous. According to the Code for Design of Steel Structures, there is a short stiffener between the compression flange and the longitudinal stiffener, and its local stability can be calculated as follows:

$$\frac{\sigma}{\sigma_{cr1}} + \left(\frac{\tau}{\tau_{cr1}}\right)^2 + \left(\frac{\sigma_c}{\sigma_{c,cr1}}\right)^2 = \frac{123.5}{295} + \left(\frac{74.92}{175}\right)^2 + \left(\frac{82.68}{295}\right)^2 = 0.68 < 1 \quad (1)$$

where, σ is the bending compressive stress at the height edge of the web calculated by the average bending moment, and σ = 123.5 MPa calculated according to the general figure; τ is the average shear stress of the web caused by the average shear force, τ = 74.92MPa; σc is the local compressive stress at the edge of the calculated height of the web, which is 82.68 MPa; $\sigma cr1$, $\tau cr1$, σc, cr1 are the critical stresses under single stress, which are 295MPa, 175MPa and 295MPa respectively. The calculation shows that the local stability of the panel web between the compressive flange and the longitudinal stiffener of the steel box girder meets the requirements.

2) Lattice calculation between tensile flange and longitudinal stiffener

In the region between the tension flange and the longitudinal stiffener, its local stability can be calculated as follows:

$$\left(\frac{\sigma_2}{\sigma_{cr2}}\right)^2 + \left(\frac{\tau}{\tau_{cr2}}\right)^2 + \frac{\sigma_{c2}}{\sigma_{c,cr2}} = \left(\frac{126}{295}\right)^2 + \left(\frac{99.7}{175}\right)^2 + \frac{31.2}{295} = 0.61 \leq 1 \quad (2)$$

Where, σ is the bending compressive stress at the height edge of the web calculated by the average bending moment, and σ = 126 MPa; τ is the average shear stress of the web caused by the average shear force, calculated τ = 99.7MPa; the transverse compressive stress of $\sigma c2$ web at the longitudinal stiffener is 31.2 MPa; $\sigma cr2$, $\tau cr2$, σc, cr2 are the critical stresses under various stresses, which are 295 MPa, 175 MPa, and 295 MPa, respectively. It can be seen from the calculation that the local stability of the grid web between the tensile flange of the steel girder and the longitudinal stiffener meets the requirements.

5 CONCLUSION

The conclusions are as follows: (1)Walking jacking construction technology has been widely used in modern bridge construction, becoming the first choice to cross deep mountains, valleys and existing traffic lines. (2)The existing technology also has the problems of poor adaptability of equipment and low degree of automation. Especially in long-distance jacking, in order to adapt to the changes of bridge alignment and jacking path, the elevation of temporary pier top needs to be constantly adjusted during construction to ensure that the beam body is always in the ideal stress state. (3) "Mechanized replacement, automatic reduction, intelligent unmanned" will become the development trend of the entire construction industry, through scientific and technological means to improve construction efficiency, reduce labor costs will also become a new direction of the development of walking push technology.

REFERENCES

Huang Jun, Zhang Hongqing, Qu Hongbo, Li Qizhi, Chen Zhi. Construction technology of steel box girder with small radius of curvature [J]. *Building technology*,2020,51(08):921–924.

Ma Qiongfeng, LIU Haiqing. Research on pushing technology of steel box girder with variable section [J]. *China and foreign highway*,2019,39(05):149–152.

Manish Kotpalliwar, Nitesh Kushwaha. Incremental Launching of the Steel Girders for Bridges[J]. *Journal of Trend in Scientific Research and Development*,2020,4(2).

Tan Xinghua, Yu Yunliang, Yang Weiping, Liu Yiqun. Research on Construction Method of Steel Groove Girder of Jiubao Bridge [J]. *Highway*,2010(06):92–98.

Xie Daoping, Liu Yiping, Wu Mingwei, Liu Dongdong. Research and application of jacking technology of long-span steel truss girder [J]. *Sino-foreign highway*,2017,37(04):190–192.

Zhang Xiaodong. Construction technology of bridge jacking [J]. *Highway*,2003(09):45–51.

Analysis of influence effect of widening subgrade fill width on deformation

Zhiqiang Wang*, Junjie Fan* & Shijie Cui*
China Power Construction Municipal Construction Group Co., Ltd, Tianjin, China

Wenbin Xiao*
School of Civil Engineering, Shandong University, Jinan, China

ABSTRACT: Based on the South Ring Road widening project in Shuozhou City, Shanxi Province, the settlement deformation of the subgrade widening project in the loess area is studied and analyzed through project site investigation and evaluation, finite difference numerical simulation, and theoretical analysis. On this basis, the influence of fill width on the deformation of new and old subgrades is studied and analyzed, which provides a reference for other subgrade widening projects.

1 INTRODUCTION

With the rapid development of China's economy, the existing road construction has gradually failed to meet the increased traffic demand of the developing economy. Coupled with the high cost of new road construction and complex construction conditions, the lower cost of re-expansion, and the close connection with the existing traffic network, road re-expansion projects are more widely used in the practice of road upgrading (Pang 2021; Yang 2022; Zhu 2020). Therefore, the various engineering problems encountered in the roadbed widening process have become a hot spot for various experts and scholars to study.

Zheng introduced a more applicable reconstruction construction technology based on roadbed widening projects (Zheng 2020). Xia proposed to follow the principle of choosing the best option according to local conditions when selecting the roadbed widening plan (Xia 2022). Yan analyzed the effects of the roadbed widening method, filling height, widening width, and soil base modulus on the differential settlement produced by widening the roadbed through ANSYS finite element calculation and analysis software (Yan 2020). Chen analyzed a new roadbed construction technology used in concrete pavement widening and reconstruction (Chen 2020). Wang studied the differential settlement of widened pavements (Wang 2018). Li studied the differential settlement characteristics of widening old and new roadbeds using FLAC3D finite difference software and concluded that the increase in widening the width of old and new roadbeds produced less impact on the old roadbed (Li 2020). Zhong chose a new material, lightweight bubble water, as the roadbed material when conducting roadbed filling and systematically analyzed the differential settlement of widened pavement (Zhong 2019).

For the aspect of highway widening project, domestic scholars have conducted a lot of related research, but there are less research on highway widening in loess areas and less research on the differential settlement characteristics of old and new roadbeds. To accurately grasp the differential settlement characteristics of the old and new roadbed widening projects, this paper uses FLAC3D finite difference software to explore the differential settlement characteristics of the old and new

---

*Corresponding Authors: 58401173@qq.com, 2587065175@qq.com, 1132453148@qq.com and 1422539796@qq.com

roadbed widening projects under different influencing factors and simulates the law of differential settlement characteristics of the old and new roadbed widening.

2 NUMERICAL SIMULATION AND ANALYSIS

2.1 Project overview

The project is located in the northwest corner of the new industrial park of Shuozhou Economic Development Zone, a municipal road network supporting a municipal pipeline project. The existing roadbed width of South Ring Road is 24.0 m, and the pavement structure adopts asphalt concrete, which has been seriously damaged. This construction is an old road renovation project. The South Ring Road is the city's main road, which has four lanes. It is designed to widen to six two-way lanes, and the road location is shown in Figure 1 below.

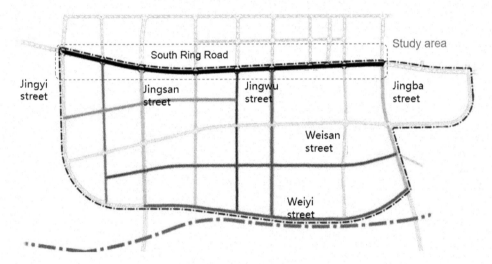

Figure 1. General layout of construction.

According to the site drilling, in-situ testing, and indoor geotechnical test results, the road foundation soil can be divided into two layers from top to bottom.

The ① layer ($Q4_2^{ml}$) for the plain fill: yellow-brown, mainly powder, containing coal chips, plant roots, etc., slightly wet to wet, slightly dense.

The ②th layer ($Q4^{al+pl}$) is loess chalk: brownish-yellow, containing mica, iron oxide, alumina, etc., slightly wet, slightly dense, with medium to high compressibility. The characteristic value of foundation bearing capacity is 100 kPa.

2.2 Old road widening method

The design width after widening is 36 m. The cross-sectional composition is. It consists of a 4.5 m non-motorized lane, 2.0 m green belt, and 11.5 m motorized lane.

Widening process simulation: the South Ring Road expansion project is used as the simulation object. The South Ring Road expansion project includes 4.2 m old roadbed excavation and removal and new roadbed filling. The filling process is divided into two parts: the first stage has a filling width of 4.2 m, and the second stage has a filling width of 6.5 m. Each part of the filling has four structural layers: 27 cm natural gravel + 18 cm cement fly ash stabilized gravel layer + 18 cm cement fly ash stabilized gravel layer + 11 cm asphalt concrete.

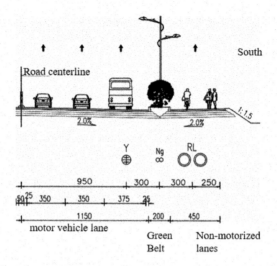

Figure 2. South Ring Road cross-sectional layout.

2.3 *Geometric conditions of the model selected in this paper*

The South Ring Road reconstruction and expansion project was used as the simulation object. The axial dimension of the road is much larger than the transverse dimension, so the spatial strain problem is considered plane strain, and a typical section of the road is selected for simulation. The calculation model size is established, as shown in Figure 3. The simulated section of the foundation soil layer is roughly divided into two layers: layer 1 is the loess layer, with a layer thickness of 2.5 m; layer 2 is a sub-clay layer, with a layer thickness of 2.5 m. The height of the old roadbed is 0.74 m. In the simulation, the length of the newly widened part is 6.5 m, and the height of the original embankment is the same, the same as 0.74 m.

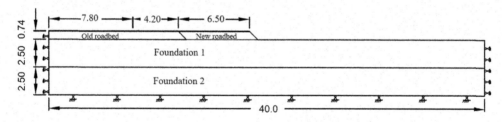

Figure 3. Geometric model.

2.4 *Assumptions of the model*

In the simulations, no water table is imposed, seepage consolidation of groundwater is not considered, and the model assumptions are as follows.

1. The simulation uses the M-C elastoplastic principal structure model.
2. The computational model is a symmetric structure; half of it is taken for the calculation.
3. The boundary conditions are horizontal and vertical constraints on the base of the foundation and horizontal constraints on both sides.
4. The model is homogeneous, continuous, and isotropic material.
5. The old roadbed under the foundation consolidation deformation is considered to have been completed.

To simplify the calculation process, the equivalent uniform load at the road surface is used to replace the effect of the traffic load. This paper uses the finite difference method to simulate the calculation, and the vehicle load is equivalent to a 10 kPa static load.

2.5 Grid division and boundary conditions

The widening project is a symmetrical bilateral widening, so it is subject to completely symmetrical loading, so half of the roadbed can be selected as the object of study, where the half-width of the old roadbed is 12m, the slope of the roadbed side slope is 1:1, each side of the widening length of 6.5 m, the grid division is shown in Figure 4.

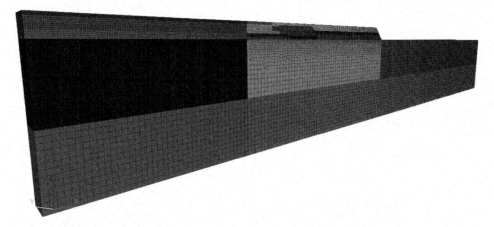

Figure 4. Schematic diagram of model meshing.

The calculation parameters of the old roadbed are determined according to the original road design information, as shown in Table 1.

Table 1. Parameters of each material.

Soil layer	Bulk modulus (Pa)	Shear modulus (Pa)	Cohesion(Pa)	friction(°)	Density(kg/m^3)
Asphalt	9.52e9	8.7e9	1e6	50	2400
Gravel	9.5e7	8.6e7	5e5	25	2200
Natural gravel	1.5e7	6.1e5	0	35	1500
Loess	3.4e6	1.5e6	6.5e4	31	1900
Sub-clay	3.1e6	1.9e6	4.1e3	13.5	1960

3 DEFORMATION IMPACT ANALYSIS

In this paper, two sections of soil backfilling with different widths of the same project are studied to analyze the internal stress-strain changes of the roadbed soil and to explore the characteristics and laws of the old and new roadbeds under different conditions. Based on the finite difference calculation model, to analyze the influence of different widening widths on roadbed deformation, this paper analyzes and calculates the two stages of roadbed filling.

Figures 5 and 6 are the vertical settlement clouds at different sections of roadbed filling widths. The figure shows that the roadbed settlement changed significantly during the filling process. Comparing one and two sections of roadbed filling can be seen that the increase of roadbed filling width not only increases the settlement of the roadbed, but also intensifies the uneven settlement. It can be analyzed that the settlement of the widened roadbed increases with the increase of the new roadbed width, and the maximum settlement produced when the widened roadbed width is 4.2 m is 1.50 cm, and when the widened roadbed width is 6.5 m, the maximum settlement produced reaches 2.42 cm. In the widening of the second section of the roadbed, the first section of the widening of the roadbed occurred to a certain extent of the bulge. The analysis is because the filling for the second section of filling, and with the first section of filling time interval is not long, filling the first section of the soil filled did not complete consolidation settlement, so the first section of filling soil extrusion produced a small amount of bulge.

Figure 7 and Figure 8 are the horizontal displacement clouds at different sections of roadbed filling width. It can be found that the trend of horizontal displacement generated at different sections of filling is the same; that is, at the location directly below the new and old roadbed lap, near the top of the foundation, there is a trend for the formation of a horizontal displacement area close to the old roadbed, at the same time, directly below the foot of the newly widened roadbed slope, there is a trend for the formation of a horizontal displacement area away from the centerline of the road displacement area. The maximum horizontal displacement generated at the widened roadbed width of 4.2 m was 0.19 cm, and when the widened roadbed width was 6.5 m, the maximum horizontal displacement generated reached 0.45 cm. It can be concluded that the horizontal displacement generated by the roadbed filling increased with the filling width.

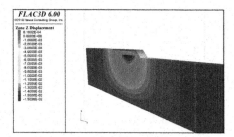   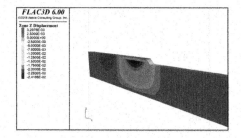

Figure 5. Settlement distribution cloud map.   Figure 6. Settlement distribution cloud map.

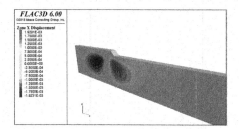   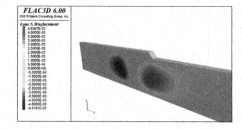

Figure 7. Horizontal displacement cloud map.   Figure 8. Horizontal displacement cloud map.

It is shown in Figure 9 that the maximum displacement of settlement occurs at 7.8 m when the first section of the roadbed is filled, and when the second section of the roadbed is filled, the maximum displacement of settlement occurs at 12 m. That is, the maximum displacement of settlement generally occurs at the junction of the old and new roadbeds. And the vertical additional settlement curve of the top surface of the newly filled roadbed is small, and there is almost no effect on the old roadbed at a longer distance. When the second section of the roadbed is widened, a certain degree of soil expansion is produced in the first filling area, which is caused by the soil extrusion by the newly filled roadbed.

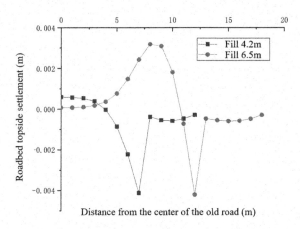

Figure 9. Effect of roadbed fill width on roadbed settlement.

4 CONCLUSION

The maximum settlement deformation and differential settlement of the top surface of the old roadbed changed when the width of the roadbed was different. With the widening of the roadbed width of 4.2 m, the maximum settlement of 1.50 cm; with the widening of the roadbed width of 6.5 m, the maximum settlement is 2.42 cm. So the increase in the width of the roadbed filling not only increases the settlement of the roadbed, but also intensifies the uneven settlement, and with the increase in the width of the widening of the roadbed significantly increases. Therefore, if the minimum width of roadbed widening can be satisfied, the control of the width of the roadbed can play an important role in the reduction of settlement deformation and differential settlement.

REFERENCES

Chen Jianhua (2020). Application of construction technology of new roadbed for concrete pavement widening and reconstruction. *Heilongjiang Transportation Science and Technology*,43(08):71+73.

Li YS, Zhang JG, Zhao JL, Zheng HP (2020). Research on differential settlement of roadbed widening based on FLAC3D. *Road Building Machinery and Construction Mechanization*,37(Z1):143–148.

Pang Jinsong, Xu Weizhong, Wang Zhiwen (2021). Analysis of settlement law of widened roadbed based on finite element model. *Shanghai Highway*,2021(01):15–19+118.

Wang Chenzhu (2018). Analysis of differential settlement characteristics and countermeasures of mountain highway roadbed. *Journal of Shandong Agricultural University* (Natural Science Edition), 49(5):45–49.

Xia Hongji (2022). Analysis of highway filling roadbed widening scheme. *Low Carbon World*,12(01):133–135.

Yang Xingping (2022). Study on technical parameters of roadbed widening construction [J]. *Transportation World*,2022(Z1):183–184.

Zhen Tianyu, Liu Jinxiu (2020). Study on the influence factors of differential settlement of highway widening roadbed. *Inner Mongolia Highway and Transportation*,2020(04):6–8+23.

Zheng Jianying (2020). Construction technology scheme of highway roadbed widening and reconstruction. *Traffic World*,2020(36):137–138+142.

Zhong Yankai, Liu Zhongshan (2019). *Research on the application of lightweight bubble soil in roadbed filling project above subway Municipal Technology*,37(3):58–60,111.

Zhu Hirong (2020). Study of mechanical behavior of widened roadbed under different positions of vehicle loads[J]. *Transportation Energy Conservation and Environmental Protection*, 16(03):90–93.

Home interior decoration design strategy based on AR technology

Li Jianjing*
Xiamen University Tan Kah Kee College, China

ABSTRACT: Home interior space is one of the essential spaces in people's lives, and the quality of its interior decoration design affects people's quality of life. Home interior decoration design based on AR technology can better meet people's requirements for home space design. It can be carried out by scanning the home interior space, constructing the interior hard decoration space, matching the interior soft decoration layout, and adjusting the interior decoration details to complete the satisfactory home interior decoration effect.

1 INSTRUCTION

With the rapid development of modern society, people's requirements for the home environment continue to increase. According to the survey and research, most families encounter various problems when carrying out interior decoration. The advancement of science and technology will lead to changes in the form of home space and innovation of customer experience. VR technology, AR technology, etc., are all essential technologies in the Metaverse. In the future, people can obtain a more exploratory and interesting immersive experience of home interior space through technological means. This experience will break the space barrier between reality and virtuality, realize the interaction between the real environment and the virtual environment, completely subvert the cognition of the existing experience, and expand the possibility of more levels of space (Cao & Shi 2021).

2 AR TECHNOLOGY INTRODUCTION

2.1 AR technology overview

AR technology, abbreviation of Augmented Reality, is a derivative technology of VR technology. It refers to superimposing the real-world environment and virtual-world objects in the same space and simultaneously displaying and realizing the virtual thing and the real world—the interactive experience between environments. Unlike VR technology, which is completely immersed in a virtual environment, AR technology focuses on superimposing computer-generated virtual objects in the real environment. The AR technology display includes three graphic modes: AR glasses, handheld, and projection. They respectively superimpose the virtual digital scene information on the physical scene, resulting in two types of mixed spatial experience modes (Wang & Xie 2021). AR technology has broad prospects for development in many fields, such as architecture, art, military, medical care, entertainment, and education, and is the development trend of a new generation of human-computer interface interaction (Chen 2017).

---

*Corresponding Author: 372256379@qq.com

2.2 Application development of AR technology

AR technology emphasizes the superposition of reality and virtuality, superimposing virtual objects in real scenes. Linking the virtual world with the real world is the principal value of AR technology. Unlike VR technology, a completely virtual environment, AR technology can see real content information, which increases customers' perception and understanding. At the same time, AR technology is more flexible in terms of equipment, and digital products that are often used, such as smartphones and tablet computers, are also one of the devices of AR technology (Weng 2019).

In recent years, AR technology has made significant progress in many fields, and many companies are making layouts in AR technology. In 2019, Huawei mobile phones launched Huawei Hetu, whose core capabilities include AR walking navigation, scene editing, rendering, etc. AR technology's virtual and reality superposition in tourism can make tourists feel immersive in tourist attractions through image reproduction. At the same time, AR technology can also increase the interaction and interest between tourists and attractions, enhancing the sense of participation of tourists in the appeal. AR technology can be used in the medical field for preoperative planning in hospitals and scenarios such as medical teaching and demonstrations, reducing surgical risks and medical disputes. In the industrial field, AR technology can be used in product display, remote assistance, and job guidance, improving work efficiency and reducing labor costs (Weng 2019).

3 THE APPLICATION OF AR TECHNOLOGY IN INTERIOR DESIGN

3.1 The advantages of AR technology in interior design

Through AR technology, interior designers can display the effect of interior design more intuitively in front of customers, giving customers a more robust experience of the interior decoration effect. At the same time, customers can participate in the interior design process; they can choose their favorite furniture and match their favorite materials and colors. Designers can adjust the interior design effect according to the customer's preferences, meet the diverse requirements of customers, and improve work efficiency and customer satisfaction (Yu 2021) (Lei & Lei 2021). AR technology provides designers with efficient visual explanations and technical support through its reality display advantages, which can help designers intuitively put forward design requirements and related concepts, bring designers closer to the sense of integration with customers, and make interior design works more easily recognized (Xu 2021).

According to the customer's needs and capabilities, the customer can do the design directly without an interior designer. AR technology can greatly improve the customer's sense of experience and autonomy and can complete the design independently through related software. Customers do not need to go to the design company in person, do not need to hire special designers, or need a smartphone or tablet, and they can feel the effect of interior design and decoration in real-time (Zhang 2020). Compared with traditional design technology, AR technology can effectively improve the use efficiency of products, improve work efficiency, save design costs, and reduce material waste and financial and human resources (Sun 2019).

3.2 The difference between VR/AR technology in interior design

VR technology and AR technology seem similar but are different yet related. VR technology is a completely virtual space that is detached from reality. Even if it feels real, it is a visual sensory experience. AR technology is based on the real space environment and brings virtual objects into real space, which combines virtual objects and real space (Li 2017). In interior design, the methods of using VR and AR technology differ, and the focus and the effects differ.

Using VR technology, the entire virtual interior design scene can be constructed. With VR eyes, users can directly enter the renovated space, feel the effect of the decoration of the interior space, see the decoration effect of each room, and handle more decoration details. At the same time, you can roam in the indoor area, walk in the space, and look around. Based on different software,

VR technology can also modify interior design content, including furniture, home appliances, decorations, etc., to achieve user-satisfied decoration effects. While using VR technology, sound can be added, tactile perception can be increased, and a better reflection effect can be achieved (Chen 2021).

Using AR technology in interior design, virtual objects can be superimposed with real indoor space. Compared with the completely virtual environment of VR technology, the perception of AR technology will be more intuitive and real. Users can use smartphones or tablet computers to superimpose AR technology in real rough room space. They can see the effect of laying the ground, painting the walls, and placing furniture and appliances in the indoor space. At the same time, the content of the indoor layout can be modified in real-time. For example, related objects' style, size, material, and color can be modified, and the effect can be previewed in real-time (Chen 2021).

3.3 *The development status of AR technology in interior design*

Although AR technology has been widely used in many fields, some fields are still in their infancy, and it is also in the early stage in the field of interior design, and the penetration rate is not very high. There have been some achievements in the application of AR technology in interior design, such as IKEA place, Creator, Taobao AR, Jingdong AR, View AR. However, some applications can only be used in the Apple system (iOS). Some applications do not work well in AR technology, so the utilization and penetration rates of interior design applications based on AR technology are not very high. It is because the utilization rate of interior design applications based on AR technology is low, the software technology is not mature enough, and the development cost is high, which are also the main reasons that hinder the widespread use of AR technology in interior design.

4 HOME INTERIOR DESIGN STRATEGY BASED ON AR TECHNOLOGY

The home interior design based on AR technology now takes the rough house as an example. First, most people like to buy rough houses, which are more extensive; second, the design based on rough houses is more comprehensive, including all aspects from hard to soft decoration. Developing an AR software application for home interior decoration is helpful. At present, the form of an App is more convenient and fast, and it is applied to the interior design of home space.

To complete the interior design more efficiently, you can have a preliminary idea of the design style of the home interior space in the early design stage. The design style can be combined with the householder's family composition, age, occupation, region, hobby, etc., and modern minimalist, Chinese, European, American, and other decoration styles.

The home space interior design strategy based on AR technology can be carried out from four aspects: scanning the home interior space, constructing the interior hard decoration space, matching the interior soft decoration layout, and adjusting the interior decoration details.

4.1 *Scan home interior spaces*

At the beginning of the design of the home interior space, the interior decoration AR APP is used to scan the existing home space, and relevant data are collected to determine the location and function of furniture that can be placed, including the length, width, and height of the space, the wall structure of the space, the position of the columns, and some other details (Figure 1).

The traditional paper and pen recording methods have low efficiency, large measurement errors, and cumbersome data sorting. Using AR technology, the data collection process can be optimized, and the efficiency of data collection can be improved. When AR technology collects data, it uses the camera to scan the space, obtains data in real-time, dimension it, and save screenshots to achieve an accurate connection between measurement data and recorded data (Sun 2019).

4.2 Build interior hard decoration spaces

Hard decoration mainly refers to the design of the ground, wall, ceiling, and other structures, which refers to fixed and immovable interior decoration. The decoration and hard decoration mainly include five major projects: ground engineering, wall engineering, roof engineering, woodworking engineering, and paint engineering. After the hard decoration design is completed, it is more difficult to modify, so the hard decoration design should be cautious (Ren 2020).

After scanning the overall space, the interior decoration AR App is used to construct the interior hard decoration space. Taking the living room as an example, you can first lay the ground; you can choose tiles to lay on the ground, choose the style, size, color, etc. of the tiles, superimpose them into the real rough room space, and feel the effect of the floor tiles have been laid (Figure 2). If you are unsatisfied with the effect, you can make changes immediately, modify the tiles' style, color, etc., and change to other materials such as wooden floors (Figure 3).

Through AR technology, because the virtual hard decoration material is superimposed on the indoor space of the real rough room, people can feel the effect of the indoor hard decoration in real-time, which is more realistic than traditional pictures and other forms. At the same time, you can modify the hard decoration part in real-time and feel the real effect during the modification process, but it is much more convenient than real modification.

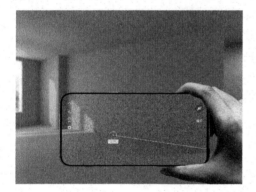
Figure 1. AR App measures indoor space.

Figure 2. AR App laying indoor floor.

Figure 3. AR App adjusts the ground material.

4.3 Match soft interior decoration

Soft decoration design refers to the later decoration based on the original structure of the building after the completion of the hard decoration, generally using furniture and decorations that are easy to move and replace. Soft objects include sofas, beds, dining tables and chairs, other furniture, curtains, bonsai green plants, and other decorations. The soft decoration design has the advantages of easy adjustment, a short construction period, and relatively small pollution (Ren 2020). Soft decoration design is generally considered based on the size of the space, the design style, cultural factors, etc. The soft decoration design style of the home space will impact the home's shape, specification, color, and material.

Through the interior decoration AR App and indoor soft decoration layout, the soft decoration can be arranged after the hard decoration of the home space. Taking the living room as an example, after constructing the floor, wall, and ceiling of the living room, sofas, coffee tables, decorations, etc., can be superimposed into the real space. For example, select the sofa style you like from the interior decoration AR App and click the space to place it (Figure 4). At the same time, you can move, rotate, and zoom the sofa. You can also change the style, material, and color of the sofa to decorate the room into an environment more in line with your style and preferences and build a living environment with personal characteristics (Figures 5 and 6).

Figure 4.   Arranging the sofa in the AR App.   Figure 5.   AR App adjusts sofa style.

Figure 6.   AR App adjusts sofa material.

4.4 *Adjust interior decoration details*

After arranging the hard and soft decoration parts of the home interior space, you can adjust the unsatisfactory parts of the interior space through the interior decoration AR App. The adjustment can be the overall adjustment of the space design or the details of the local space. For example, when adjusting the living room, you can modify the hard parts such as the floor tiles, TV background wall, and ceiling shape of the living room, as well as modify the color of the sofa, adjust the style of the coffee table, and replace the decorations and other soft decoration parts.

While arranging the hard and soft decoration of the home interior space, the interior decoration AR App can also change the lighting effect of the home interior space. For example, the lighting effect of the living room at night can be modified, which can be overall or partial lighting. The light source or the surface light source can be a chandelier, a spotlight, a light strip, etc. Different lighting forms present other lighting effects to achieve different lighting atmospheres in the living room at night (Figures 7 and 8).

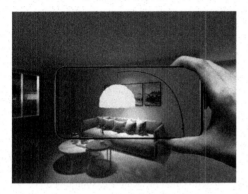

Figure 7. AR APP is adding lights.   Figure 8. AR APP adjusts lighting style.

5 CONCLUSION

Home and interior decoration design development are closely related to people's daily lives. It needs continuous innovation and adapts to more needs to adapt to the development of the times. The interior decoration design uses emerging technologies such as VR, AR, MR, and AI to present the interior space in a richer form. Among them, AR technology has brought great imagination and creativity to people's home life, allowing people to participate in interior decoration design and interact more with interior space (Rao & Li 2021). AR technology has brought better development prospects to people's lives and provided more changes and innovations in interior decoration design. Home interior design based on AR technology starts from people's psychological factors. It aims to create a multidimensional experience, which brings people an unprecedented new experience and provides more prospects for the innovation and development of the home interior design.

ACKNOWLEDGMENT

This project is supported by the Education and Research Project for Young and Middle-aged Teachers in Fujian Province (JAT191082), the Social Science Planning Project in Fujian Province (FJ2018C082), and the Xiamen Social Science Research Project (Xiashe Scientific Research [2020]C18).

REFERENCES

Cao Lei, Shi Yulin. Research on the design of immersive experience dining space [J]. *Furniture and Interior Decoration*, 2021, 274(12): 117–121.
Chen Rowen. *Design and implement AR-based home display platform in e-commerce system_Chen Ruowen* [D]. Chongqing University, 2017.
Chen Xiaolian. Design and application of VR_AR indoor cloud [J]. *Journal of Heilongjiang Institute of Technology* (Comprehensive Edition), 2021, 21(1): 72–77.

Lei Xianzhen, Lei Fuyuan. The application of AR technology in interior decoration design [J]. *Jiangxi Building Materials*, 2021(09):120+123.

Li Weizhuo. *Research on the application of AR technology in interior space design* [D]. Jilin Art Institute, 2017.

Li Yao, Fan Linlin. Talking about the combination of brand home display and AR technology [J]. *Drama Home*, 2019, 332(32): 243.

Rao Yong, Li Xinyu. Research on experiential museum display design in the age of digital technology [J]. *Furniture and Interior Decoration*, 2021, 274(12): 127–129.

Ren Zheng. Analysis of aesthetic fusion of interior soft decoration design and interior hard decoration design [J]. *Ju She*, 2020, (26): 18–19, 101.

Sun Yuge. Discussion on the application of VR and AR technology in architectural interior design [J]. *Building Materials and Decoration*, 2019(33):127–128.

Wang Chen, Xie Xin. Research on VR application in stage space and viewing experience [J]. *Furniture and Interior Decoration*, 2021, 272(10): 10–13.

Weng Linwei. The application of AR technology in museum exhibitions: Taking Liangzhu culture as an example [J]. *Furniture and Interior Decoration*, 2019, 250(12): 15–17.

Wu Yiguo, Zhang Li. Research on mobile AR marketing application for offline home furnishing retail [J]. *Design*, 2021, 34(7): 158–160.

Xu Chao. Research and application of architectural interior design based on MR technology [J]. *Furniture and Interior Decoration*, 2021(11):120-122.DOI:10.16771/j.cn43-1247/ts.2021.11.023.

Yu Hong. The application of VR and AR technology in the dissemination of intangible cultural heritage and the integration of Xizhuang brocade elements into interior design [J]. *Guangxi Urban Construction*, 2021, 221(4): 77–79.

Zhang Guomei. Based on Vuforia_SDK. AR home decoration system design and development [J]. *Computer Knowledge and Technology*, 2020, 16(19): 80–81.

Application analysis of BIM technology in electromechanical design

Yang Xinghua*
Chongqing Yugao Engineering Design CO., LTD, Chongqing, China

ABSTRACT: Building Information Modeling (BIM) is an emerging computer information technology in the construction industry in recent years. By integrating Datamation and informatization models for buildings, this technology enables engineering technicians to handle various building information efficiently and provides the basis of collaborative work for the main construction bodies, which is indispensable in improving production efficiency, and saving costs as well as shortening construction periods.

This paper discusses the current application status and process of BIM technology at home and its role in the electromechanical design of a typical project. It could provide a reference for similar projects in electromechanical design to better serve construction participants with the adoption of BIM technology.

1 INTRODUCTION

Building Information Modeling (BIM for short) is an emerging information-based computer technology in the construction industry in recent years. Unlike the two-dimensional model established by CAD software, BIM technology integrates the project characteristics, information, and functions of the entire lifecycle into a visualized 3D model. This integration of data and information models for building makes the sharing and transmission of projects can be realized during the process of planning, design, procurement, construction, operation, and maintenance throughout the entire lifecycle, assisting engineering technicians in correctly understanding and efficiently responding to various building information. Besides, it provides the basis of collaborative work for the main construction bodies and plays an important role in improving production efficiency, saving costs, and shortening the construction period (Zhenqing, Y. et al. 2014).

Since 2010, several government departments have formulated and published relevant policies and subsidy measures to accelerate the R & D and application process of BIM technology. It is explicitly pointed out in the Report on Informatization Development of China Construction Industry (2021) issued by the Ministry of Housing and Urban-Rural Development that "great efforts should be made to energetically develop a digital design, intelligent production, intelligent construction, and intelligent operation and maintenance to accelerate the R&D and application of BIM technology, exploring a high-quality development approach of the construction industry."

2 THE APPLICATION STATUS OF BIM TECHNOLOGY IN DESIGN

Currently, two design modes of BIM technology are adopted in China, the BIM forward design and the BIM model conversion design.

---

*Corresponding Author: 76559906@qq.com

2.1 BIM forward design

First, a complete BIM implementation plan shall be formulated in the preparation stage of a project. Meanwhile, all professional designs adopt a 3D design environment.

Second, a 3D model will be established based on the architectural plane during the preliminary design stage. After inspection, structural and electromechanical professionals will provide related information. Professionals from each field shall coordinate with each other during deployment and management and carry out the detailed design of the 3D model according to different expertise. Collaborative design and real-time collision checks between different professions can urge them to realize and correct their errors. In the later stage, different professions need to share the necessary information with each other and carry out collision checks and detailed design of models.

Next, each profession shall conduct detailed design, annotation of dimensions and text of the view, then export the drawings and 3D models after inspection.

Finally, when designing construction drawings, each profession shall conduct model deepening, collision check, and other work based on the floorplan and 3D views, followed by detailed work, including detailed design and dimensioning of construction drawings. With perfection and inspection of geometric information, finally, they will provide drawings and export 3D models for delivery (Runsheng, W. & Wenlue, W. 2014).

2.2 BIM model conversion design

Model conversion means that the BIM design is not involved in the preparation or the preliminary design stage of a project, and the digital model will be established during the design stage or after the completion of construction drawings, in which the model creation work of the BIM team lags behind the design work of the current 2D design team. Based on the foregone design process, the BIM team can discover the problems in 2D design drawings and propose correction suggestions through the creation of the 3D model, which can be instructive for the design results (Guorui, P. & Liang, Z. 2021).

The optimization effect of construction drawings will be influenced to a certain extent due to BIM model conversion professionals' comprehending deviation and lack of 2D design experience. Meanwhile, BIM technology plays a supportive role in 2D design, so the value of BIM technology in the design process cannot be fully effective (Chao P. 2019).

At present, BIM model conversion design is the most common mode because of the following factors:

1) BIM software: Currently, most BIM adopts foreign software such as REVIT, CATIA, etc. Compared with traditional CAD, the localization level is comparatively low, thus the service efficiency is not as good as that of various 2D software developed based on CAD (Wenjuan, Y. 2020);
2) Personnel capacity: BIM design is an information technology that has not been promoted for too long. The current practitioners are mainly post-90s generation. However, the main body of architectural design, the pre-90s generation, is not proficient in BIM technology. This leads to a dilemma that "designers do not understand BIM personnel and BIM personnel do not understand designers," which inhibits the development of BIM forward design;
3) Construction party's understanding of BIM: As a project investor, the construction party failed to realize the positive significance of BIM design and is unwilling to pay for BIM forward design.

In the following contents, the author will analyze the process and value of the current BIM technology in practical application in our country through the application of BIM in the mechanical and electrical design of a typical project.

3 BIM TECHNOLOGY APPLICATION IN A COMMERCIAL ELECTROMECHANICAL DESIGN

3.1 Project overview and difficulty analysis

This project is a large-scale commercial complex in Yinchuan, Ningxia, covering a total construction area of 86,000 square meters, with one underground floor and four floors above, including a central shopping mall, cinema, supermarket, catering area, garage, and other business formats. Various mechanical and electrical pipelines and equipment exist in the building due to the complicated business formats, including sprinklers, fire hydrant pipes, water supply, and drainage pipes, sewage pipes, rain pipes, ventilation pipes, air-conditioning ducts, air-conditioning water pipes, heating pipes, oil fume exhaust pipes, fire smoke exhaust pipes, hangers, electric smoke screens, cable trays for strong electricity and weak electricity, etc.

The detailed heights of the building space are shown in the following table:

Table 1. Detailed heights of the building space.

Building floor	Building net story height(m)	Requested net height after decoration (m)	The maximum depth of girder (m)	Depth of girder in the aisle (m)	The minimum installation space in the suspended ceiling (m)
1F	6.0	4.1	0.9	0.8	0.85
2F	5.4	3.1	1.5(Atrium)	0.8	0.55
3F	5.4	3.1	1.5(Atrium)	0.8	0.55
4F	5.4	3.1	1.5(Atrium)	0.8	0.55

*Notes:

1. The inner height of the suspended ceiling is deducted from the thickness of 0.2 m for the structural panel of each floor and surface thickness of 0.05 m for decoration;
2. The atrium of the first and second floors is connected, and the atrium of the third and fourth floors are sealed, but the corresponding areas of the second, third and fourth floors are all equipped with 1.5 m high steel girders.

The table reveals that the installation space in the suspended ceiling is cramped, especially for the atrium, due to the setup of steel structural beams. The installation space under the inner beam of the second floor's suspended ceiling is only 0.55 m, while the thickness of the mechanical smoke exhaust pipe in the atrium has reached 0.32 m. The installation height of the smoke exhaust system has reached 0.47 m as the thickness of the heat insulation layer and the anti-seismic supports and hangers will take up 0.15 m. The net after-decoration heights cannot be satisfied unless all the mechanical and electrical pipelines avoid the smoke exhaust pipes.

Therefore, it is crucial to reasonably design the electromechanical pipelines in the suspended ceiling of the building, reduce the intersection of pipelines and ensure the net height of the suspended ceiling to ensure the quality and construction period of the entire project. As three-dimensional spatial information technology, BIM design can play its role.

3.2 Intervention of BIM design in the process of electromechanical design

Due to the construction unit's insufficient understanding of BIM forward design, short design cycle, frequent adjustments of the design scheme, and other factors, the designing institute did not receive the task assignment of BIM 3D design or the requirement of cooperating with other BIM design teams in the process of 2D design. Therefore, only a rough plan of pipeline direction and a simple pipeline layout were given by the electromechanical professionals when designing before the official drawings.

After the design institute finished the construction drawings, the construction unit appointed a third-party BIM design team to work out a directional 3D model conversion design without communicating with the design institute on the proofreading and adjustment of the mechanical and electrical pipelines on the 3D model conversion results.

Hereafter, the design institute made great adjustments to the building plane as well as mechanical and electrical pipelines (especially the aisles in the public areas) on account of the decoration requirements of the construction unit and the adjustments of the shops during the process of investment promotion, resulting in the loss of reference value for BIM model conversion results. Nonetheless, the construction unit has already started the installation of the mechanical and electrical pipelines on the first floor according to the second detailed design drawings provided by the design institute. After measurements, the on-site supervising engineer found that the net height after decoration would be if they continued the construction according to the drawings. Therefore, the construction must be shut down immediately. Simultaneously, the construction unit also required the BIM design team to re-cooperate with the design institute for the second design drawings to avoid the problems of pipeline crossing and insufficient floor height.

3.3 Problems and solutions in BIM design

3.3.1 Establishment of 3D model and unification of different professions

Based on secondary design drawings of architecture, structure, water supply, drainage, HVAC, electrical and other professions, the BIM design team built a 3D information model and checked the model.

Through inspection, the drawings of the mechanical and electrical profession were found to be inconsistent with the final version of the architectural plan due to excessively adjusted versions of the architectural plan resulting in overlaps of some equipment, pipelines, partition walls and shear walls, which affected the installation (see Figure 1 below). Along with the change of separation for some shops, the equipment profession still needed to adjust the layout and number of the corresponding equipment.

Figure 1. Conflict between vertical drainage pipe and girder.

According to the feedback report of BIM design, the mechanical and electrical professionals of the design institute have modified the relevant problems detail by detail and unified the architectural interface, ensuring the operation of five main professions on the same architectural plane.

3.3.2 *Pipeline collision check and nalysis on spatial net height of mechanical and electrical profession*

BIM design is based on the mechanical and electrical pipelines, equipment dimensions, and installation heights in a two-dimensional design model, combined with construction technology, sequence, and operation of space reservation to locate the mechanical and electrical pipelines in the building space and construct a detailed three-dimensional model. Through collision detection and height analysis of the 3D model, corresponding analysis reports will be put forward for the key points, pipeline intersections, and areas without reasonable maintenance space affecting the floor height setting (see Figures 2 and 3 below).

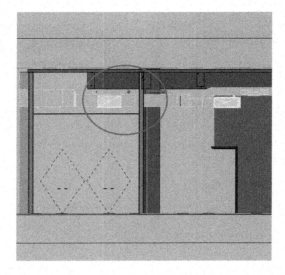

Figure 2. Influence of collision between exhaust duct and fresh air duct on net height.

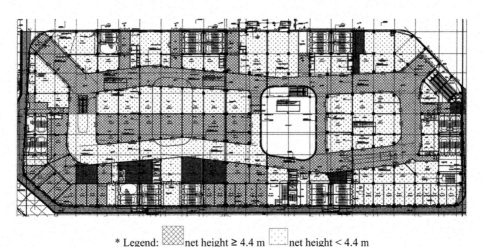

* Legend: net height ≥ 4.4 m   net height < 4.4 m

Figure 3. Drawing of net height analysis.

According to the analysis report provided by the BIM team, the electromechanical profession of the design institute follows the principle that "smaller pipelines shall give place to larger pipelines, pressure pipelines shall give place to non-pressure pipelines" and adjusts the elevation and direction of electromechanical pipelines. Meanwhile, the electromechanical profession has provided technical bottom-line and question answering for the installation unit concerning the installation sequence and precautions of electromechanical pipelines to avoid secondary demolition and renovation as well as rework during construction, which ensures the quality and progress of the project.

Particularly, for the second floor's atrium corridor, in which the installation space is only 0.55 m, the design institute has adjusted the arrangement of mechanical and electrical pipelines according to the analysis of the floor plan and section of the BIM 3D digital model. After passing through the 1.5 m vertical beam outside the atrium, the smoke exhaust pipe with a total height of 0.47 m immediately turned up to the hollow on the beam between the transverse steel beams to avoid intersection with other pipelines. The floor plan and section of the 3D model after adjustments are shown in Figure 4:

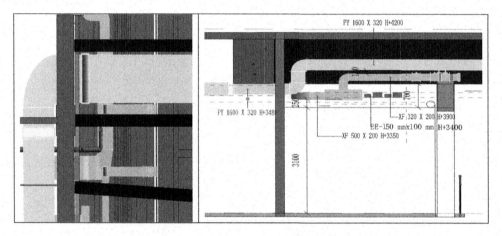

Figure 4. Floor plan and section of the atrium after adjustments of BIM.

3.3.3 *BIM design of equipment room*

Due to the complex business format of this project, the HVAC profession alone has one heat exchange station, two central air-conditioning control rooms, sixteen terminal air-conditioning control rooms, and multiple smoke exhaust machine rooms. The equipment and pipelines in each machine room are also very complicated, especially the central air-conditioning control room of the large commercial mall on the first floor underground, which contains multiple air-conditioning equipments and five sets of water systems such as chilled water, cooling water, heating hot water, supplementary water, and softened water, let alone the electrical cable trays, sprinklers and vent pipes in the machine room.

BIM has guided and optimized the layout of each electromechanical equipment in such an originally narrow space by establishing a 3D model and applying sections and floor plans. Meeting the requirements of extubation space, equipment installation distance, and maintenance of the refrigerating machine, BIM has created a favorable working environment inside the machine room and laid the foundation for the appraising of the project.

4 CONCLUSIONS

In the field of mechanical and electrical design of public buildings, it is essential to utilize the three-dimensional information model established by BIM technology to guide the design direction in the early stage of design, inspect the design results and make corrections in the middle and later stages to ensure the quality and progress of a project.

At present, during the application process of BIM technology, situations such as a lack of designers, insufficient understanding of BIM among construction parties, uneven performance of BIM software, and lag in BIM design are inevitable. Nevertheless, it is believed that BIM technology will better play a valuable role with the continuous progress of BIM technology itself, popularization of information resources sharing and collaboration, and constant deepening of intellectualization in the construction industry.

REFERENCES

Chao, Peng. (2019). Analysis of the application of BIM technology in the detailed design of the architectural mechanical and electrical installation. *Building Technology Research*, (06): 187–188.

Guorui, P. & Liang, Z. (2021). Application of BIM forward design in municipal projects. *Construction and Design of Project*, (10): 138–141.

Runsheng, W. & Wenlue, W. (2014). Study on the application of BIM in architectural design. *Journal of Qingdao University of Technology*: 43–48.

Wenjuan, Yang. (2020). Analysis of key points of BIM collaborative design based on revit software. *Building Technology Research*, (05) : 133–134+137.

Zhenqing, Y. & Lili, Z. & Xiaoling, Z. & Yi, L. & Hua, W. (2014). Application of BIM technology in deepening design of super high-rise building engineering. *Architecture Technology*, 115–118.

Research on elderly-friendly indoor renovation for rural houses in Northeast China

Jingdong Liu* & Jingwei Chang*
Shenyang Jianzhu University, Shenyang, China

ABSTRACT: This paper presents an elderly-friendly renovation solution for rural houses in northeast China to provide a better living environment for the rural elderly. Through a questionnaire survey on the rural elderly in Liaoning Province and a field survey of their houses, we collected the current living conditions and habits of the rural elderly, studied the types and layout characteristics of rural houses, and summarized some elderly-friendly renovation strategies. An optimal elderly-friendly renovation solution was developed for rural houses, which can guide the rural elderly to renovate their own houses.

1 INTRODUCTION

According to the traditional concept of elderly care and the 9073 plan (taking care of 90% of seniors at home, 7% at adult daycare centers, and 3% at nursing homes) advocated by the state, home-based elderly care has become the mainstream in China at present. The state is also exploring the model of mutual-assistance elderly care in rural areas. The rural senior daycare centers, rural nursing homes, and other elderly care facilities mainly provide care services for the elderly who rely on facilities including wheelchairs and handrails or are dependent on the care of others. Most rural elderly have chosen to spend the rest of their lives at home.

The *National Bulletin on Development of Undertakings for the Aged 2020* clearly shows that the aging level in rural areas is significantly higher than in towns. The proportions of the elderly population aged 60 and above and 65 and above in rural areas to the total rural population are 23.81% and 17.72%, respectively, which are 7.99 and 6.61 percentage points higher than the proportions of the same group in towns to the total urban population. This indicates that rural areas face a more difficult aging situation.

The *Rural Revitalization Strategic Plan* (2018-2022) clearly states that to adapt to the increasingly severe rural aging situation, a multi-level rural elderly care service system based on homes, communities, and institutions will be established. Many elderly people in rural areas want to spend the rest of their lives in their homes. A great amount of social research shows that 98% of the elderly in China rely on home-based elderly care, and only 2% go to nursing institutions for the aged. However, due to the slow renewal of rural houses, many rural elderly people face challenges in their living environments.

2 SURVEY ON CURRENT LIVING ENVIRONMENTS OF RURAL ELDERLY

2.1 Overview of plan layout of rural houses

According to the questionnaire survey on the elderly in most rural areas of Liaoning Province, it can be concluded that the rural elderly mainly live in their own houses built from 1980 to 1999.

---

*Corresponding Authors: 1274685830@qq.com and 867532358@qq.com

Specifically, the houses built from 1950 to 1959 account for 3%, that from 1960 to 1969 account for 9%, from 1970 to 1979 account for 12%, from 1980 to 1989 account for 23%, from 1990 to 1999 account for 26%, from 2000 to 2009 account for 15%, and from 2010 to 2019 account for 12%. But houses built from 1980 to 1999 were usually constructed according to the actual needs of families. Due to the lack of unified planning in design, it does not consider the convenience for the life of the elderly.

The simple farming life has resulted in a single housing layout, so most houses are designed with three to four rooms. Generally, the bathroom in rural areas is independently situated in the corner of the yard, which is very inconvenient for the elderly. People usually rely on Kang (heatable brick bed) and some electric heaters to provide heating in winter in rural areas. Some families also build a sunroom in front of their windows to expand the indoor space and increase the indoor temperature. The sunroom can not only supply heating in winter but also create the elderly an outdoor space, yet it may cause poor ventilation in summer.

This paper conducted a field survey in the Dongbajiazi Village, Hunnan District, Shenyang, China. This village is located in the southeast mountainous area of Hunnan District, Shenyang, 37 km from the city center, 37 km from Fushun, and 36 km from Benxi. It is located in the center of Shenyang, Fushun, and Benxi. The village faces a severe aging situation, with over 75% of the population over 60 years old. Due to its proximity to Shenyang, many young people have migrated to the city, resulting in numerous vacant courtyards and many older people living alone in the countryside. The author conducted a field survey on ten rural households with aged people in this village, and Table 1 shows the basic data of the survey subjects.

Table 1. Basic data of survey subjects.

Subject	Year Built	Floor Area	Floor	Generations Lived	Number of Senior Residents
01	2010	72	One	One	2
02	1990	53	One	One	2
03	1994	76	One	Two	2
04	1983	72	One	One	2
05	1983	62	One	One	2
06	1968	90	One	Three	2
07	2000	50	One	One	1
08	2009	70	One	Two	1
09	1999	60	One	Two	1
10	1967	84	One	One	2

Figure 1 shows the plan layout and site photos of the surveyed rural three-room houses. Both house types have three rooms, but their area is different. The plan layout of the house consists of two spaces, namely the sleeping space and the kitchen and dining space. In the sleeping space, the Kang is sub-divided into the south Kang and the north Kang, which is mainly determined by the location of the kitchen. In Case 1, the kitchen occupies a relatively independent space in the north of the house, so a north Kang is built. In Case 2, as the indoor area is relatively small, a south Kang is built to ensure sufficient lighting and improve the indoor heating effect in winter.

2.2 Survey on living conditions of rural elderly

Through a questionnaire survey, the author made statistics on the living and psychological conditions of the rural elderly over 60 years old in Liaoning Province. The survey aims to collect the troubles encountered by the rural elderly in their life and their views on elderly-friendly house renovation. A total of 100 questionnaires were distributed, and 82 valid questionnaires were collected. The ratio of men to women elderly interviewed was 4:3 (47:35). The oldest was 91 years old, and the youngest was 61.

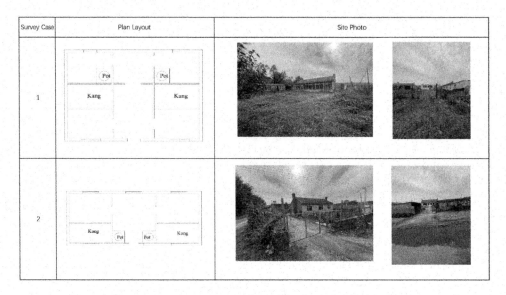

Figure 1.　Plan layout and site photos of houses (drawn by the author).

The survey results showed that 15% of the elderly lived alone, 56% lived with their spouses, 27% lived with their children, and only 2% lived in their children's homes, as shown in Figure 2. It can be seen that most of the elderly live with their spouses.

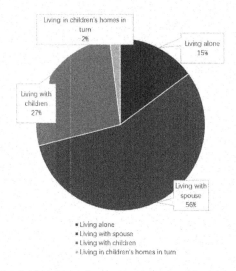

Figure 2.　Living conditions of elderly in rural areas (drawn by the author).

As they grow older, their physical functions deteriorate to some extent. The survey results showed that 59% of the elderly have stumbled or fallen at home. Among them, 40% have fallen at the thresholds (steps), 21% have fallen in their yards, 11% have fallen in their rooms, 10% have fallen in the bathroom. Many of them even have fallen in more than one place. Due to deteriorating physical functions, once fallen, the elderly may suffer irreversible damage as they cannot recover as quickly as young people.

Due to a lack of relevant facilities, rural older people rarely have bathing conditions in their homes. The survey results show that 51% of them shower in their homes, while others take a shower in public baths. Only 22% of them did not have troubles in the bathing process, while others, more or less, suffered some troubles, such as difficulty in mobility, no assistance in bathing, low indoor temperature, and improper anti-slip measures for the bath. To some extent, these will cause a decline in bathing quality and bathing frequency. The questionnaire also shows that more than 40% of the elderly think their bathing rooms need to be renovated. The field survey found that some houses only have simple bathing facilities built in the yards that can only be used in summer. These factors need to be considered in elderly-friendly house renovation.

In the survey on the items that need to be renovated in the opinion of the rural elderly people, over 35% think that bathrooms need to be renovated, and the affordable price is within CNY 3,000, over 27% think that kitchens need to be renovated, and that price is within CNY 5,000, and over 22% think that their homes should be equipped with aging-friendly furniture.

3 RURAL RESIDENTIAL RENOVATION STRATEGIES

In the design of the elderly-friendly renovation of rural houses, the following four design strategies should be observed. Considering the difference between rural and urban houses and that between rural and urban elderly people, it is necessary to develop house renovation strategies based on the living habits and psychological characteristics of rural elderly people. The five strategies below can better solve the problems encountered by the rural elderly in their lives.

3.1 Elderly-friendly design

Unlike the disabled, the problem faced by the elderly is not the loss of one body function, but the functional deterioration of the whole body. Therefore, unlike the barrier-free design, which often needs more space to facilitate the use of equipment, the elderly-friendly design needs to provide a relatively compact space so that the elderly can grasp or hold the handrail easily. Nevertheless, the latent design requirement also should be considered, for example, the need to narrow the distance between furniture to provide the space for wheelchair rotation. So, in the elderly-friendly renovation, the elderly-friendly design requirements should be preferentially met, and then the barrier-free design can be considered needed.

Rural older adults often do physical labor, so they have better physical conditions than urban ones. For that reason, the elderly-friendly house renovation should consider the physical functions of the elderly instead of just following the unified building standards for them. That is, the houses of the rural elderly should be renovated based on the graded general renovation design that suits the different physical functions of the elderly.

3.2 Expansion of storage space

Due to the relatively backward living conditions in rural areas, many elderly people keep things, including clothes, daily necessities, medicines, food, and some items from their children. However, their houses were not built with enough storage space, which has resulted in the accumulation and random placement of items over time. Their mobility and eyesight decline will cause great safety hazards to their indoor activities, such as tripping. To this end, we should increase the storage space as much as possible in elderly-friendly house renovation, but try not to change the storage location, in case the elderly cannot find their items after renovation, which will only cause trouble to them. Moreover, it is necessary to shorten the route and increase the efficiency when designing the storage space, so that the elderly can easily get the items.

3.3 *Latent design*

Many rural houses are designed with only spatial functions at the beginning and do not consider the possible living conditions of the elderly in the future. In elderly-friendly house renovation, various cases that the elderly may encounter in the future, such as bedridden, wheelchair-bound, and short stay in bed (fracture), should be considered to meet the housing needs and living conditions of the elderly in the long term. In addition, some space also should be reserved for the caregiver to move around to facilitate care.

3.4 *Smaller changes in spatial location*

Elderly people are usually nostalgic and have fixed living habits. They are very familiar with the placement of their home items, furniture forms, and furniture characteristics. These are the spatial cognition that the elderly have for their own homes. In elderly-friendly house renovation, we should try to retain the function of the original space, keep the position of furniture in the space unchanged, and ensure that the original spatial cognition of the elderly for their own homes will not be changed. If the original position of furniture is changed, the elderly may not find familiar items, easily making them anxious. For those used to getting up at night, changing the furniture's position is more likely to cause falling.

3.5 *Design specific to current needs*

First, the design of elderly-friendly renovation should suit the living habits of the local elderly, not just copying the urban design but following the excellent design principles of urban elderly-friendly renovation and integrating them with the living habits of the rural elderly. Second, it should also meet the aspiration of rural areas to the city. For example, the latest and modern interface materials should be used.

4 ELDERLY-FRIENDLY RENOVATION DESIGN FOR RURAL HOUSES

4.1 *Sleeping space*

According to the living habits of rural elderly people, Kang, the most important activity space, performs functions such as sleeping, dining, hospitality, and indoor activities. Elderly people usually spend most of their time here, so Kang will be the focus of renovation. Kang is the main way to supply heating in northern rural houses in winter, and it usually covers the whole room to ensure the heating effect. However, there is a popular word puzzle, "An old lady gets on the Kang—Jinzhou," which describes the difficulty for the elderly to get on the Kang, and the pronunciation sounds similar to a city name Jinzhou.

To address these problems of Kang, the renovation strategy for rural houses is adopted. Here are three renovation solutions: First, a 150 mm high step can be built at the front edge of the Kang as a foot platform to help the elderly move to the Kang and increase the space for storing shoes (Figure 3). Second, a 450 mm high side cabinet can be added at the head/tail of the Kang, and a 900 mm high side cabinet can be placed on the ground near the edge of the Kang, so that the elderly can temporarily place and store items on the Kang and get on and off the Kang using side cabinets as handrails, to avoid falling and increase the storage space in the room (Figure 4). Third, soft mats can be laid on the Kang. Traditionally, the Kang is covered by a layer of leather mats, which is very uncomfortable for the elderly to sit on. Thus, soft mats like wool felt and quilts can be laid on the Kang, depending on the actual conditions of the houses.

For other problems in the sleeping space, here are two renovation solutions: First, a few houses built from 1980 to 1999 are dilapidated, with windows on only one side of the room, which will easily cause poor indoor air circulation and stifling summer heat. So, in the renovation, another window should be added on the other side as much as possible to improve air circulation. Second,

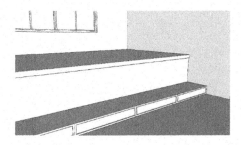 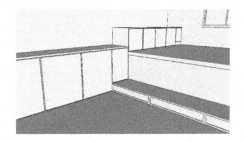

Figure 3. Step in front of Kang (drawn by the author).

Figure 4. Side cabinets for Kang (drawn by the author).

in the past, rural houses are usually built with high thresholds to prevent the outdoor dust from entering the indoor space, but this may easily cause the elderly to fall. So, lowering the threshold height can prevent the elderly from falling and block the dust. The threshold height should be kept within 120 mm, and materials with a non-slip surface such as wood should be used.

In addition, the only entertainment for most rural elderly is watching TV. The TV set should be placed in a convenient position for the elderly to watch it directly while sitting on the Kang. The installation height should be below the sight level of the sitting elderly so as not to harm their cervical vertebrae.

4.2 Kitchen and dining space

Generally, there is no separate kitchen space in small three-room rural houses, but only the entrance space doubles as the kitchen space with some storage areas, which undertake meal preparation, cooking, heating supply, and storage of domestic water. So, the kitchen space is always the center of a rural house.

Rural elderly people are accustomed to using straws as fuel and preparing meals on the stove countertop, while the stove also supplies heat for the Kang. But the countertop is unsuitable for the elderly. As it is usually 1.2 m × 1.2 m square in size, elderly people easily suffer from pain in the waist and back when preparing meals, and they are even more resistant to use it as their physical functions decline. Accordingly, in the elderly-friendly renovation, the stove should be retained for supplying heat for the Kang only, while its cooking function should be removed and replaced by the cooking system of urban kitchens. This will not only eliminate the shortcomings of the countertop to facilitate the elderly, but also expand the indoor storage space and make the space more orderly.

According to the elderly-friendly design principles for cabinets in urban houses, the cabinet bottom should be 1,400–1,500 mm above the ground. For kitchens to be used by wheelchair-bound people, the bottom of the wall cupboard should be 1,200 mm above the ground; the cupboard's top elevation is generally not greater than 2,200 mm; the depth of the 1,400–1,800 mm high cupboard should be 250–300 mm and 250 mm away from the countertop edge, so as to avoid touching the head of the elderly when cupboard doors are opened and allow them to take and put items (Figure 5) easily.

Meanwhile, most rural residents usually dine in the sleeping space. Due to different living habits, some elderly people are used to dining on the Kang, while others dine on the ground. However, when dining on the 450–500 mm high table placed on the Kang, the elderly need to sit cross-legged for a long time, which is harmful to their joints. Given that, a cushion with a height of 150–200 mm can be added so that the elderly can squat on the Kang to dine. For the elderly who dine on the ground, tables and chairs suitable for the elderly should be provided (Figure 6).

4.3 Indoor bathroom

Traditionally, there is an indoor bathroom in rural houses, and they are all independent in the courtyard. The squat toilet in the rural bathroom will cause great inconvenience to the elderly. For

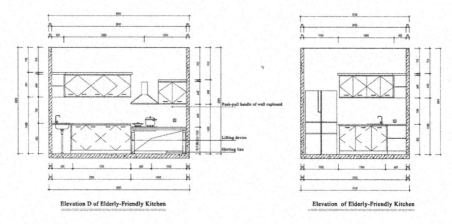

Figure 5. Elderly-friendly cabinets (drawn by the author).

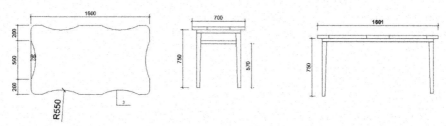

Figure 6. Elderly-friendly table (drawn by the author).

example, as the elderly's digestive function is declining, squatting for a long time will make it difficult for the elderly to get up or even fall. In elderly-friendly indoor renovation, the toileting space and indoor bathing space shall be added.

Here are four elderly-friendly renovation solutions for the indoor bathroom. First, the partition of the new space can be made of matte glass, which takes up little space, and an observation hole should be reserved on the door to observe the condition of the elderly in the bathroom when needed. Second, the bathroom should not have a height difference from outer space. If unavoidable, it can be eliminated by a gentle slope that uses non-slip materials to prevent the elderly from falling. Third, the bathroom door should not be an inward opening door. An outward opening, sliding, or folding door can be used depending on the size of the space. Fourth, as the rural elderly are accustomed to using the squat toilet, U-shaped handrails can be designed on both sides to facilitate the elderly getting up. These u-shaped handrail parameters are for reference: 650–700 mm in height and a minimum width of 700 mm between two handrails (Figure 7).

Figure 7. Elderly-friendly handrails for flush toilet (Source: Internet).

Here are four renovation solutions for the outdoor bathroom: First, handrails are provided on both sides of the toilet to help the elderly get up. Second, the height difference should be removed as far as possible. If unavoidable, non-slip materials should be used to avoid falling. Third, a roof should be provided so that the elderly can use it on rainy days, and the ground will not be muddy due to rain. Fourth, an SOS emergency button should be provided so that the elderly can quickly call for help when they have an accident in the outdoor bathroom.

4.4 Lighting design

For the rural houses built from 1980 to around 2000, there is only one lighting lamp in one space to provide indoor lighting. However, as the age increases, the eyesight of the elderly is getting worse and worse, so one lamp cannot meet their lighting needs anymore, and it is easy to cause danger. To that end, in elderly-friendly indoor design, local lighting should be added according to the needs of the elderly, and this also can provide them with psychological security.

Here are three elderly-friendly renovation solutions for the indoor lighting problem. First, sufficient lighting fixtures should be provided for the sleeping and kitchen space. Especially in functional places like the kitchen, if there is insufficient illuminance, proper local lighting should be added. Some lamps with brightness regulation functions can be used to avoid dazzling. Second, the indoor lighting should be of an intermediate color (white light), so that the elderly can see objects more clearly. In the sleeping space, warm lighting can be provided locally (Kang), as warm light can give the elderly a warm, relaxing, and soft feeling, making them easy to fall asleep. Third, in choosing interior materials, materials including organic glass and stainless steel should be avoided, as they may easily cause dazzling. So matte materials that will not reflect are more suitable for the elderly to observe.

5 CONCLUSION

The following conclusions were reached based on analyzing the questionnaire and field survey data.

First, home-based elderly care is prevalent in rural areas of Northeast China. There are still many problems in rural houses that trouble the elderly. It is necessary to conduct relevant studies and guide farmers to make elderly-friendly renovations to their own houses combined with relevant policies, regulations, and social welfare systems, to create a comfortable living environment for the rural elderly.

Second, this paper only studied the elderly-friendly indoor renovation of rural houses and did not analyze the outdoor space. There are also many problems in the outdoor space that need to be solved.

Third, in the elderly-friendly renovation of rural areas, more attention should be paid to the rational use of rural natural resources, green buildings, and environmental protection in the future. A green, healthy, and friendly living environment should be built for the elderly while achieving carbon neutrality and protecting the ecological environment.

REFERENCES

Liu D W, Jia L, Wang S S. A study on universal housing design with home-based care for the aged [J]. *Architectural Journal*. 2015:11–18.

Liu J D, Han M, Wang W D. Reconstruction strategy research of elderly-adapting lighting design in rehabilitation buildings [J]. *Journal of Shenyang Jianzhu University Social Science*. 2020, 22(4):7.

Wang H Y, Zhou B, Lu W. A study on barrier-free design adaptable for elderly houses taking rural elderly families in northern China as examples [J]. *Time Architecture*. 2012:38–42.

Wang X L. Research on the design of indoor facilities of houses lived by the elderly in home-based elderly care [J]. *Decoration*. 2014:86–87.

Wang X Y. *A study of the aged housing optimal design method of rural residents in southern Liaoning of China* [D]. Dalian University of Technology. 2016.

Zhou N, Wang X Y, Hu W H. The inheritance of morphological characteristics of traditional rural residence of southern Liaoning [J]. *Development of Small Cities & Towns*, 2010(2):3.

Preferential study on environmental protection for highway slopes in rainy areas of South China based on the amount of water-based polyurethane

Enlian Xie*

Guangxi Tianxin Highway Co., Ltd., Guangxi, China

ABSTRACT: Soil erosion remains an acute problem in rainy areas of south China due to precipitation and farming. As the construction of highways aggravates slope erosion and soil erosion, it is necessary to take measures to conserve and restore the environment of slopes. In this paper, a dose selection test of water-based polyurethane is carried out to protect slopes based on the Bama-Pingxiang highway and the effect of different doses of water-based polyurethane on the environmental protection of slopes is analyzed through the slope erosion resistance test and plant growth monitoring test. The results indicate that the surface of the slope protected by water-based polyurethane can rapidly cure the soil in the slope and accelerate the drainage on the slope surface, thus improving the anti-erosion performance of the slope surface by 41.7%~65.5%. As the intensity of the anti-erosion performance is affected by rainfall, the anti-erosion performance tends to reduce in heavy rains. The monitoring test of plant growth shows that the slope plants protected by water-based polyurethane still grow normally, and the water retention performance of the slope soil is better, which provides sufficient water supply for the later growth of plants and reduces the influence of leaching. However, an excessive amount of water-based polyurethane is likely to inhibit the germination of plants. As for the test plants, Paspalum notatum, and Dianthus barbatus, the best protection effect is achieved when water-based polyurethane with a 3–5% mass fraction is used. Therefore, the results of the study provide a theoretical and experimental basis for the application of water-based polyurethane in the environmental protection of slopes in rainy areas of South China and also offer new ideas for the environmental protection of slopes with the help of chemical materials.

1 INTRODUCTION

The red soil area in South China accounts for about 23% of the total land area in China. South China enjoys a subtropical monsoon climate with abundant heat and precipitation. With frequent farming and unreasonable exploitation of land resources, South China has suffered from the severity of soil erosion, second only to the Loess Plateau (Liu 2017). In recent years, the rapid construction of highways in the region has led to many exposed slopes. Due to the high pore ratio and low compressibility of the soils on the slope (Tian 2019), soil erosion is more serious in areas with frequent rainfall, resulting in a large amount of water and soil loss. Meanwhile, the low nutrient of the excavated slope soils seriously restricts the ecological protection and restoration of slopes (Zhang 2021).

Currently, common technologies for protecting slops at home and abroad can be divided into engineering protection and ecological protection. For engineering protection, slopes can be protected and reinforced in a short period, but environmental impacts aren't considered, so this method

---

*Corresponding Author: enlianxie@163.com

cannot meet the current demands for ecological protection. Ecological protection means protecting plants and traditional engineering protection (Zhang 2021). While the stability of slopes is ensured, the roots and branches of plants anchor the soil and intercept rainfall to enhance the anti-erosion performance of the soil. Currently, the commonly used ecological protection means mainly include spray seeding, grass planting, 3D net grass planting, ecological-bag grass planting, etc. Although progress has been made in ecological protection, some problems remain acute such as high reworking rate, weak vegetation structure layer, poor plant growth, and long restoration period (Liu 2021; Peng 2017; Shan 2016).

Consolidation of materials and ecological measures provide a new idea for erosion control (Wang 2020; Zhou 2014). Water-based polyurethane, whose main component is water-based polyurethane resin, is a new environmental-friendly polymer material that can form an elastic and porous consolidation layer shortly after spraying onto the slope surface, which improves the erosion resistance of the slope surface. Water-based polyurethane has been applied to erosion control of sandy soil and red clay soil (Liang 2020; Qin 2021; Wang 2020), but the first research results mainly focus on soil erosion characteristics without considering the effect of water-based polyurethane on plant growth. As ecological restoration of slopes is a comprehensive process, it is necessary to consider both the erosion resistance of soils and the effects on plant growth.

In this paper, based on water-based polyurethane for ecological protection of slopes in rainy areas in South China, a rainfall simulation test and a planting monitoring test are conducted to study the erosion resistance and the effects on plant growth. The paper aims to analyze the erosion resistance, effects on plant growth, and water retention performance of slopes under the effect of different concentrations of water-based polyurethane. Therefore, the findings provide a theoretical basis and experimental foundation for applying water-based polyurethane in the ecological protection of slopes in the rainy areas of South China.

2 MATERIALS AND METHODS

2.1 *Test materials*

2.1.1 *Soil samples*
The soil samples used in the test are collected from the slopes of the Bama-Pingxiang highway in Tiandeng County, Chongzuo City, Guangxi Zhuang Autonomous Region, and the sampling area is the bare slopes newly formed during construction. After clearing the debris and weeds on the surfaces of slopes, multipoint sampling is used to collect soils from 0–30 cm on the surface of the slopes with a shovel, and then the soils are mixed and sealed in bags for preservation.

2.1.2 *Water-based polyurethane*
The main component of the water-based polyurethane used in this test is a modified water-based polyurethane resin with light yellow or brown oil, a density of 1.08 g/cm^3 and pH 6.8~7.0. After mixing with water, the material reacts and cures rapidly to form a porous and elastic cementing colloid. Therefore, when used on the slope, it can be mutually cemented with the soil on the surface of the slope to resist erosion (Li 2019). The material uses water as a curing agent and reacts with water to produce green and environmentally friendly carbon dioxide.

$$2R - NCO + H_2O \rightarrow NHCONH + CO_2 \tag{1}$$

2.1.3 *Other materials*
The water retention agent is selected from polyacrylamide (Wei 2020), which can improve soils, regulate soil moisture, and enhance soil nutrients. Wood fiber, processed from natural raw materials such as wood, coconut shell, bamboo, and straw, can enhance the porosity of soil after addition and provide nutrients for plant growth after natural degradation. Peat, rich in nutrients, can improve the nutrient contents of the soils after addition.

2.2 Rainfall simulation test

2.2.1 Rainfall simulation device

The rainfall simulation device is shown in Figure 1, mainly composed of a water pump, flow meter, intelligent water pressure valve, spray head, fixed bracket, etc. The rainfall intensity can be adjusted and controlled by the water pump and water pressure, which can meet the needs of the rainfall intensity under different test requirements. The size of the simulated slope device is 1.0m (length) × 0.4m (width) × 0.3m (height), with a runoff collection port and a runoff bucket for collecting runoff and sediment from the slopes.

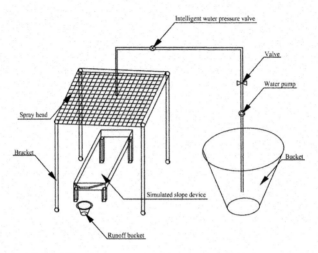

Figure 1. Rainfall scours simulation device.

2.2.2 Experimental design

During the test, the soil samples collected in the field are mixed and evenly laid in layers, with each layer 10 cm thick. Then, the soil samples are compacted while lying evenly. The surface of slopes is scraped with wooden boards to avoid sliding between layers and ensure that the surface remains natural. The simulated slope is set at 1:1, and the runoff bucket of precipitation and the sediment collection device is placed at the runoff collection port of the simulated slope. The runoff bucket should be placed outside the spraying range to avoid the simulated rainfall directly falling into the runoff bucket.

After the soil samples of the simulated slope are filled, water-based polyurethane with mass fractions of 3%, 5%, and 7% is sprayed on the surface of the slope at a dosage of 3 L/m^2. Another slope without any treatment is built as a control test. One day before the rainfall simulation test, preprecipitation with 0.5 mm/min of rainfall intensity is carried out; the rainfall is terminated after the runoff production and is left for 24 hours to ensure the consistent moisture content in the slope soils.

The simulated rainfall tests are conducted for 30 minutes with a rain intensity of 1.0 mm/min to simulate light and moderate rainfall and 3.0 mm/min to simulate heavy rainfall, and each group is repeated three times. The beginning of rainfalls is timed, and the time when the runoff of each slope is produced is recorded. After the runoff appears on the slope, it is collected at the exit of the simulated slope with a numbered runoff bucket, and the sampling starts from the second minute in the first six minutes to reduce the influence of the floating soil on the surface of the slope on the test results. The samples are taken once every 2 minutes, and the sampling lasts 1 minute; after 6 minutes, the samples are taken once every 4 minutes, and the sampling lasts 1 minute each time until the end of the test. The entire sampling for the runoff production lasts 30 minutes, with a total of 9 sampling sessions. After the test, the liquid in the runoff bucket is stirred, and the sampling bottles with uniform specifications are selected and numbered. The samples are taken from the runoff bucket in turn, and each runoff bucket is sampled three times to reduce the error caused by the uneven mixing of sediment samples. After the runoff samples are taken, each sample is dried in an oven; the sediment mass is weighed with an electronic scale with an accuracy of 0.01 g to calculate the sediment carried by the runoff, and the amount of sediment erosion per unit area is obtained by area conversion. With the set runoff carrying sediment of bare slopes as a reference, the sediment-reducing effects of different water-based polyurethane dosages used in slopes are calculated separately, and the calculation formula is:

$$EI = \frac{Y_b - Y_i}{Y_b} \times 100\% \qquad (2)$$

EI denotes sediment-reducing effects; Y_b is the sand production from bare slopes, and Y_i is the sand production from the sample with spraying mass fraction i.

2.3 Planting monitoring trials

The planting monitoring test is carried out in pots with a diameter of 30 cm and a depth of 20 cm, and a total of nine tests are set up, each with three identical samples. The test plants are commonly used in South China to protect slopes, such as the herb Paspalum notatum and shrub Dianthus barbatus, and the seeds are purchased from Chongzuo City, Guangxi Zhuang Autonomous Region. The soil samples collected in the field are filled into the pots for 15 cm and compacted; then, after mixing with a water retention agent, wood fibers, peat, and plant seeds, they are spread on the surface of the soil in pots. In the tests, the amount of the water retention agents is 5 g/m², the amount of wood fibers is 100 g/m², the amount of peat is 4 L/m², the number of seeds is 15 g/m², and the seed dosage of Paspalum notatum and Dianthus barbatus is matched at 1:0.3. After the plants are sown, the water-based polyurethane with mass fractions of 3%, 5%, and 7% are sprayed onto the pots according to the number. The sample plants grow under natural conditions, and after their seeds germinate, the number of sprouts in each sample is counted. After 28 days of growth, the plant stems and leaves in each sample are collected by cutting along the surface of soils, while the withered stems and leaves on the surface of the sample are collected, dried, and then weighed to determine the aboveground biomass of the plants under the action of different mass fractions of water-based polyurethane. After that, the roots in each sample plant are removed intact, rinsed, and dried to determine their belowground biomass.

Soil nutrient test: After the plant biomass sampling is finished, soil samples 5~10 cm below the soil surface are selected to determine the soil nutrient content. An intelligent soil nutrient tester measures nutrient indexes, including alkaline hydrolyzable nitrogen, fast-acting phosphorus, and fast-acting potassium. The soil that determines the nutrients is sampled three times to ensure accuracy.

To better explain the test results, the samples with the mass fraction of 3%, 5%, and 7%, and the blank control group without being sprayed with water-based polyurethane are replaced by numbers C3, C5, C7, and B.

3 RESULTS AND ANALYSIS

3.1 Erosion resistance of slopes

3.1.1 Time of initial runoff

The time of the initial runoff of the soils on the surface of the slope body can reflect the response of the soil to the rainfall scour and the resulting runoff in the slope. The longtime of initial runoff indicates that the infiltration effect is obvious when the rainfall reaches the slope; the longer it takes to form the runoff in the slope, the better the effect of reducing the runoff. The time of initial runoff of different samples is shown in Table 1. As shown in the Table, when the rainfall intensity increases, the time of initial runoff in the sample soils reduces. When the simulated rainfall is light or moderate, the time of the initial runoff in sample C3 is 13.2% longer than that of the blank control sample B. The time of the initial runoff in samples C5 and C7 reduce by 8.5% and 18.6%; when the heavy rainfall is simulated, the time of the initial runoff in the samples C3, C5, and C7 decreased by 7.1%, 12.5%, and 26.8%, which is significantly lower than that of sample B. The analysis shows that the effect of water-based polyurethane to protect slopes is related to the mass fraction of material used and rainfall intensities. For the slopes protected by water-based polyurethane with the same mass fraction, the time of producing initial flow in the samples with the lower mass fraction is significantly longer when the rainfall intensity is lower, and the time of producing initial flow in the samples with the higher mass fraction is significantly shorter. When the rainfall intensity is higher, the time of the initial runoff in the samples with water-based polyurethane is shorter than that of the blank control samples. The results reveal that the runoff characteristics in the slope with water-based polyurethane for ecological protection will be significantly changed.

Table 1. Time of initial runoff in different samples.

Number	Simulated Rain Intensity	
	Light and moderate rainfall	Heavy rainfall
B	129	36
C3	146	33
C5	118	29
C7	105	23

3.1.2 Total runoff

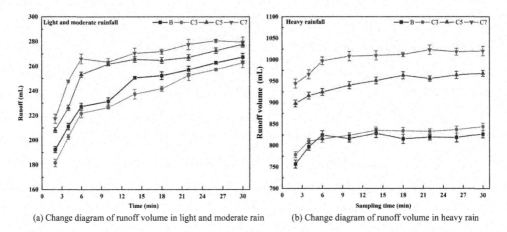

(a) Change diagram of runoff volume in light and moderate rain   (b) Change diagram of runoff volume in heavy rain

Figure 2. Change diagram of runoff volume under different rainfall intensity.

Table 2. Initial stabilization of slope runoff.

Simulated rain intensity (mm·min^{-1})	Runoff Volume/mL			
	B	C3	C5	C7
1.0	252.3c	251.4c	265.6b	270.6a
3.0	824.2c	809.8c	963.6b	997.5a

The variation of slope runoff collected under the different intensities of rainfall is shown in Figure 2. From the Figure, under the effect of light and moderate rainfall, the volumes of slope runoff in all samples show a trend of rapid growth in the early stage and steady fluctuation later. However, as the mass fraction of water-based polyurethane is different, the time of maximum runoff is different from that of stable runoff. Among them, the volume of runoff in sample B starts to stabilize from the 14th minute, with the stable volume of runoff reaching 252.3 mL/min. In sample C7, the runoff volume starts to stabilize from the 6th minute, while the stabilization time of samples C3 and C5 is later than that of C7, which is earlier than that of the blank control sample. Their stabilized runoff rates are 270.6 mL/min, 251.4 mL/min, and 265.6 mL/min, which indicate that the higher the mass fraction of water-based polyurethane is, the bigger the stabilized value of slope runoff reach. However, when the mass fraction is 3%, the stabilized value of slope runoff is smaller than that of the blank control sample. During the simulated downpour, the slope runoff volumes of sample B, sample C3, and sample C7 show a trend of stable fluctuation after a short but rapid rise. The stabilization time of samples B and C7 occur in the 6th minute, with the slope runoff volume reaching 824.2 mL/min and 997.5 mL/min. The stabilization time of sample C3 is in the 4th minute, with a slope runoff volume of 809.8 mL/min at the initial stabilization. However, sample C5 reveals no notable growth but a trend of stable, slow growth followed by stable fluctuation, with the runoff rate reaching 963.6 mL/min at the initial stabilization time. After the comparison, the volume of stable runoff is consistent with that of moderate and light rainfall. The analysis shows that when water-based polyurethane with a mass fraction of 3% is used to protect slopes, the infiltration effect of the slope surface is better, and so does the effect of runoff reduction. Nevertheless, with the increase in mass fraction and the runoff volume of the surface of the slope, the greater the rain intensity tends to be, the more notable the increase of the runoff volume is. It means that the use of water-based polyurethane with a higher mass fraction can reduce the retention of rainwater on the slope surface, and accelerate the drainage of the surface. A large amount of rainwater infiltration increases the moisture content of the soils on the slope, but the high moisture content affects the stability of the slope, thus causing mudslides and landslides. As a hydrophilic material, water-based polyurethane can quickly react with water and form a film structure on the slope's surface, as shown in Figure 3. The film structure that covers the soils reduces the infiltration of rainwater into the slope surface, thus improving the scour resistance of the surface. However, the water-based polyurethane with a low mass fraction forms the solution, which fails to build a complete protective film structure on the surface of the slope due to the low content of water-based polyurethane. After the solution infiltrates into the soil, a channel similar to a pipe is formed to accelerate the infiltration of rainwater into the surface of the slope. Therefore, water-based polyurethane with a higher mass fraction can promote drainage on the surface and reduce the possibility of secondary disasters.

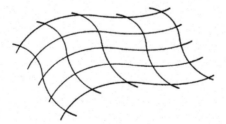

Figure 3. Gel network structure. (Liang 2016).

3.2 *The sediment volume carried by runoff*

The change in sediment volume carried by runoff of each test sample under different rainfall intensities is shown in Figure 4. During light and moderate rainfall, the sediment volumes carried by runoff in sample B, sample C3, and sample C7 increase at first and then decrease with time. The highest sediment volume carried by runoff of sample B reaches 54.2 g, while the maximum

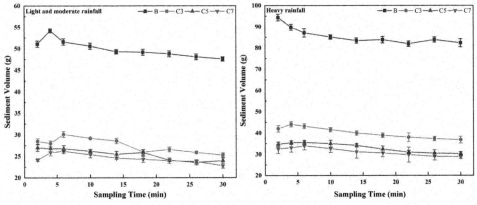

(a) Sediment volume carried by runoff during light and moderate rainfall (b) Amount of sediment carried by runoff during heavy rainfall

Figure 4. Change diagram of sediment volume carried by runoff with time

sediment volumes of sample C3 and sample C7 are 30.1 g and 26.2 g. The sand production of sample C5 decreases with time, with the maximum sediment volume reaching 27 g. From the Figure, the sediment volume of the slopes treated with water-based polyurethane is fewer than that of the bare slopes during light and moderate rainfall, with the sediment-reducing effects of 41.7% and 52.6%. During heavy rain, the trend of sediment volume of runoff with scouring time is similar to that of light and moderate rainfall, but it is more stable, showing a decrease in the sediment volume. From the Figure, compared with sample B, sample C7 records the best sediment-reducing effect, reducing the sediment by 58.8~65.5%, followed by sample C7, and sample C3 reduces sediment by 50.4~55.5%. The test results show that compared with the natural slope, the anti-scouring performance in the slope's surface protected by water-based polyurethane has been improved; a higher mass fraction of water-based polyurethane leads to a higher mass fraction of water-based polyurethane leads marked increase in the anti-scouring performance, and water-based polyurethane is more effective during heavy rains.

When runoff is formed on the slope surface during rainfalls, fine soil particles are first carried by the surface, which increases sediment volume during light rains. However, with the increased runoff volume, the fine particles on the surface will decrease, and so does the sediment volume washed down with the runoff. When the rain intensity is higher, the rainfall will form runoff directly on the surface of the slope. While carrying the fine soil particles on the surface, the slope runoff also carries and strips the large agglomerates on the slope surface. Therefore, the sediment volume carried by the runoff tends to fluctuate and remain consistent when the rain intensity is higher. From the reaction mechanism, the -NCO group on the polymer chain of water-based polyurethane reacts quickly with the -OH of water molecules and a high-strength elastic membrane structure can be generated in a short time. As the membrane structure does not react with water, it ensures the integrity of the soil on the surface. To reduce the amount of sediment carried by slope runoff, two aspects need to be considered. First, to reduce the runoff volume of the slope is to reduce the erosive force of runoff; the other is to enhance the soil consolidation to reduce the supply source of the material carried by slope runoff(Li 2021). Thanks to the characteristics of water-based polyurethane, its ability to protect slopes mainly relies on enhancing the consolidation of the soils on the slope. Although this leads to the consequent increase in the runoff volume of the slope, the test results show that it's more effective in inhibiting the sediment volume carried by runoff.

It should be noted that the simulated rainfall scouring test mainly focuses on the initial effect of water-based polyurethane on protecting slopes without considering the interception and drainage effect of slope plants. The water-based polyurethane can prevent the loss of plant seeds from scouring the slope while consolidating the soil, which ensures the plant coverage and uniformity of the slope at the later stage. In addition, the effect of water-based polyurethane on plant growth and soil improvement is also important to the ecological protection of slopes, which needs additional experimental research.

4 PLANT GROWTH MONITORING

4.1 *Plant germination capacity*

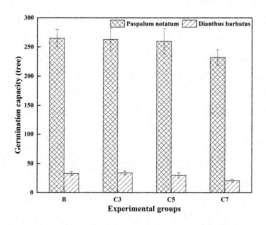

Figure 5. Comparison of germination effects.

The germination capacity of plants with different mass fractions of water-based polyurethane is shown in Figure 5. For the slopes protected by water-based polyurethane, the germination capacity of both plants is the same as that of the control sample B when the mass fractions of water-based polyurethane are 3% and 5%. However, when the mass fraction of water-based polyurethane is increased to 7%, the germination of Paspalum notatum decreases by 12.5% compared with sample B, while the germination of *dianthus barbatus* decreases by 36.4% compared to sample B. The analysis shows that when water-based polyurethane with a low mass fraction is used to protect slopes, it seldom influences the growth and germination of plants, but when the dosage is higher, it is likely to inhibit plant germination, exerting different influences on various plants. This is because water-based polyurethane with a higher mass fraction brings about the tight and thick film-like structure formed on the surface of soils. Plant seeds cannot penetrate the structure after germination, which inhibits the germination of plants. Therefore, higher mass fractions should be avoided when water-based polyurethane is adopted for protecting slopes. Meanwhile, the effects are related to the type of planting plants. When other plants are used with water-based polyurethane to protect slopes, corresponding tests should be conducted to study the growth effect of selected plants under the action of water-based polyurethane.

4.2 *Plant biomass*

For each test sample, the aboveground biomass measured from the test is shown in Figure 6. For the test plant, Paspalum notatum treated with water-based polyurethane, the aboveground biomass of samples C3, C5, and C7 is increased by 44.2%, 38.5%, and 26.9%, and the belowground biomass is increased by 23.7%, 20.2%, and 16.2% compared to sample B. For the test plant *Dianthus barbatus*, compared to sample B, the aboveground biomass of samples C3, C5, and C7 increased by 67.6%, 62.2%, and 45.9%, while the belowground biomass increased by 24.7%, 21.2%, and 13.5%. From the Figure, the aboveground and belowground biomass of the samples treated with water-based polyurethane is higher than those of the blank control samples. Still,

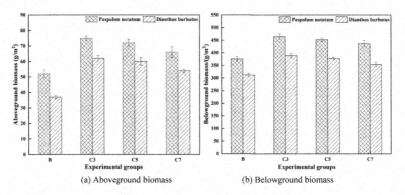

Figure 6. Plant biomass

with the increase in the mass fraction of water-based polyurethane, the enhancement effect of aboveground and belowground biomass decreases compared to the blank control samples. This indicates that water-based polyurethane can boost plant growth, but water-based polyurethane with a higher mass fraction is ineffective in promoting plant growth. At the same time, when the plant height is measured during growth, it is found that the plant growth rate of the sample treated with water-based polyurethane is faster than that of the control sample B. Moreover, the higher the mass fraction of water-based polyurethane is, the more rapidly the plants grow. The analysis shows that the "film" formed by the water-based polyurethane in the soil can simultaneously achieve the thermal insulation effect on the soil, thus providing the appropriate temperature for plant growth. Yet, the effect of water-based polyurethane on plant growth at different temperatures needs to be further tested. The plant's root system can reinforce the topsoil of the slope; therefore, the larger the root system is, the higher the value of the root biomass, which better helps stabilize the soil on the slope (Zhong 2022).

As water-based polyurethane improves the soil's structure on the slope's surface, it makes the loose clay particles tightly bound, playing a key role in retaining water and preventing the soil nutrients from losing. All this helps the plants better absorb water and nutrients in the soil, making the soil on the slope's surface more suitable for plants' growth. However, since the effect of water-based polyurethane on soil consolidation varies with different mass fractions, there are differences in the initial germination and later plant growth. For the selected plants, the water-based polyurethane with a mass fraction of 3%-5% can boost the later plant growth.

4.3 *Soil nutrient contents*

Soil nutrients are the general term for all nutrients provided by the soil that can be used for plant growth. Among them, the mineral components directly absorbed by plant roots or absorbed after transformation include 13 elements such as nitrogen, phosphorus, potassium, etc. In addition to mineral components, soil nutrients include organic matter (Liu 2022). This experiment selects alkaline-hydrolyzable nitrogen, fast-acting phosphorus, and fast-acting potassium for determination and analysis. With the test group as the horizontal coordinate and the nutrient contents as the vertical coordinate, the comparison of the nutrient contents of different groups is shown in Figure 7.

As can be seen from the Figure, the nutrient contents and total nutrients of the blank control sample B and sample C3 are the same, while the total nutrients of sample C5 are higher than those of sample C3 by about 7.8% and those of sample C7 by about 12.6%. This is because the time to measure the soil nutrient contents is close to the plant sowing time. Organic matters such as wood fibers have not been naturally degraded and transformed into soil organic matter and then into plant-absorbable nutrients such as alkaline-hydrolyzable nitrogen. The total amount of nutrients in sample C7 is higher than in the other samples because the water-based polyurethane plays a

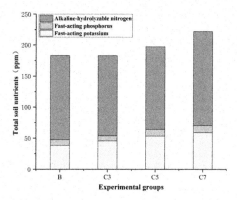

Figure 7. Total soil nutrients of experimental groups.

cementing and curing role. When its mass fraction is higher, the film-like structure in the soil surface is more compact. This means less runoff infiltration in the sample and fewer losses of soil nutrients with the infiltration during regular rains, which can better retain fertilizers. Meanwhile, the membrane structure layer on the surface of sample C7 provides a higher temperature for the soil in the lower layer, which promotes the degradation and transformation of the substrate, such as wood fibers in the soil, so its total amount of nutrients is higher than other samples. In addition, based on the data on plant germination and plant biomass, the analysis indicates that the water-based polyurethane with a higher mass fraction means less plant germination, poor growth later on, and less nutrient uptake by plants to retain most nutrients. Therefore, when water-based polyurethane materials are used to protect slopes, higher mass fractions should be avoided; otherwise, it will inhibit the growth of plants and affect the ecological restoration of slopes.

5 CONCLUSIONS

In this paper, to study the effect of water-based polyurethane on anti-erosion performance and the promoting effect on plant growth to protect slopes in rainy areas of South China, rainfall simulation tests and planting monitoring tests are carried out to analyze the six indicators: initial runoff time, total runoff volume, sediment volume carried by runoff, plant germination capacity, plant biomass, and soil nutrient contents. The comprehensive conclusions are as follows.

(1) The runoff on the slope surface protected by water-based polyurethane has changed significantly, manifested by the marked increase in runoff volume and the decrease in rainfall infiltration. Moreover, the higher the mass fraction of water-based polyurethane is, the more obvious the effect is. In addition, the runoff volume on the slope's surface is also influenced by the rainfall intensity. During light rainfall, there is a small correlation between runoff volume, sediment volume on the surface, and the mass fraction of water-based polyurethane, and the change is not obvious with the increase in its mass fraction; when the rainfall intensity is higher, the runoff volume increases with the rise in the water-based polyurethane dosage, but the sediment volume carried by runoff reduces, which means the better effect of soil consolidation and sand reduction.

(2) The use of water-based polyurethane to protect slopes will have a certain impact on the growth of plants. The water-based polyurethane with a low mass fraction seldom influences growth, but a higher mass fraction inhibits plant growth to a certain extent, leading to lower plant germination and poorer growth later on. Yet, water-based polyurethane with a higher mass fraction is better at preserving soil fertilizers.

(3) Based on the erosion resistance and promoting effect on plant growth on the slope's surface, suggestions are made that the mass fraction of water-based polyurethane should be 3–5% when used to protect slopes in rainy areas of South China. However, the tolerance of other plants to water-based polyurethane needs to be studied to prevent the situation that plants cannot germinate and grow under the influence of water-based polyurethane.

In summary, water-based polyurethane plays a good role in the ecological protection of the soils on the slopes in the rainy area of South China and ensures the normal growth of plants. However, the effect of the water-based polyurethane is affected by the slope, vegetation type, and temperature, which requires further study.

REFERENCES

Li G. D. *Study on damage of plant-growing consolidation material/pisha sandstone under drying-wetting cycle* [D]. Xiangtan University, 2019.

Li Z. Y., Zhang M. J., Chen M. Y., et al. Effects of Alfalfa on runoff and sediment yield and soil moisture on slope [J]. *Research of Soil and Water Conservation*, 2021, 28 (05): 54–60.

Liang Z. S., Liu H. W., Zhang L. X., et al. Effect of water-based polyurethane material on soil erosion rate and microstructure of arsenic sandstone slope [J]. *Journal of Soil and Water Conservation*, 2020, 34 (05): 355–360.

Liang Z. S., Wu Z. R. Sand fixation and growth promotion properties and mechanism of modified water-soluble polyurethane [J]. *Transactions of the Chinese Society of Agricultural Engineering*, 2016, 32 (22): 171–177.

Liu K., Ma J. Research on slope protection technology in highway subgrade design [J]. *Transportation world*, 2021 (18): 96–97.

Liu L. M., Song Y. S., Zhong B., et al. Research progress on ecological restoration technology of vegetation concrete [J]. *Journal of Environmental Engineering Technology*, 2022, 12(03):916–927.

Liu T. T., Han L. X., Sun M. Y., et al. Simulation on the time progress of the non-point source pollution load in runoff for small watershed [J]. *Environmental Science and Technology*, 2017, 30 (05): 31–35.

Peng A. X., Zhang M. X., Zhu H. C. Triaxial test of high strength geocell reinforced soil [J]. *Journal of Shanghai University* (Natural Science Edition), 2017, 23(04): 590–599.

Qin X. C., Ni A. C., Zhang N., et al. Erosion control and growth promotion of water-based polyurethane material on red clay highway slopes: A case study in South China[J]. *Sustainability*, 2021, 13.

Shan Y. T., Hu L., Wang Q., et al. Impacts of runoff scouring on high-grade highway slope erosion in alpine and high-altitude regions [J]. *Journal of Traffic and Transportation Engineering*, 2016, 16(04): 88–95.

Tian Y. C., Huang Y. L., Zhang Q., et al. Soil erosion and Selenium loss in Qinjiang River Basin in Beibu Gulf coastal zone [J]. *China Environmental Science*, 2019, 39(01): 257–273.

Wang X., Zhu X. C., Liang Y., et al. Effects of new water-based polyurethane materials on infiltration and runoff and sediment yield of typical eroded soils in South China [J]. *Science of Soil and Water Conservation*, 2020, 18 (06): 123–131.

Wang Y. B., Tang Z. G., Yang Y. L. Experimental study on improving plateau red clay with mineral powder soil solidifier [J]. *Journal of North University of China* (Natural Science Edition), 2020, 41(05): 443–449.

Wei Y. M., Liao Z. W., Hong J. L., et al. Study on water and fertilizer retention effect of new water retaining agent and its components [J]. *South China Forestry Science*, 2020, 48 (05): 69–73.

Zhang F. Y., Xin Y. X., Hong J., et al. Optimization of matrix ratio for ecological protection of expressway slope in alpine canyon area [J]. *Highway*, 2021, 66(08): 333–337.

Zhang H., Su C. Analysis on the stability of borrowed soil in ecological slope under rainfall effect [J]. *Water Resources and Hydropower Engineering*, 2021, 52(04): 186–191.

Zhong C. Y., Cui P., Zhu S. R., et al. Analysis of the influence of root water absorption on the stability of unsaturated soils slope [J]. *Journal of Soil and Water Conservation*, 2022, 36(02): 99–105.

Zhou H. L., Shen X. D. Application research situation and prospect of soil stabilizer [J]. *Materials Reports*, 2014,28(09): 134–138.

Study on diagonal brace resistance to lateral loads in frame structure building

Keding Wang*

School of Mechanics and Civil Engineering, China University of Mining and Technology, Beijing, China

ABSTRACT: Diagonal braces are often installed in the frame structure in architectural design. The diagonal brace plays an important role in resisting lateral load and improving the lateral stiffness of the building in the frame structure, which can improve the earthquake and wind resistance of the building structure. However, it is unclear to what extent the strength of skew braces is strengthened in the frame structure. Therefore, this paper uses two kinds of finite element analysis software, ETABS, and SAP2000, to establish a simplified model of the frame structure and a model of a single unit containing diagonal braces in the building, respectively, and applies horizontal loads to the model to simulate the real stress situation. The analysis of the simulation results of the software shows that the diagonal braces significantly improve the lateral stiffness of the whole frame structure, and the failure of the diagonal braces occurs before that of the frame yield in a single frame element, the ability of the diagonal braces to resist transverse loads is also significantly improved.

1 INTRODUCTION

High-rise buildings use a lot of structures such as shear walls, core tubes, trusses, and diagonal braces to resist horizontal loads, among which the diagonal supports are of great help to enhance the stability of the structure. The diagonal brace is generally connected with the beam and column of the building, which can effectively increase the stiffness and seismic capacity of the structure (Bao 2014).

A diagonal brace across several floors is arranged on the outside of the building to form a space frame, which can effectively increase the stiffness and seismic capacity of the structure (Gong 2021). Through the diagonal brace, the seismic horizontal force becomes the axial force of the column transmitted to the foundation and foundation. The diagonal brace is installed on the main stress components of the building, which can use structural materials to a greater extent. The Alcoa Building shown in Figure 1 is a typical frame structure with diagonal braces. It is an efficient and economic seismic and wind-resistant structural component. Therefore, it is very important to clarify the contribution of a diagonal brace against lateral stiffness and the force mechanism of the diagonal brace in frame structure (Wang 2019).

Study of braces within China and abroad mainly focused on changing the shape of a brace, materials, and the connecting way of brace and architecture subject to ensure the strength of the brace to meet the design required, to maximize the use of the strength of materials and structure of the brace itself intensity, but there are few studies to brace for the quantitative analysis of the strength of the frame structure building research. Therefore, the research of this paper mainly focuses on the improvement of the strength of the building.

Finite element analysis of building structure is an effective building design and analysis method. In this paper, the finite element analysis software ETABS and SAP2000 is used to carry out finite

---

*Corresponding Author: 1910610220@student.cumtb.edu.cn

Figure 1. A typical frame structure with diagonal brace: Alcoa Building, San Francisco.

element analysis on the model containing the diagonal brace simplified according to the actual situation, quantitatively analyze the enhancement effect of the diagonal brace on the overall lateral stiffness of the model and obtain the stress state of the diagonal brace when the model is damaged.

2 THE FORM AND ADVANTAGE OF DIAGONAL BRACE FRAME STRUCTURE

In frame structure buildings, diagonal support is generally arranged according to the modulus of story height and column-span, and its setting height is usually $1 \sim 2$ floors. This arrangement method is still preferred and widely used at present. But giant braces that span multiple floors and spans are also being used more and more. The diagonal brace makes the beam and column structure system more coordinated when resisting gravity load and horizontal load, enhances the lateral force stiffness of the outer frame structure, promotes the progress of building structure, and especially creates a more effective structure form for super high-rise buildings. The diagonal bracing frame system consists of a shear bracing structure and a beam-column arranged vertically. Horizontal shear force is mainly supported by diagonal braces rather than columns, which bear vertical loads from walls, beams, and plates. Compared with general frame structures, this structural system can not only improve the overall stiffness of the structure, but also greatly enhance the anti-lateral stiffness of the system.

The frame structure with diagonal brace has the following advantages:

(1) The height of the building is often proportional to the size of the section of the beam and column of the building, and the section size of the giant beam and column with diagonal support is not only much larger than the conventional beam and column, plus the addition of diagonal support, so its stiffness is far greater than the ordinary frame structure (Chen 2014).

(2) The lateral stiffness is large, the distribution along the height is uniform, and the force transmission path is clear, which is an ideal lateral force resistance structural system (Ding 2014).

(3) The horizontal earthquake effect is large in a high-rise building. The giant structure system with diagonal support can have different combinations. The main and secondary structures can use different materials and systems, so that the irregular building can take the appropriate structural units combined into regular giant structures for wind resistance and earthquake resistance is very favorable (Bie 2018).

(4) The secondary structure of the giant frame structure with diagonal braces is only the force transmission structure, so the pillars of the secondary structure need not be continuous, and the

building can be arranged in a large space or green space in the sky. The columns in the secondary structure mainly bear a small load between the giant beams, and the sections can also be made very small, creating good conditions for the flexible arrangement of the room (Hang 2011).

(5) The construction speed is fast. The giant frame structure system with a diagonal brace can be constructed from the main structure first, and the secondary structure will be constructed on each working face at the same time after the completion of the main structure, greatly shortening the construction period of the building structure (Yang 2014).

(6) It has greater stability and higher structural performance, can save materials and reduce cost, and has strong economic practicability (Zhao 2013).

3 FINITE ELEMENT ANALYSIS OF DIAGONAL BRACE REINFORCEMENT FOR MULTI-STORY BUILDINGS

The finite element analysis software ETABS is used to model the simplified structure of two multi-story buildings of the same size. Model 1 is a frame multi-story building model, and Model 2 is a frame multi-story building model with X-type diagonal support between floors based on model 1. Figures 2 and 3 show that the only difference between the two structures is whether to add an X-type brace between floors. Therefore, by comparing the maximum story displacement and maximum story drifts of the two buildings under the same load, the degree of lateral stiffness of the building model improved by diagonal supports can be quantitatively analyzed.

3.1 The multi-story building model

This is a multi-story building model of a frame structure, as shown in Figures 2 and 3. The dimensional parameters of the building are shown in Table 1. The steel bars and concrete selected in the model are from China steel bar standards and China concrete standards. The concrete strength level is C30, and the steel strength level is HRB400. The geometric dimensions and reinforcement of beam and column sections are shown in Table 2. The thickness of the floor is 100mm, and the type of the floor is Membrane Specify floors as rigid partitions. The column, beam, beam, and foundation are rigidly connected in this model.

Figure 2. Schematic diagram of building Model 1.

According to the architectural design load code (GB50009-2010), a constant load of 2kN/m² in the vertical direction is applied to the building floor, with a load component coefficient of 1.3, a

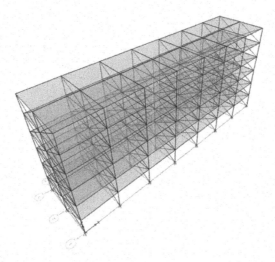

Figure 3. Schematic diagram of building Model 2.

Table 1. Basic structural attributes.

Attribute types	Data m
Overall length	42
Overall width	10
Overall height	18
Story height	3
Column spacing in the X direction	6
Column spacing in the Y direction	5

Table 2. Component infographic.

Component type	Frame column	Frame beam
Cross-sectional dimensions	240mm*240mm	600mm*300mm
Configuration of reinforcement	8Φ24 (longitudinal bar) Φ8 @100 (stirrup)	3Φ10 (longitudinal bar) Φ8 @100 (stirrup)

Table 3. Seismic parameters table.

Parameter	Parameter values
Maximum seismic influence coefficient α	0.16
Seismic fortification coefficient SI	8 (0.20g)
characteristic period of ground motion Tg	0.4
Period reduction coefficient PTDF	1
Damping ratio	0.05

live load of $2kN/m^2$, and a load component coefficient of 0.6. The seismic load is applied to the model using the response spectrum method, and the load analysis coefficient is 1.2. The reaction spectrum function in ETABS was selected, and its parameters are shown in Table 3. The action direction of seismic load is the Y direction.

3.2 Results and analysis of finite element

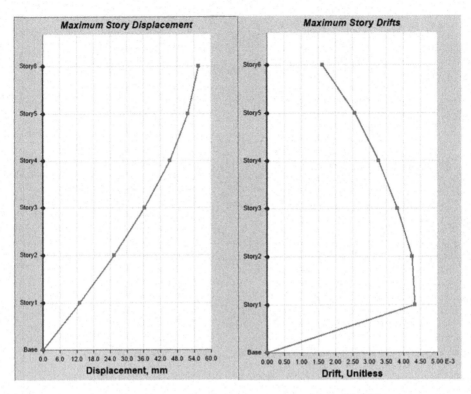

Figure 4. Maximum story displacement diagram and maximum story Drifts Model 1.

Table 4. Base shear of Model 1 and Model 2.

Framework form	Base shear
Without brace (Model 1)	12384.30 KN
With brace (Model 2)	21424.84 KN

Figure 4 and Figure 5 show the maximum story displacement diagram and maximum story drifts of Model 1 and Model 2. The maximum story displacement and the maximum story drift are important indexes to reflect the lateral stiffness of building structures. The finite element analysis shows that the maximum story displacement is 55.57mm and the maximum story drift is 0.004332 in Model 1, while the maximum floor displacement is 8.80mm, and the maximum story drifts is 0.000588 in model 2.

By analyzing the data, it can be concluded that the maximum story displacement of Model 2 is only 15.84% of that of Model 1, and the maximum story drift is 13.57% of that of Model 1. The maximum story displacement and the maximum story drift in model ii are 10% ~ 20% of that in Model 1. At the same time, the base shear of Model 1 is 58.74% of that of Model 1, as shown in Figure 4. The results indicate that the X-shaped diagonal brace significantly improves the overall lateral stiffness of the model, and the maximum story displacement angle of STORY1 in Model 2 is significantly smaller than that in model 1. It is only 6.18% of Model 1. The reduction was the smallest of any floor, indicating that the X-shaped diagonal supports greatly improve the

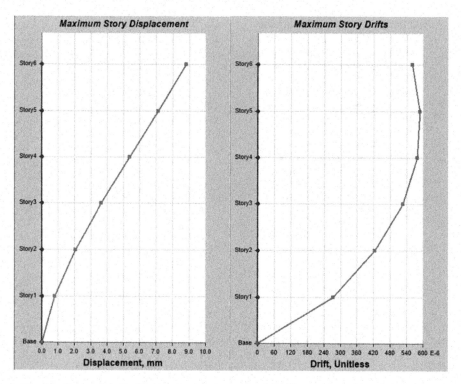

Figure 5. Maximum story displacement diagram and maximum story Drifts Model 2.

lateral stiffness of the underlying structure of the model and play an important role in improving the overall stability of the structure.

By analyzing the results, it can be found that the base shear force of the model with diagonal braces is larger than that of the model without diagonal braces. Therefore, it is necessary to strengthen the shear strength of the base column of the frame structure with diagonal braces to improve the overall safety of the building.

The seismic performance of the frame structure can be improved effectively by adding diagonal braces, which mainly shows that the vertex displacement is greatly reduced and the seismic performance is improved. Under the earthquake action, the base shear of the frame structure with inclined brace composite wall panels increases by about 41%, and the vertex displacement decreases by about 33%. The seismic performance of the structure is improved effectively. (Qing 2021). The conclusion of this paper is similar to that of this paper because it can prove that the conclusion of this paper is correct.

4 STRESS ANALYSIS AND FAILURE PROCESS OF DIAGONAL BRACE IN SINGLE-LAYER FRAME

From the results of the finite analysis in the previous section, it can be seen that the diagonal brace contributes greatly to enhancing the overall lateral stiffness of the frame structure. However, it is not clear about the stress state of the diagonal brace in the structure and the stress state when the structure reaches the load limit from loading. Therefore, SAP2000 is used in this paper to conduct stress analysis on the single-story frame structure with a diagonal brace and analyze its stress characteristics and failure process when subjected to load. It is important to understand the principle of improving the overall lateral stiffness of frame structures with diagonal braces.

4.1 The model of a single-story frame structure with the diagonal brace

The frame structure of single layer reinforced concrete diagonal brace is 5m in span and 3m in height. Beams and columns are all I-steel, and the steel used is Q235. The specific dimensions of the I-steel are shown in Table 5. Due to the joint mode being a rigid connection, the joint strength is large, and the plastic hinge zone's position shifts from the beam's end to the middle of the span (Liang 2017). Therefore, in this model, the plastic hinge is set straight on the beam at $h1=0.5m$ away from the endpoint, as shown in Figure 6. By force analysis of the model, the maximum bending moment is found in the center of the diagonal brace, so the plastic hinge is set at the midpoint of the diagonal brace.

Table 5. The dimensions of I-beams.

Attribute types	Frame beam mm	Frame column mm
Overall height	200	200
Upper and lower flange width	200	100
Upper and lower flange thickness	12	8
The web thickness	8	8

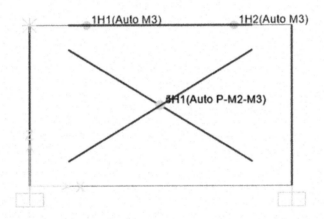

Figure 6. Plastic Angle of frame structure.

4.2 Boundary conditions of the model

The selected horizontal loading mode is equivalent to the inertia force under earthquake action, and a reasonable horizontal loading mode will reflect the real failure mode of the structure. Common horizontal loading modes: uniform loading, exponential loading, node loading, and so on (Liang 2011). This structure is a single-layer skew braced frame structure with a relatively simple structure. The displacement load applied is 200 mm. The node loading mode shows in Figure 7.

4.3 Results and analysis of finite element

Figure 8 reflects the relationship between stress and strain of plastic hinges. Point A begins to load, point B begins to yield, point C reaches the limit, point D is a failure, and point E is a complete failure. Figure 9 shows the process of structural damage. When the displacement load is 1mm, diagonal support enters the BC stage; when the displacement load is 5mm, a plastic hinge on the

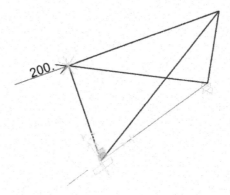

Figure 7. Boundary conditions of the model.

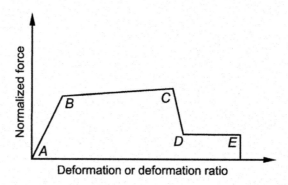

Figure 8. The stress-strain relationship in each stage.

diagonal support enters the CD stage; when the displacement load is 20mm, the plastic hinges on the two inclined braces enter the BC and CD stages respectively; when the displacement load is 45mm, the plastic hinges on the two skew supports both enter the CD stage; when the displacement load is 100mm, the plastic hinges on the two skew supports both enter the DE stage; when the displacement load is 150mm, the two plastic hinges on the beam both enter the BC stage.

In loading the structure, the plastic hinges of reinforced concrete diagonal braces occur and finally reach the limit state. When the plastic angle of the diagonal brace reaches the failure state at the beginning of loading, the frame does not produce a plastic angle and does not enter the plastic state. Under the horizontal load, the diagonal brace plastic hinge produces plasticity and failure before the frame. The diagonal brace is the first line of defense against horizontal load in the frame structure and is the main component that resists horizontal load in the structure.

In the established finite element model, the reinforced concrete oblique brace is the first to be destroyed and becomes the first k of the structure (Liang 2017). The conclusion is similar to that obtained from the analysis of the results of this model, so it can explain the correctness of the conclusion of this model to a certain extent.

5 CONCLUSION

It can be concluded by analyzing the above two finite element models that there are a lot of advantages in setting the diagonal brace in the frame structure. The diagonal brace plays an important role in improving the stiffness of the building structure in the frame structure. In this paper, a simple model of a frame structure and a model of a single unit containing diagonal braces with

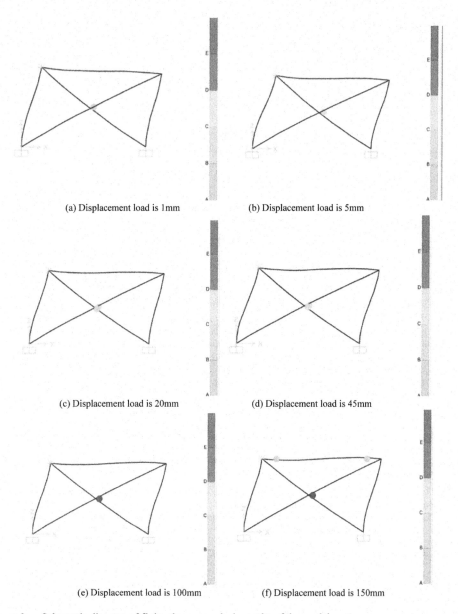

Figure 9. Schematic diagram of finite element analysis results of the model.

inclined braces are established and analyzed by the finite element analysis software. The following conclusions can be drawn:

(1) The maximum story displacement and the maximum story drift of the model with diagonal braces are only 10%~20% of that of the model without diagonal braces, and the lateral stiffness of the frame structure with diagonal braces is significantly improved.
(2) The maximum story drift of the model with the diagonal brace is much smaller than that of the model without the diagonal brace, so the reinforcement effect of diagonal braces on the lateral stiffness of the bottom building is significant;

(3) Base shear force of the model with diagonal braces is larger than that of the model without diagonal braces. Thus, it is necessary to strengthen the shear strength of the base column of the frame structure with diagonal braces to improve the overall safety of the building.

(4) When the single-layer frame structure with the diagonal brace is destroyed under the action of horizontal load, the diagonal brace is destroyed first, and the plastic hinge of the diagonal brace is generated before the frame. Therefore, the diagonal brace has a significant effect on improving the lateral stiffness of single-layer frame structures.

In this paper, the finite element analysis is carried out on the model of the frame structure containing the diagonal brace to quantify the degree of the lateral stiffness of the building, and the analysis method used in this paper has a certain reference value to analyze the influence of other building components on the building strength. However, the model established in this paper is more theoretical and does not simulate and analyze the actual building model. The actual model can be simulated in the future to improve the accuracy and persuasiveness of the conclusion.

REFERENCES

Bao, L.J., Wang, D.S., Zhou, J.L., Chen, J. X., Tong, J. & Dao-Yuan, L.U. (2014) *Design and rethinking of mega brace in Tianjin 117 tower Progress in Steel Building Structures*. 16, 43–48.

Bie, Y., Liu, W., Xie, W., Kong, G. & Gao, J. (2018) *Experimental study of tensile failure on seismic connecting components of inclined struts of hanging brackets Port Engineering Technology*. 55, 49–53.

Chen, W. Q., Yang, D. & Wang, Z. (2017) *Analysis of mechanical properties of a super high-rise building's tilt-column transition structure joints Shanxi Architecture*. 43, 61–62.

Ding, J., Wu, H. & Zhao, X. (2014) Current situation and discussion of structural design for super high-rise buildings above 250 m in China *Journal of Building Structures*. 35, 1–7.

Gong, Z. L. (2021) Comparison of the design of mega braces in super high-rise buildings *Journal of Building Structures*. 51, 106–110.

Hang, Y. (2011) Analysis of the performance of mega hybrid frame-corewall structure. *Industrial Construction*. 41, 63–66.

Liang, H.X. (2011) *Research on the practicability of pushover analysis procedure in the building structures* Southwest Jiaotong University.

Liang, Y.P. (2017) *Analysis of Mechanical Behavior of The Total Precast Reinforced Concrete Frame Braced*. Structure South China University of Technology.

Qing, L.L., Zhao, L.X. & Qian, K. (2021) *Comparison of Seismic Performance of Frame Structures with and Without Diagonal Braces*, North Building.6

Wang, D.J. & Zhou, J.L. (2019) Development and the prospect of hybrid high-rise building structures in China *Journal of Building Structures*. 49, 62–70.

Yang, Z.Q., Zhang, L.L., Zhang, X.L., Luo, Y. & Hua, W.U. (2014) Application of bim technique in the in-depth design of super high building *Architecture Technology*.

Zhao, X., Wang, B., Chen, Y. & Qin, H. (2013) Monotonic static tests on outrigger truss and its connection with mega column and core tube of the shanghai tower *Journal of Building Structures*. 34, 20–28.

Study on the optimal proportion of ecological protection substrate for highway slopes in rainy areas of South China

Enlian Xie*
Guangxi Tianxin Highway Co., Ltd, Guangxi, China

Xuejun Ma* & Bin Xue*
Jiaoke Transport Consultants Ltd., Beijing, China

ABSTRACT: Heat-rich and precipitation-rich areas in South China have serious soil erosion, and slope erosion is aggravated by slope excavation during highway construction. Thus, it is imperative to carry out the ecological protection of highway slopes. In this regard, relying on the Bama-Bingxiang Highway, the slope ecological protection substrate proportion test was carried out, and the new fiber spray seeding agent was selected, together with pH regulator, water retaining agent, binding agent, and peat to form the slope ecological restoration substrate material. The orthogonal test was carried out with Paspalum Natatum as the single test plant to observe and monitor the plant germination, plant biomass, soil nutrients, and the corrosion resistance of the substrate under different substrate proportioning. The orthogonal test results were analyzed to obtain the optimal proportion of each substrate material. The results showed that the optimal dosage of each substrate material was 0.6 kg/m² of new fiber spray seeding agent, 30 g/m² of pH regulator, 4 g/m² of water retaining agent, and 5 g/m² of the binding agent. The actual implementation in the field was good, and the experiment provided a theoretical and practical basis for using a new fiber spray seeding agent for slope protection in rainy areas in South China.

1 INTRODUCTION

In recent years, along with the rapid development of infrastructure construction in China, the mileage of highways has increased rapidly, and by the end of 2021, the mileage of highways in China has reached 169,100 km. South China is a subtropical monsoon climate zone characterized by abundant heat and precipitation. The area of South China accounts for about 23% of the total land area of China, and due to the frequent farming activities and unreasonable exploitation and utilization of land resources in the region, the severity of water loss and soil erosion is second only to that of the Loess Plateau region (Liu 2017). The highway construction projects have formed a large number of exposed slopes, and coupled with frequent rainfall in the region, the erosion effect on the slopes is more serious, resulting in a large amount of water loss and soil erosion while causing secondary disasters that seriously threaten the operational safety of highways. Therefore, achieving rapid slope restoration and ensuring the restoration effect through slope ecological protection technology is an important issue to be solved to protect the ecological environment and guarantee the safety of highway operations.

Common slope protection technologies at home and abroad can be divided into engineering protection and ecological protection. Although engineering protection can protect and reinforce slopes quickly, it lacks consideration of the impact on the ecological environment and cannot meet the current demand for ecological protection. Ecological protection is mainly the combination of

---

*Corresponding Authors: enlianxie@163.com, maxuejun20120622@163.com and xuebin1213@163.com

plant protection and traditional engineering protection. While ensuring the stability of the slope surface, the roots, branches, and leaves of plants are used to anchor the soil and intercept the rainfall to enhance the anti-corrosion performance of the soil. Currently, the commonly used ecological protection means mainly include grass sowing by spraying, three-dimensional vegetative net, environmentally-friendly bag grass planting, etc. Although a certain ecological protection effect has been achieved, problems include a high rework rate, poor vegetation structure layer, poor plant growth effect, and a long restoration period (Shan 2016; Zhang 2021, 2021).

The combination of material science and ecological protection measures provides new ideas for slope ecological protection. The new fiber spray seeding agent, with cured wood fiber as the main raw material, can achieve a good plant growth effect and cause little harm to the ecological environment, which is one of the focuses of attention in the field of slope ecological protection. The fiber substrate spray seeding technology has been widely used at home and abroad (Zhang 2020); however, the technology of slope ecological protection based on cured wood fibers has rarely been applied in a large area, and the technical application of new fiber spray seeding agent for slope ecological protection in rainy areas of South China is urgently needed.

In this paper, we conducted orthogonal comparison tests based on the new fiber spray seeding agent for ecological restoration and protection of slopes in rainy areas in South China and conducted experimental research and analysis on the growth-promoting effect and anti-erosion effect of slopes under the effect of substrate materials with different dosage ratios. The findings provide a theoretical basis and experimental foundation for applying new fiber substrate in the ecological restoration of slopes in rainy areas in South China.

2 EXPERIMENTAL MATERIALS

2.1 Experimental soil

The soil samples used in the test were collected from the slope of the Bama-Bingxiang Highway in Tiandeng County, Chongzuo City, Guangxi Zhuang Autonomous Region. The sampling area is the newly formed bare slope during construction. After clearing the surface gravel and weeds, the method of multi-point sampling was adopted. $0 \sim 30$ cm soil on the surface of the slope was collected with a shovel, mixed, and sealed for storage.

2.2 New fiber spray seeding agent

The main material of the new fiber spray seeding agent selected in this experiment is fully biodegradable cured wood fiber, mainly made of straw, coconut shell, bamboo, wood, and other natural raw materials after dissolution, curing, and spinning. The cured wood fiber has higher physical tensile strength and can form a self-locking structure between the fibers, which can quickly heal and cover the slope after use, and the formed covering layer is porous and has good moisture absorption performance. It is a new, non-toxic, pollution-free green material devoid of plastic components, curing period, and chemical substances (Zhang 2020).

Figure 1. Schematic diagram of new fiber spray seeding agent.

2.3 Other materials

Water retaining agent (polyacrylamide) has the functions of soil improvement, soil moisture regulation, and soil nutrient enhancement (Wei 2020). pH regulators are intended to adjust the pH value of the substrate material and mitigate the effect of pH value on soil fertility (Liu 2016). Binding agents can improve the slope soil adhesion and bonding between materials, ensuring the sprayed substrate's anti-scouring performance. Peat is a kind of latent soil with a thickness of more than 50cm, distributed in low-lying cold and wet areas. Adding peat to the substrate can improve the water retention capacity, air permeability, and fertilizer retention.

3 EXPERIMENTAL DESIGN

3.1 Orthogonal experimental design

As a material for slope ecological restoration in the rainy area of South China for the first time, the dosage ratio of the new fiber spray seeding agent, when used with other materials as a substrate material, needs to be studied to explore the most suitable dosage and ratio for the soil quality and natural environment of the slope in the use area. In this experiment, we considered the effects of the new fiber spray seeding agent, water retaining agent, pH regulator, binding agent, and peat in the substrate material on the ecological restoration effect, and finally, five orthogonal test factors for the five substrate materials were determined. Without considering the interaction among the factors, a total of 16 groups of substrate schemes with different ratios are designed (Wu 2019). Germination number, biomass, soil nutrient content, and slope erosion resistance were measured and compared, and the proportions of the test substrates are shown in the table below.

Table 1. Experimental substrate proportioning table.

S/N	New fiber spray seeding agent (kg/m^2)	pH regulator (g/m^2)	Water retaining agent (g/m^2)	Binding agent (g/m^2)	Peat (L/m^2)
1#	0.3	15	2	5	0
2#	0.3	30	4	7	3
3#	0.3	45	6	9	6
4#	0.3	60	8	11	9
5#	0.4	15	4	9	9
6#	0.4	30	2	11	6
7#	0.4	45	8	5	3
8#	0.4	60	6	7	0
9#	0.5	15	6	11	3
10#	0.5	30	8	9	0
11#	0.5	45	2	7	9
12#	0.5	60	4	5	6
13#	0.6	15	8	7	6
14#	0.6	30	6	5	9
15#	0.6	45	4	11	0
16#	0.6	60	2	9	3

3.2 Experimental method

The soil samples obtained in the field and each test material were weighed with a balance according to the test substrate composition proportion table in Table 1, and the test substrate materials of each group were stirred and filled into the pots, which are 20 cm in diameter and 15 cm in depth.

Figure 2. Experimental process.

3.3 *Measurement method*

To study the effect of different substrate materials on plant germination, growth, and soil nutrient loss more accurately, only Paspalum Natatum was used in this experiment, and the number of seeds was uniformly applied at 15g/m². The optimal substrate proportion was determined according to the germination number of Paspalum Natatum, biomass, soil nutrients, and erosion resistance of the slope.

4 ANALYSIS OF TEST RESULTS

4.1 *Analysis of germination number of substrate plants with different proportion*

The germination amount of plant seeds is an important indicator to test whether the substrate affects the normal development of plants (Wu 2019). After the substrate sample was made and sown, the germination number of Paspalum Natatum seeds was tracked, observed, and recorded. The recording time of effective germination data is ten days, and the subsequent plant germination amount is no longer included in the data range of this study. According to the test records, the germination of Paspalum Natatum began on the second day after sowing, with basically no dead seedlings. To reflect the germination number of different substrates more intuitively, the germination number of Paspalum Natatum under different substrates was drawn, with the substrate number as the horizontal coordinate and the plant germination number as the vertical coordinate, as shown in Figure 3.

It can be seen from the figure that the highest germination number is 281 of 16 # plant, with the least of 1#, which is 188. The average germination number of 16 substrates is 243, and the number of substrates exceeding the average is 10, accounting for 62.5% of the total test quantity, indicating that the substrate scheme design of the quadrat is reasonable. The range of the plant germination number of 16 substrate quadrats is 93, the upper quartile is 263, the lower quartile is 224, and the ratio of the maximum to the minimum germination is 1.49, indicating that different substrate proportioning schemes affect the plant germination number, but the degree of influence is not obvious.

4.2 *Analysis of plant biomass in substrates with different proportions*

Biomass refers to the total amount of organic matter per unit area of the plant body at a given time, including the dry weight of living organisms and the dry weight of withered litter (Guo 2022).

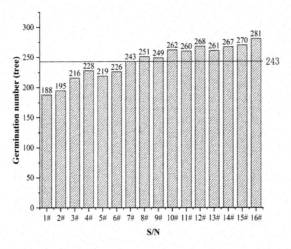

Figure 3. Statistics of germination number of different substrate schemes.

After 90 days of plant germination and growth, fresh plant stems and leaves of each specimen were collected by cutting along the soil surface, while wilted stems and leaves were collected, dried, and processed to calculate plant biomass under the action of different substrates. To compare the effects of different substrates on plant biomass, the biomass of Paspalum Natatum under the action of different proportions of substrates was drawn, with the substrate number as the horizontal coordinate and plant biomass as the vertical coordinate, as shown in Figure 4.

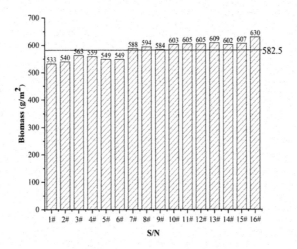

Figure 4. Biomass statistics of different substrate schemes.

It can be seen from the figure that there are significant differences in the biomass of plants under the effect of different substrate proportioning schemes, but the overall level is at a high level. Among them, 16# had the highest biomass value of 630 g/m^2; 1# had the lowest biomass value of 533 g/m^2; the average value of biomass of different substrates was 582.5 g/m^2, and the number of substrates with biomass exceeding the average value was 10, accounting for 62.5% of the total number of substrate schemes. Further analysis showed that the effect of 1# and 2# was poor, with plant biomass values lower than 550g/m^2; the effect of 7 substrates, namely: 10#, 11#, 12#, 13#, 14#, 15#, and 16# was better, with biomass values higher than 600g/m^2, but the difference between high and low values was not significant.

The range analysis results of plant biomass are shown in Table 2. The data in the table shows the influence of different substrate compositions on plant biomass can be analyzed.

Table 2. Range analysis of plant biomass (g/m^2).

Factor level	New fiber spray seeding agent	pH regulator	Water retaining agent	Binding agent	Peat
N1	548.75	568.75	579.25	582	584.25
N2	570	573.5	575.25	587	585.5
N3	599.25	590.75	585.75	586.25	581.5
N4	612	597	589.75	574.75	578.75
Range	63.25	28.25	14.5	12.25	6.75

It can be seen from Table 2 that according to the range analysis results of plant biomass, the degree of influence of each component material of the substrate proportioning scheme on the mean value of plant germination number from high to low is the new fiber spray seeding agent, pH regulator, water retaining agent, binding agent, and peat. Among them, the change in the dosage level of the new fiber spray seeding agent has the greatest impact on the plant biomass, with a range of about 63g/m^2; The change in peat dosage level had the least impact on the plant biomass, about 7g/m^2. The analysis shows that different dosage levels of the new fiber spray seeding agent have a great impact on the plant biomass, indicating that the substrate formed by adding the new fiber spray seeding agent has an obvious promoting effect on the plant growth, and the higher the dosage, the more obvious the growth-promoting effect; peat has less effect on plant biomass at different dosage levels and has the least effect in the material composition of the spraying substrate, so it cannot have a greater impact on plant growth.

4.3 Analysis of soil nutrients in substrates with different proportions

Soil nutrients are the general term for all types of nutrients provided by the soil for plant growth, among which the mineral components that can be directly absorbed by plant roots or can be absorbed by plant root system after transformation include 13 elements, such as nitrogen, phosphorus, potassium, etc. In addition to mineral components, soil nutrients include organic matter (Liu 2022). In order to study the soil fertility status after a certain period of plant growth under different substrate schemes, alkaline nitrogen, fast-acting phosphorus, and fast-acting potassium contents were selected for quantitative analysis, and the time of soil nutrient determination was chosen after the completion of plant biomass sampling.

In this experiment, an intelligent soil nutrient tester was used to determine the alkaline nitrogen, fast-acting phosphorus, and fast-acting potassium contents of the test samples. Taking the nutrient content as the horizontal coordinate and the substrate number as the vertical coordinate, the histogram of soil nutrient accumulation for different substrates was drawn, as shown in Figure 5.

Figure 5 shows that the measured results of total soil nutrients at different dosage levels of five substrate materials, including the new fiber spray seeding agent, are different, indicating that different dosages of the substrate materials can significantly affect the total soil nutrients. It can be seen that different dosages of the new fiber spray seeding agent have the most obvious effect on the change of the total soil nutrients, while the other four materials do not have obvious effects on the change of the total soil nutrients. The peat in the substrate materials cannot be converted into a large amount of alkali-hydrolyzable nitrogen and other nutrients that can be directly absorbed and utilized by plants in a short period. However, the new fiber spray seeding agent has high nutrient conversion efficiency and can provide nutrients for plants in a more timely manner. In addition, the total amount of soil nutrients is significantly affected by the amount of new fiber spray seeding agent. Combined with the data on the germination number and plant biomass, the larger the amount of the new fiber spray seeding agent, the greater the germination number and biomass, indicating

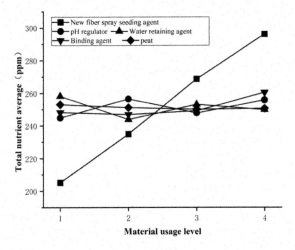

Figure 5. Influence of five substrate materials at different levels on total soil nutrients.

that increasing the amount of new fiber spray seeding agent can not only prevent rain seepage and scouring protect soil fertility from loss, but also can be degraded and transformed into a nutrient supply source for plants, providing some nutrients for plant growth.

4.4 *Analysis of erosion resistance of substrates with different proportions*

The rainfall simulation device is used to analyze and test the anti-corrosion performance of substrates with different proportions. The schematic diagram of the rainfall simulation device is shown in Figure 6. Before the test, 5 cm fine sand is filled at the bottom of the simulated slope to ensure good drainage conditions during the test. The soil samples collected on site are evenly mixed and laid in layers, 5 cm for each layer, and the compaction is ensured simultaneously. The slope is leveled with wood to avoid sliding between layers and ensure that the slope is similar to the natural state. The slope of the simulated slope is set at 45°. At the same time, a runoff bucket is placed at the runoff collection outlet of the simulated slope. Meanwhile, it should be kept away from the rainfall range to avoid interference (Zhao 2022).

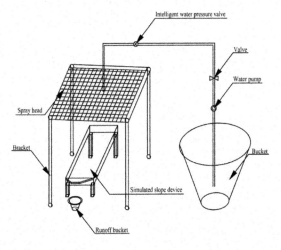

Figure 6. Rainfall simulation test device.

A rainfall simulation test was conducted for 30 min with a rainfall intensity of 3.0 mm/min (rainstorm), and each group of tests was repeated twice. The timing started at the beginning of the simulated rainfall, and the time when each slope started to produce runoff was recorded. After the runoff was generated on the slope, runoff sediment samples were collected at the outlet of the catch basin with the numbered runoff buckets, and the sampling was started from the second min in the first 6 min to reduce the influence of the floating soil on the slope on the test results. Samples shall be taken every 2 minutes, each time shall be 1min; after 6 min, samples shall be collected once every 4 min, and the sampling time shall be 1 min until the end of the test. The sampling time of flow production shall be 30 min in total, and a total of 9 samples shall be collected. At the end of the test, the sediment samples in the runoff bucket were stirred thoroughly according to the sampling sequence, so the sediment particles were evenly dispersed. After stirring, samples were taken quickly in the runoff bucket with the sampling bottle of known number and weight, and the sampling was repeated three times in each bucket to reduce the error caused by the uneven stirring of the sediment samples in the bucket. After sampling, the collected runoff sediment samples were dried in an oven. The sediment mass was weighed with an electronic scale with an accuracy of 0.01 g to calculate the runoff sediment yield, and the sediment yield per unit area was obtained by unit conversion. The comparison chart of sediment volume of different substrates was drawn with the substrate number as the horizontal coordinate and sediment volume as the vertical coordinate, as shown in Figure 7.

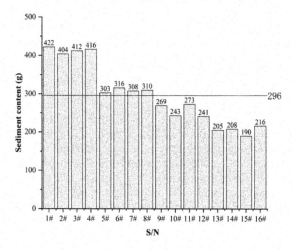

Figure 7. Statistical chart of sediment carried by slope runoff of different substrates.

According to the analysis, the influence of different substrates on the sediment content of slope runoff varies a lot. The maximum sediment content of different substrates is 422g, corresponding to No. 1#; the minimum sediment content is 190g, corresponding to No. 15#; the average sediment content data corresponding to the 16 groups of substrates is 296g. As seen from the figure, the substrates with sediment content in the slope runoff exceeding the average value are mainly distributed in the first eight groups, and the sediment content of the latter eight groups is lower than the average value. To determine the influence of different components and different amounts of the same component in the substrate proportioning scheme on the sediment content of slope runoff, it is necessary to summarize and analyze the test data, respectively. To more clearly compare and analyze the relationship between different dosages of new fiber spray seeding agent, binding agent, peat, and the sediment amount, the influence curve of the sediment amount affected by the three materials of different concentrations is drawn according to the statistical data results, as shown in Figure 8. It can be seen from the figure that, with the increase of the dosage of the three materials, the sediment content data corresponding to the new fiber spray seeding agent showed a substantial decreasing trend, indicating that when the dosage of the new fiber spray seeding agent increased, the anti-scouring performance of the slope improved significantly; while the change of the dosage of binding agent and peat did not cause change to the sediment content, and the sediment amount maintained at the same level with different amounts of binding agent or peat. To compare the correlation between substrate materials and sediment amount more accurately, the mean data of sediment amount corresponding to the three materials were fitted utilizing the linear fitting. The fitting equation for the mean sediment content A affected by the new fiber spray seeding agent is y=-679x+601.55, R^2=0.949; the fitting equation for the mean sediment content C affected by the binding agent is y= 0.225x+294.2; the fitting equation for the mean value of peat content influenced by peat is y=-9x+300.05.

According to the function fitting results, for each 0.1kg increase in peat amount per unit area of the slope, the sediment reduction is about 0.9g, indicating that the change of increasing peat dosage relative to the anti-scouring performance of the slope is small; for each 1g increase in binding agent dosage per unit area of the slope, the increase of sediment amount is about 0.225g, indicating that the addition of binding agent in the substrate has no effect on the anti-scouring performance of the slope, and even weakens the anti-scouring performance of the slope. For each 0.1kg increase of the new fiber spray seeding agent per unit area of the slope, the sediment will decrease by about 68g, indicating that the new fiber spray seeding agent can form a relatively compact anti-corrosion layer on the slope surface, and the more the amount of new fiber spray seeding agent, the compacter the anti-erosion layer formed, and the better the anti-scouring performance of the slope.

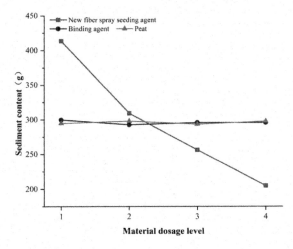

Figure 8.   Influence of different dosages of substrate components on sediment content of slope runoff.

4.5 Range analysis of the optimal substrate proportion

In this paper, the optimal proportion of substrate is determined by the comprehensive weight scoring method. The method comprehensively considers the influence of different substrate compositions on four indicators: plant germination number, plant biomass, soil nutrients, and substrate erosion resistance. However, considering the high price of the new fiber spray seeding agent, in order to ensure the economic feasibility of the proportion of substrate materials, the price of the materials was taken as an independent indicator in the comprehensive scoring, the germination number, plant biomass, soil nutrients, runoff sediment content were scored separately, and the comprehensive scores of 16 substrates with different proportions were calculated according to the scoring values of the five indicators of sprouting volume, plant biomass, soil nutrients, sediment content in runoff and material cost, which account for 20%, as shown in Table 3.

The range analysis is carried out according to the comprehensive scoring results of different substrate schemes, and the analysis results are shown in Table 4.

Table 3. Comprehensive scoring of different substrates.

S/N	New fiber spray seeding agent	pH regulator	Water retaining agent	Binding agent	Peat	Comprehensive score
1#	67	85	68	45	100	73
2#	69	86	66	47	67	67
3#	77	89	67	46	50	66
4#	81	89	72	46	40	66
5#	78	87	74	63	67	74
6#	80	87	79	60	50	71
7#	86	93	78	62	40	72
8#	89	94	81	61	33	72
9#	89	93	84	71	50	77
10#	93	96	96	78	40	81
11#	93	96	87	70	33	76
12#	95	96	91	79	29	78
13#	93	97	100	93	40	84
14#	95	96	100	91	33	83
15#	96	96	98	100	29	84
16#	100	100	96	88	25	82

Table 4. Analysis of orthogonal test results.

S/N	New fiber spray seeding agent	pH regulator	Water retaining agent	Binding agent	Peat	Comprehensive score
1#	1	1	1	1	1	73
2#	1	2	2	2	2	67
3#	1	3	3	3	3	66
4#	1	4	4	4	4	66
5#	2	1	2	3	4	74
6#	2	2	1	4	3	71
7#	2	3	4	1	2	72
8#	2	4	3	2	1	72
9#	3	1	3	4	2	77
10#	3	2	4	3	1	81
11#	3	3	1	2	4	76
12#	3	4	2	1	3	78
13#	4	1	4	2	3	84
14#	4	2	3	1	4	83
15#	4	3	2	4	1	84
16#	4	4	1	3	2	82
K_{21}	272	308	302	306	310	
K_{22}	289	302	303	299	298	
K_{23}	312	298	298	303	299	
K_{24}	333	298	303	298	299	
k_{21}	68	77	75.5	76.5	77.5	
k_{22}	72.25	75.5	75.75	74.75	74.5	
k_{23}	78	74.5	74.5	75.75	74.75	
k_{24}	83.25	74.5	75.75	74.50	74.75	
Range	15.25	2.5	1.25	2	3	

It can be seen from Table 4 that the k24=83.25 is the largest value of different new fiber spray seeding agents (compared with 68, 72.25, 78, and 83.25), so the dosage of new fiber spray seeding agent material should take as the 4th level, i.e., the dosage of new fiber spray seeding agent is $0.6kg/m^2$; K21=77 is the largest dosage of pH regulator, so the dosage of pH regulator should be the first level, i.e., the dosage of pH regulator is $15g/m^2$. K22=k24=75.75 is the largest value for the water retaining agent. Considering the material costs, the water-retaining agent should take the second level, i.e., the amount of water-retaining agent is $4g/m^2$. K21=76.5 is the largest amount of binding agent, so the amount of binding agent should be the first level, i.e., the amount of binding agent should be $5g/m^2$. K21=77.5 is the largest value of peat, so the amount of peat should be the first level, i.e., the amount of peat should be $0L/m^2$, indicating that peat does not need to be added to the substrate material. In conclusion, the optimal test proportioning scheme is not included in the current 16-group test scheme.

According to the range calculation results, the range values are new fiber spray seeding agent, pH regulator, peat, binding agent, and water retaining agent in descending order, i.e., among all the factors, the new fiber spray seeding agent has the greatest influence on the overall effect of slope protection, followed by pH regulator, peat, binding agent and water retaining agent.

The comprehensive analysis shows that the optimal substrate proportioning scheme is $0.6kg/m^2$ of new fiber spray seeding agent, $15g/m^2$ of pH regulator, $4g/m^2$ of water retaining agent, and $5g/m^2$ of binding agent.

5 CONCLUSION

In this paper, by designing an orthogonal test with Paspalum Natatum as the test plant, the slope protection substrate materials with different proportions were formed by adjusting the dosage of the new fiber spray seeding agent, pH regulator, water retaining agent, binding agent, and peat. The slope protection effects of different substrates were studied with four indicators: plant germination number, plant biomass, soil nutrient content, and slope anti-scouring performance, and the following conclusions were obtained:

(1) Rapid realization of slope ecological protection can not only ensure highway landscape reconstruction but also relate to the safety of highway traffic operations. This paper selected a new fiber spray seeding agent, pH regulator, water retaining agent, binding agent, and peat as substrate materials to form the spraying substrate. A total of 16 orthogonal tests are designed with Paspalum Natatum as the test plant, and the plant germination number, plant biomass, soil nutrient content, and slope anti-scouring performance of different substrates are tracked and monitored. The test results show that the design of this test scheme is scientific and reasonable, and the optimal proportion of substrates can be selected, which provides a solid foundation for field application.
(2) According to the test results, the orthogonal test range analysis was carried out on the four indicators of plant germination number, plant biomass, soil nutrient content, and slope erosion resistance of different substrates. It was found that among the five selected substrate materials, the new fiber spray seeding agent had the greatest impact on the overall effect of slope protection, followed by pH regulator, peat, binding agent, and water retaining agent. The optimal dosage of each material is $0.6kg/m^2$ for the new fiber spray seeding agent, $15g/m^2$ for the pH regulator, $4g/m^2$ for the water retaining agent, and $5g/m^2$ for the binding agent.
(3) In heat-rich and precipitation-rich areas in South China, slopes formed after highway slope excavation are widely distributed. In this paper, combining material science with ecological protection measures provides new ideas for slope ecological protection in this area. Subsequently, based on this study and in combination with the characteristics of regional projects, we will actively explore and study the feasibility of introducing new materials at home and abroad for the ecological protection of slopes.

REFERENCES

Guo Qiang, Guan Fengying, Hui Chaomao, et al. Effects of density and fertilization on growth and biomass characteristics of newly grown Dendrocalamus sinicus [J]. *Journal of Beijing Forestry University*, 2022, 44(04):95–106.

Liu Guofei, Xu Yongli, Li Fuping. Effect of additive amount on ecological characteristics of artificial Soil [J]. *Environmental Science & Technology*, 2016, 39(09):28–31+60.

Liu Liming, Song Yansong, Zhong Bin, et al. Research progress on ecological restoration technology of vegetation concrete [J]. *Journal of Environmental Engineering Technology*, 2022, 12(03):916–927.

Liu Tiantian, Han Longxi, Sun Mingyuan, et al. Simulation on the time progress of the non-point source pollution load in runoff for small watershed [J]. *Environmental Science and Technology*, 2017, 30 (05): 31–35.

Shan Yongti, Hu Lin, Wang Qi, et al. Impacts of runoff scouring on high-grade highway slope erosion in alpine and high-altitude regions [J]. *Journal of Traffic and Transportation Engineering*, 2016, 16(04): 88–95.

Wei Youming, Liao Zongwen, Hong Jiale, et al. Study on water and fertilizer retention effect of new water retaining agent and its components [J]. *South China Forestry Science*, 2020, 48 (05): 69–73.

Wu Xiaoping, Ding Jian, Guo Jianfang, et al. Effects of gibberellin and high-temperature germination promotion on root germination of dioscorea esculenta (Lour.) Burkill [J]. *Journal of Anhui Agricultural Sciences*, 2019, 47(14):15–17.

Wu Yongping, Luo Yuen, He Sheng-lin. Analysis of factors affecting slope safety factor based on orthogonal experimental method [J]. *Coal Technology*, 2019, 38(12):70–73.

Zhang Fufu, Xin Yongxin, Hong Jie, et al. Study on optimization of matrix ratio for ecological protection of expressway slope in alpine canyon area [J]. *Highway*, 2021, 66(08): 333–337.

Zhang Heng, Su Chao. Analysis of stability of borrowed soil in ecological slope under rainfall effect [J]. *Water Resources and Hydropower Engineering*, 2021, 52(04): 186–191.

Zhang Nan. *Study on new ecological restoration technology of red clay slope of highway in rainy areas of South China* [D]. Beijing Jiaotong University, 2020.

Zhang Ping, Wang Shusen, Ma Yingmei, et al. Effects of plant fiber blankets of different herbaceous plant growth stages on runoff and sediment yield in the Loess Hilly and Gully Region [J]. *Journal of Soil and Water Conservation*, 2020, 34(05):49–55.

Zhao Weikang, Jing Changqing, Guo Wenzhang, et al. Effects of simulated rainfall on carbon and water fluxes in alpine meadow on the Northern Slope of Tianshan Mountain [J]. *Chinese Journal of Grassland*, 2022, 44(02):16–23.

Research progress of asphalt soot detection technology and odor removal technology

Hongchao Zhang* & Lianghao Sun*
The Key Laboratory of Road and Traffic Engineering, Ministry of Education, Beijing, China

ABSTRACT: Asphalt smoke detection technology and deodorization technology have become a research hotspot in the road infrastructure industry under the background of carbon peak and carbon neutralization. In order to more accurately determine the composition and concentration of each component of asphalt soot, analyze the generation mechanism of asphalt soot and inhibit the generation of asphalt soot from the source, this paper summarizes the experimental design and main methods of asphalt soot testing, including thermogravimetric method, UV-vis spectrophotometry, thermogravimetric mass spectrometry, gas chromatography-mass spectrometry, and high-performance liquid chromatography. The applicable conditions, advantages, and disadvantages of various methods and the calculation model of the total emission of asphalt smoke and dust are analyzed. For the inhibition of asphalt smoke and dust, combined with relevant test data, this paper focuses on the asphalt deodorization technology developed in recent years and has broad market prospects, including physical adsorption, chemical inhibition, plant extract, and microorganism. The deodorization effect of various deodorizers, their influence on asphalt performance, and the analysis model of the deodorization mechanism of deodorizers are analyzed. The conclusions are given as follows: GC-MS is easy to operate, can separate each component efficiently and quickly, and has the characteristics of sensitive detection and accurate qualitative analysis. It is suggested to use this method to test asphalt soot. Plant extract deodorant has wider application conditions and a more obvious deodorant effect. It is suggested to use this deodorant and conduct further research on the road performance of asphalt mixture and its application evaluation in engineering practice.

1 BACKGROUND

The outline of the construction of a strong transportation country emphasizes the need to adhere to green development, promote new construction materials, and control pollution emissions. The construction of green, environment-friendly asphalt pavement, and the implementation of the green road concept. This is to help China's "carbon peak" and "carbon neutral" ambitious vision become the future development of the transport industry's top priority. According to the statistical bulletin on the development of the transportation industry in 2020, by 2020, China's total road mileage will reach 5,198,100 km, and more than 90% of the new roads have adopted asphalt pavement. However, behind the continuous growth of road mileage is the increasingly prominent environmental protection problems in China's road construction industry. Under the background of carbon peaking and carbon neutralization, the promotion and application of green, low-carbon asphalt pavement materials and technology must be the general trend of the development of the transportation industry.

Research shows that China currently consumes more than 30 million tons of asphalt and about 600~700 million tons of asphalt mixture every year. Under the construction temperature of 160°C,

---
*Corresponding Authors: zhanghc@tongji.edu.cn and 2133433@tongji.edu.cn

848 grams of asphalt smoke and dust are produced per hour per ton of asphalt. Based on the mixing construction time of 4 hours, nearly 120000 tons of asphalt smoke and dust are discharged from asphalt pavement construction in China every year. These asphalt fumes contain a large amount of volatile organic compounds (VOCs), which will harm the human body and lead to environmental problems such as haze and acid rain (Cai et al. 2014). Currently, the research on the generation mechanism of asphalt soot is not deep enough. Researchers generally believe that the generation of asphalt soot includes two processes: one is the volatilization of light components in asphalt under heating conditions; the second is the parallel sequential reaction between oxygen and asphalt molecules under heating conditions. The reaction includes cracking and condensation. The cracking reaction is the main cause of asphalt flue gas (Jullien et al. 2006). Under photocatalysis, other components in the atmosphere will have a photochemical reaction with volatile organic pollutants in asphalt smoke and produce photochemical smoke (Fryazinov & Grudnikov 1976). When mixing at a high temperature of 160–180°C, sulfide (including naphthenic group, alkyl group, mixed group sulfide, and aromatic group), homology of Tetrahydrothiophene, and thiophene are the main substances that produce a malodorous smell and harmful gas. In 1990s, China's emission standard for odor pollutants (GB-14554-93) set very strict regulations on the emission of sulfur-containing volatile organic compounds (VOCs). Among them, mercaptan is one of the typical pollutants in VOCs. When the mass concentration of mercaptan in the air is higher than $0.7\mu m/L$, it will produce malodorous smell and make people feel uncomfortable, which will seriously impact people's work and life quality (Cavallari et al. 2012). Living in the air containing high concentration of mercaptan for a long time may cause human discomfort and even leukemia and anemia (Xiu et al. 2004). In addition, VOCs gas may cause diseases in human respiratory tract, lung, kidney, liver, digestive system, nervous system, and hematopoietic system (Agostini et al. 2013). When the concentration of VOCs in the air is too high, it will lead to headaches, nausea, coma, convulsions, and other symptoms. In addition, VOCs are also important precursors for the formation of fine particulate matter (PM2.5) and ozone (O3), which will cause direct health hazards to the human body and exacerbate global warming (Huang 2013).

Therefore, this paper analyzes the test design and methods of asphalt smoke and dust, summarizes various asphalt smoke and dust suppression technologies, and summarizes the asphalt deodorization technology developed in recent years and with broad market prospects combined with relevant test data.

2 TEST DESIGN AND TEST METHOD OF ASPHALT SMOKE AND DUST

The composition of asphalt soot is very complex and is closely related to many factors, such as the type of modifier and the source of asphalt. Asphalt is a mixture, and its constituent elements mainly include carbon, hydrogen, sulfur, oxygen, etc. when mixing hot asphalt mixture, it needs to be heated to about 180°C, a high temperature to flow state, and the heating process needs to be continuously stirred. Full contact between high-temperature asphalt and air will produce much smoke and dust. Asphalt is a mixture of organic matter. Therefore, the inorganic component in smoke and dust is the product after heating. Among them, the inorganic solid particles do not produce a peculiar smell, and the inorganic liquid is the water generated after heating and condensing the hydrogen element in the asphalt, which will not cause pollution. Therefore, when analyzing the components of smoke and dust, only inorganic gas and organic matter are usually taken as the research object (Cao et al. 2021; Li 2020), as shown in Figure 1.

Some scholars have designed a set of asphalt smoke collection devices to better analyze the composition of asphalt smoke. The typical device is shown in Figure 2.

The device brings air into the container by the pump, controls the heating temperature, mixing state, and heating time of asphalt, and sets three collection devices to filter solid particles, absorb organic gas and collect inorganic gas, respectively. Based on the physical and chemical characteristics of different adsorption and separation materials, the purpose of fully collecting asphalt smoke and dust is achieved (Cao et al. 2021). Another scholar adopted the method of rapid condensation,

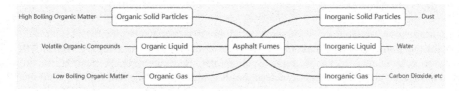

Figure 1. Composition of asphalt fumes.

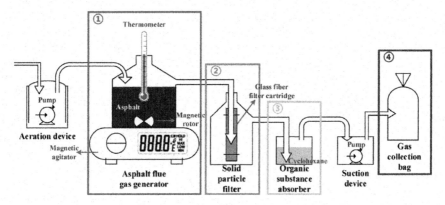

Figure 2. Asphalt dust collection device (Cao et al. 2021).

absorbed the asphalt smoke and dust through pure polypropylene fiber cotton, and finally passed the remaining gas into pure water and discharged it into the air (Huang 2013).

Currently, the main methods for testing asphalt smoke and dust are the thermogravimetric method, ultraviolet-visible spectrophotometry, thermogravimetric mass spectrometry, gas chromatography-mass spectrometry, and high-performance liquid chromatography.

2.1 Thermogravimetric method

Asphalt will not release smoke and dust at normal temperatures. After cooling, the asphalt smoke and dust generated after heating will be adsorbed on the corresponding medium. After removing water vapor, the quality of asphalt smoke and dust can be determined by weighing the mass changes before and after sampling in the container (Huang 2013; Huang et al. 2015). The operation of the thermogravimetric method is simple, but only the total mass of adsorbed asphalt smoke can be obtained, and the composition of asphalt smoke can be analyzed qualitatively.

The thermogravimetric analysis studied the effects of different components on the thermal stability of asphalt. It is pointed out that thermogravimetric analysis can be used as an initial step in studying the physical and chemical properties of asphalt and related compounds (JimenezMateos et al. 1996). Thermogravimetric analysis (TG) is used to determine the change of mass loss with temperature. It can be carried out in the air to simulate real working conditions or inert environments such as nitrogen (Elkashef et al. 2018). TG in a nitrogen environment can characterize the asphaltene content in different asphalt adhesives. The higher the asphaltene content, the lower the thermal stability (Firoozifar et al. 2011). The mass loss of asphalt binder in nitrogen is stable at about 600°C, while it needs 800°C in the air (Wielinski et al. 2015).

In addition, some scholars combine thermogravimetry with other methods. The decomposition stage of SBS-modified asphalt was studied by thermogravimetric analysis of Fourier transform infrared spectroscopy (Mothe et al. 2008). TG and nuclear magnetic resonance (NMR) were combined to study the chemical structure changes of oil sand asphalt during pyrolysis (Wang et al. 2017).

2.2 Ultraviolet-visible spectrophotometry

The determination principle of UV-vis spectrophotometry is to generate specific substances through the color reaction between asphalt smoke and corresponding color-developing agents. After the substance is irradiated by visible light or ultraviolet light, the valence electrons in the substance molecules absorb radiation to determine. It is an effective method for structural analysis, quantitative analysis, and qualitative analysis of substances (lu 2012).

After the asphalt smoke is absorbed by the cyclohexane solution, it is placed under the ultraviolet spectrophotometer with a wavelength of 288 nm to test, and its absorbance value is obtained. Then the asphalt smoke concentration is calculated according to the linear relationship between the absorbance value and the asphalt smoke concentration (Mao 2000). This method can effectively determine the content of asphalt smoke and dust, which is fast, convenient, and feasible. However, due to the limited solubility of cyclohexane to asphalt smoke, the absorption peak measured with cyclohexane as the absorption solution is not very significant. Using benzene as an absorption liquid, the benzene solution absorbing asphalt smoke and dust has a characteristic absorption peak of 286 nm. When the asphalt smoke and dust content is not greater than $500 \mu g$, it is directly proportional to the extinction value, obeys Lambert-Beer law, and the detection limit should be $0.5 \mu g/ml$ (Yan et al. 2004). However, this method cannot qualitatively and quantitatively analyze each component (Li 2017).

2.3 Thermogravimetric-mass spectrometry coupling

The principle of thermogravimetry mass spectrometry is to place the asphalt sample on the heating device for heating, use the capillary to introduce the asphalt smoke into the mass spectrometer, and then the mass spectrometer separates the asphalt smoke according to the charge-to-mass ratio of the substance, and finally compare the spectrum library to determine which substance it is.

Some research used this method to study the smoke and dust release of asphalt with different deodorizers and matrix asphalt (Cui et al. 2014a, 2014b, 2015). This method can qualitatively analyze the organic matter in asphalt dust with high accuracy and sensitivity. However, when the asphalt is heated in the thermogravimeter, the gas introduced is inert gas (generally helium). In the actual construction and mixing process, the asphalt is in full contact with the air and oxidizes some volatile organic compounds. Therefore, this method cannot reflect the release law of asphalt smoke and dust under real construction conditions.

2.4 Gas chromatography-mass spectrometry (GC-MS)

The principle of GC-MS is that substances with different partition coefficients in the stationary and gas phases have different properties. The carrier gas carries the asphalt dust the sample produces into the chromatographic column. The substances with different properties are distributed repeatedly between the two phases. After moving the column long enough, they are separated and come to the mass spectrometer in a certain order. After arriving at the mass spectrometer, it is separated by ionization and mass spectrometry. Finally, it is detected and recorded by the detector (Rao 2011).

The asphalt soot samples were analyzed by gas chromatography-mass spectrometry and detected 196 kinds of organic pollutants, including 81 kinds of pollutants with large content and can be determined, mainly polycyclic aromatic hydrocarbons (Shi et al. 2001). Li (2017) optimized the test parameters of gas chromatography-mass spectrometry and studied the smoke generation characteristics of rubber asphalt and matrix asphalt and the smoke suppression effect of organic montmorillonite. The test parameters of GC-MS were optimized, and the smoke generation characteristics of rubber asphalt and matrix asphalt and the smoke suppression effect of organic montmorillonite were studied (Li 2020). Four main components were analyzed by gas chromatography-mass spectrometry combined with the NIST library. It was found that the four components were mainly composed of alicyclic compounds, polycyclic aromatic hydrocarbons (PAHs), monocyclic aromatic hydrocarbons, and heterocycles (Feng et al. 2011). The concentration of volatile organic compounds in asphalt was quantitatively analyzed by gas chromatography-mass spectrometry. The main factors affecting its emission were found to be asphalt temperature and asphalt source (Gasthauer et al. 2008; Mo et al. 2019).

Gas chromatography has the characteristics of rapid and efficient separation characteristics, and mass spectrometry has the characteristics of sensitive detection and accuracy characteristics. Gas chromatography-mass spectrometer has both advantages, which can more accurately analyze complex mixed organic compounds quantitatively and qualitatively. It is worth noting that the gasification chamber and chromatographic column have limited temperatures, while some components in polycyclic aromatic hydrocarbons have high boiling points. Their analysis temperature is close to the limit temperature, which will shorten the service life of the instrument and chromatographic column (Bai et al. 2016).

2.5 High-performance liquid chromatography

High-performance liquid chromatography is a high-performance separation method. This method improves the disadvantage of the limited application of traditional liquid chromatography and combines it with the traditional gas chromatography theory to expand its detection range (Xiong 2020). This method mainly uses a high-efficiency particle stationary phase, high-pressure infusion pump, and high-sensitivity detector to analyze samples' substances and improve detection accuracy and efficiency (Chen 2019; Yang 2017; Zeng 2019). Due to the limited length of the liquid chromatography column, the separation ability of traditional liquid chromatography is greatly limited; the boiling points of some heterocyclic compounds and polycyclic aromatic hydrocarbons in asphalt soot are high, so the results of traditional liquid chromatography are not accurate (Bai et al. 2016).

The column layer separation method adsorbs heterocyclic aromatic hydrocarbons and other non-target aromatic hydrocarbons. In order to reduce the interference to the peak of the liquid phase, the toluene extraction liquid column chromatography separation method is used to more accurately determine the content of 16 carcinogenic polycyclic aromatic hydrocarbons in coal tar pitch. This method has high accuracy and precision, good linear relationships, and stable test results (Bai et al. 2016). Combining high-performance liquid chromatography with ultraviolet, diode array, or fluorescence detector, quantitative analysis methods were established to determine the quantification of 16 EU priority polyaromatic hydrocarbons (PAHs) in smoke flavors (Brasseur et al. 2007).

Some scholars have established models to calculate the total emission of asphalt smoke and dust quantitatively. The prediction model of "road condition - vehicle speed - energy consumption and emission" is established, and the total emission of asphalt soot is quantified from the macro level based on the life cycle method (Yang 2012).

With the deepening of research, researchers are now more inclined to adopt quantitative testing methods, and some scholars have comprehensively adopted the above methods. Among them, gas chromatography-mass spectrometry and high-performance liquid chromatography can achieve quantitative analysis. When the boiling point of the tested component is lower than the limit temperature of the chromatographic column and the gasification chamber, the former is recommended because the former is relatively simple to operate, can separate each component efficiently and quickly, and has the characteristics of sensitive detection and accurate qualitative determination. The latter requires toluene as an extractant, and toluene is volatile, flammable, and explosive. It is controlled by the public security department according to the regulations on the administration of precursor chemicals and the safety management of hazardous chemicals. Therefore, it is recommended to use the latter when the use conditions of the former are not met.

3 DEODORIZING EFFECT OF DEODORIZER AND ITS INFLUENCE ON ASPHALT PERFORMANCE

For the problem of a large amount of asphalt smoke and dust produced in the mixing and construction of traditional asphalt mixture, researchers have conducted in-depth research and adopted some technical means to reduce the smoke and dust emission after asphalt heating and inhibit the release of carbon oxides, sulfur oxides, nitrogen oxides, and polycyclic aromatic hydrocarbons. The existing technologies mainly include cooling construction technology, odor masking method, source improvement method, and odor removal method. Due to the low construction temperature and poor adhesion between asphalt and aggregate, the road performance and durability of the cooling construction method are worse than that of the hot mix in engineering practice (Tatari et al. 2012). As the name suggests, the odor masking method only eliminates the influence of asphalt odor in olfactory smell and cannot fundamentally inhibit the generation of asphalt smoke and dust. It should be used as a supplementary means to other methods. The source improvement method is selecting higher quality crude oil or reducing the generation of asphalt smoke and dust by improving the refining process flow and parameters (Li 2005). However, as a petroleum derivative, asphalt is not suitable for selecting crude oil types to reduce the emission of asphalt smoke and dust, which greatly increases the cost. The deodorization method is mainly to add deodorization additives into asphalt to prepare deodorization and environmental protection asphalt, so as to make the additives react with volatile substances in asphalt physically or chemically, inhibit the generation of asphalt smoke and dust, or generate new non emission substances, so as to fundamentally reduce the emission of harmful gases and protect the surrounding environment.

According to different deodorants, deodorization methods can be divided into physical adsorption, chemical inhibition, plant extract, and microorganism.

3.1 Physical adsorption class

Physical adsorption mainly uses porous materials with small particle sizes and large specific surface areas such as slag, coke particles, dolomite, talc, or fly ash to adsorb asphalt smoke (Wu et al. 2011).

After adding 2–3% activated carbon into asphalt, it is found that the smoke suppression rate can reach 20%, which has a good smoke suppression effect. However, a large amount of smoke will be produced in preparing activated carbon-modified asphalt, resulting in new environmental problems (Huang 2013). Biological asphalt from biological waste replaced petroleum-based asphalt. Using styrene butadiene styrene (SBS) and rubber crumbs (CR) as raw materials, it was found that only physical reaction occurred in the process of blending and modification by gel permeation chromatography (GPC) and Fourier transform infrared spectroscopy (FTIR). This composite modification method made full use of biological waste and waste tires and improved the performance of the mixed biological asphalt (Dong et al. 2019).

The adsorbent used in this method does not need regeneration and has the advantages of a simple process, less investment, and high purification efficiency; however, the system resistance is largeand thus, it is rarely used in asphalt deodorization.

3.2 Chemical inhibition class

Chemical inhibition mainly refers to adding deodorant into asphalt to prepare deodorant and environment-friendly asphalt. Deodorants can directly react with volatile substances in asphalt or play a catalytic role in generating pollution-free new substances to fundamentally inhibit the generation of asphalt smoke and dust.

Shell Group of Companies has conducted some research on inhibiting the emission of hydrogen sulfide gas from sulfur-modified asphalt and obtained many patents (Feng 2019). Hong et al. common chemical deodorants include hydrogen peroxide, calcium chloride, ferrous sulfate, potassium permanganate, and calcium hydrogen phosphate (Hong et al. 2013). For sulfur-modified asphalt, its high-temperature stability is improved through modification to reduce free small molecular sulfur elements and reduce the generation of harmful gases such as hydrogen sulfide. It is suggested that the best addition ratio is 30%. Adding polymers such as PE and SBS can greatly reduce the release of asphalt smoke. Adding 1% SBS and 5% SBS reduced the emission of asphalt smoke by 9.15% and 22.90%, respectively (Li & Peng 2015). Layered halogen-free high-efficiency smoke suppressor also has an inhibitory effect on asphalt smoke. It is found that when the mass fraction is 2%, the total emission of asphalt smoke and dust decreases by 27.0% (Zhu et al. 2019). Through experimental comparison, it is found that when the content of expanded graphite is 0.25–0.75%, it can reduce the release of asphalt smoke and dust by 68%, but it will lead to a sharp decrease in asphalt ductility; when the content of gum alone resin is 0.5%, the emission of asphalt smoke and dust can be reduced by 83%, but the penetration of asphalt will be reduced sharply. Both modifiers will lead to the performance of asphalt not meeting the specification requirements (Liu et al. 2014). The deodorization effect of flame retardant deodorizing asphalt and nonpolar adsorption deodorizing asphalt and their influence on the three indexes of asphalt are studied, and it was found that most deodorizing agents have limited deodorizing effect, and some materials will have segregation. Finally, expanded graphite was selected as deodorizing agent, which makes the smoke suppression rate of asphalt stable by more than 60%, but will lead to a sharp reduction in asphalt ductility (Huang 2013). Nano titanium dioxide has optical catalytic properties. An additional dose of 8‰ is recommended to be added as a modifier to the asphalt pavement due to the optical catalytic performance of nano titanium dioxide. Through indoor testing and engineering application, it was found that its decomposition effect on various harmful gases in tail gas was stable up to 20%–30%, which could play a role for a long time, and had no significant negative impact on the performance of the mixture (Sun et al. 2011; Xu et al. 2011). Alumina trihydrate (ATH) and organic montmorillonite (OMMT) are mixed into an asphalt binder, and the emission characteristics of volatile organic compounds are evaluated. It was found that the compounds composed of the two prevented the fracture of molecular chains in asphalt and promoted the carbonization of asphalt in the combustion process, thus reducing the emission of asphalt smoke and dust, and significantly improved the high-temperature performance of asphalt mixture. However, it reduced the water sensitivity and thermal cracking resistance of asphalt mixture (Yang et al. 2020).

Compared with traditional hot asphalt, the chemical inhibition method can effectively reduce the emission of irritant gas in asphalt by 20%–90% through a chemical reaction. It has the characteristics of green environmental protection and adding with use.

3.3 Plant extracts class

Plant extracts are the mixture formed by mixing the volatile oil extracted from trees, flowers, and plants with water after emulsification, which is added to the asphalt as a deodorant (Zhang et al. 2015).

Emulsifiers, penetrants, and solvents are added to the rosin extract as a deodorizer. It was found that the removal rates of H_2S, NH_3, and C_3H_8S were 71.8%, 72.6%, and 70.5%, respectively (Zhang et al. 2015). Powder deodorant (mainly composed of high-carbon alcohol organics) and liquid deodorant (mainly composed of plant alcohol organics) are added to rubber asphalt. It was found that when the content of deodorant was 5‰, the deodorant effect is the best, which can reduce the emission of hydrogen sulfide by 80% and has little impact on the basic properties of rubber asphalt. The action principle was to inhibit the degradation of rubber powder in asphalt and reduce the free sulfur element in rubber asphalt. In addition, liquid deodorant can not only absorb rubber powder but also slow down the reaction of rubber powder in asphalt and absorb sulfur-containing flue gas (Li 2020). The natural macromolecular material Eucommia ulmoides gum is used to replace the expensive trans-polyctenamer rubber so that a three-dimensional network structure was formed in the blend, which helped to form a solid and reliable chemical bond between rubber chips and asphalt, thus contributing to the compatibility of polymer modified asphalt and promoting the sustainable development of rubber asphalt pavement construction (Deng et al. 2017).

The action mechanism of plant extracts is a physical and chemical reaction, but different from physical adsorption and chemical inhibition, plant extract deodorant can play a role in acidic, alkaline, and neutral gases. On the premise of deodorization, it can be completely degraded to turn toxic substances into non-toxic substances without toxic pollution to the environment (Yuan and Huang 2005).

3.4 *Microbiology*

Microbial deodorization technology transforms or degrades odor substances into harmless or low-harmful substances by microorganisms. Due to the existence of active groups in the odor gas, it is easy to be oxidized after being absorbed by the liquid containing microorganisms, so as to weaken the odor and achieve the purpose of odor removal (Liu et al. 2018). Microbial deodorizer has the advantages of low cost, wide treatment range, long-lasting effect, non-toxic, and no secondary pollution. However, deodorization takes a certain time and can not produce a deodorization effect immediately. Moreover, most microorganisms can not survive under asphalt high-temperature mixing, so it is not suitable for application in the process of asphalt mixing.

Some scholars have established models to analyze the deodorization mechanism of deodorizers deeply. Based on the theory of Newtonian mechanics, a molecular dynamics model was established to simulate and analyze the deodorization mechanism of deodorizers in rubber asphalt.

For the above four deodorizers, the microbial deodorization technology is unsuitable for asphalt due to the lag of the deodorization effect and the requirements of temperature conditions. Physical adsorption, chemical inhibition, and plant extract deodorizers can be used to inhibit asphalt smoke and dust. Among them, plant extract deodorizer has wider application conditions and obvious deodorization effect. Currently, it is rarely used in asphalt deodorization, which may be a development direction in the future.

4 CONCLUSION

The detection methods of asphalt smoke and dust can be divided into two categories. One is qualitative determination, which only analyzes the components in asphalt smoke and dust. The determination methods include the thermogravimetric method, UV-vis spectrophotometry, and thermogravimetric mass spectrometry; the other is the quantitative determination of the concentration of each component in asphalt dust. The determination methods include gas chromatography-mass spectrometry and high-performance liquid chromatography. The two methods have advantages and disadvantages, and their application is also different.

Asphalt deodorization technology can fundamentally reduce the emission of harmful gases from the production and construction of asphalt and asphalt mixture. This method is simple to operate. It is the main development direction of smoke and dust suppression technology and has broad market prospects. According to different deodorizing agents, asphalt smoke deodorization methods are mainly divided into physical adsorption, chemical inhibition, plant extract, and microorganisms. However, microorganisms are not suitable for high-temperature mixing asphalt deodorization. However, asphalt deodorization technology is not mature. Most scholars only evaluate the deodorization effect of deodorizer and its impact on asphalt performance but rarely evaluate the road performance of asphalt mixture and its application in engineering practice.

ACKNOWLEDGMENT

Sichuan Transportation Science and Technology Project 2022-ZL-05.

REFERENCES

Agostini, M., Ferro, G., Burstyn, I., De Vocht, F., Portengen, L., Olsson, A., Boffetta, P., Kromhout, H. & Stud, I. E. A. W. 2013. Does a more refined assessment of exposure to bitumen fume and confounders alter risk estimates from a nested case-control study of lung cancer among European asphalt workers? *Occupational and Environmental Medicine*, 70, 195–202.

Bai, S., Ouyang, Z. & Luo, D. 2016. Determination of 16 polycyclic aromatic hydrocarbons in coal tar pitch by high-performance liquid chromatography. *Chinese Journal of Analysis Laboratory*, 35, 1078–1082.

Brasseur, C., Brose, F., Pirlot, A., Douny, C., Eppe, G., Maghuin-Rogister, G. & Scippo, M. L. 2007. Validation of the analytical procedure for the determination of polyaromatic hydrocarbons in smoke flavorings using high-performance liquid chromatography coupled to an ultraviolet, diode array, or fluorescence detector. *Accreditation and Quality Assurance*, 12, 535–542.

Cai, H., Li, Z., Li, J. & Tang, Q. 2014. The evaluation of the potential harm of asphalt fumes to the environment. *New Building Materials*, 41, 47–50.

Cao, L. P., Yang, C., Li, A., Wang, P., Zhang, Y. & Dong, Z. J. 2021. Flue gas composition of waste rubber modified asphalt (WRMA) and effect of deodorants on hazardous constituents and WRMA. *Journal of Hazardous Materials*, 403.

Cavallari, J. M., Osborn, L. V., Snawder, J. E., Kriech, A. J., Olsen, L. D., Herrick, R. F. & Mcclean, M. D. 2012. Predictors of airborne exposures to polycyclic aromatic compounds and total organic matter among hot-mix asphalt paving workers and influence of work conditions and practices. *Annals of Occupational Hygiene*, 56, 138–147.

Chen, G. 2019. Application of high-performance liquid chromatography in food detection. *Modern Food*, 181–183.

Cui, P. Q., Wu, S. P., Li, F. Z., Xiao, Y. & Zhang, H. H. 2014. Investigation on using SBS and active carbon filler to reduce the VOC emission from bituminous materials. *Materials*, 7, 6130–6143.

Cui, P. Q., Wu, S. P., Xiao, Y., Wan, M. & Cui, P. D. 2015. Inhibiting effect of layered double hydroxides on the emissions of volatile organic compounds from bituminous materials. *Journal of Cleaner Production*, 108, 987–991.

Cui, P. Q., Wu, S. P., Xiao, Y. & Zhang, H. H. 2014. A study on the deteriorations of bituminous binder resulted from volatile organic compounds emissions. *Construction and Building Materials*, 68, 644–649.

Deng, X. Y., Li, Z. G., Huang, Y. X. & Luan, Y. B. 2017. Improving mechanism and effect analysis of sulfurated and grafted Eucommia Ulmoides Gum modified rubber asphalt. *Construction and Building Materials*, 148, 715–722.

Dong, Z. J., Zhou, T., Luan, H., Williams, R. C., Wang, P. & Leng, Z. 2019. Composite modification mechanism of blended bio-asphalt combining styrene-butadiene-styrene with crumb rubber: A sustainable and environmental-friendly solution for wastes. *Journal of Cleaner Production*, 214, 593–605.

Elkashef, M., Williams, R. C. & Cochran, E. 2018. Thermal stability and evolved gas analysis of rejuvenated reclaimed asphalt pavement (RAP) bitumen using thermogravimetric analysis-Fourier transform infrared (TG-FTIR). *Journal of Thermal Analysis and Calorimetry*, 131, 865–871.

Feng, F., Qin, L., Wu, Y., Li, Y. & Wu, Y. 2011. Analysis of components of flue gas extract from coal tar pitch heating by GC/MS. *Industrial Health and Occupational Diseases*, 37, 198–203.

Feng, T. 2019. Shell asphalt: upgrade and start again. *China Highway*, 48–49.

Firoozifar, S. H., Foroutan, S. & Foroutan, S. 2011. The effect of asphaltene on thermal properties of bitumen. *Chemical Engineering Research & Design*, 89, 2044–2048.

Fryazinov, V. V. & Grudnikov, I. B. 1976. Cleanup of emissions from asphalt production. *Chemistry and Technology of Fuels and Oils*, 12, 867–870.

Gasthauer, E., Maze, M., Marchand, J. P. & Amouroux, J. 2008. Characterization of asphalt fume composition by GC/MS and effect of temperature. *Fuel*, 87, 1428–1434.

Hong, X., Huang, L. & Ma, H. 2013. Research progress of deodorant and its application prospect in the leather industry. *Leather and Chemical Industry*, 30, 23–25.

Huang, G. 2013. *Development of smoke suppression modified asphalt and Study on mixture performance under high temperature.* Dissertation, Chongqing Jiaotong University.

Huang, G., He, Z. & Huang, T. 2015. Indoor measurement of asphalt smoke emission under high temperature and analysis of influencing factors. *Journal of Building Materials*, 18, 322–327.

Jimenezmateos, J. M., Quintero, L. C. & Rial, C. 1996. Characterization of petroleum bitumens and their fractions by thermogravimetric analysis and differential scanning calorimetry. *Fuel*, 75, 1691–1700.

Jullien, A., Moneron, P., Quaranta, G. & Gaillard, D. 2006. Air emissions from pavement layers composed of varying rates of reclaimed asphalt. *Resources Conservation and Recycling*, 47, 356–374.

Li, A. 2020. *Mechanism and performance evaluation of purifying odor of rubber asphalt.* Master's Thesis, Harbin Institute of Technology.

Li, J. 2005. *Study on optimization method and application of refinery process system.* Dissertation, National University of Defense Technology.

Li, L. 2017. *Study on release characteristics and inhibition methods of VOCs from rubber asphalt.* Master's Thesis, Wuhan University of Technology.

Li, Z. & Peng, X. 2015. Effect analysis of polymer on inhibiting high-temperature asphalt smoke. *Industrial Safety and Environmental Protection*, 41, 24–26.

Liu, J., Zhao, Y., Huang, G. & Wang, L. 2014. Development and application of smoke suppressant. *Petroleum Asphalt*, 28, 63–67.

Liu, Y., Zhao, P., Zhang, Z., Lian, X. & Zhang, Z. Research status of microbial deodorization technology. The 12th Annual Conference of Chinese society of bioengineering and 2018 National Biotechnology Conference, 2018 Changsha, Hunan, China. 335–339.

Lu, F. Brief introduction of odor monitoring and analysis methods. The 4th National odor pollution testing and Control Technology Seminar, 2012 Zibo, Shandong, China. 52–56.

Mao, J. 2000. Analysis and improvement of asphalt smoke determination method. *Qinghai environment*, 66–70.

Mo, S. C., Wang, Y. H., Xiong, F. & Ai, C. J. 2019. Effects of asphalt source and mixing temperature on the generated asphalt fumes. *Journal of Hazardous Materials*, 371, 342–351.

Mothe, M. G., Leite, L. F. M. & Mothe, C. G. 2008. Thermal characterization of asphalt mixtures by TG/DTG, DTA, and FTIR. *Journal of Thermal Analysis and Calorimetry*, 93, 105–109.

Rao, Z. 2011. Detection technology of environmental organic pollutants and its application. *Acta Geologica Sinica*, 85, 1948–1962.

Shi, B., Xu, G. & Liu, J. 2001. Online analysis of chemical components of asphalt smoke by gas chromatography-mass spectrometry. *Environmental Chemistry*, 200–201.

Sun, L., Xu, H., Li, J. & Liu, L. 2011. Study on the effect and application method of nano titanium dioxide in treating automobile exhaust. *Journal of Highway and Transportation Research and Development*, 28, 153–158.

Tatari, O., Nazzal, M. & Kucukvar, M. 2012. Comparative sustainability assessment of warm-mix asphalts: A thermodynamic based hybrid life cycle analysis. *Resources Conservation and Recycling*, 58, 18–24.

Wang, Z. C., Wang, Q. & Jia, C. X. 2017. Structural changes in oil sand bitumen during pyrolysis. *Journal of Thermal Analysis and Calorimetry*, 127, 2215–2223.

Wielinski, J., Kriech, A., Huber, G., Horton, A. & Osborn, L. 2015. Analysis of vacuum tower asphalt extender and effect on bitumen and asphalt properties. *Road Materials and Pavement Design*, 16, 90–110.

Wu, S., Yu, Y. & Chen, M. 2011. Research progress of asphalt volatiles. *Petroleum Asphalt*, 25, 1–6.

Xiong, S. 2020. Characteristics and application of high-performance liquid chromatography. *Modern Food*, 199–201.

Xiu, T., Wang, Y., Wang, Y., Xu, X., Sun, Y. & Liu, G. 2004. Measurement Volatile HCX in the Atmosphere of Beijing by a Method of Concentrated Large Volume Air Sample/GC – MS. *Journal of Instrumental Analysis*, 161–165.

Xu, H., Liu, L., Sun, L. & Li, J. 2011. Application of nano titanium dioxide in practical road engineering. *Highway Engineering*, 36, 189–192+198.

Yan, X., Mu, X. & Liu, G. 2004. Determination of asphalt smoke by Ultraviolet Spectrophotometry. *Northern Environment*, 61–62.

Yang, B. 2012. *Study on quantitative analysis method and evaluation system of energy conservation and emission reduction of Asphalt Pavement.* Dissertation, Chang'an University.

Yang, X. L., Shen, A. Q., Su, Y. X. & Zhao, W. D. 2020. Effects of alumina trihydrate (ATH) and organic montmorillonite (OMMT) on asphalt fume emission and flame retardancy properties of SBS-modified asphalt. *Construction and Building Materials*, 236.

Yang, Y. 2017. Application of high-performance liquid chromatography in food analysis. *China Food Safety Magazine*, 67.

Yuan, W. & Huang, C. 2005. Research progress on the treatment of malodorous gas with plant extracts. *Environmental Protection of Chemical Industry*, 441–445.

Zeng, D. 2019. Application of high-performance liquid chromatography in food quality detection. *Modern Food*, 173–175.

Zhang, W., Zhang, Q. & Zhang, H. 2015. Study on preparation and deodorization effect of turpentine deodorant. *Environmental Science and Technology*, 38, 273–275+329.

Zhu, K., Tang, D., Huang, Y., Wang, Q. & Wu, K. 2019. ZnMgAl-CO_ Flame retardant and smoke suppression performance and mechanism analysis of 3-ldhs asphalt. *Journal of Building Materials*, 22, 599–605.

Research on construction safety evaluation of prefabricated medical building based on cloud model

Aiping Song & Fanghong Tao*
Yunnan University of Business Management, Yunnan, Kunming, China

ABSTRACT: Traditional building construction has disadvantages such as long periods, low industrial production efficiency, and many potential safety hazards. In order to advocate green and sustainable development, it is necessary to change the traditional construction method in China and adopt the prefabricated building construction method, which not only improves construction efficiency but also can effectively solve the problem of construction safety. Considering the characteristics of prefabricated buildings, this paper proposes a set of construction safety evaluation system for prefabricated medical buildings based on cloud model theory, to standardize the construction safety of prefabricated medical buildings, help enterprises to supervise and guide the construction process of prefabricated buildings scientifically and reasonably, and effectively improve the problem of frequent safety accidents in China's construction industry. Regarding the construction safety of prefabricated medical buildings, China should improve relevant laws and regulations, adjust the hidden dangers in the safety construction system, and standardize the pricing of various materials in the prefabricated building market, so as to ensure that stakeholders can seek certain benefits. At the same time, the safety of prefabricated construction can be guaranteed.

1 INTRODUCTION

Due to the characteristics of high-risk construction in the construction industry, various construction safety accidents frequently occur, which hinder construction progress, delay the construction period, and bring huge economic losses to the owners. The occurrence of safety accidents has seriously hindered the healthy and steady development of the construction industry, damaged the interests of all parties, and wasted social resources. The construction unit bears economic losses which affects the company's reputation (Gu 2022). At the same time, casualties and property losses caused by safety accidents bring sadness and pain to the families of casualties and affect social harmony and stability. Therefore, the construction safety of prefabricated buildings needs attention and cannot be ignored. This paper studies the construction safety evaluation of prefabricated medical buildings and analyzes the relationship between construction safety indicators, identifies safety evaluation indicators, and establishes a safety evaluation system (Gao et al. 2022). The prefabricated medical building construction safety management plan enables the relevant management personnel to control the factors affecting construction safety effectively and improves the construction safety management ability. Finally, taking the X prefabricated medical building project as an example, by proposing the theoretical concept of the cloud model, the evaluation cloud model was established to carry out safety evaluation based on the evaluation results. Corresponding countermeasures and suggestions were put forward, and the scientific and cloud-based evaluation index system was verified. The practicability of the model provides a reference for the construction safety management of prefabricated buildings.

---

*Corresponding Author: 83335673@qq.com

2 ESTABLISHMENT OF A CLOUD MODEL FOR CONSTRUCTION SAFETY EVALUATION OF PREFABRICATED MEDICAL BUILDINGS

2.1 *Formatting the title*

Cloud models can comprehensively evaluate complex systems and convert qualitative linguistic values suitable for analysis into appropriate ones. In the security evaluation, clouds represent evaluation sets and evaluation values (Lin 2022). Cloud models are universal and scientific, and their operability is also very strong. Therefore, in the detailed analysis of the prefabricated medical building construction safety, this study selected the cloud model for safety evaluation to obtain a more reasonable, accurate, and intuitive evaluation result (Lin 2022). The prefabricated medical building construction safety cloud model is shown in Figure 1.

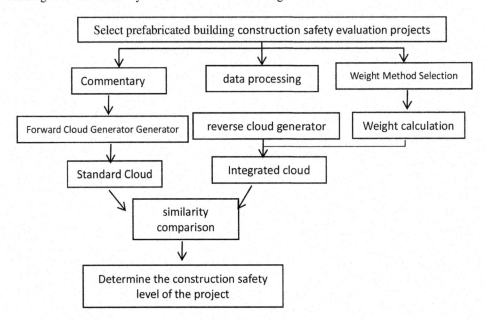

Figure 1. Safety cloud model of prefabricated medical building construction.

2.2 *Determination of construction safety evaluation system for prefabricated medical buildings*

The prefabricated building construction safety evaluation index system is not simple and changeable. It involves the identification and screening of safety evaluation indexes, and the corresponding influencing factors are divided through relevant theories and actual construction problems of safety accidents (Miao & Chen 2022). Most of the prefabricated construction projects in China implement the construction technology combined with prefabrication and cast-in-place, so it is necessary to use text mining and questionnaire survey to summarize and analyze the identified construction safety hazards, and then according to the construction safety management points and prefabricated building construction standards and the safety standards of related literature at home and abroad, comprehensively identify and screen the construction safety evaluation indicators, and provide the basis for the establishment of the construction safety evaluation system.

The factors affecting the construction safety of prefabricated buildings are diverse and difficult to give a comprehensive overview. Through the analysis of the construction safety system, they are classified into human, physical, environmental, and policy factors. Besides, various safety evaluation indicators are classified to jointly build the prefabricated building (Su et al. 2022). The evaluation system of building construction safety influencing factors. The significance analysis draws the prefabricated medical building construction safety evaluation index, as shown in Table 1.

Table 1. Construction safety evaluation indicators of prefabricated medical buildings.

First-level indicator	Secondary indicators
Human factor B_1	Construction workers' safety protection wearing C_{11}
	Safety measures for construction workers C_{12}
	Professional operation level of construction personnel C_{13}
	Construction workers' safety awareness C_{14}
	management skills of managers C_{15}
	Qualifications of construction personnel C_{16}
	Safety production inspection C_{17}
	Construction safety education and training C_{18}
Object factor B_2	Component factory safety inspection C_{21}
	Equipment assembly safety simulation C_{22}
	Equipment regular safety inspection C_{23}
	Component transportation and fixing measures C_{24}
Environmental factor B_3	Weather change C_{31}
	Force majeure C_{32}
	On-site construction environment C_{33}
Policy factors B_4	Quality acceptance specification C_{41}
	Improvement of the measurement specifications of quotas and lists C_{42}
	Implementation of the management and supervision mechanism C_{43}
	Implementation of government incentive policies C_{44}
	Improvement of construction safety management system C_{45}
	Implementation of safety management responsibility system C_{46}
	Compliance with safety regulations C_{47}

2.3 Determination of weight of safety evaluation index for prefabricated medical building construction

2.3.1 Determination of subjective weights

Analytic Hierarchy Process (AHP) first poses a complex multi-objective decision-making problem, decomposes it into several levels, then uses the qualitative index fuzzy quantitative method to determine the final calculation result, the target optimization, and multiobjective system. Therefore, we use this method for quantitative analysis to obtain the weights of relevant factors. The specific steps are as follows:

First, the hierarchical model of the research topic is established, the decision matrix A is formed, and the value is allocated on a 9-level scale (Shan 2022). Through calculation, the maximum eigenvalue A_{max} of the decision matrix is normalized to obtain the corresponding eigenvector W and the weight vector W = (W_1, W_2, W_3, ..., W_n). The determination matrix obtained by the first-level indicators is as follows:

$$A = \left(a_{ij}\right)_{m \times n} = \begin{bmatrix} a_{11} & a_{12} & \cdots & a_{1n} \\ a_{21} & a_{22} & \cdots & a_{2n} \\ \cdots & \cdots & \cdots & \cdots \\ a_{m1} & a_{m2} & \cdots & a_{mn} \end{bmatrix} \quad (1)$$

Judgment Matrix Consistency Determination (Shen 2022).

$$CR = \frac{\lambda_{max} - n}{RI(n-1)} \quad (2)$$

In the formula, CR is the satisfactory consistency index, λ_{max} is the largest eigenvalue of the matrix, RI is the average random consistency index value, and n is the order.

The value table of the 1–10th order matrix RI is shown in Table 2.

Table 2. Value list of average random consistency index.

Order n	1	2	3	4	5	6	7	8	9	10
RI	0	0	0.58	0.9	1.12	1.24	1.32	1.41	1.45	1.49

Generally, the smaller the CR, the better the consistency of the judgment matrix (Wang 2022). When CR≤0.1, it is considered that the judgment matrix has satisfactory consistency; when CR≥0.1, it is considered that the judgment matrix does not meet the consistency requirements, and the matrix needs to be modified.

Multiply the rows of each element of the decision matrix to obtain M_i:

$$M_i = \prod_{j=1}^{n} b_{ij} \tag{3}$$

Calculate the nth root of M_i, and obtain W^*:

$$W^* = \sqrt[n]{M_i} \tag{4}$$

Normalize the W^* of the vector to obtain W_i representing the weight of each indicator:

$$W_i = W^* / \sum_{i=1}^{n} W^* \tag{5}$$

2.3.2 Determination of objective weight

Entropy is a measure of disorder. The more chaotic a system is, the less information it provides. The greater the role entropy plays in the overall evaluation, the higher the weight it has. The entropy weighting method is an objective weighting method that integrates the certainty of entropy weight through the subjective evaluation of experts (Yang et al. 2022). When determining the weight of each index, it needs to be confirmed by the method of entropy weight to avoid differences between human subjective factors and objective samples (Yu 2022). The error is caused by the influence of the size of the uncertainty. The specific process of processing is as follows:

First, assume n indicators, among which $X_i = \{X_1, X_2, ..., X_n\}$. By standardizing each index, the obtained values are $Y_1, Y_2, ..., $ and Y_n. The original matrix form is $Y = (y_{ij})_{m \times n}$, and the matrix is normalized by calculation to obtain the matrix Y. This paper uses the normalization formula of positive indicators to standardize the indicators and then normalize them (Zhu, 2022).

$$y_{ij} = \frac{x_{ij} - \min_i (x_{ij})}{\max_i (x_{ij}) - \min_i (x_{ij})} \tag{6}$$

Get the normalized matrix:

$$Y = \begin{bmatrix} y_{11} & y_{12} & \cdots & y_{1n} \\ y_{21} & y_{22} & \cdots & y_{2n} \\ \cdots & \cdots & \cdots & \cdots \\ y_{m1} & y_{m2} & \cdots & y_{mn} \end{bmatrix}_{m \times n} \tag{7}$$

Based on the above matrix, the entropy value of the risk index can be calculated.

$$e_i = -K \sum_{j=1}^{n} j \ f_{ij} \ln f_{ij} \tag{8}$$

In the formula, K=1/Inn

$$f_{ij} = y_{ij} / \sum_{i=1}^{n} y_{ij} \qquad (9)$$

Among them, when $f_{ij}=0$ is specified, f_{ij} In$f_{ij}=0$

Calculate the difference coefficient of the risk index according to the calculated entropy value of the risk index: $g_i=1-e_i$

Finally, the entropy weight of the difference coefficient risk index is obtained:

$$W_{ei} = g_i / \sum_{i=1}^{m} g_i \qquad (10)$$

2.3.3 Determination of comprehensive weights

The final weight is obtained by using the optimized comprehensive weight formula of the AHP-entropy weight method. Assume that the weight coefficients of each safety evaluation index determined by the AHP method and the entropy weight method are V = (V$_1$, V$_2$, V$_3$······V$_n$) and W = (W$_1$, W$_2$, W$_3$······W$_n$), respectively), then each evaluation index weight coefficient Wj:

$$W_j = \frac{v_i w_i}{\sum_{1}^{n} v_i w_i} \qquad (11)$$

3 SAFETY EVALUATION RESULTS OF PREFABRICATED MEDICAL BUILDING CONSTRUCTION BASED ON CLOUD MODEL

3.1 Evaluation method

The comments of the cloud model are embodied in the concepts of "excellent," "good," and "poor," and each evaluation index can be replaced with a specific comment. Therefore, the digital feature values of the standard cloud, evaluation cloud, and comprehensive cloud are determined using the cloud model (Zhang 2022). Considering the actual situation of the project and expert suggestions, combined with the analysis of a large amount of related literature and the habit of safety evaluation language expression, the construction safety evaluation level is scientifically and reasonably divided into five grades, which are dangerous, mildly dangerous, safe, very safe. In order to give a scientific and reasonable scoring interval for each level, it is assumed that the value of the first level is 0, and the value of the fifth level is 100, then the interval [0, 100] is the level score. The relevant experts conduct multiple independent evaluations of the interval according to the language description, divide the grade standard of the second, third and fourth grades, and take the average value as the evaluation grade interval (Zhao 2022). Most of the previous standards are fixed values, which makes some samples. The wrong division into other intervals affects the reliability of the evaluation criteria, thus affecting the scientific rationality of the evaluation results. Therefore, it is necessary to set the upper and lower limits of bilateral constraints on the critical points of each evaluation level to calculate the cloud parameters.

3.2 Analysis of evaluation results

In order to determine the safety status of the X prefabricated medical building construction, ten experts were invited to score the safety evaluation indicators of the prefabricated building construction, and each secondary index was scored. The results are shown in Table 3.

The final comprehensive cloud evaluation result is C(88.5636, 2.6783, 0.9481).

Therefore, the evaluation result of this project is consistent with the above and is "very safe." Therefore, the successful construction of this project and its safety management methods and experience have certain practical significance and reference value for future research on the safety evaluation and management of prefabricated buildings.

Table 3. Cloud model parameters evaluated by secondary indicators.

First-level indicator	Secondary indicators	W_{BC}	Cloud parameters (ExU, EnU, HeU)
Human factor B_1	Construction workers' safety protection wearing C_{11}	0.0355	(81.7, 2.6320, 1.7405)
	Safety measures for construction workers C_{12}	0.0369	(82.9, 2.1557, 0.9813)
	Professional operation level of construction personnel C_{13}	0.0451	(83.6, 2.6570, 1.1004)
	Construction workers' safety awareness C_{14}	0.0354	(84.5, 3.8853, 1.9548)
	management skills of managers C_{15}	0.0429	(81.9, 2.3813, 0.8528)
	Qualifications of construction personnel C_{16}	0.1180	(81.7, 2.6320, 1.5031)
	Safety production inspection C_{17}	0.0357	(81.1, 1.8800, 0.5586)
	Construction safety education and training C_{18}	0.0338	(81, 2.5066, 1.1280)
Object factor B_2	Component factory safety inspection C_{21}	0.0338	(82, 1.7546, 0.9598)
	Equipment assembly safety simulation C_{22}	0.0311	(80.6, 1.6544, 0.2566)
	Equipment regular safety inspection C_{23}	0.0336	(81.8, 2.8074, 1.0633)
	Component transportation and fixing measures C_{24}	0.0365	(82, 3.0080, 1.5836)
Environmental factor B_3	Weather change C_{31}	0.0681	(81.7, 2.3813, 0.7728)
	Force majeure C_{32}	0.0721	(81.6, 2.2560, 0.0629)
	On-site construction environment C_{33}	0.0714	(83.3, 4.3866, 0.4749)
Policy factors B_4	Quality acceptance specification C_{41}	0.0513	(88.8, 2.1306, 0.5474)
	Improvement of the measurement specifications of quotas and lists C_{42}	0.0517	(88.2, 2.0554, 1.2264)
	Implementation of the management and supervision mechanism C_{43}	0.0498	(85.5, 1.8800, 0.2215)
	Implementation of government incentive policies C_{44}	0.0445	(80, 2.8826, 1.5558)
	Improvement of construction safety management system C_{45}	0.0500	(80, 2.8826, 1.5558)
	Implementation of safety management Responsibility system C_{46}	0.0455	(81.7, 2.5066, 0.6650)
	Compliance with safety regulations C_{47}	0.0480	(80.6, 1.5040, 0.1878)

4 CONSTRUCTION SAFETY COUNTERMEASURES OF PREFABRICATED MEDICAL BUILDINGS BASED ON CLOUD MODEL

We can learn from the successful construction safety management of this project and summarize its safety management methods and experience. Since the laws and regulations on prefabricated buildings are comprehensive, there are no loopholes and hidden dangers in the relevant responsibilities and systems in construction safety. When a safety accident occurs, relevant processing methods and measures can be provided in a timely manner (Zhang 2022). The list pricing standard is perfect. While stakeholders seek greater benefits, the market is also in a state of healthy competition. The safety of prefabricated building construction can be guaranteed, and the management and supervision mechanism is sound, so that the supervision and management units can perform their corresponding responsibilities. Government incentives can also be provided. The specific implementation measures are mentioned in the policy, which improves people's enthusiasm and concern for the construction safety of prefabricated buildings and strengthens the construction safety management of prefabricated buildings.

5 CONCLUSION

In recent years, prefabricated building safety accidents still occur frequently, and the analysis of construction safety factors plays an increasingly important role in the prevention and control of prefabricated building accidents, whether from the perspective of social benefits or economic benefits. From this point of view, analyzing influencing factors is of great significance to the safe development of prefabricated buildings. The research on construction safety evaluation of prefabricated buildings is relatively complicated. Due to the broad scope of construction safety, the evaluation indicators may be omitted in the identification process, and the selection of construction safety evaluation indicators is not comprehensive enough. The construction safety evaluation system is imperfect and needs further improvement. Based on the actual data of X-built prefabricated construction projects, AHP and entropy weight methods are combined to avoid the influence of human subjective factors and objective sample differences. Although the combination of these methods can make up for the defects of related parties, this paper cannot analyze all related. The influencing factors of prefabricated buildings are still insufficient in accuracy. Some factors are eliminated because the data is too small, leading to certain deviations in the data and affecting the integrity of relevant factors. Therefore, more reasonable and effective research methods need to be further explored and strengthened.

REFERENCES

Gao Xianwu, Wang Jun, Guan Dujuan.(2022).Risk assessment of prefabricated building construction based on entropy weight fuzzy comprehensive evaluation method. *Journal of Shanxi Datong University* (Natural Science Edition), 1, 45–51.

Gu Shoupu. (2022).Rationalization of prefabricated decoration design in the context of the development of prefabricated buildings. *China Building Decoration*, 6, 36–38.

Li Shuo. (2022). Analysis of the design points and development trend of prefabricated building structure system. *Real Estate World*, 5, 52–54.

Li Yongjun. (2022).Research on safety management of prefabricated building construction. *Jushe*, 11, 135–137.

Miao Zehui, Chen Xiao. (2022). Research on sustainable development evaluation of prefabricated buildings based on improved three-scale fuzzy analytic hierarchy process. *Intelligent Building and Smart City*, 2, 108–111.

Shan Hao. (2022). Analysis of influencing factors and countermeasures of prefabricated construction project management. *Public Standardization*, 4, 87–91.

Shen Yu. (2022).Common quality problems and preventive measures in prefabricated building construction. *Building Materials Development Orientation*, 4, 87–89.

Su Xia, Zhang Jingjing, Zhang Weiguang, Liu Xiaofeng. (2022).Research on risk auditing of prefabricated construction projects: Taking the State Grid Xiong'an Zhuhe Substation as an example. *Friends of Accounting*, 8, 132–139.

Wang Wei, Yu Shichen. (2022). Analysis of quality control points and common problems in prefabricated building construction. *Juye*, 3, 48–50.

Yang Yanping, Xie Qiyang, Xie Yongkang, Xie Qisheng. (2022). Analysis of the quality control of prefabricated components of prefabricated buildings. Housing Industry, 1, 80–83.

Yu Qi. (2022). Production and construction quality problems and improvement of prefabricated buildings. *Public Standardization*, 5, 25–27.

Zhang Jun, Hu Longwei, Sun Yu, Huang Baolun, Xia Siyu. (2022). Evaluation model of prefabricated building suppliers based on AHP and BP neural network. *Journal of Qingdao University of Technology*, 1, 18–23.

Zhang Linzhi. (2022).Analysis of prefabricated building construction technology and quality management. *Jushe*, 8, 166–168.

Zhao Benyu. (2022). Thoughts on energy saving and emission reduction of green and sustainable prefabricated buildings. *Ceramics*, 3, 154–156.

Zhu Guofeng. (2022). Research on construction technology and quality control methods of prefabricated buildings. *Science and Technology Innovation and Application*, 8, 105–107.

Evolution characteristics of displacement and crack of rock mass under the shallowly buried explosion loading

Qindong Lin
Xi'an Modern Chemistry Research Institute, Xi'an, Shaanxi, China

Chun Feng
Key Laboratory for Mechanics in Fluid Solid Coupling Systems, Institute of Mechanics, Chinese Academy of Sciences, Beijing, China

Wenjun Jiao*, Yundan Gan, Yulei Zhang & Jianfei Yuan
Xi'an Modern Chemistry Research Institute, Xi'an, Shaanxi, China

ABSTRACT: The shallowly buried explosion technology is widely used in the military and civilian fields. Based on the continuum-discontinuum element method, the evolution characteristics of displacement and crack of rock mass under shallowly buried explosion loading are studied. First, a full-time numerical simulation of rock mass is conducted. Then, the displacement evolution characteristic of rock mass is investigated. Finally, the crack evolution characteristic of rock mass is investigated. The numerical results show that the rock mass undergoes three stages of extrusion deformation, slippage, and dispersion, and finally, an obvious infundibular crater appears. The interface undergoes tensile failure and shear failure, and the interface near the explosive mainly undergoes shear failure. The cracked interface mainly appears in the explosion stage, and the cracked interface in the explosion stage accounts for 94.16% of the overall cracked interface.

1 INTRODUCTION

When an explosive explodes in the geotechnical bodies, the explosive position has an important influence on the displacement and crack evolution characteristics. Since the shallowly buried explosion technology has a wide range of applications in the military and civilian fields. it is important to study the displacement and crack evolution characteristics of geotechnical bodies under shallowly buried explosion loading.

The current research methods for the shallowly buried explosion are composed of theoretical analysis, experimental study, and numerical simulation. By introducing the damage variable, many scholars proposed the damage constitutive model and studied the dynamic mechanical response of geotechnical bodies (Wang et al. 2021; Xie et al. 2019). However, due to the complexity of geotechnical properties and the shallow buried explosion process, it is difficult to conduct a detailed theoretical analysis and establish a mathematical model. In addition, there are some assumptions and simplifications in the theoretical analysis. Therefore, it is necessary to obtain the dynamic mechanical response of geotechnical bodies based on experimental study. Denefeld (Denefeld et al. 2017), Hu (Hu et al. 2014), Peng (Peng et al. 2020), Ridby (Rigby et al. 2016) and Wang (Wang et al. 2018) conducted many explosion tests, and studied the effect of some parameters (e.g., burial depth, confining pressure, explosive charge) on the dynamic mechanical response of geotechnical bodies.

---

*Corresponding Author: jiaowj@mail.ustc.edu.cn

With the rapid development of computer technology, many numerical methods are proposed. According to the inherent assumption, the methods are categorized into the continuum-based method (e.g., FEM, FVM), discontinuum-based method (e.g., DEM, DDA), and mesh-free method (e.g., SPH, MPM). Since each numerical method has advantages and disadvantages, many coupled methods are proposed. Since the convenience of implementation, Ambrosini (Ambrosini & Luccioni 2006), Qian (Qian et al. 2021), Wei (Wei et al. 2009), Zhu (Zhu et al. 2018) and Liu (Liu et al. 2020) studied the dynamic mechanical response of geotechnical bodies under shallowly buried explosion loading based on numerical simulation.

Currently, scholars have conducted lots of numerical studies on the dynamic mechanical response of geotechnical bodies under shallowly buried explosion loading. Since most of the numerical methods belong to the continuum-based method and mesh-free method, they cannot accurately portray the crack evolution characteristic of the research object. To investigate the displacement and crack evolution characteristics of rock mass, this study conducts the numerical simulation based on the continuum-discontinuum element method, and the evolution characteristics of displacement and crack are studied.

2 NUMERICAL SIMULATION

2.1 Continuum-discontinuum element method

The continuum-discontinuum element method (CDEM) is a dynamic explicit numerical algorithm, and it can simulate the whole process of material from continuous deformation to crack and movement. The basic model in CDEM includes block and interface. A block includes one or more elements, and it is used to represent the continuous features. The common boundary between blocks is defined as an interface, which is used to represent discontinuous features. The interface includes the real interface and the virtual interface. The real discontinuous features are characterized by the real interface. The virtual interface has two main purposes: to connect two blocks and transfer mechanical information; and to provide potential space for crack initiation and expansion (Ju et al. 2016; Wang et al. 2019; Zhang et al. 2019). CDEM establishes a governing equation, which is written as

$$Ma(t) + Cv(t) + Ku(t) = F(t) \quad (1)$$

where $a(t)$, $v(t)$, and $u(t)$ represent the acceleration vector, velocity vector, and displacement vector, respectively. M, C, and K denote the mass matrix, damping matrix, and stiffness matrix, respectively. $F(t)$ denotes the external force vector.

2.2 Numerical model and mechanical parameters

The numerical model of rock mass and explosive is shown in Figure 1, the horizontal length of rock mass is 20 m, the vertical height is 8 m, and there are 26810 elements in the numerical model. The JWL equation of state is used to describe the explosion process, and the mechanical parameters of the explosive are listed in Table 1. The mechanical parameters of rock mass are listed in Table 2. The strength parameters of the real interface are set to zero, while the strength parameters of the virtual interface are determined according to the weak value of elements on both sides of the interface.

Figure 1. Numerical model of rock mass and explosive.

Table 1. Mechanical parameters of JWL.

Material	Charge density (kg/m³)	Initial internal energy (J/m³)	CJ pressure (GPa)	Detonation velocity (m/s)
TNT	1630	7e9	20	6930

Table 2. Mechanical parameters of rock mass.

Density (kg/m³)	Elastic modulus (GPa)	Cohesive strength (MPa)	Tensile strength (MPa)	Friction angle (°)
2500	50	6	2	40

2.3 Displacement characteristic

The displacement nephograms of rock mass under shallowly buried explosion loading are plotted in Figure 2. It can be seen that the rock mass undergoes three stages of extrusion deformation, slippage and dispersion. At the initial moment of explosion (Figure 2(a)), only the rock around the explosive undergoes movement and extrusion deformation. As the time increases (Figure 2(b)), the stress wave reaches the top boundary, where the displacement is larger than that in a certain depth region below. With the action of explosion gas, the displacement of rock above the explosive increase continuously, and the rock region with large vertical displacement is infundibular. Due to the difference in displacement between the inner and outer sides of the funnel, the rock on both sides undergoes obvious slippage. When the lasting time of detonation gas ends (Figure 2(c)), the infundibular region with large displacement is evident. Subsequently, with the increase of time, the rock continues to move, and there is a clear dispersion phenomenon. When $t = 0.03$ s (Figure 2(d)), the infundibular crater has clearly appeared.

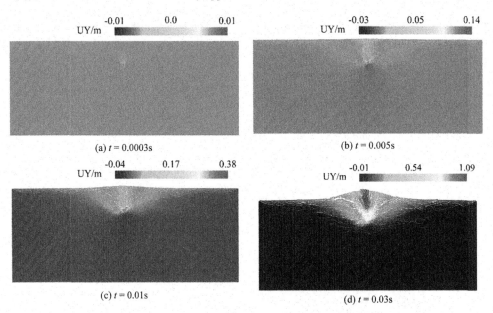

Figure 2. Displacement nephograms of rock mass at different moments.

The displacement at the top boundary is plotted in Figure 3, and it is observed that the changing trend of the displacement curve at different moments is similar. From $x = -10$ m to $x = 10$ m, the displacement first increases and then decreases, and it reaches the maximum at the position $x = 0$ m. In addition, the displacement increases slowly and then increases sharply when x increases from -10 m to 0 m, and it decreases sharply and then decreases slowly when x changes from 0 m to 10 m. Therefore, it can be concluded that there are two inflection points on the displacement curve, and the horizontal coordinate of inflection points is symmetric about $x = 0$, which is caused by the symmetry of the boundary condition and loading condition.

2.4 *Crack characteristic*

To quantitatively describe the changing trend of interface crack degree, a dimensionless index, crack ratio α, is introduced, and the time-history curve is plotted in Figure 4. In the explosion stage, α first increases sharply and then increases slowly. At the initial moment, the explosion gas pressure is high, which leads to the α increase sharply. As the time increases, the explosion gas pressure gradually decreases, resulting in a gradual decrease in the growth rate of α. Once the explosion gas disappears, the time-history curve enters the post-explosion stage. Since the dislocation displacement and stress between elements increase slowly, the growth rate of α decays, and finally α no longer increases. Since $\alpha = 14.02\%$ at $t = 0.01$ s and $\alpha = 14.89\%$ at $t = 0.03$ s, it is concluded that the cracked interface in the explosion stage accounts for 94.16% of the overall cracked interface.

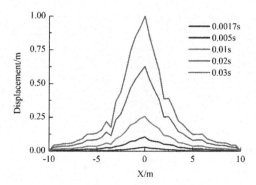

Figure 3. Displacement at the top boundary.

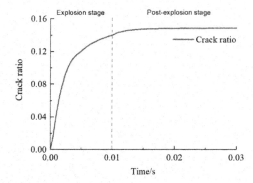

Figure 4. Time-history curve of crack ratio α.

To accurately study the crack evolution characteristic of rock mass, the initial failure nephogram is plotted in Figure 5. At the initial moment (Figure 5(a)), the interface around the explosive first cracks, the region of the cracked interface is circular, and the interface mainly undergoes shear failure. With the increase of time (Figure 5(b)), the region of the cracked interface expands. Although the compressive stress wave transforms into the tensile stress wave at the top boundary, the interface mainly undergoes shear failure. At the end of the explosion stage (Figure 5(c)), there is a clear fracture zone (the region around the explosive) and cracking zone (outside of the fracture zone) in the rock mass. It is known that the failure type of fracture zone is mainly a shear failure, and the failure type of cracking zone includes shear failure and tensile failure. When the model enters the post-explosion stage, it is observed that only a small amount of cracked interface appears in the cracking zone (Figure 5(d)).

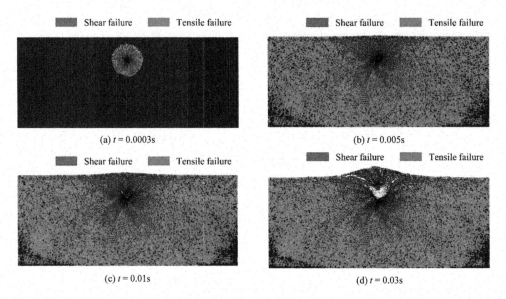

Figure 5. Initial failure nephograms of rock mass.

3 CONCLUSION

Based on the Continuum-discontinuum element method (CDEM), the displacement and crack evolution characteristics of rock mass under shallowly buried explosion loading are studied. First, a full-time numerical simulation of rock mass is conducted. Then, the displacement evolution characteristic of rock mass is investigated. Finally, the crack evolution characteristic of rock mass is studied. The following conclusions can be drawn:

(1) For the evolution characteristic of displacement, the rock mass undergoes three stages of extrusion deformation, slippage, and dispersion, and finally an obvious infundibular crater appears. There are two obvious inflection points on the displacement curve, and the horizontal coordinate of inflection points are symmetric at about $x=0$.
(2) For the evolution characteristic of crack, with the increase of time, the growth rate of α gradually decays, and finally, α remains unchanged. The cracked interface mainly appears in the explosion stage, and the cracked interface in the explosion stage accounts for 94.16% of the overall cracked interface. The initial failure type of interface includes shear failure and tensile failure, and the interface undergoing shear failure is mainly distributed near the explosive.

In this study, the dynamic mechanical response of rock mass under blast loading is studied, which lays the foundation for the subsequent analysis of the destructive effect of underground fortifications under blast loading. Under long-term geological action, rock mass has the typical heterogeneity and complex geological structure (e.g., joints, faults), which affect the dynamic response characteristic of the rock mass. To more accurately study the mechanical response of rock mass under blast loading, it is necessary to introduce the heterogeneity and geological structure into the numerical model.

REFERENCES

Ambrosini R D, Luccioni B M. (2006) Craters produced by explosions on the soil surface. *J Appl Mech*, 73: 890–900.
Denefeld V, Heider N, Holzwarth A. (2017) Measurement of the spatial specific impulse distribution due to buried high explosive charge detonation. *Def. Technol.*, 13(3): 219–227.
Hu D A, Long T, Liu C H, Yang G, Han X. (2014) Swelling movement induced by the underground explosion of aluminized explosive in multilayered compact material. *Int. J. Rock Mech. Min. Sci.*, 71: 330–339.
Ju Y, Liu P, Chen J L, Yang Y M, Ranjith P G. (2016) CDEM-based analysis of the 3D initiation and propagation of hydrofracturing cracks in heterogeneous gluten items. *J Nat Gas Sci Eng*, 35: 614–623.
Liu G K, Wang W, Liu R C, Zhang W M, Zhao Q. (2020) Deriving formulas of loading distribution on underground arch structure surface under close-in explosion. *Eng Fail Anal*, 115: 104608.
Peng J Y, Zhang F P, Du C, Yang X H. (2020) Effects of confining pressure on crater blasting in rock-like materials under electric explosion load. *Int J Impact Eng*, 139: 103534.
Qian H M, Zong Z H, Wu C Q, Li J, Gan L. (2021) Numerical study on the behavior of utility tunnel subjected to ground surface explosion. *Thin Wall Struct.*, 161: 107422.
Rigby S E, Fay S D, Clarke S D, Tyas A, Reay J J, Warren J A, Gant M, Elgy I. (2016) Measuring spatial pressure distribution from explosives buried in dry Leighton Buzzard sand. *Int J Impact Eng*, 96: 89–104.
Wang H Z, Bai C H, Feng C, Xue K, Zhu X G. (2019) An efficient CDEM-based method to calculate full-scale fragment field of the warhead. *Int J Impact Eng*, 133: 103331.
Wang M Y, Qiu Y Y, Yue S L. (2018) Similitude laws and modeling experiments of explosion cratering in multi-layered geotechnical media. *Int J Impact Eng*, 117: 32–47.
Wang Y B, Ren B, Wang D C. (2021) Research on the process of crack growth induced by explosion stress waves in rock masses with open joints. *Theor. Appl. Fract. Mech.*, 115: 103038.
Wei X Y, Zhao Z Y, Gu J. (2009) Numerical simulations of rock mass damage induced by an underground explosion. *Int. J. Rock Mech. Min. Sci.*, 46: 1206–1213.
Xie L X, Yang S Q, Gu J C, Zhang Q B, Lu W B, Jing H W, Wang Z L. (2019) JHR constitutive model for rock under dynamic loads. *Comput Geotech*, 108: 161–172.
Zhang Q L, Yue J C, Liu C, Feng C, Li H M. (2019) Study of automated top-coal caving in extra-thick coal seams using the continuum-discontinuum element method. *Int. J. Rock Mech. Min. Sci.*, 122: 104033.
Zhu J B, Li Y S, Wu S Y, Zhang R, Ren L. (2018) Decoupled explosion in an underground opening and dynamic responses of surrounding rock masses and structures and induced ground motions: A FEM-DEM numerical study. *TUNN UNDERGR SP TECH*, 82: 442–454.

Research on underwater nondestructive testing technology of hydraulic culvert based on ROV

Chao Zhang & Mangqiang Li
Gansu Runyuan Environmental Resources Technology Co., Ltd, Jiayuguan, P.R. China

Kai Zhang* & Xin Yang
Nanjing Hydraulic Research Institute, Nanjing, P.R. China

ABSTRACT: The hidden danger of hydraulic culvert structure is always the focus and difficulty of detection work because of its concealment. As a nondestructive (NDT) testing technology, the underwater robot can replace the human to enter the engineering environment which is difficult to enter and reflect the actual operation of the engineering well. In this study, a remote-operated vehicle (ROV) equipped with a variety of detection technologies was used to design a multi-angle underwater NDT testing scheme that integrated acoustics, optics, and electricity. Then a long-distance water culvert of Dacaotan Reservoir in Gansu Province, China was tested. The practice shows that the NDT scheme proposed in this paper has good feasibility. At the same time, based on the existing detection results, the future development of detection schemes is prospected.

1 INTRODUCTION

During the construction and operation period of the culvert in hydraulic structures, it will be affected by the long-term scouring and erosion of high-speed sand flow, which will lead to different degrees of silting, deterioration of material properties, and decrease in service function and apparent defects. Especially long-distance hydraulic culverts have become important hidden dangers of hydraulic and traffic engineering safety because of their long distance, high operating frequency, the huge difficulty of underwater inspection, and great risk of engineering accidents (Clarke & Fletcher 2014).

Therefore, finding out the health status of hydraulic culvert engineering can eliminate the hidden danger of safety and reduce the risk of culvert accidents. This will greatly improve the overall safety management level of the hydraulic structure, so as to minimize the culvert accident to public safety, people's life and property, and economic and social development caused by the great damage. Then public safety and sustainable development of economic and social can be ensured, which will gain significant and far-reaching social benefits (Pidi et al. 2018).

But on the other hand, due to the lack of underwater detection and service performance evaluation technology of the corresponding hydraulic underwater structures, the detection of them has been mainly carried out by divers' exploration, observation, and optical photography for a long time in the past (Hirai & Ishii 2019). However, there are various unfavorable factors in the underwater environment of hydraulic culverts, such as low visibility, debris, turbulence, complex structure, and so on, which pose a great threat to the personal safety of divers (Shimono et al. 2016).

With the development of modern underwater remote control robots, underwater sounding sonar, and positioning technology, it has become possible to use ROVs carrying relevant sonar equipment to detect water conservancy facilities and underwater structures (Aras et al. 2017; Trsli et al. 2020).

---

*Corresponding Author: kzhang@nhri.cn

In this research, the advanced underwater robot detection technologies which integrated acoustics, optics, and electricity were developed, expecting to promote the development of intelligent water conservancy and greatly reduce the cost of inspection and safety risks. Then a ROV equipped with these multi-angle underwater NDT testing technologies was applied in a long-distance hydraulic culvert to verify the efficiency and inspection quality.

2 ROV DETECTION SYSTEM DESIGN

ROV is a high-performance system designed for underwater structure inspection of hydraulic engineering. The system has the characteristics of large thrust, strong communication and carrying capacity, robustness, and reliability. Compared with other similar products, it has higher overall performance and diversified adaptability (Landstad et al. 2021).

The main components of ROV include an underwater vehicle, umbilical cable, and water control system (console, retractable system, power supply system, etc.). Navigation and diving under the control of water operators can not only operate in the conventional underwater environment, but also be applied to ship traffic, offshore oil, and other engineering fields, with wider adaptability.

ROV, as an underwater motion carrier, can carry different detection equipment to achieve corresponding detection work. There are three detection technologies designed based on ROV in this study.

2.1 Underwater camera technology

An underwater camera is used to detect targets in water with a camera mounted by ROV, and perform real-time TV display and image storage on the overwater equipment (Yang et al. 2016). The composition of an underwater camera system generally includes a camera, data cable, control system, display system, etc. The advantage of using underwater camera technology is that ROV can be used for close detecting with the flexibly selecting of observation angle and position. But it will be a challenging job under the condition of poor water quality and high turbidity.

Figure 1. Underwater camera.

2.2 Underwater multi-beam technology

The working principle of the multi-beam system is that the ultrasonic system locates accurately through the phased array method of wave theory (Dima & Sjostrom 2016), so it is also called a sonar array sounding system. The signal receiving unit consists of a number of transducers that are independent of each other and at an Angle, and the depth is determined by the amplitude and phase methods based on the echo signal at each beam position. The transducers of the multi-beam system are arranged at a certain angle, which can cover the measurement data of a strip at the same time as each launch. The size, shape, and height of the underwater target can be obtained through data analysis, so as to draw the underwater three-dimensional topography and geomorphic features of the scanned area.

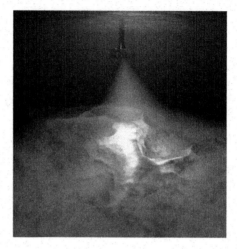

Figure 2. Underwater multi-beam terrain strafing.

2.3 Underwater sonar imaging technology

The basic principle of underwater sonar imaging is acoustic ranging and the morphological characteristics of the target are judged by the difference in the backscattering characteristics of the target (Blain et al. 2003). It is an active sonar that transmits a wide-angle beam of sound to both directions that are perpendicular to each other and images the target based on the backscattered data it receives. It can cover a large area simultaneously in deep water and can transmit at different frequencies depending on the target. Underwater image sonar system has the advantages of small size, lightweight and convenient operation. It can generate a high-resolution image with almost the same as the practical condition in a muddy water environment, which makes up for the defects of the optical imaging system to a large extent.

3 MAIN CONTENT AND PURPOSE

Based on the long-distance hydraulic culvert detection technology and ROV system, this study fully integrates multi-source information through field investigation, on-site underwater multi-angle detection tests, and data analysis. Through comparing and verifying, the actual operation of the hydraulic culvert is analyzed.

In view of such problems as low visibility of hydraulic culverts, difficult underwater inspection, serious consequences of engineering accidents, and imperfect underwater detection technology, the main objectives, and realization of this study are as follows:

(1) In view of the turbid water body and complex operating environment, it is difficult for a single detection method to reflect the real operation status of water culverts. Based on acoustics and optoelectronics, a comprehensive underwater non-destructive detection technology for hydraulic culverts is studied to further improve the discrimination and recognition ability of target defects in underwater detection.
(2) It is needed to select points that can represent typical structures of culverts for monitoring, and form optical video images and acoustic profiles of culverts to judge the surface defects,

 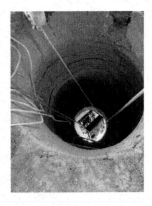

Figure 3. Inspection well at point no. 3. 　　　　Figure 4. ROV enters the inspection well.

deformation and damage. Then the practical application of underwater NDT testing technology is verified in long-distance hydraulic culverts by means of field investigation and data analysis.
(3) The practical application of long-distance hydraulic culvert environmental detection equipment is studied. With the change in the underwater detection environment and operating conditions, the detection methods are different. It is necessary to deepen the research of underwater detection methods based on the analysis of the actual application environment.

4 CASE STUDY

Dacaotan Reservoir project was constructed from 1959 to 1971 and formally completed in 1972. It is an injection reservoir with a total storage capacity of 64 million cubic meters. The water source of the reservoir is drawn from the south of the Taolai River. A flood diversion hub on the Taolai River was constructed. From the left bank of the diversion hub to build tunnels and channels, the water will be transported to the Dacaotan reservoir. Dacaotan Reservoir mainly undertakes the task of supplying water to Jiuquan Iron and Steel Company. Dacaotan Reservoir supplies more than 90% of its production process, which is the lifeline project of Jiuquan Iron and Steel production. Once an accident occurs, it will cause incalculable consequences to the development of Jiuquan Iron and Steel Company. In addition, this hydraulic culvert runs through railways, highways, residential buildings, industrial plants, and other industrial and civil buildings, once problems occur, it will directly endanger the safety of surrounding people's property. At the same time, due to the operation needs, the culvert project does not have the conditions of emptying, leading to the culvert and other hydraulic structures in service with water pressure, the corresponding underwater detection and service performance evaluation technology is more difficult.

Therefore, the ROV equipped with forward-looking multi-beam sonar, pipeline sonar, and an underwater high-definition camera was used to inspect the appearance, acoustics, and defect detection of the culvert downstream of Dacaotan Reservoir. Five typical inspection points were selected for the underwater inspection. Due to the limited space of this paper, we mainly aimed at the detection process and results of no. 3 points to verify the feasibility of the proposed method and technology.

The equipment adopts the way of front to back to detect the culvert at no. 3 point. The inspection covered a total length of about 35 meters from the time the ROV was placed at the inspection well to the time the culvert was blocked and the equipment could not move forward.

This test started from the entrance of the inspection well which was regarded as the reference point. It was found that a small amount of erosion at the bottom of the culvert was about 6 ∼ 7 meters away from point 3 (see Figure 5). Scour cracks were found at the bottom of the culvert about

25 meters away from point 3, and scour and settlement were found at the bottom of the culvert about 26 meters away from point 3 (see Figure 6).

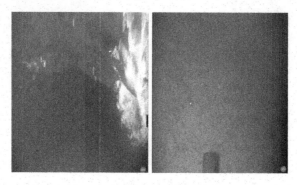

Figure 5.   Underwater camera observation results at about 6 ~ 7 meters far from point no. 3.

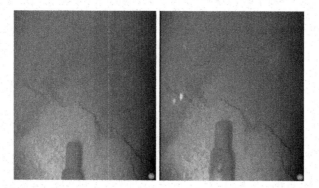

Figure 6.   Underwater camera observation results at about 25 ~ 26 meters far from point no. 3.

The culvert was measured on both sides of the culvert with forward-looking multi-beam sonar at about 13 meters away from point no. 3 (see figure 8). According to the test results, the width of the culvert was about 1.27 meters.

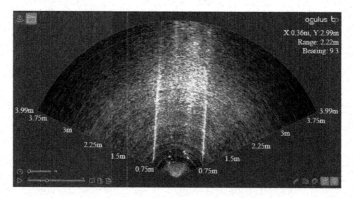

Figure 7.   Underwater forward-looking multi-beam sonar detection results at about 6 meters far from point no. 3.

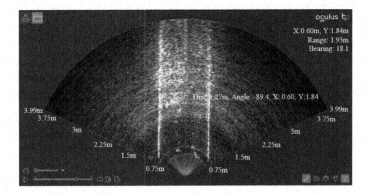

Figure 8. Underwater forward-looking multi-beam sonar detection results at about 13 meters far from point no. 3.

According to the pipeline sonar test results, the overall structure of the culvert was measured by using pipeline sonar at about 15 meters away from the no.3 point. It was found that the width of the culvert was 1.371m and the depth of water was 0.635m (see Figure 9).

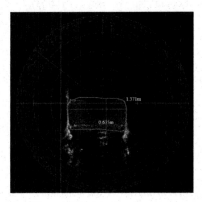

Figure 9. Pipeline sonar test results at about 15 meters far from point no.3.

5 CONCLUSION AND FOLLOW-UP DETECTION METHOD DESIGN

To sum up, through optical and acoustic inspection, it is confirmed that this section of the culvert is a square culvert. It is found that the overall structure of both sides of the culvert is normal without deformation.

In this study, a multi-angle underwater NDT testing technology that integrated acoustics, optics, and electricity is proposed based on ROV. The applicability of the method is verified for a hydraulic culvert structure, but in order to promote engineering informatization and improve the level of engineering management, further research should be focused on the following aspects:

(1) By using the scanning modeling data visualization technology of the inspection robot, the culvert simulation model consistent with reality is mapped on the terminal according to the original data and robot positioning information. Finally, the view and analysis of the reality culvert are realized on the data terminal. Through the integration of sonar, video, and measurement data in the culvert, the variation of culvert data can be visualized through the three-dimensional view.

(2) Using doppler velocity log (DVL), inertial navigation, pressure sensors, and obstacle avoidance sonar, combined with the pipeline image sonar, culvert images at different points are drawn. Through the modeling technique, a three-dimensional image of the culvert will be formed. It is convenient for managers to view the status of the whole culvert and select a point for careful observation and analysis. This system will effectively improve the efficiency of culvert monitoring and explore the deep integration of informatization and industrialization in the field of supervision

(3) The forward-looking sonar image target detection system adopts the combination of traditional features and deep learning to improve the target detection rate. Three-dimensional point clouds of hydraulic culverts can be generated by changing the single beam scanning sonar into the multi-beam cooperating with pipeline sonar detection of three-dimensional data. Then any point can be able to select on careful observation and analysis to enhance the efficiency of culvert monitoring and truly achieve the depth of information and industrialization integration.

ACKNOWLEDGMENTS

This research was jointly funded by the Fundamental Research Funds for the Central Non-profit Research Institution of the Chinese Academy of Forestry (Y721007) and the Water Conservancy Science and Technology Project of Jiangsu Province (2018023).

REFERENCES

Aras M, Harun M H, and Azmi M. 2017 Modelling and control of underwater remotely operated vehicle (ROV) for depth control using system identification. In: 4th Mechanical Engineering Research Day (MERD). *Melaka* 57–59.

Blain M, Lemieux S and Houde R. 2003 *Implementation of a ROV navigation system using acoustic/Doppler sensors and Kalman filtering.* In: MTS/IEEE Conference on Celebrating the Past – Teaming Toward the Future. San Diego 1255–1260.

Clarke B and Fletcher R. 2014 High-resolution tunnel surveys by ROV. *Sea Technol.* 55.

Dima E and Sjostrom M. 2016 Camera and lidar-based view generation for augmented remote operation in mining applications. *IEEE ACCESS* 9 82199–82212.

Hirai H and Ishii K. 2019 *Development of dam inspection underwater robot.* In: Proceedings of International Conference on Artificial Life and Robotics. Japan 528–531.

Landstad O, Halvorsen HS, Overseas H, et al. 2021 Dynamic positioning of ROV in the wave zone during launch and recovery from a small surface vessel. *Ocean Eng.* 235.

Pidi A, Aasbe E, Almankaas J S, et al. 2018 *Low-cost autonomous underwater vehicle (AUV) for inspection of water-filled tunnels during operation.* In: ASME International Design Engineering Technical Conferences (IDETC) / Computers and Information in Engineering Conference (CIE). Quebec City.

Shimono S, Matsubara O, Toyama S, et al. 2016 Development of underwater inspection system for dam inspection. In: MTS/IEEE Oceans Conference. Washington.

Trsli P, Omerdic E, Dooly G, et al. 2020 Neuro-fuzzy dynamic position prediction for autonomous work-class ROV docking. *Sensors* 20.

Yang Y, Hirose S, et al. 2016 Development of a stable localized visual inspection system for underwater structures. *Adv. Robotics* 30 1415–1429.

Research on the application technology of the integrated scaffolding and formwork system with steel platform alternately supported by steel columns and tubular frames for high-rise structure

Ma Wei* & Wu Lianding
Shanghai Construction Group Co., Ltd., Shanghai, China
Shanghai Engineering Research Centre of Mega Structure Construction Technology and Equipment, Shanghai, China

ABSTRACT: The main structural form of high-rise buildings usually adopts the core-frame structural form, and the core-frame structural construction usually adopts the integrated scaffolding and formwork system with a steel platform alternately supported by steel columns and tubular frames. This formwork system uses alternate support of instrumental steel column and formwork system to realize the change of support forces between the climbing phase and working phase and uses a hydraulic cylinder to drive the climbing shoe to climb along the instrumental steel column to realize the overall climbing operation. This paper introduces the system and component design based on the modular concept of the integrated scaffolding and formwork system with a steel platform alternately supported by steel columns and tubular frames in the construction application of the specific high-rise structure construction, as well as the results of the force analysis of the formwork system under complex working conditions, and also introduces the highly adaptable construction technology of the formwork system for the special construction requirements such as the deformation of structural shape.

1 INTRODUCTION

Compared with the traditional formwork forms such as integral lifting scaffolding and hydraulic climbing formwork, integrated scaffolding and formwork system with steel platform alternately supported by steel columns and tubular frames has obvious advantages in terms of sealing, safety, green environmental protection, efficient construction, and comfort, it has been widely used in many major super high-rise projects such as Sinar Mas Plaza (Hight of 320m), Hangzhou Gate Tower (Hight of 310m), Shanghai International Aviation Service Center (Hight of 230m), and achieved relatively excellent engineering results (Fu et al. 2014; Gong et al. 2014; Xia & Huang 2017).

When the integrated scaffolding and formwork system with a steel platform alternately supported by steel columns and tubular frames is applied in construction, it is necessary to focus on solving the problems of adaptive design and construction technology that match the needs of engineering construction, and the modular structure is the basis for solving the above problems.

This paper focuses on the application of the key technology of the integrated scaffolding and formwork system with steel platform alternately supported by steel columns and tubular frames in the construction of specific high-rise structures construction in Hubei Province, mainly involving the system design based on the modular concept, the force analysis, and the highly adaptable construction technology.

---

*Corresponding Author: mawei345543@163.com

2 CONSTRUCTION OVERVIEW

The specific high-rise building has 3 floors underground and 56 floors above ground, with a building height of 278.60m and the main structure height of 275.95m. The main structure of this high-rise building is a frame-core tube structure system. The core tube structure consists of the core tube wall, the inner wall of the core tube (including hidden columns), beams, and slabs, and the core tube wall is a reinforced concrete structure. The plane of the core tube is a pentagon, the plane size of the cylinder is about 35.6m×19m, there are 6 inner walls, and the plane of the core tube is divided into 12 grids, as shown in Figure 2 (a), the shape of the core tube wall is in 35F has undergone major changes, some of the walls have disappeared, and the plane of the core wall has been reduced from 12 to 10, as shown in Figure 2 (b).

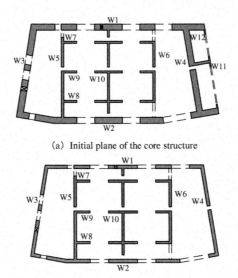

(a) Initial plane of the core structure

(b) Plane of core tube structure after deformation

Figure 1. Planes of the core tube structure.

The core wall has 13 typical planes. As the height increases, the thickness of the wall gradually decreases. When it reaches 35F, W1 and W2 are reduced from 1200 mm to 600 mm, W3 is reduced from 1300 mm to 800 mm, and W4 is reduced from 1200 mm to 70 mm, a total reduction of 200mm.

Selecting the appropriate form of integrated scaffolding and formwork system is the key to realizing the safe, economical and efficient construction of the core tube structure. The structure of the core tube of this specific high-rise building is complex and changeable, which has a high demand for the adaptability of the formwork equipment and brings great difficulties to the vertical transportation of the formwork equipment. The construction difficulties of the core tube structure are as follows:

- The width of the core tube wall and the inner wall has been reduced several times, ranging from 100 to 200 mm each time. It is necessary to optimize the design of the external hanging scaffolding to meet the requirements of the wall.
- The core tube structure has a total of 56 floors, and the super high height has high demands on the choice of formwork form, vertical transportation capacity, safety, and convenience of the construction platform.
- As shown in Figure 2, the core tube wall was deformed in a large area on the 35th floor, and the right tube disappeared, which brought great difficulties to the design of the internal and external

hanging scaffolding and the installation and removal of the integrated scaffolding and formwork system.
- There are great changes in the floor height of the core tube. In addition to the standard floor height of 4.40m, there are also many non-standard floor heights such as 4.5 m, 4.39 m, 4.26 m, 4.55m, 5.82m, and 4.10 m. The climbing process of the standard floor is optimized to meet the needs of floor height changes.

According to the characteristics and construction requirements of the core tube of this specific high-rise building, such as the plane structure form, wall fraction, storey height, and body shape change, the integrated scaffolding and formwork system supported by alternating steel columns and tube frames is selected for the construction of the core tube structure.

3 THE INTEGRATED SCAFFOLDING AND FORMWORK SYSTEM DESIGN

3.1 The steel platform system design

The steel platform system is composed of a steel platform frame, cover plate, grating plate, and safety enclosure. The plane area of the steel platform system used in this project is about 947m². The main beam and the secondary beam are composed of H400mm × 200mm × 8mm × 13mm, which are located on the same horizontal plane; the grid plate is set above the wall, and the length is determined according to the thickness of the wall; According to the construction requirements, paving slabs are laid on the steel beams to form an operating platform. The size of the paving slabs is 1800mm×1800mm, and 4mm patterned steel plates are used; around the steel platform, a 2m-high enclosure plate is set to form a closed operating space. The outer edge of the steel platform is 1400mm away from the inner wall of the shear wall of the core tube, which is convenient for the construction personnel to adjust the scaffolding and install and remove the formwork. The layout of the steel beam is shown in Figure 2.

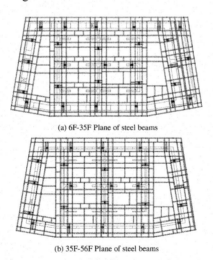

(a) 6F-35F Plane of steel beams

(b) 35F-56F Plane of steel beams

Figure 2. Planes of steel beams.

3.2 The hanging scaffolding system design

The hanging scaffolding system consists of scaffolding hangers, stairs, enclosure baffles, anti-falling baffles, walkway boards, sliding devices, and other components, and the components are connected by bolts. The scaffolding hanger is divided into the outer hanger and inner hanger. The width is 900mm, and there are 3 specifications in the height direction: 1200mm, 1500mm, and

1800mm. The walkway board is divided into an inner scaffold walkway board and an outer scaffold walkway board. The standard width of the inner scaffold walkway board is 1100mm, the standard width of the outer scaffold walkway board is 900mm, and the length of the walkway board is 300mm, 600mm, 1200 mm, 1500 mm, 1800 mm, and other specifications. Other components such as enclosure baffles, anti-falling baffles, and stairs are standard components of modular design, and components of suitable specifications can be selected according to the distance between the hangers and assembled on the hanger by bolting.

The external hanging scaffold used in this project has a total of six layers. The upper three layers are steel and formwork construction areas. The height of the top layer is 2.05m, the height of the other two layers is 1.90 m, and the width is 0.90 m. Its height is 1.90 m and its width is 0.70 m.

When designing the external hanging scaffolding, the side of the wall is slidable, and the side that does not have a swivel is fixed. The sliding form of the external scaffold is connected to the top of the steel platform system through sliding steel beams. The fixed form of external scaffolding is fixed to the bottom of the frame beam of the steel platform system with bolts, and the entire externally suspended scaffolding climbs synchronously with the steel platform system. The layout of the externally suspended scaffolding is shown in Figure 3.

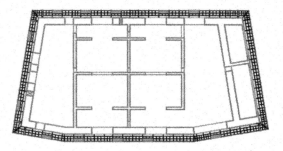

Figure 3. Plane of external scaffolding.

There are six floors of inner hanging scaffolding, the height of the top floor is 2.05m, and the height of the other five floors is 1.90m. One or two upper and lower stairs are set in each independent shaft of the inner hanging scaffold, and the width of the stairs is 600mm. The inner hanging scaffold is composed of independent frames installed in twelve cylinders and is provided with main frame columns, wall-attached top wheels, and anti-tilt devices.

3.3 *The large formwork system design*

The large formwork of the core tube used in this project has been put into use since the construction of the 6th floor. The formwork system adopts a 5mm steel plate as the panel, double 10# channel steel is used as the horizontal purlin, the average spacing is 800mm, and the 6.3# channel steel is used as the vertical purlin, and the spacing is not more than 300mm.

The large formwork is configured according to the standard layer height of 4400mm, and the high formwork is connected to the top when the non-standard layer is constructed. The large template adopts Ø20 screws as tie rod bolts, and the spacing is less than or equal to 900mm. Two 16mm steel plate lifting lugs are set on each large formwork, and each 16mm steel plate lifting lug is hung on the lifting point lugs of the steel platform frame beam with a 3-ton manual hoist. For the formwork on the side of the wall body, the corresponding standard strips are set at the corners according to the number of modules and times to meet the construction requirements.

3.4 *The instrumental steel column climbing system design*

The instrumental steel column climbing system includes an instrumental steel column, steel column base, upper and lower climbing components, power system, etc. The instrumental steel column is the guide rail for integrated scaffolding and formwork system to climb and uses standard general components with a size of 10000mm × 250mm × 300mm; the steel column base and the upper and lower climbing components also use standard general components (Qing et al. 2018). The power system consists of 5 hydraulic pump stations, 26 hydraulic jacking cylinders, and 1 centralized control system.

During the construction of the core tube, according to the distribution of the structural walls, 26 instrumental steel columns were initially set up, and when the 35F core tube was deformed, it was adjusted to 25 instrumental steel columns, as shown in Figure 4.

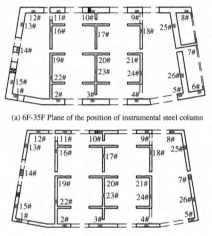

Figure 4.   Planes of the position of instrumental steel column.

3.5 *The cylinder frame support system design*

The cylinder frame support system consists of a vertical support device, horizontal limit device, supporting bottom beam, and cylinder frame support unit installed in the core tube.

The horizontal limit device and vertical support device use standard general components; the length of the support bottom beam is 1800 mm, 3600 mm, and 5400 mm, a total of 3 specifications, and the width is 1100 mm; the support unit of the cylinder frame is composed of 4 cylinder frame support columns and horizontal cylinder frame support beams assembled, the support column of the cylinder frame adopts 2 specifications of 200 mm×8 mm and 150 mm×8 mm, and the plane size of the lateral support beam is 1100 mm×1100 mm.

4   FORCE ANALYSIS

4.1 *Model building and computational assumptions*

In order to ensure the reliability and safety of the integral integrated scaffolding and formwork system, the finite element software Midas Gen is used to model and stress the integral climbing integrated scaffolding and formwork system structure. The model is shown in Figure 5.

4.2 *Working condition analysis*

According to the construction process, the calculation conditions of the formwork structure of the integrated scaffolding and formwork system can be divided into the working phase and climbing phase, of which the working phase can be subdivided into the steel bar binding construction phase, formwork lifting construction phase and concrete pouring construction phase. According to the

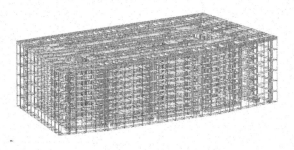

Figure 5. A computational model of integrated steel platform.

characteristics of different working phases, the corresponding loads and boundary conditions are determined, and the most unfavorable load combination is determined for stress analysis.

4.3 *Load analysis*

In the construction process, the loads considered in each calculation phase mainly include dead load, construction live load, and wind load.

The dead load mainly includes the dead weight of the formwork structure G_1, the dead weight of the hydraulic cylinder and the instrumental steel column G_2, and the dead weight of the electrical operation room and the pump station G_3. The values are as follows:

- The self-weight G_1 of the formwork structure is calculated according to the structure size and material density.
- The weight G_2 of the hydraulic cylinder and the instrumental steel column is 20kN for one machine position.
- The dead weight of the electrical operation room and the pumping station is G_3, and each group is valued at 9.8kN.

The live load mainly includes the construction live load Q_1, the steel mold line load Q_2, the rebar stacking load Q_3, the core tube concrete pouring a live load Q_4, and the climbing phase live load Q_5. The values are as follows:

- The construction live load Q_1 is taken as 1 kN/m^2, and the inner and outer hanging scaffolds are arranged in two consecutive layers, and the most unfavorable arrangement is taken.
- The steel large form line load Q_2 acts on the beams on both sides of the formwork, with a value of 5.3kN/m on one side, which only occurs in the construction phase of formwork lifting.
- Rebar stacking load Q_3, which is taken as 5 kN/m^2, only appears in the construction condition of rebar binding.
- The live load Q_4 of the concrete pouring of the core cylinder; according to the value of 1 kN/m^2, it only appears in the concrete pouring construction condition.
- The live load Q_5 in the climbing phase, the live load in the climbing phase is only applied to the top and bottom layers of the integrated scaffolding and formwork system under the climbing phase, which is 0.5kN/m^2

The wind load w_k is calculated by converting the surface load acting on the external hanging scaffold into the line load acting on the steel beam of the hanging scaffold.

For the consideration of construction safety, when the wind force is below level 6 (including level 6), the integrated scaffolding and formwork system shall perform normal climbing operations. If the wind force is greater than level 6, climbing should be prohibited, and the stacking loads on each layer of the platform should be cleaned before climbing operations, to prevent falling, the non-climbing operators are evacuated, and it is strictly forbidden to stay. In the calculation, the force analysis of the climbing phase is carried out according to the wind of grade 8, and the maximum wind speed is taken as 20.7m/s.

When the wind is below level 8 (including level 8), the integrated scaffolding and formwork system should be constructed normally. When the wind is above level 8, the workers should be evacuated. Construction operations are strictly prohibited. The maximum wind speed is taken as 36.9m/s.

Under the working phase, the integrated scaffolding and formwork system is supported by the cylinder frame support system, the wind load is considered according to the 12th-grade wind, and the load combination of each calculation condition is calculated according to the following formula:

- Construction conditions of formwork lifting:

$$1.2\,(G_1 + G_2 + G_3) + 1.4(Q_1 + Q_2 + w_k)$$

- Construction conditions of steel bar binding:

$$1.2\,(G_1 + G_2 + G_3) + 1.4(Q_1 + Q_3 + w_k)$$

- Concrete pouring construction conditions:

$$1.2\,(G_1 + G_2 + G_3) + 1.4(Q_1 + Q_4 + w_k)$$

In the climbing state, the integrated scaffolding and formwork system is supported by instrumental steel columns, the wind load is considered according to the 8th-grade wind, and the load combination is calculated according to the following formula:

$$1.2\,(G_1 + G_2 + G_3) + 1.4(Q_5 + w_k)$$

4.4 Analysis results

The stress ratio cloud diagram under the working conditions before the body shape conversion is shown in Figure 6. Except for the relatively large stress of the individual columns at the 1F corner of the integral steel platform formwork (about 0.74), the stress ratio of most of the components Within 0.5, the strength reserve of the formwork structure is sufficient, and the stability meets the requirements.

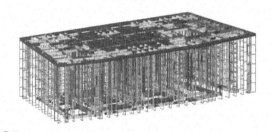

Figure 6. Stress ratio of scaffolding and formwork system under the normal construction condition.

The stress ratio cloud diagram of the components under the climbing condition is shown in Figure 7. The design stress ratio of the components is all within 0.51, which indicates that the structure has sufficient strength and the ability to maintain its own stability in the climbing state.

The stress ratio cloud diagram of the components under the working conditions after the integral steel platform formwork is converted is shown in Figure 8. The maximum stress ratio is 0.84, which is located at the instrumental steel column at the 1F corner of the integral steel platform formwork. The stress ratio of the remaining components is within 0.5; in the climbing condition, the design

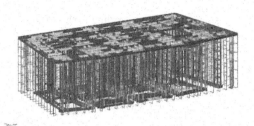

Figure 7. Stress ratio of scaffolding and formwork system under the climbing condition.

stress ratio cloud diagram of the components is shown in Figure 9, and the design stress ratios of the components are all within 0.41. This shows that the integral steel platform formwork still has high stability and safety after the 35F is deformed.

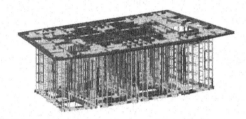

Figure 8. Stress ratio of scaffolding and formwork system under normal the construction condition.

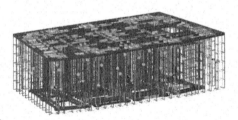

Figure 9. Stress ratio of scaffolding and formwork system under the climbing condition.

5 HIGHLY ADAPTABLE CONSTRUCTION TECHNOLOGIES

In view of the situation that the core tube is deformed in the air at 35F, it is necessary to convert the integral steel platform formwork in the air when the core tube is constructed to 35F. In order to ensure the smooth transition of part of the inner hanging scaffolds to the outer hanging scaffolds during the conversion, the inner hanging scaffolds on the outside of the W4 web wall were designed to be slidable when designing the inner hanging scaffolding system. During the aerial conversion, only the main frame column on the inner side of the original W11 web wall needs to be removed, and the conversion of the internal and external hanging scaffolds can be realized. The specific conversion process is described as follows:

- Remove the equipment pipelines of the hydraulic cylinders at the 6#, 7#, and 8# positions, and then remove the 6#, 7#, 8# hydraulic cylinders and instrumental steel columns.
- Remove the steel platform cover plate and grid plate on the top of the integral steel platform formwork, and then lift the outer hanging scaffold and its upper steel platform frame beam. Fill in the missing safety enclosure at the edge formed by the unremoved part.

- Dismantle the inner cylinder part, and dismantle the inner cylinder steel platform frame beam, the inner hanging scaffold and the bottom steel platform frame beam. Fill in the gaps on the top edge of the integral steel platform formwork and the gaps in the spanning wall of the safety enclosure.
- The integral steel platform formwork is climbed to a standard layer, and the vacancies of the 4F, 5F and 6F spanning walls of the external hanging scaffolds are filled with the aisle slabs and side nets, and then the 35F wall construction is completed.
- The integral steel platform formwork is climbed to a standard layer, and the vacancies of the 2F and 3F spanning walls of the external hanging scaffolds are filled with aisle slabs and side nets, and then the 36F wall construction is completed.
- The integral steel platform formwork is climbed to a standard layer, the vacancy of the 1F cross-wall of the external hanging scaffold is filled with the walkway board and side net, the 35F external hanging scaffold is slipped, and the walkway board and side net on the 1st to 6th floors are adjusted and filled. So far, the aerial conversion of the integral steel platform formwork is completed.

6 CONCLUSION

In this paper, the application technology of the integral steel platform formwork supported by the steel column and the cylinder frame alternately in the construction is researched, and the main conclusions are as follows:

- The formwork system adopts the alternate support method of instrumental steel column and cylinder frame support system, which can effectively reduce the construction cost; most of the components in the formwork are standardized components, which can be reused to further improve economic benefits and meet the requirements of the development needs of green and industrialized high-rise buildings.
- The working environment provided by the integral steel platform formwork is safe and reliable, the construction efficiency can be improved by self-climbing, the construction operation is convenient, and the bearing capacity is large, which can meet various complex requirements of super high-rise construction.
- The integral steel platform formwork can meet the air deformation requirements of super high-rise building structure changes through module assembly, so it has strong engineering adaptability.

ACKNOWLEDGMENTS

This research was sponsored by the Shanghai Municipal Science and Technology Committee of Shanghai's outstanding academic leaders' plan (No. 2020XD1431800).

REFERENCES

Fu X, Li Y and Liang Y.2014. Research and application of formwork equipment technology for steel column and cylinder frame alternately supported integral climbing steel platform. *Building Construction*, vol. 36:390–394.

Gong J, Yu X and Huang Y.2014. Alternately supported hydraulic climbing integral steel platform formwork technology for steel column and cylinder frame. *Building Construction*, vol. 36:47–50.

Qing P, Wang X and Mu Y.2018. Modular design and application of integral climbing steel platform formwork supported alternately by steel beams and cylinder frames. *Building Construction*, vol. 40:919–921.

Xia J and Huang Y.2017. Stability analysis and design of climbing system of steel column frame alternately supported hydraulic climbing integral steel platform formwork system. *Building Construction*, vol. 39:1533–1535.

Research on ventilation support parameters in high altitude tunnel construction

Mingzhu Zhang*
Yunnan Province Dianzhong Water Diversion Project Construction Management Bureau, Yunnan, China

Guoquan Xu
China Railway First Bureau Group Co., Ltd, Xi'an, China

ABSTRACT: The ventilation design of high-altitude tunnel construction is of great significance to ensure the safety of tunnel constructors and mechanical efficiency. Among the four calculation methods of air halo, air volume elevation correction is required for personnel air demand, air demand for diluting gun smoke, and air demand for diluting construction machinery sewage. The fan efficiency loss includes the loss of fan machinery itself and the efficiency loss of altitude factors. Taking Laoqingshan Tunnel with an altitude of over 4,300 m as an example, its fan efficiency is only 0.64 of the designed power; the air leakage rate is proportional to the altitude, and the higher the sea level, the greater the air leakage rate. Taking Laoqingshan Tunnel with an altitude of over 4,300 m as an example, its air leakage rate reaches 3%. The tunnel construction over 3000m above sea level needs to start with oxygen supply, and the oxygen supply mode is mainly the combination of dispersion and individual oxygen supply, and the oxygen supply standard based on the comfort and safety of construction personnel is established. For some high-altitude tunnels located in the meteorological separation zone, the influence of natural wind on tunnel construction ventilation should be considered.

1 INTRODUCTION

Underground foundation projects such as roads, railway tunnels, and subways are widely used, especially the application of ventilation technology. The air quality in tunnel construction affects the work efficiency and the health of workers. In order to ensure the physical and mental health of tunnel constructors and provide a good construction environment, it is especially important to ventilate and reduce dust, cool down, and remove harmful gases in the tunnel work area. This paper summarizes the latest research results on key parameters of ventilation in high-altitude tunnels, such as air demand, mechanical efficiency, air leakage rate, and oxygen supply, mainly including the coefficient related to altitude in air demand calculation, the influence of altitude on fan efficiency, and the law of air leakage rate changing with altitude.

2 PROJECT OVERVIEW

The research on the ventilation characteristics of single-heading roadways started earlier in foreign countries, which first appeared in the research of railway tunnel construction ventilation. The technical problems of tunnel ventilation were further studied after the appearance of the highway tunnel. A large number of scholars from the former Soviet Union did a lot of work in the study of ventilation in single-head tunneling and achieved a lot of results.

*Corresponding Author: 27943055@qq.com

In the early 1920s, some foreign scholars began to study the wind flow characteristics of tunneling faces. Until the 1960s, they had a complete theoretical analysis and model experiment research, thus gradually gaining a qualitative understanding of the ventilation characteristics of tunneling faces in tunnels (Likar & Cadez 2000). On the basis of the research results of two scientists, A. R. Kesenovontova and B. H. Voronin, foreign scholars have made detailed theoretical and experimental research on the smoke exhaust and air demand calculation of single-head tunneling in drilling and blasting tunnel construction, and obtained different calculation formulas. Scientists in the Soviet Union have the largest workload and the most meticulous research work. In addition to Wo Luoning's formula obtained by scholar B.H. Wo Luoning applied the theory of fluid dynamics to solve the calculation problem of the ventilation process, and Musteli scholars conducted chromosome hydraulic model tests and calculated the air volume calculation formula of forced ventilation, which was called Musteli's formula. In addition, it also includes the Kshengnuovontova formula, Butcherev formula, Sergei Voronov and Olihanfsky formula, static dilution formula, Kuo-Malov formula, Iosijing formula, the calculation formula of mine ventilation manual (Russian version), Vrakimirsky formula, etc. The representative research results of other countries are the Japanese formula and the Swedish formula.

In the 1950s and 1960s, the United States and Japan studied the concentration of harmful gases in tunnel environment during tunnel construction and put forward the allowable concentrations of various harmful gases, which provided important standards for tunnel environmental quality evaluation and laid a foundation for the formulation of various health standards in the world in the future (Modic 2003). A great deal of research work has been done in the field of tunnel ventilation in Japan, and the "Design Essentials of Japanese Road Corporation" compiled by it has been used for reference by all countries in the world, making great contributions to the development of tunnel ventilation in the world. During tunnel construction and tunneling, the United States began to test and study the exhaust gas in underground tunnels in the 1940s, such as Ash SH and others, and Berger LB conducted in-depth research on the exhaust gas emitted by diesel construction machinery and its pollution to the working environment in tunnels. According to the test results of air sampling analysis, the highest volume concentration of CO in the tunnel is 0.53%, the content of CO2 formation is 0.014%, and the content of nitrogen oxides represented by NO2 formation is as high as 21 pm (Garcia & Harpalani 1989).

In addition, on the basis of studying the pollutant emission model and pollutant emission factors of highway vehicles, foreign scientists have started to study the environmental air pollution in tunnels. Since the 1970s, serious motor vehicle exhaust pollution and photochemical pollution have occurred in western Europe, the United States, Japan, and other industrial developed countries and regions, and environmental protection has been paid more and more attention all over the world. Therefore, countries all over the world began to study the composition, emission intensity, and emission characteristics of motor vehicle exhaust pollutants, and based on this, established a series of calculation models of motor vehicle exhaust pollutants. Among many computing models, the CORINAI model proposed by European countries and the MOBILE model proposed by EPA (Setta et al. 2010) are the most representative. Since the 1980s, with the construction of various long tunnels, on the one hand, for the prevention and treatment of air pollution in highway tunnels, and on the other hand, for the safety problems of tunnel traffic and the design of mechanical ventilation in tunnels, the Federal Highway Administration (FHWA), FORD Motor Company, GM Motor Company, etc. measured the concentrations of various pollutants in highway tunnels in detail to determine Based on a series of research results of vehicle pollutant emission models and emission factors, more and more foreign scientists and technicians have done a lot of research work on pollutant concentration distribution and ventilation system in highway tunnels, among which the theoretical research and field test of Vancouver Cassiar Tunnel, Gubrist Highway Tunnel, Tuscarora Tunnel, and Allegeny Highway Tunnel are typical (McPherson 2009).

For the problem of the air leakage rate of the tunnel ventilation system, ToranoAlvarez used a simple calculation method to calculate the ventilation system at first, and Gary Auld used the Atkinson formula to evaluate the influence of various factors such as air duct diameter, air duct friction resistance, air duct length change and air volume in an air duct on air leakage. The concept of "ventilation efficiency" is put forward to quantify the influence of air leakage in the ventilation system on the work of ventilation pipes. The air leakage coefficient of a ventilation system is determined by electronic data representation, and the air leakage characteristics of ventilation pipes in the ventilation system are analyzed in detail (Gary Auld 2004; Vutukuri 1983).

The technology of improving the ventilation system by using circulating air in tunnels dates back to 1933. Lawton, B.R of England reported the application of new ventilation technology to increase air volume in some tunnels. Until 1983, as many as 4% of British mines used circulating ventilation technology in tunneling faces, and it was successfully applied to deep mine ventilation in South African gold mines (Arif Widiatmojo et al. 2015).

3 VENTILATION DESIGN

The ventilation control standard and the maximum air volume should be determined in the design of ventilation air demand for construction, so as to ensure the adequate delivery of air volume. Three key parameters related to altitude are air demand, fan efficiency, and air leakage rate.

3.1 Ventilation calculation

The ventilation control standards are mainly related to adverse geological conditions. The existing tunnel construction ventilation control standards mainly refer to the relevant construction codes of hydraulic, railway, and highway tunnels, while the construction ventilation of coal-bearing strata containing harmful gases such as gas and H2S mainly refers to the Technical Code for Construction of Coal Mines and Other Gas Channels. For high ground temperature tunnels, it is necessary to control the construction temperature below 28°C through ventilation and other measures. Therefore, the control standards of construction ventilation are different according to the different geological characteristics of the tunnel. For a special tunnel, it is necessary to study the control standards of construction ventilation according to its characteristics.

The determination of the required air volume for ventilation is mainly based on the personnel, the smoke, and dust produced by dilution blasting, the exhaust gas of the internal combustion engine, and the four required air volumes corresponding to the minimum wind speed in the tunnel. Take the maximum value among the four as the design value of tunnel air demand. The calculation formula is as follows :

Air demand of personnel:

$$Q_p = v_p M k \quad (1)$$

Where: vp needs air volume for people, taking 3m3/min; M is the extreme number of construction people in the hole, generally taking 100 people; K is the reserve coefficient of air volume.

Generally, there are four formulas for calculating the required air volume of smoke and dust produced by dilution blasting: railway tunnel gauge calculation method, Wuzhong simplified calculation method, Soviet Union calculation method, and Japanese calculation method. Generally, the railway tunnel gauge calculation method is widely used, and the formulas are as follows:

$$Q_s = \frac{5Ab}{tK} \quad (2)$$

Where: A is the maximum charge for one blasting (kg); B is the amount of harmful gas produced by the explosion of 1kg explosive (L/kg); T is the ventilation time, usually 30min; K is the altitude correction coefficient, which is generally 0.85.

Air demand for diluted exhaust gas of internal combustion engine:

$$Q = K \times n_i \times A \quad (3)$$

Where: ni is the total power of all construction machinery in the tunnel (kW); K is the altitude coefficient of internal combustion engine air volume, generally 1.2 ~ 3.9; A to dilute the exhaust gas of internal combustion engine, the required air volume is generally 3m3/min.

Small wind speed needs phoenix quantity.

$$Qd = 60v_{min}S_{max} \qquad (4)$$

Where: v_{min} is the minimum allowable air volume of the tunnel, which is generally greater than 0.15m/s; S is the tunnel cross-sectional area (M2).

3.2 Fan efficiency

In order to ensure that the air demand of the tunnel face at a high altitude can meet the construction needs, besides the accurate control standard and air demand calculation, how to transport enough air from outside the tunnel to the tunnel face, fan efficiency and air leakage rate are the research focuses and hotspots, and many domestic scholars have made many valuable achievements.

Yan Tao tested the fan efficiency in the Balangshan tunnel and found that its efficiency was only 43% of that in the plain tunnel. Considering the flow, leakage, wheel resistance, and mechanical loss of the machine itself, the efficiency loss caused by the environmental change caused by the elevation was 36.3%.

Li Qi et al. made a theoretical study on the mechanical efficiency of diesel construction in high-altitude areas by using the mechanical efficiency model and established the calculation method of diesel mechanical power loss and effective power. The research results showed that with the increase of altitude, the oxygen content gradually decreased, and the effective power decreased by 3% ~ 5% every time the atmospheric pressure decreased by 20kPa; in order to ensure the efficiency of tunnel construction machinery in high altitude areas, it is necessary to consider aeration operation or the modification and selection of high altitude tunnel construction machinery.

3.3 Oxygen supply in construction

Oxygen supply in construction is of great significance to ensure the safety and efficient operation of high-altitude tunnel constructors. For example, Wang Mingnian and other domestic scholars have systematically studied the high-altitude tunnel.

Yan Prayer conducted a laboratory test of dispersed oxygen supply in the control room of Balangshan Tunnel at an altitude of 3800m m.

Xie Wenqiang gave the starting elevation of oxygen supply in construction based on safety and comfort considerations and put forward the classification of tunnel labor intensity for the first time. The relationship between labor intensity, altitude and oxygen consumption of construction personnel was established, and oxygen supply standards were formulated according to comfort and safety, as shown in Table 1 and Table 2.

Table 1. Oxygen supply standard (comfort).

Work Intensity	2500m	3000m	3500m	4000m	4500m	5000m	5500m	6000m
Very light	0	0.04	0.09	0.14	0.20	0.26	0.32	0.40
light	0	0.09	0.18	0.29	0.40	0.52	0.65	0.79
medium	0	0.13	0.28	0.43	0.60	0.78	0.97	1.19
heavy	0	0.18	0.37	0.57	0.80	1.04	1.30	1.58
Very heavy	0	0.22	0.46	0.72	1.00	1.30	1.62	1.98

Oxygen supply/(L/min)

To sum up, based on the comfort and safety of construction personnel, an oxygen supply is required for tunnel construction from 3000m above sea level.

Table 2. Oxygen supply standard (safety).

Work Intensity	Oxygen supply/(L/min)			
	4500m	5000m	5500m	6000m
Very light	0	0.06	0.13	0.20
light	0	0.12	0.25	0.39
medium	0	0.18	0.38	0.59
heavy	0	0.24	0.50	0.78
Very heavy	0	0.30	0.63	0.98

4 CONCLUSION

In this paper, the research on key ventilation parameters of high-altitude tunnel construction is summarized. Under the condition of mechanized operation, ventilation can provide fresh air for the tunnel construction site, eliminate toxic and harmful gases and various kinds of dust, create a good working environment, and ensure the health and safety of construction personnel. The calculation of required air volume and air leakage rate provides a theoretical basis for tunnel construction ventilation. and the following conclusions are obtained:

(1) Among the four methods for calculating wind halo, air volume elevation correction is required for personnel, dilution of cannon smoke, and dilution of construction machinery sewage;
(2) The fan efficiency loss includes the loss of fan machinery itself and the efficiency loss of altitude factors. Taking Laoqingshan Tunnel with an altitude of over 4,300 m as an example, its fan efficiency is only 0.64 of the designed power;
(3) The air leakage rate is proportional to the altitude, and the higher the sea level, the greater the air leakage rate. Taking Laoqingshan Tunnel with an altitude of over 4,300 m as an example, its air leakage rate reaches 3%.
(4) It is suggested that oxygen supply should be started in the tunnel construction at an altitude of over 3000m, and the oxygen supply mode is mainly the combination of dispersion and individual oxygen supply, and the oxygen supply standard based on the comfort and safety of construction personnel is established;
(5) For some high-altitude tunnels located in the meteorological separation zone, the influence of natural wind on tunnel construction ventilation should be considered.

REFERENCES

Arif Widiatmojo, Kyuro Sasaki, Yuichi Sugai, Yoshiaki Suzuki, Hiroyuki Tanaka, Kagemi Uchida, Hiroyuki Matsumot. Assessment of air dispersion characteristic in underground mine ventilation: Field measurement and numerical evaluation[J]. *Process Safety and Environmental Protection*, 2015, 93(1): 173–181.
Gary Auld. An estimation of fan performance for leaky ventilation ducts[J]. *Tunnelling and Underground Space Technology*, 2004, 19(6): 539–549.
J Modic. Air velocity and concentration of noxious substances in a naturally ventilated tunnel[J]. *Tunnelling and Underground Space Technology*, 2003,18(4): 405–410.
J.Likar, J. Cadez. Ventilation design of enclosed underground structures[J]. *Tunnelling and Underground Space Technology* C200, 15(4)F477–480.
M.M.Garcia, S. Harpalani. Distribution and characterization of gases produced by detonation of explosives in an underground mine [J]. *Mining Science and Technology* C1989, 8(1):49–58.
McPherson, MJ. *Subsurface Ventilation Engineering*, second ed[M].Ventilation Services Inc, Fresno, Californina, 2009.
V.Setta, F. Cascetta, M. Musto. G. Rotondo. Fluid dynamic performances of traditional and alternative jet fans in tunnel longitudinal ventilation systems[J]. *Tunneling and Underground Space Technology* C2010, 25(4): 415–422.
VS, Vutukuri, Air leakage in ventilation ducting and the design of auxiliary ventilation systems [J], *Mining Engineer*, 1983, 143(262): 37–43.

Analysis of vibration reduction effect of vibration reduction hole parameters in tunnel blasting construction

Baofu Duan & Zhaowen Yu
Hubei Key Laboratory of Blasting Engineering of Jianghan University, Hubei Wuhan, China
Shandong University of Science and Technology, Shandong Provincial Civil Engineering Disaster Prevention and Mitigation Key Laboratory, Shandong Qingdao, China

Chunwu Zhang
Qingdao Ruihan Technology Group Co, Ltd, Shandong Qingdao, China

Zongjun Sun*
China Railway Wuhan Survey and Design Institute Co., Ltd, Hubei Wuhan, China

ABSTRACT: In order to study the influence of vibration-damping holes on blasting seismic waves, the MIDAS/GTS NX finite element simulation software is used to establish three-dimensional numerical calculation models of rock and soil, tunnels, and blast holes. The distance between the damping hole and the blasting source, and the row distance of the double-row damping hole, are used to study the law of the change of the damping hole parameters. The analysis shows that the vibration reduction effect is better by increasing the distance between the orifice the explosion source, and the diameter of the orifice, and by reducing the spacing, depth, and line spacing of the orifice.

1 INTRODUCTION

At present, in the construction of urban rail transit, mining method excavation is a commonly used construction method for subway tunnels to pass through hard rocks due to its economical and efficient advantages (Editorial Office of China Journal of Highway and Transport 2015). But in blasting projects close to important buildings, blasting vibration is very serious.

In this regard, some scholars have studied various measures to reduce the impact of blasting vibration. On the one hand, the blasting parameters are studied. For example, Xu Hongtao et al. (Xu et al. 2008) used the LS-DYNA software to analyze the blasting vibration and proposed a method of combining the fluid-structure coupling algorithm and the equivalent simplified blasting load application, and the error between the simulation results and the actual data was small. Yu Deyun et al. (2011) analyzed and studied the attenuation effect of the additional vibration-damping trenches on the propagation of surface waves and body waves by means of numerical simulation methods. Studies have shown that both the width and depth of the vibration-damping trench affect the propagation of bulk waves, while the propagation of surface waves is only affected by the depth of the vibration-damping trench. Mu Yuanbing et al. (Miao & Wu 2014) studied the newly built and uploaded existing long-span tunnels with the help of the dynamic finite element software MIDAS/GTS NX. The research results obtained the most unfavorable stress positions of the existing tunnels and gave suggestions on the most unfavorable points of the existing tunnels. blasting vibration safety limits. Mu et al. (2011) used the dynamic finite element software LS-DYNA

---

*Corresponding Author: 3519808967@qq.com

to simulate the propagation and attenuation of stress waves in weak interlayers with different thicknesses and pointed out that the influence of weak interlayers should be fully considered when blasting holes around the tunnel.

On the other hand, reasonable isolation measures and related vibration blasting laws were studied. For example, Mindlin et al. (1953)compared the rock and soil mass to an entity composed of many particles. The propagation of blasting seismic waves and the transmission of energy are essentially the interaction between the seismic wave and the rock and soil particles. There is friction between the rock and soil mass to move each other and requires work to be done. Overcome, this will cause the energy attenuation of seismic waves. Savage, Armstrong, et al. (Savage 1996) pointed out that the blasting seismic waves interact in the process of propagating in the rock, and heat must be generated in the process. This heat will be dissipated into the air, and the dissipation of heat will lead to the attenuation of blasting seismic wave energy.

The research of scholars has proved that in the propagation of seismic waves, applying vibration-damping holes on the propagation path of the waves can change the propagation path of the waves, and it will cause reflection, refraction, and diffraction of the wave, which will greatly reduce the energy carried by the wave and reduce the harm caused by vibration. Moreover, the construction process of the vibration-damping hole is simple and easy to popularize, but it is not common to use the vibration-damping hole on the tunnel face. The author will use the actual parameters in tunnel construction to conduct qualitative research on the vibration-damping hole, and the obtained results can be directly applied in practical engineering.

2 BUILD A FINITE ELEMENT MODEL

2.1 Engineering background

Shenzhen City Rail Transit Line 6 Phase II Project 6111 Biaoyi Work Area. The project includes Meilinguan Station, Shen-Mei section, and Mei-Han section. It is located in Longhua New District and Futian District, with a total length of 5.45km. Among them, the Shen-Mei section starts from the reserved project interface of Shenzhen North Station and is arranged along the central green belt of New District Avenue. Goufa Tunnel will go from the newly added shaft to Shenzhen North Station with a length of 180m on the left line, ZDK13+161~ZDK13+341; However, due to geological reasons, the overall construction period of the Shen-Mei shield tunnel was adjusted to the mining method. From top to bottom in the project area are plain fill, clay soil, and granite. Figure 1 is a schematic diagram.

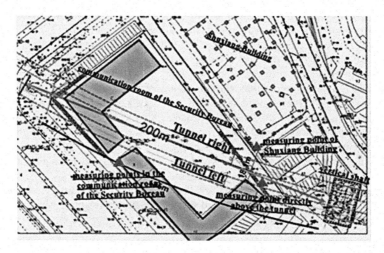

Figure 1. Location of on-site monitoring points.

2.2 Build a numerical model

MIDAS/GTS NX dynamic finite element simulation software is used to establish three-dimensional numerical calculation models of rock and soil mass, tunnel, and blast hole. According to the tunnel engineering numerical simulation boundary range of 3~5 times the tunnel length (Fan et al. 2016), the tunnel buried depth is 30m. The selected size of the model is 60m×60m×70m, and the model has a total of 277545 units. The numerical calculation model is shown in Figure 2:

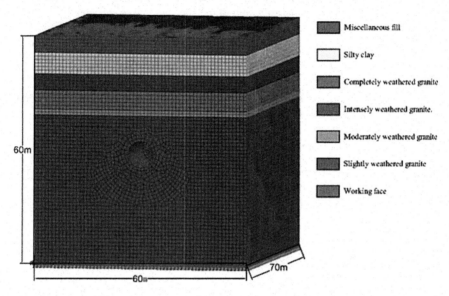

Figure 2. Numerical model.

2.3 Size selection and feasibility verification of numerical calculation model

(1) Choice of model size
The model mainly changed five sets of data, by changing one of the data and keeping the other data unchanged for a control experiment. Among them, the diameter of the damping hole is 60, 80, 100, and 120. The distance between the damping hole and the explosion source is 1300, 1500, 1700, and 2000. The distance of the damping hole is 60, 90, 120, and 150; the depth of the damping hole chooses 1200, 1500, 1800, and 2100, and choose 50, 100, 150, and 200 for the double-row shock-absorbing hole spacing (unit: mm).

(2) Feasibility verification
According to the research of many articles, in the actual project, the vertical vibration velocity can be used instead of the three-vector vibration velocity to simplify the control standard (Su 2012), so only the z direction is selected for the research, as shown in Table 1 below. It can be seen

Table 1. Comparison of monitoring data and numerical simulation results.

Measuring point	On-site monitoring results	Numerical Simulation Results	error (%)
Measuring point directly above the tunnel	0.326	0.315	3.37
Scholar Building measuring point	0.249	0.268	7.63
Security Bureau measuring point	0.00785	0.00862	9.80

Maximum vibration velocity in Z direction (cm/s)

from the table that except for the peak vibration velocity in the Z direction of the measuring point directly above the tunnel, the numerical simulation results of all other measuring points are greater than the on-site monitoring data. The reason for this phenomenon is that the numerical model has made considerable assumptions and optimizations, but the actual geological situation is very complex. The fissures of the underground rock and the variability of the stratum are all assumed to be isotropic, and the influence of groundwater is also ignored. The error between the results of on-site monitoring and numerical simulation is within 10%, which ensures that the numerical calculation can well restore the actual situation of the site, and makes sufficient preparations for the later study of vibration damping hole parameters to ensure the correctness of the numerical calculation model in the future.

3 ANALYSIS OF NUMERICAL SIMULATION RESULTS OF VIBRATION DAMPING HOLES WITH DIFFERENT PARAMETERS

In some scientific research articles (Li et al. 2018), scholars generally use the peak vibration speed of the particle for comparison. A single-speed comparison can only show how much the vibration-damping hole is damped, but cannot see the magnitude of the vibration damping. Therefore, the vibration-damping hole is introduced. With the concept of the vibration reduction rate η here, you can intuitively see the reduction amplitude values of the five groups of vibration reduction parameters.

$$\eta = \frac{v_{no} - v_{yes}}{v_{no}} \times 100\% \quad (1)$$

In the formula: η is the damping rate;

V_{no} is the vibration speed of the measuring point when there is no vibration-damping hole;

V_{yes} is the vibration speed of the measuring point when there is a vibration-damping hole.

From the above formula and the vibration velocity in Table 2, the vibration reduction rate of various factors can be obtained, and then use the origin drawing software to draw the peak vibration velocity and vibration reduction rate curve of the three measuring points under different parameters, as shown in Figures 3 and 4 shown:

3.1 *Analysis of different damping hole diameters and distances from different damping holes to the explosion source*

From the two curves in Figure 3, it can be seen that the diameter of the vibration-damping hole and the distance between the vibration-damping hole and the explosion source increase with the increase of the distance and the aperture, and the peak vibration velocities of the three measuring points all tend to decrease. The peak vibration velocity of the points is higher than that of other measurement points. The changing trend of the peak vibration velocity of the measurement point of the Security Bureau is not obvious and is at the lowest level, but the vibration reduction effect of the measurement point of the Security Bureau is the best. As the distance increases, the slight speed change will produce a larger vibration reduction effect. The vibration reduction rates of these two groups are on the rise with the increase of the distance and the aperture. The vibration reduction effect of the vibration reduction hole diameter is relatively flat when the aperture reaches 120mm, and the curve of the distance between the vibration reduction hole and the explosion source is 1900mm. The curve continues to rise, the vibration reduction rate continues to increase, and the speed continues to decrease. Therefore, a larger distance and a larger aperture can be selected from these two sets of parameters to have a better vibration reduction effect. According to the upward trend of the curve, the diameter of the damping hole is 120mm, and the distance between the damping hole and the explosion source is recommended to be more than 2000mm.

Table 2. Summary table of the peak vibration speed and damping rate in the Z direction of each influencing factor

Influencing factors	parameter settings	Scholar Building measuring point Peak vibration speed (mm)	Vibration reduction rate	Security Bureau measuring point Peak vibration speed (mm)	Vibration reduction rate	Measuring point directly above the tunnel Peak vibration speed (mm)	Vibration reduction rate
No damping holes	0mm	0.269		0.009		0.315	
Vibration damping hole diameter D	60mm	0.257	0.045	0.008	0.061	0.290	0.078
	80mm	0.246	0.086	0.007	0.163	0.279	0.114
	100mm	0.240	0.106	0.006	0.331	0.266	0.155
	120mm	0.232	0.137	0.005	0.378	0.247	0.214
The distance R from the vibration-damping hole to the explosion source	1300mm	0.265	0.013	0.008	0.024	0.304	0.036
	1500mm	0.260	0.031	0.008	0.046	0.295	0.064
	1700mm	0.250	0.070	0.008	0.081	0.276	0.124
	1900mm	0.246	0.086	0.007	0.163	0.279	0.114
Vibration damping hole distance L	60mm	0.243	0.096	0.007	0.197	0.274	0.131
	90mm	0.246	0.086	0.007	0.163	0.279	0.114
	120mm	0.258	0.040	0.008	0.093	0.290	0.080
	150mm	0.261	0.030	0.008	0.053	0.280	0.110
Vibration damping hole distance L	1200mm	0.241	0.102	0.007	0.178	0.275	0.128
	1500mm	0.246	0.086	0.007	0.163	0.279	0.114
	1800mm	0.254	0.054	0.008	0.104	0.284	0.097
	2100mm	0.260	0.032	0.008	0.071	0.297	0.058
Double row vibration damping hole row spacing S	50mm	0.214	0.204	0.006	0.289	0.244	0.226
	100mm	0.224	0.166	0.007	0.160	0.252	0.198
	150mm	0.235	0.126	0.007	0.142	0.276	0.123
	200mm	0.239	0.110	0.008	0.116	0.281	0.106

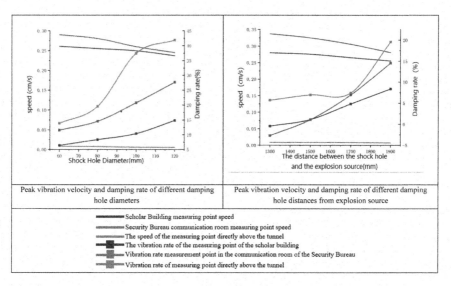

Figure 3. Peak vibration velocity and vibration-damping rate change curve of the damping hole diameter and the distance from the explosion source change curve of the damping rate.

3.2 Analysis of different damping hole spacing, hole depth, and double-row damping hole spacing

As shown in Figure 4, the three sets of data of the hole spacing, hole depth, and double-row shock-absorbing hole spacing show an overall upward trend with the increase of the distance. The peak vibration velocity of the measuring point directly above the tunnel is the highest and the peak value of the measuring point of the Security Bureau. The changing trend of the vibration speed is the smallest and the vibration speed is the lowest, so the smaller hole diameter, hole depth, and row spacing should be selected as much as possible. The damping rate curves are all the curves of the measuring points of the Security Bureau. The damping effect is the best. The damping rate curves of the damping hole distance and hole depth are similar, and the curve shows a relatively smooth downward trend. According to the trend of the curve, the hole distance is selected. 60–90mm is the best, and the hole depth is 1200–1500mm. However, the measurement points of the Security Bureau for the vibration reduction rate of the double-row shock-absorbing hole row distance have the lowest peak value at 150mm, and the other two measurement points also have a relatively flat curve after this point. It is noted that a depth of 50–100mm is the best;

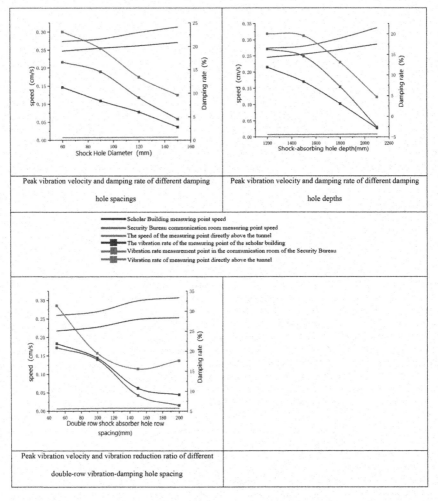

Figure 4. Vibration damping hole pitch, hole depth, peak vibration velocity of double-row damping holes and change curve of the damping rate.

3.3 Overall analysis

By comparing and combining the initial control conditions, some experience can be drawn: under the condition that other parameters of the damping hole remain unchanged, the greater the distance between the damping hole and the explosion source, the better the damping effect of the damping hole, and the better the damping effect of the damping hole. The higher the vibration reduction rate, the larger the diameter of the vibration reduction holes, the lower the peak vibration velocity of each measuring point on the ground, and the greater the vibration reduction rate. If the distance between the vibration-reduction holes is increased, the vibration reduction effect of the vibration-reduction holes will be worse, and the vibration reduction rate will be worse and lower; the depth of the shock-absorbing holes is increased due to the existence of the cavity effect[10], the vibration-absorbing effect of the shock-absorbing holes is worse, and the vibration-absorbing rate is lower; as the row spacing of the double-row shock-absorbing holes increases, the vibration-absorbing increases. The worse the damping effect of the hole, the lower the damping efficiency of the damping hole.

Due to the cavity effect and the interference that the lower the speed, the higher the damping rate, the depth of the damping hole, the diameter of the hole, and the distance from the explosion source are not the main factors that affect the damping, and the double-row damping holes will not appear in practical applications. In the case of the lower spacing and the trend of the curve, it is concluded that the vibration reduction rate of the double-row shock-absorbing holes will be extremely low, so the influence of this factor on the vibration-absorbing effect of the shock-absorbing holes is excluded, so the hole spacing of the shock-absorbing holes is regarding the main factors affecting vibration reduction, which is also in line with the conclusion of most scholars.

4 CONCLUSION

(1) Analyze the influence of the parameters of the single-row damping hole on the damping effect. Under the condition that other parameters of the vibration-damping hole are kept unchanged, increase the distance of the vibration-damping hole from the explosion source, increase the diameter of the vibration-damping hole, and reduce the distance between the vibration damping holes. The lower the peak vibration velocity of the ground measuring point, the better the damping effect of the damping hole, and the higher the damping rate. In the case of controlling other parameters of the damping hole unchanged, increasing the depth of the damping hole, due to the existence of the cavity effect, the damping effect of the damping hole is worse, and the damping rate is lower.

(2) The influence of the parameters of the double-row damping holes on the damping effect is analyzed. Under the condition that other parameters of the damping holes are kept unchanged, the lower the vibration damping efficiency, the double-row damping holes are arranged in a plum blossom shape.

(3) Through the analysis, it is concluded that the hole distance is the main influencing factor. Generally, 60-90mm is the best choice. The distance between the shock-absorbing hole and the explosion source is 2000mm, the diameter of the shock-absorbing hole is 120mm, and the hole depth is 1200-1500mm. The spacing of the double-row shock-absorbing holes is 50-100mm.

ACKNOWLEDGMENTS

This research was funded by the Shandong Natural Science Foundation of China, grant number ZR2020ME096 and the work is supported by the Foundation of Hubei Key Laboratory of Blasting Engineering, grant number BL2021-24 and Qingdao West Coast New Area High-level Talent Team Project, grant number RCTD-JC-2019-06.

REFERENCES

Editorial Office of China Journal of Highway and Transport 2015 Summary of Academic Research on Chinese Tunnel Engineering·2015 J. *China Journal of Highway and Transport*, 28(05): 1–65.

Fan H, Qiu J, Xie Yongli, Guo Chunxia. Effects of blasting vibration of tunnels under villages on surface buildings [J]. *Journal of PLA University of Science and Technology* (Natural Science Edition), 2016, 17(03): 209–214.

Li Z, Yin R, Meng Y, Deng W, Chen L. Analysis of vibration response and cavity effect of tunnel blasting in soil and rock interlaced strata[J]. *Tunnel Construction* (Chinese and English), 2018, 38(04): 588–593.

Miao Y, Wu L. Analysis of influence of surface blasting vibration on existing tunnels [J]. *Highway Traffic Technology* (Applied Technology Edition), 2014, 10(03): 177–180.

Midlin R D. Effects of an oscillating tangential force on the contact surface of elastic spheres. Proc. L SU Cong. *Appl. Mech*, 1953: 203–208.

Mu C M, Zhang Q, Liu Z K, et al. Numerical simulation of the tunnel blasting process in weak intercalated layer[J]. *Highway*, 2011, 314: 452–456.

Savage J C. Theroelastic attention of elastic waves by cracks. *J. Geophys, Res*. 1996, (71): 3929–3938.

Su Y. *Research on the influence of tunnel blasting vibration on the ground and nearby buildings*[D]. Ocean University of China, 2012.

Xu H, Lu W, Zhou X. Equivalent application method of blasting load in dynamic finite element simulation of blasting vibration field [J]. *Journal of Wuhan University* (Engineering Science), 2008(01):67–71+103.

Yu D, Yang J, Zhao M. Discussion on shock absorption mechanism of shock absorbing trench to bench blasting seismic wave[J]. *Chinese Journal of Coal*, 2011, 36(02): 244–247.

Simplified analysis of breach outflow hydrograph of Embankment Dam break

Jiayi Lin
China Institute of Water Resources and Hydropower Research, Beijing, China

Yao Xu* & Ronglu Wang
China Institute of Water Resources and Hydropower Research, Beijing, China
Beijing IWHR-KHL Co., Ltd, Beijing, China

Fang Xiao
China Institute of Water Resources and Hydropower Research, Beijing, China

Xiulin Li
China Institute of Water Resources and Hydropower Research, Beijing, China
Beijing IWHR-KHL Co., Ltd, Beijing, China

ABSTRACT: Based on 22 cases of embankment dam breaks and the related existing prediction models of dam breaching parameters, the breach outflow hydrograph of the embankment dam break is studied in this paper. The breach outflow hydrograph is simplified, and a corresponding prediction model is proposed to realize a quick prediction for the breach outflow hydrograph. Finally, the simplified prediction model proposed in this paper is demonstrated in the dam break analysis of Houtun Reservoir and Banqiao reservoir.

1 INTRODUCTION

In recent years, risk analysis has been used with increasing frequency in the safety management of reservoir dams (Lin & Chen 2018; Xian et al. 2018). In the risk analysis of reservoir dams, both the possibility of dam breaks and the assessment of loss suffered in the lower reaches caused by disastrous floods after dam outbursts should be considered. To assess the routing process of the dam-break flood and the loss in the downstream areas, it is necessary to analyze the breach outflow hydrograph of dam break. The failure process of an embankment dam generally consists of two phases: the breach initiation phase and the breach development phase (Xu & Zhang 2007). During the breach initiation phase, the downstream face starts to erode away, and then the erosion gradually reaches the upstream face with relatively slow erosive velocity and small outflow. During the breach development phase, the erosive velocity, outflow rate, and the expansion of the breach are rapidly increasing until the end of the dam break. Most dam-break floods occur in the breach development phase. Therefore, in practical calculations, only the outflow hydrograph during the breach development phase is required in the analysis. In this paper, 22 cases of embankment dam failures due to overtopping are collected (Hassan et al. 2004; Hanson et al. 2005; Ru & Niu 2001;

---

*Corresponding Author: xuyao@iwhr.com

Vaskinn et al. 2004; Xie 1993; Zhong et al. 2016). Basic information about these reservoir dams is shown in Table 1, and their detailed breach outflow hydrographs are shown in Figure 1 (except for Shimantan). Based on these cases, a simplified analysis of the breach outflow hydrograph is presented in this paper, and a corresponding prediction model is proposed for predicting the outflow hydrograph of an embankment dam break in a quick way.

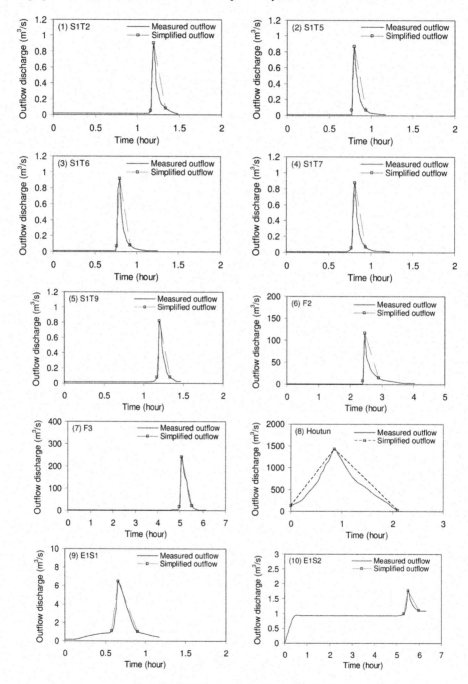

Figure 1. 21 cases of outflow hydrographs from overtopping breach of embankment dams.

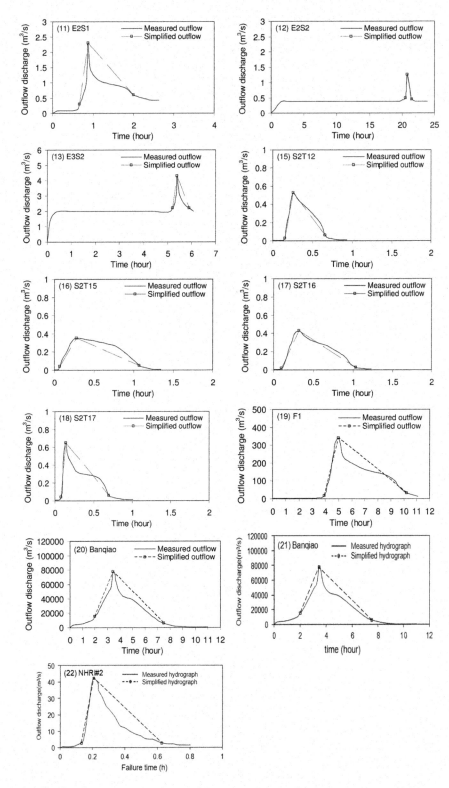

Figure 1. Continued.

2 SIMPLIFIED BREACH OUTFLOW HYDROGRAPH

As shown in Figure 2, the breach outflow hydrograph is simplified in this paper to a triangular diagram. Only three parameters are required to define the simplified hydrograph: Q_p (peak outflow rate), T_p (duration from the start of breach development to the peak outflow), and T_f (failure time). The failure time in this paper refers only to the breach development time, which did not contain the previous breach initiation time. The value of Q_p and T_f can be predicted by using many existing models (Wahl 1998; Xu & Zhang 2009). Therefore, once T_p or the rate of T_p/T_f is estimated, the simplified outflow hydrograph is finally obtained. If a dam fails, it is usually accompanied by the continuous inrush of floodwater into the reservoir. Therefore, the impact of the additional reservoir inflow must be considered. For the purposes of demonstration, it is assumed that the value of the additional reservoir inflow is constant in this paper, thus increasing the outflow hydrograph by the value of Q_{in} (flow rate into the reservoir, as shown in Figure 2). The adjusted peak outflow rate, Q_{pa} is:

$$Q_{pa} = Q_p + Q_{in} \quad (1)$$

It is found that for two dams with different heights but the same storage capacity, the failure of the higher dam would result in a larger Q_p, a smaller T_f, and a smaller ratio of T_p/T_f, while the failure of the lower dam would result in a smaller Q_p, a larger T_f, and a larger ratio of T_p/T_f (Xu & Zhang 2009). Therefore, it can be deduced that the value of T_p/T_f increased with the reservoir shape coefficient (C_r), which is verified in the following. The reservoir shape coefficient (C_r) in this paper reflected the relationship between the reservoir storage capacity (V) and dam height (H), which is defined as $C_r = V^{1/3}/H$.

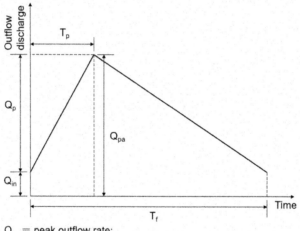

Q_p = peak outflow rate;
Q_{in} = flow rate into reservoir;
Q_{pa} = adjusted peak outflow rate;
T_p = duration from the start of breach development to the peak outflow;
T_f = failure time.

Figure 2. Simplified outflow hydrograph from the breach.

In addition to the C_r mentioned above, the dam material is also a significant influencing factor. For example, the breach development model varies widely from granular embankments to cohesive embankments (Xu & Zhang 2007). As shown in Table 1, there are 14 granular embankments and 8 cohesive embankments among 22 cases of embankment dam overtopping failures. For granular embankments, as shown in Figure 3, the breach initiation and development make the dam body appear to be sliced diagonally into pieces with the increasingly flatter erosion surface and larger breach in the shape of an inverted trapezium. On the other hand, as shown in Figure 4, the failure of

Table 1. 22 cases of failure of embankment dams due to overtopping.

No.	Dam name	Location	Case type	Embankment type	Dam height (m)	Reservoir capacity (m^3)	Reservoir shape coefficient	Peak outflow time, T$_p$(hour)	Failure time, T$_f$(hour)	T$_p$/T$_f$	References
1	S1T2	England	Laboratory	Granular	0.49	245	12.8	0.04	0.18	0.22	[4]
2	S1T5	England	Laboratory	Granular	0.48	240	12.9	0.03	0.17	0.18	[4]
3	S1T6	England	Laboratory	Granulars	0.49	245	12.8	0.04	0.16	0.25	[4]
4	S1T7	England	Laboratory	Granulars	0.49	245	12.8	0.04	0.17	0.24	[4]
5	S1T9	England	Laboratory	Granulars	0.48	240	12.9	0.03	0.17	0.18	[4]
6	F2	Norway	Field	Granulars	5	31,000	6.3	0.06	0.50	0.12	[5]
7	F3	Norway	Field	Granulars	6	65,000	6.7	0.09	0.53	0.17	[5]
8	Houtun Reservoir*	China	Field	Granulars	9.6	4,600,000	17.3	0.85	2.10	0.40	[6]
9	E1S1	USA	Field	Granulars	2.29	5,300	7.6	0.08	0.32	0.25	[7]
10	E1S2	USA	Field	Granulars	2.29	5,300	7.6	0.19	0.66	0.29	[7]
11	E2S1	USA	Field	Granulars	1.52	5,700	11.8	0.21	1.33	0.16	[7]
12	E2S2	USA	Field	Granulars	1.52	5,700	11.8	0.25	1.00	0.25	[7]
13	E3S2	USA	Field	Granulars	2.29	5,300	7.6	0.20	0.70	0.29	[7]
14	Shimantan	China	Accident	Granulars	25	91,800,000	18.0	1.20	5.50	0.22	[8]
15	S2T10	England	Laboratory	Cohesive	0.6	300	11.2	0.39	1.54	0.25	[4]
16	S2T12	England	Laboratory	Cohesive	0.59	295	11.3	0.11	0.51	0.22	[4]
17	S2T15	England	Laboratory	Cohesive	0.59	295	11.3	0.21	1.00	0.21	[4]
18	S2T16	England	Laboratory	Cohesive	0.59	295	11.3	0.22	0.93	0.24	[4]
19	S2T17	England	Laboratory	Cohesive	0.59	295	11.3	0.06	0.62	0.10	[4]
20	F1	Norway	Field	Cohesive	6	54,000	6.3	1.05	6.25	0.17	[5]
21	Banqiao Reservoir	China	Accident	Cohesive	24.5	492,000,000	32.2	1.45	5.50	0.26	[8]
22	NHRI#2	China	Field	Cohesive	9.7	100,000	4.8	0.08	0.50	0.16	[11]

Note: In the case of the Houtun Reservoir, the height and storage of the dam are the dam height and reservoir volume corresponding to the reservoir water level when the dam failure occurred.

cohesive embankments is characterized by the formation of a series of nearly vertical slopes along the downstream face of the embankments. The erosion surface forms near the downstream face and advances to the upstream face. In the following analysis of the ratio of T$_p$/T$_f$, different prediction models of T$_p$/T$_f$ are developed respectively for granular embankments and cohesive embankments.

Based on the above 22 cases, the relationship between the ratio of T$_p$/T$_f$ and C$_r$ is shown in Figure 5. For granular embankments, it is clearly indicated that the ratio of T$_p$/T$_f$ increases with the reservoir shape coefficient (C$_r$); For cohesive embankments, the relationship is not distinct based on the original date, but the trendline reflects the increasing trend of the ratio of T$_p$/T$_f$ with the reservoir shape coefficient (C$_r$). Moreover, as shown in Figure 5, the trendline for granular embankments is on top of that for cohesive embankments, which means that with the same C$_r$, it takes more time required for the peak outflow rate of the granular embankments than that of the cohesive embankments after a dam failure.

Theoretically, the peak outflow rate occurs when the reservoir water level and the breach geometry reach an optimal combination. When the reservoir shape coefficient (C$_r$) is relatively large, the reservoir level does not change significantly during the early stage of the embankment breach, and hence allows a longer time of lateral erosion while the reservoir level remains high. In such a case, the peak outflow rate will occur in the later lateral erosion stage. Therefore, the larger the reservoir shape coefficient (C$_r$) is, the later the peak outflow rate is reached. When the fill material is more erodible, i.e., granular embankments, the erosion at a high rate enlarges the breach rapidly while the reservoir level does not change significantly. Hence, the peak outflow rate will occur in the later stage of the breach reaching or approaching its maximum size. Therefore, the time to peak outflow rate for the granular embankments is longer than that for the cohesive embankments after a dam failure.

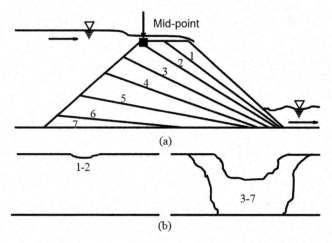

Figure 3. (a) Overtopping and erosion process of granular embankments; (b) Corresponding breach initiation and development diagram ("1-2" refers to the breach initiation phase; "3-7" refers to the breach development phase).

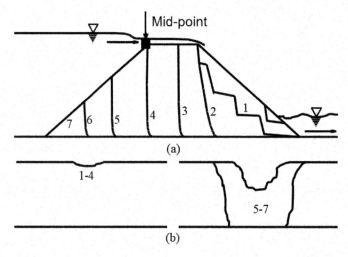

Figure 4. (a) Overtopping and erosion process of cohesive embankments; (b) Corresponding breach initiation and development diagram ("1-4" refers to the breach initiation phase; "5-7" refers to the breach development phase).

According to the above analysis, the time to peak outflow rate depends on the reservoir shape coefficient (C_r) and erosion resistance of the dam material. The relationship between the ratio of T_p/T_f and these two controlling factors is shown in Figure 3. Moreover, the mathematical equations between the value of T_p/T_f and the reservoir shape coefficient (C_r) of granular embankments and cohesive embankments are shown as follows:

$$\left(T_p/T_f\right)_{granular} = 0.063 \ln C_r + 0.079 \qquad (2)$$

$$\left(T_p/T_f\right)_{cohesive} = 0.055 \ln C_r + 0.069 \qquad (3)$$

These two empirical equations, deduced from dam overtopping failure cases, are not applicable to other dam failure modes. In addition, the adoption of the empirical equation in the prediction

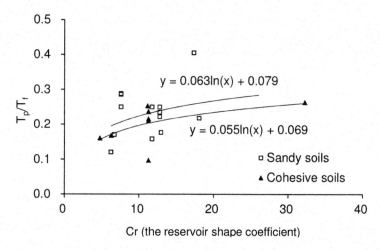

Figure 5. Relationship between the ratio of T_p/T_f and C_r.

of the value of T_p/T_f should be in line with applicable conditions because of the relatively small number of cases analyzed in this paper, some of which are even laboratory tests.

3 DAM BREAK ANALYSIS OF HOUTUN RESERVOIR AND BANQIAO RESERVOIR

The Houtun Reservoir Dam is a homogeneous earthfill dam with a maximum height of 17 m. At the time of dam failure, the water depth was 9.6 m with a 4.6 million m³ reservoir storage. The filed test of dam failure was conducted after the breach was intentionally destroyed. Its measured breach outflow hydrograph is presented in Figure 6. As a clay core wall dam, the Banqiao Reservoir Dam has a maximum storage capacity of 492 million m³ and a maximum height of 24.5 m. The Banqiao Reservoir dam failure, attributed to overtopping, occurred on August 8, 1975. The measured breach outflow hydrograph is shown in Figure 7.

To predict Q_p and T_f, the following prediction models were adopted (Xu & Zhang 2007):

$$Q_p = 0.133 C_r^{-1.276} e^{-0.877} \sqrt{g V_w^{5/3}} \tag{4}$$

$$T_f = 0.038 (H/15)^{0.654} C_r^{1.246} \tag{5}$$

In the above equations, V_w represents the water volume of the reservoir above the bottom level of the eventual breach at the beginning of the dam failure.

In the case of Houtun Reservoir Dam, V_w is about 4.6 million m³. By using Equations (4) and (5), the predicted values of Q_p and T_f are as follows: $Q_p = 1626$ m³/s, $T_f = 1.44$ hours. The equation (2) was adopted in the calculation of T_p/T_f, of which the result is 0.26, slightly smaller than the measured value, 0.40 (as shown in Table 1). Therefore, the prediction of a simplified breach outflow hydrograph of Houtun Reservoir Dam (Figure 6) is achieved based on the value of Q_p, T_f, and T_p/T_f. As shown in Figure 6, in comparison to the measured results, the predicted value of Q_p is relatively larger, while the predicted value of T_f is relatively smaller. The result of this comparison is mainly concerned with applicable conditions of Equations (4) and (5) that are developed mainly based on dam failure cases of full reservoirs with high water levels and large flow at the time of dam failure, as well as relatively fast scouring velocity. In such cases, the predicted value of T_f is smaller, and that of Q_p is larger. On the contrary, the dam failure of the Houtun Reservoir is attributed to the intentional destruction of the breach that led to a significantly smaller water level than the dam height at the time of dam failure. As a result, the actual dam failure of the Houtun Reservoir exhibits lower scouring velocity, longer failure time, and smaller peak outflow rate.

In the case of Banqiao Reservoir Dam, V_w is 607.5 million m³. By using Equations (4) and (5), the predicted values of Q_p and T_f are as follows: $Q_p = 52981$ m³/s, $T_f = 3.2$ hours. The equation (3) is adopted in the calculation of T_p/T_f, of which the result is 0.27, almost equal to the measured value, 0.26 (as shown in Table 1). Therefore, the prediction of a simplified breach outflow hydrograph of Banqiao Reservoir Dam (Figure 7) is achieved based on the value of Q_p, T_f, T_p/T_f, and Q_{in}. The value of Q_{in} varied over time. At the onset of the dam failure, the value of Q_{in} was 9650 m³/s; When the peak outflow rate was reached, the value of Q_{in} was 5250 m³/s; At the end of the dam failure, the value of Q_{in} was 890 m³/s. As shown in Figure 7, in comparison to the measured results, the predicted value of the outflow curve, including Q_p and T_f, is relatively smaller. There are two main reasons for the result of this comparison. First, the dam filling quality could not be ensured with backward construction equipment and techniques during the construction phase, resulting in poor erosion resistance of the dam. Secondly, after the start of the overtopping, up to 239 million m³ of floodwater continued to flow from upstream into the reservoir, accounting for 40% of the initial reservoir storage (V_w = 607.5 million m³). A great inrush of much additional floodwater had a significant impact on the breach development, thus prolonging the time of breach erosion processes and increasing the breach size and peak outflow rate. Therefore, the predicted values in this paper are smaller than the measured results for the above two reasons.

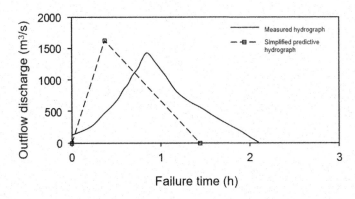

Figure 6. Simplified breach outflow hydrograph of Houtun Reservoir Dam.

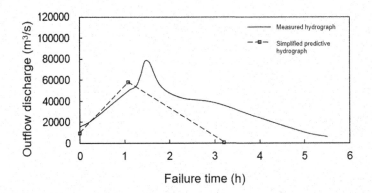

Figure 7. Simplified breach outflow hydrograph of Banqiao Reservoir Dam.

4 CONCLUSION

The simplified analysis of the breach outflow hydrograph is conducted in this paper for achieving a quick prediction of the breach outflow hydrograph of an embankment dam. Only three parameters, Q_p (peak outflow rate), T_p (duration from the start of breach development to the peak outflow), and T_f (failure time), are required to predict the outflow hydrograph. Based on 22 cases of embankment dam failures due to overtopping, two different mathematical prediction models for the time to peak outflow rate for granular embankments and cohesive embankments are developed, respectively. By using the existing prediction models of peak outflow rate and failure time, it is available to predict the simplified breach outflow hydrograph in a quick way. Finally, the simplified prediction model of the breach outflow hydrograph proposed in this paper is demonstrated in the dam break analysis of Houtun Reservoir and Banqiao reservoir. The simplified prediction model can be applied to the rapid prediction of the breach outflow hydrograph in emergencies, which in turn can simulate the routing process of the dam-break flood in downstream areas and assess the loss of inundated areas. All these efforts help ensure that strategies for disaster mitigation and emergency response can be specified in a timely manner.

ACKNOWLEDGMENTS

This research was funded by the IWHR Basic Research Fund (SM0145B022021).

REFERENCES

Hanson G., Cook K., Hunt S. Physical modeling of overtopping erosion and breach formation of cohesive embankments[J]. *Transactions of the ASAE*, 2005, 48(5): 1783–94.

Hassan M., Morris M., Hanson G., et al. *Breach formation: Laboratory and numerical modeling of breach formation*[C]. Proc. Dam Safety 2004. Phoenix: Association of State Dam Safety Officials (ASDSO), 2004.

Lin P. Z., Chen Y. Risk analysis of dam overtopping for cascade reservoirs based on bayesian network. *Advanced Engineering Sciences*[J], 2018, 50(03): 46–53.

Ru N. H., Niu Y. G. *Embankment dam incidents and safety of large dams*[M]. Beijing: China Water & Power Press, 2001

Vaskinn K., Lovoll A., Hoeg K., et al. *Physical modeling of breach formation: Large-scale field tests*[C]. Proc. Dam Safety 2004. Phoenix: Association of State Dam Safety Officials (ASDSO), 2004.

Wahl T. *Prediction of embankment dam breach parameters*[R]. Report DSO-98-004. Denver: U.S. Department of the Interior Bureau of Reclamation, Dam Safety Office, 1998.

Xian J., Gu S. P., Lin L. M., et al. Risk analysis of reservoir over-storage at flood season based on stochastic simulation method. *Yellow River*[J], 2018, 40(05): 39–43.

Xie R. Z. *Dam-break hydromechanics*[M]. Jinan: Shandong Science and Technology Press, 1993.

Xu Y., Zhang L. M. Study on break development model of earth-rock dams[J]. *China Flood and Drought Management*, 2007, Suppl.: 18–21.

Xu Y., Zhang L.M. Breaching parameters for earth and rockfill dams[J]. *Journal of Geotechnical and Geoenvironmental Engineering*, 2009, 135(12): 1957–70.

Zhong Q. M., Chen S. S., Deng Z. Research on mathematical model for homogeneous earthen dam breach process due to overtopping failure and its application[J]. *Journal of Hydraulic Engineering*, 2016, 47(12): 1519–27.

Theoretical investigation on the crack initiation mechanism of brittle rock specimen with a 3D internal open-type flaw

Yusong Zhao & Qi Qi
Zijin School of Geology and Mining, Fuzhou University, Fujian, Fuzhou, China

Congcong Chen*
School of Civil and Resource Engineering, University of Science and Technology Beijing, Beijing, China

ABSTRACT: The existence of an internal 3D open-type flaw subsequently leads to uneven deformation and secondary failures in surrounding rocks. Accordingly, the crack initiation mechanism analyses are finished at the tips of the 2D (for comparison) and 3D preset flaws, and on the main free surfaces of the internal 3D flaws. The results indicate that the pure Mode II and Mode III failures occur at the inclination and strike boundary of the internal 3D flaw, respectively. Besides, the application of the thin plate models (circle plate) proves that the internal free surface can be divided into two regions; secondary tensile failures initially appear in the central Destruction Region (rock bears tensile stress in at least one direction), which surrounded by the annular-shape Anti-destruction Region (rock bears triaxial compressive stress here, and the central tensile cracks cannot penetrate this region and extend outwards).

1 INTRODUCTION

Commonly, there are many types of original or secondary fracture structures distributed inside rock masses resulting from the complicated geological forces or construction of artificial geotechnical works, which has bad continuity and leads to severe risks in related projects. Especially, the structural-controlled rock bursts occurring in brittle rock masses are one of the hottest issues in this field, which has characteristics of severe damage, and rapid development, and are hard to be predicted.

There are large amounts of 2D fracture rock studies finished with various types of occurrence, shape, spatial relation between fracture structures, loading method, filling state, and material property; and the mechanical properties, acoustic characteristics, deformation features, initiation, propagation, and coalescence of secondary failure structures under different preset conditions are discussed in those studies (Bobet & Einstein 1998; Bobet 2000; Li et al. 2005; Sagong & Bobet 2002; Xu & Li 2019; Yang et al. 2017; Zhuang et al. 2014; Zhao et al. 2016; Zou et al. 2016). However, the 2D settings of former studies are selected simplification of the real 3D conditions, which cannot reflect the real behaviors of rock under 3D conditions. Therefore, it is important to conduct 3D-type tests and research in this field.

The most widely used method for preparing 3D internal structures is installing a thin sheet into a transparent material, which is fixed by some thin lines during the curing period (Adams 1978; Dyskin et al. 2003; Fu et al. 2016; Li et al. 2020; Mei et al. 2020). Currently, the hottest, most accurate, and most efficient method used is the 3D-printing technology, which can construct complex fracture structures in rock-like samples layer-by-layer (Zhou & Zhu 2018; Zhou et al. 2020).

---

*Corresponding Author: chencong0428@126.com

Although there are many special results and conclusions obtained by laboratory tests or numerical simulations, the corresponding theoretical analysis is not comprehensive, especially for the condition of the 3D open-type flaw. Accordingly, the stress status of surrounding rocks at various positions was discussed in this work, which explains the mechanism of corresponding failures and provides an important reference for 3D fracture mechanics in future works under similar conditions.

2 BOUNDARY OF THE 2D PRESET FLAW

Referring to the work finished by P.Z. Pan and S.T. Miao et al. (Miao et al. 2018; Pan et al. 2019), the 2D preset flaw with the rectangular cutting section was simplified as an ellipse model. The long (l_1) and short (l_2) axes of the ellipse model represented the long and short edges of the rectangular flaw (Figure 1-left). Constructed an x-y local coordinate system based on the centroid point, long and short axials of the ellipse model (the x axial along the long axial and y axial along the short axial). We defined positive stress as compression and negative stress as tension in this theoretical model. The relationship between axial stresses and shear stress after disassembly was as follows:

$$\begin{aligned} \sigma_x &= \sigma \sin^2 \alpha \\ \sigma_y &= \sigma \cos^2 \alpha \\ \tau_{xy} &= \sigma \sin \alpha \cos \alpha \end{aligned} \quad (1)$$

Where α was the flaw inclination angle; σ was the external loading.

The stress concentration status caused by the above three stresses along the periphery of an open flaw can be roughly obtained through an analytical solution, and the tangential stress (σ_β) on the boundary of the elliptical flaw was given:

$$\sigma_\beta = \frac{\sigma_y\left[m(m+x)\cos^2\beta - \sin^2\beta\right] + \sigma_x\left[(2m+1)\sin^2\beta - m^2\sin^2\beta\right] - \tau_{xy}\left[2(1+m^2)\sin\beta\cos\beta\right]}{m^2\cos^2\beta + \sin^2\beta} \quad (2)$$

Where m was the ratio of l_2 to l_1; β defines the position of a point on the boundary of the flaw.

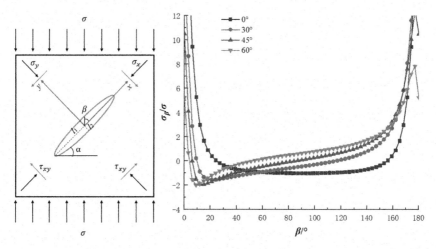

Figure 1. Schematic of an inclined ellipse flaw subjected to uniform compressive stress and corresponding results.

Applied geometric parameters of the 2D preset flaw into the Formula (2), and the tangential stresses along the periphery of the preset flaw with various inclinations (0°, 30°, 45°, and 60°) are shown in Figure 1-right. The maximum tensile stress is obtained at the middle point of the preset flaw

(β is 90°) when the flaw inclination angle α is 0°. It is noticed that the value of β approaches zero as the flaw inclination increase, which represents that the position of the maximum tensile stress becomes closer to the top flaw tip. The value of the maximum tensile stress also shows a downward trend, which gets the peak value (180.1% σ) in the sample with 60° of the flaws, and the bottom value (96.4% σ) in the sample with 30° of flaw. Furthermore, compression stresses are concentrated in the upper and bottom edges of the preset flaw. Because the maximum ratio of the peak compression stress and the peak tensile stress of the 2D flaw is 19.63, which is similar to the traditional brittle rock like granite and limestone, tensile failure is thus the first secondary destruction structure in surrounding rock. Accordingly, as the flaw inclination increased, the initiation positions of surface secondary failures gradually approached the edges of the preset flaws, which were high and coincided with the calculations of theoretical analysis.

3 BOUNDARY OF THE 3D INTERNAL FLAW

To make the research results more universal, the ellipse internal flaw is selected as the research object, and the simplified model is shown in Figure 2, where a is the long axes, b is the short axes, α is the elliptic polar angle, β is the included angle between the long axes of the ellipse and the compression direction. The X-axis is the flaw inclination direction, the Y-axis is the flaw strike direction, and the Z-axis is the normal direction of the elliptic surface. In conclusion, the 3-D propagation surface morphology of internal elliptical crack depends on deflection angle (θ) and torsion angle (φ).

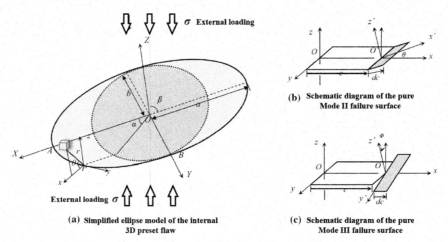

Figure 2. Schematic diagram of 3D internal crack fracture analysis under uniaxial loading (modified from reference (Zhang et al. 2020)).

Based on the previous works (Guo et al. 2011; Zhang et al. 2020) about the internal 3D flaw, it can be assumed that the singular stress field at the boundary of the 3D preset flaw is composed of Mode I, Mode II, and Mode III stress expressions, namely:

$$\sigma_{xx} = \frac{K_I}{\sqrt{2\pi r}} \cdot \cos\frac{\theta}{2} \cdot \left(1 - \sin\frac{\theta}{2} \cdot \sin\frac{3\theta}{2}\right) - \frac{K_{II}}{\sqrt{2\pi r}} \cdot \sin\frac{\theta}{2} \cdot \left(2 + \cos\frac{\theta}{2} \cdot \cos\frac{3\theta}{2}\right) \quad (3a)$$

$$\sigma_{zz} = \frac{K_I}{\sqrt{2\pi r}} \cdot \cos\frac{\theta}{2} \cdot \left(1 + \sin\frac{\theta}{2} \cdot \sin\frac{3\theta}{2}\right) + \frac{K_{II}}{\sqrt{2\pi r}} \cdot \sin\frac{\theta}{2} \cdot \cos\frac{\theta}{2} \cdot \cos\frac{3\theta}{2} \quad (3b)$$

$$\tau_{xz} = \frac{K_I}{\sqrt{2\pi r}} \cdot \sin\frac{\theta}{2} \cdot \cos\frac{\theta}{2} \cdot \cos\frac{3\theta}{2} + \frac{K_{II}}{\sqrt{2\pi r}} \cdot \cos\frac{\theta}{2} \cdot \left(1 - \sin\frac{\theta}{2} \cdot \sin\frac{3\theta}{2}\right) \quad (3c)$$

$$\tau_{yz} = \frac{K_{III}}{\sqrt{2\pi r}} \cdot \cos\frac{\theta}{2} \quad (3d)$$

$$\tau_{xy} = \frac{K_{III}}{\sqrt{2\pi r}} \cdot \sin\frac{\theta}{2} \quad (3e)$$

The corresponding tangential stress at the flaw boundary is expressed as:

$$\sigma_{yy} = v \cdot (\sigma_{xx} + \sigma_{zz}) \quad (4)$$

For the previous studies finished by the internal filling type 3D flaw, there is no secondary tensile stress that occurs at the flaw boundary under the uniaxial compression, the K_I is thus 0 (Zhang et al. 2020). On the other hand, the internal open type 3D flaw builds a real cavity and many free surfaces in rock specimens, and there is thus no secondary shear stress appearing at the flaw boundary (K_{II} and K_{III} are thus 0 (Guo et al. 2011; Guo & Zhu 2011)).

When the flaw inclination angle is not 0°, both tensile failure and shear failure can exist at the end of the preset 3D flaw, the K_I, K_{II}, and K_{III} are expressed as:

$$K_I = \sigma \cdot \frac{\sqrt{\pi b}}{E(k)} \cdot \left(\sin^2\alpha + \frac{b^2}{a^2}\cos^2\alpha\right)^{1/4}; \quad K_{II} = \tau \cdot \frac{k'k^2\sqrt{\pi b}\cdot\cos\alpha}{B\cdot\left(\sin^2\alpha + \frac{b^2}{a^2}\cos^2\alpha\right)^{1/4}};$$

$$K_{III} = -(1-v)\tau \cdot \frac{k^2\sqrt{\pi b}\cdot\sin\alpha}{B\cdot\left(\sin^2\alpha + \frac{b^2}{a^2}\cos^2\alpha\right)^{1/4}} \quad (5)$$

Where, $k^2 = 1 - \frac{b^2}{a^2}$, $k'^2 = \frac{b^2}{a^2}$; $\tau = \sigma \cdot \sin\beta \cdot \cos\beta$; $B = (k^2 - v)\cdot E(k) + vk'^2 \cdot K(k)$;

$$K(k) = \int_0^{\pi/2} \frac{1}{\sqrt{1-k^2\sin^2\xi}}d\xi; \quad E(k) = \int_0^{\pi/2} \sqrt{1-k^2\sin^2\xi}\,d\xi.$$

The tangential tensile stress on the boundary of the elliptical flaw is given:

$$\begin{aligned}\sigma_N &= \sigma_{xx}\cdot\sin^2\theta\cdot\cos^2\varphi + \sigma_{zz}\cdot\cos^2\theta\cdot\cos^2\varphi + \sigma_{yy}\cdot\sin^2\varphi \\ &\quad -2\tau_{xz}\cdot\sin\theta\cdot\cos\theta\cdot\cos^2\varphi - 2\tau_{yz}\cdot\cos\theta\cdot\sin\varphi\cdot\cos\varphi - 2\tau_{xy}\cdot\sin\theta\cdot\sin\varphi\cdot\cos\varphi\end{aligned} \quad (6)$$

When $\sigma_{N\,max} = \sigma_t$, the surrounding rock shows typical tensile failure initiates at the corresponding position.

Besides, when $\frac{\partial \sigma_N}{\partial \theta} = 0$, and $\frac{\partial \sigma_N}{\partial \varphi} = 0$, to solve the above two equations, we can get the variations of deflection angle (θ) and torsion angle (φ) with elliptical polar angle (α) in the initial fracture state. As shown in Figure 3 ($a = 7.5$ mm, $b = 5.0$ mm, $v = 0.25$, $r = 1.5$ mm, $\beta = 45°$), the calculation results indicate that:

1) When the polar angle is 0° (flaw inclination boundary), the corresponding deflection angle and torsion angle are 0° and -46.0°, respectively, which proves that the pure Mode II failure appears at this position (downwards) and no Mode III failure occurs here.
2) When the polar angle is 90° (flaw strike boundary), the corresponding deflection angle and torsion angle are 31.7° and 0°; this result indicates that the pure Mode III failure appears at this position and no Mode II failure occurs here.
3) Compared with the results obtained in reference (Zhang et al. 2020), it is obvious that the pure Mode II and Mode III failure occurs at the flaw inclination and strike boundary, respectively; while the Mode II failure has different extension directions in internal 3D filling type and open type preset flaws. In addition, the deflection angle becomes closer to 0 as the polar angle increases, and the torsion angle shows a two-steps change (a sharp increase when the polar angle is 0~15°, and a steady increase when the polar angle is 15~90°).

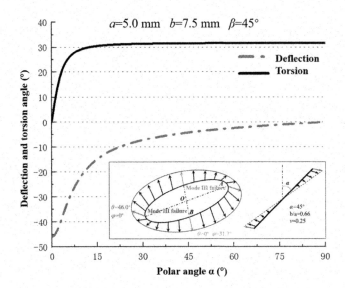

Figure 3. Main results of the theoretical crack initiation mechanism analysis.

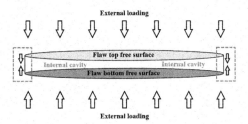

Figure 4. Schematic diagram of a 3D internal open-type flaw when the flaw inclination angle is 0°.

Besides, for a special condition where the flaw inclination angle is 0° (Figure 4), the flaw boundary sides are under the compressive stress concentration (the K_I is thus 0 here), and the corresponding region only shows secondary shear failure (no tensile stress occurs here). The main free surfaces of the internal open type flaw are vertical to the external loading, which may lead to secondary tensile failure in the corresponding regions. Therefore, a new analytical method is necessary to be introduced for solving this issue.

4 THE MAIN INTERNAL FREE SURFACE

The boundary fixed thin plate model is also available to solve the stress state of internal round open flaw, and the radial stress (σ_r) and circumferential stress (σ_θ) fields in the free surface can be calculated. The sides of the round plate model satisfied the conditions:

$$r = R, \frac{dw}{dr} = 0; \; r = R, w = 0 \tag{7}$$

Where r was the distance between a point and the centroid point of the round plate model, R was the radius of the round plate model, and w represented the deflection of the round plate model:

$$M_r = \frac{p}{16}[R^2(1+\mu) - r^2(3+\mu)]; \; M_\theta = \frac{p}{16}[R^2(1+\mu) - r^2(1+3\mu)] \tag{8}$$

Therefore, the slope and deflection equations at a point in this model were:

$$\frac{dw}{dr} = -\frac{pr}{16D'}(R^2 - r^2); \quad w = \frac{p}{64D'}(R^2 - r^2)^2 \tag{9}$$

Where p represented the uniform loading works on the free surface, D' was the bending stiffness of the material ($D' = Et^3/12(1-\mu^2)$), and t was the thickness of the model.

Based on the relations between the deflection and bending moments along the radial and circumferential directions of the board model, the radial stress (σ_r) and circumferential stress (σ_θ) were obtained as:

$$\sigma_r = \mp\frac{3}{8}\frac{p}{t^2}[R^2(1+\mu) - r^2(3+\mu)]; \quad \sigma_\theta = \mp\frac{3}{8}\frac{p}{t^2}[R^2(1+\mu) - r^2(1+3\mu)] \tag{10}$$

The above parameters were substituted into Formula (10), and the external uniform load was set as 0.001 MPa. Finally, the stress field clouds in radial and circumferential directions of the internal free surface (Figure 5) were obtained, and the 2D clouds below were the horizontal projections of 3D clouds on the x-o-y plane. Obviously, σ_r and σ_θ reached the peak values at the centroid point of the model, and the positions of $\sigma_r=0$ and $\sigma_\theta=0$ were fixed by the geometric shape of the model. Besides, the maximum value of σ_r and σ_θ was the same, while the minimum value of σ_r was significantly smaller than that of σ_θ. There were three regions with different stress states illustrated on the round surface (Figure 6):

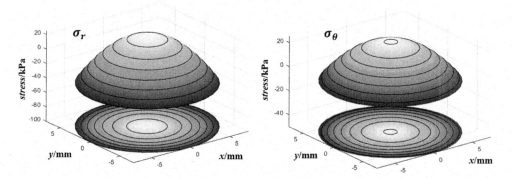

Figure 5. Calculation results of stress states along the radial and circumferential directions on the internal round free surface.

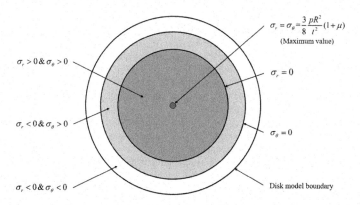

Figure 6. Distributions of the Destruction Region and Anti-destruction Region in round free surface.

1) $\sigma_r>0$ and $\sigma_\theta>0$, the corresponding rock under biaxial tension condition;
2) $\sigma_r<0$ and $\sigma_\theta>0$, the corresponding rock under tension-compression conditions;
3) $\sigma_r<0$ and $\sigma_\theta<0$, the corresponding rock under biaxial compression condition (if consider the uniform load p works on the rock, it can be considered as a triaxial compression state).

Consequently, there was a Destruction Region (marked by blue colors) and an Anti-destruction Region (a mark by white color) occurring on the round free surface. Rock in the Destruction Region suffers tensile failures, and rock in the Anti-destruction Region would restrict the development of tensile failures.

5 CONCLUSIONS

The crack initiation mechanism analyses are conducted at the tips of the 2D and 3D preset flaw and on the free surface of the 3D internal flaw. It is evident that as the flaw inclination increases, the initiation positions of surface secondary failures gradually approach the edges of the preset flaws. The pure Mode II and Mode III failures occur at the inclination and strike boundary of the internal 3D flaw, respectively. The deflection angle becomes closer to 0 as the polar angle increases, and the torsion angle shows a two-step change. Calculation results of the theoretical plate models prove that the maximum normal deflection, bending moments and tensile stresses occur at the centroid point of the internal free surface, which can be considered as the initiation position of the internal secondary tensile failures. Furthermore, rock in the Anti-destruction Region is under a triaxial compression condition and has a strong blocking effort on the secondary tensile failures that occur in the Destruction Regions. Finally, the thin plate model with a fixed boundary belongs to the elasticity issue, and the fracture mechanics analysis (more suitable for rock mechanics problems) will be applied in the future.

ACKNOWLEDGMENT

This work is supported by the Education and Research Project for Young Teachers in Fujian Province (JAT210016), and the Science Foundation of the Fuzhou University [grant number 511069]. We declare that we do not have any commercial or associative interest that represents a conflict of interest in connection with the work submitted.

REFERENCES

Adams (1978) Jet Propulsion Laboratory, Pasadena, Calif. 91103 (U.S.A.) Materials Dept., School of Engineering, U.C.L.A., Los Angeles, Calif 90024 (U.S.A)
Bobet A (2000) The initiation of secondary cracks in compression. *Eng Fract Mech* 66: 187–219. https://doi.org/10.1016/S0013-7944(00)00009-6
Bobet A, Einstein HH (1998) Fracture coalescence in rock-type materials under uniaxial and biaxial compression. *Int J Rock Mech Min* 35: 863–888. https://doi.org/10.1016/S0148-9062(98)00005-9
Dyskin AV, Sahouryeh E, Jewell RJ, Joer H, Ustinov KB (2003) Influence of shape and locations of initial 3-D cracks on their growth in uniaxial compression. *Eng Fract Mech* 70: 2115–2136. https://doi.org/10.1016/S0013-7944(02)00240-0
Fu J, Chen K, Zhu W, Zhang X, Li X (2016) Progressive failure of new modelling material with a single internal crack under biaxial compression and the 3-D numerical simulation. *Eng Fract Mech* 165: 140–152. https://doi.org/10.1016/j.engfracmech.2016.08.002
Guo Y, Ma J, Ji Y (2011) Three-dimensional initial fracture states of an inclined elliptical flaw. *Progress in Geophysics* 26 (04): 1206–1213. https://doi.org/10.3969/j.issn.1004-2903.2011.04.010 (In Chinese)
Guo Y, Zhu W (2011) Experimental study on three-dimensional (3-D) propagation from a pre-existing ellipse flaw under compression-shearing. *ACTA MECHANICA SOLIDA SINICA* 32(1): 64–73. https://doi.org/10.19636/j.cnki.cjsm42-1250/o3.2011.01.008

Li B, Yu S, Zhu W, Cai W, Yang L, Xue Y, Li Y (2020) The microscopic mechanism of crack evolution in brittle material containing 3-D embedded flaw. *Rock Mech Rock Eng.* https://doi.org/10.1007/s00603-020-02214-z

Li Y, Chen L, Wang Y (2005) Experimental research on pre-cracked marble under compression. *Int J Solids Struct* 42: 2505–2516. https://doi.org/10.1016/j.ijsolstr.2004.09.033

Mei J, Yang L, Sheng X, Song G, Yang W, Zhang B (2020) Time-dependent propagation of 3-D cracks in rocks under hydromechanical coupling. *Rock Mech Rock Eng* 53: 1923–1934. https://doi.org/10.1007/s00603-019-02020-2

Miao S, Pan P, Wu Z, Li S, Zhao S (2018) Fracture analysis of sandstone with a single filled flaw under uniaxial compression. *Eng Fract Mech* 204: 319–343. https://doi.org/10.1016/j.engfracmech.2018.10.009

Pan P, Miao S, Jiang Q, Wu Z, Shao C (2019) The influence of infilling conditions on flaw surface relative displacement induced cracking behavior in hard rock. *Rock Mech Rock Eng.* https://doi.org/10.1007/s00603-019-02033-x

Sagong M, Bobet A (2002) Coalescence of multiple flaws in a rock-model material in uniaxial compression. *Int J Rock Mech Min* 39: 229–241. https://doi.org/10.1016/S1365-1609(02)00027-8

Xu J, Li Z (2019) Crack propagation and coalescence of step-path failure in rocks. *Rock Mech Rock Eng* 52: 965–979. https://doi.org/10.1007/s00603-018-1661-4

Yang S, Huang Y, Tian W, Zhu J (2017) An experimental investigation on strength, deformation and crack evolution behavior of sandstone containing two oval flaws under uniaxial compression. *Eng Geol* 217: 35–48. https://doi.org/10.1016/j.enggeo.2016.12.004

Zhang Z, Yu S, Yang E (2020) Theoretical and numerical study on three-dimensional internal crack specimen under uniaxial compression. *Geotechnical and Geological Engineering* 38: 4059–4072. https://doi.org/10.1007/s10706-020-01278-6

Zhao Y, Zhang L, Wang W, Pu C, Wan W, Tang J (2016) Cracking and stress-strain behavior of rock-like material containing two flaws under uniaxial compression. *Rock Mech Rock Eng* 49: 2665–2687. https://doi.org/10.1007/s00603-016-0932-1

Zhou T, Zhu J, Xie H (2020) Mechanical and volumetric fracturing behaviour of three-dimensional printing rock-like samples under dynamic loading. *Rock Mech Rock* Eng 53: 2855–2864. https://doi.org/10.1007/s00603-020-02084-5

Zhou T, Zhu JB (2018) Identification of a suitable 3D printing material for mimicking brittle and hard rocks and its brittleness enhancements. *Rock Mech Rock Eng* 51: 765–777. https://doi.org/10.1007/s00603-017-1335-7

Zhuang X, Chun J, Zhu H (2014) A comparative study on unfilled and filled crack propagation for rock-like brittle material. *Theor Appl Fract Mec* 72: 110–120. https://doi.org/10.1016/j.tafmec.2014.04.004

Zou C, Wong LNY, Loo JJ, Gan BS (2016) Different mechanical and cracking behaviors of single-flawed brittle gypsum specimens under dynamic and quasi-static loadings. *Eng Geol* 201: 71–84. https://doi.org/10.1016/j.enggeo.2015.12.014

A method of reinforcing stringer with silver ingot tenon

Yucheng Li*, Xiaofang Li* & Qiang Sun*
School of Urban Construction, Anhui Wenda Information Engineering College, Hefei, China

Shouyi Bu*
School of Mechanical Engineering, Anhui Sanlian college, Hefei, China

ABSTRACT: In order to study the repair and reinforcement of the stringer, prevent the original structural damage, and understand the different failure forms of the stringer, due to the different reasons for the damage, the stringer was strengthened with silver ingot tenon; however, when the tenon of the test member is broken or decayed, the truss will be damaged seriously, if it is not caused by the deterioration of tenon and mortise and the bending of stringer body, the tenon, and mortise of the stringer can be returned to its original position when the beam frame is installed, and iron raking nails are added on both sides of the truss joint. The method of using silver ingot tenon to strengthen the longeron has a simple structure, reasonable structure, and novel structure, which can effectively repair and strengthen the longeron, greatly improve the performance of the structure and reduce the risk of damage to the performance of the specimen, which is beneficial to the protection and utilization of ancient buildings.

1 INTRODUCTION

This paper discloses a method for reinforcing a stringer with silver ingot tenon, which includes repairing and reinforcing the structure body of the original stringer; the repair and reinforcement structure body of the original stringer is composed of the original stringer, silver ingot tenon, iron hoop, and steel plate; it can be broken between two pieces of the original truss. In addition, the silver ingot tenon is made of hardwood, and the original stringer and the silver ingot tenon are connected with each other through the tenon. The iron hoop is embedded in one end of the silver ingot tenon. The steel plate is balanced and erected on the top of the column and is arranged along the stringer side to support two stringers and is fixed with screws. The method of reinforcing stringer with silver ingot tenon is simple in structure, reasonable in structure, and novel in structure, which can effectively repair and strengthen the stringer, it greatly improves the performance of the structure, reduces the risk of damage to the performance of the test specimen, which is conducive to the protection and utilization of the ancient architecture (Han 2022; Pu 2022; Tang 2022; Yang 2022; Zhang et al. 2022). The purpose of this design is to be able to effectively repair and reinforce the joist, which greatly improves the performance of the structure, reduces the risk of damage to the performance of the test specimen, and facilitates the conservation and utilization of ancient buildings.

2 THE BASIC COMPOSITION OF THE STRUCTURE

We designed the silver ingot tenon (Kang et al. 2016) and reinforcing stringer (Zheng et al. 2021) as shown in Figures 1 ~ 3. In this design, a kind of repair and reinforcement structure for stringers,

---

*Corresponding Authors: 947080764@qq.com, 2284755750@qq.com, 1399484228@qq.com and 2461521347@qq.com

including the repair and reinforcement structure body of the original truss. The new stringer is composed of the original stringer 1 and the silver ingot tenon 2. The original stringer 1 is composed of two parts. The silver ingot tenon 2 is between the two original stringers 1. When the tenon of the original stringer 1 is broken or rotten, the rotten tenon can be removed. In addition, hardwood is used to make spindle tenon. A wall is embedded into the truss bar, and a fiber hoop or iron hoop is added. When installed, it is inserted into the mortise and tenon of the stringer. If necessary, a steel plate is erected at the top of the column along the direction of the stringer to support the two trusses, which are fixed with screws.

The iron hoops, two in number, are added after being bonded with water-resistant adhesive.

The size of the steel plate supporting the balanced erection of the two trusses shall not be less than 100 mm in width and 10–15 mm in thickness, and shall be fixed with screws.

The specific size of the silver ingot tenon 2 is determined according to the intact degree of the original truss head, and the bearing capacity shall be checked.

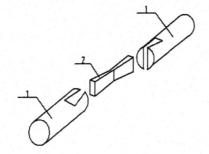

Figure 1. It is a structural schematic diagram of a truss tenon reinforced with silver ingot tenon.

Figure 2. It is a structural schematic diagram of the original stringer of a kind of silver ingot tenon reinforced stringer.

Figure 3. It is a structural schematic diagram of a kind of silver ingot tenon for reinforcing the truss bar.

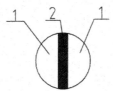

Figure 4. It is a cross-sectional structural diagram of a silver ingot tenon for reinforcing stringer silver ingot tenon.

3 WORKING PROCESS AND PRINCIPLE OF THE METHOD OF REINFORCING STRINGER WITH SILVER INGOT TENON

The working process of this design is as follows:

The utility model relates to a repair of the original truss body of a pair of truss structures. The repair and reinforcement structure body of the original stringer is composed of the original stringer, silver ingot tenon, iron hoop, and steel plate. The original stringer is composed of two parts. The silver ingot tenon is between the two original stringers. The original stringer can remove the rotten tenon when the tenon is broken or rotten. In addition, the silver ingot tenon is made of hardwood, and the original stringer and the silver ingot tenon are connected with each other through the tenon. The iron hoop is embedded in one end of the silver ingot tenon. The steel plate is balanced and erected on the top of the column along the stringer side to support two stringers and is fixed with screws.

As a further scheme of the design: the silver ingot bar tenon should be inserted tightly and neatly between the two original stringers. The specific size of the silver ingot tenon should be determined according to the integrity of the truss head, and the bearing capacity should be checked.

As a further scheme of this design: if the original stringer in the tenon is broken or rotten, the rotten tenon should be removed, and in addition, the hardwood used to make silver ingot tenon should meet the material selection standard.

As a further scheme of the design: the iron hoop is embedded in the truss bar at one end of the silver ingot tenon, which is bonded with water-resistant adhesive and nailed firmly, and there are two iron hoops.

As a further scheme of the design: the steel plate size should meet the conditions, the width of the steel plate should be at least 100 mm, and the thickness of the steel plate should be 10 ~ 15 mm.

As a further scheme of the design: for the original truss section size does not meet the requirements after the structural bearing capacity calculation, the new truss should be replaced.

4 INNOVATIVE DESIGN OF THE METHOD OF REINFORCING STRINGER WITH SILVER INGOT TENON

The utility model relates to a method for reinforcing a stringer with a silver ingot tenon. The repair and reinforcement structure body of the original stringer is composed of the original stringer, silver ingot tenon, iron hoop, and steel plate. The original stringer is composed of two parts. The silver ingot tenon is between the two original stringers. The original stringer can remove the rotten tenon when the tenon is broken or rotten. In addition, the silver ingot tenon is made of hardwood, and the original stringer and the silver ingot tenon are connected with each other through the tenon. The iron hoop is embedded in one end of the silver ingot tenon. The steel plate is balanced and erected on the top of the column along the stringer side to support two stringers and is fixed with screws.

A method of reinforcing stringer with silver ingot tenon is designed, which is characterized in that the said silver ingot tenon shall be inserted tightly and neatly between the two original stringers, and the specific size of the silver ingot tenon shall be determined according to the integrity of the truss head, and the bearing capacity shall be checked.

We designed a method of reinforcing the stringer with silver ingot tenon. The feature of this method is that the original stringer should remove the rotten tenon when the tenon is broken or rotten. In addition, the hardwood used to make silver ingot tenon should meet the material selection standard.

A method of reinforcing the stringer with silver ingot tenon is designed, which is characterized in that an iron hoop is inserted into the stringer at one end of the silver ingot tenon and bonded with water-resistant adhesive and nailed firmly, and there are two iron hoops.

The feature of the method is that the size of the steel plate should meet the requirements. The width of the steel plate should be at least 100 mm and the thickness of the steel plate should be 10–15 mm.

The reason is that the bearing capacity of the new truss should not meet the requirements of the new design method.

5 CONCLUSION

The beneficial effect of this design is that it has a simple structure and reasonable and novel construction, which can effectively repair and strengthen the joist, greatly improve the performance of the structure, reduce the risk of damage to the performance of the test specimen, and is conducive to the protection and utilization of ancient buildings. This design is important for future research on the structural performance and stability of the silver ingot tenon-reinforced truss method.

ACKNOWLEDGMENTS

Fund Project: Research on plastic mechanical properties and reinforcement and repair method of key components of concrete-filled steel tubular composite frame under fire environment (No.:KJ2020A0805), Teaching team of Civil Engineering, Project (No.:2021xjxtd02), the Duration prediction model of three-dimensional frost heave deformation of stratum by tunnel freezing method, project number: (No.:XZR2019B04), Mechanical properties of bucket arches and braces of Huizhou ancient buildings(No.: XZR2022B07), Repair and reinforcement test of wood beams of ancient Hui style buildings(No.:XZR2022B01), Beichuang teaching assistant project (phase II), Project (No.:2021bcc02006).

A BRIEF INTRODUCTION TO THE AUTHOR

Li Yucheng (1994-), male, born in Suzhou, Anhui Province, is a master engineer and teaching assistant. He is mainly engaged in the research of fire resistance theory and safety assessment of steel structures. Email: 947080764@qq.com Tel: 18226635643

REFERENCES

Han Yongxin. Conservation technology of ancient buildings [J]. *Hos*, 2022(13): 161–163+167.
Kang Kun, Qiao Guanfeng, Chen Jinyong, Niu Qingfang, Li Tieying, Wei Jianwei. Finite element analysis of the influence of the gap between tenon and mortise on the bearing capacity of dovetail tenon joint in ancient timber structure [J]. *Chinese scientific papers*, 2016, 11(01): 38–42.
Pu Li. Technical research on improving the protection and utilization of cultural relics in the process of ancient building renovation [J]. *Art Review*, 2022(11): 26–29.
Tang Xiaowen. Application of ancient architectural elements in modern architectural design [J]. *America and the times* (City Edition), 2022(02): 26–28.
Yang Ping. Discussion on repair and protection measures of ancient buildings [J]. *Collection and investment*, 2022, 13(02): 108–110.
Zhang Yuanyi, Zhang Ying, Liu Shuhu, Tang Xiang, Wu Yue. An experimental study on cognition of large wooden components of Chinese ancient architecture in a virtual environment [J]. *Experimental technology and management*, 2022, 39(03): 80–84.
Zheng Nana, Zhao Qian, Zhao Zhifeng, Zhang Yong, Yu Chunhua. Research on the design of truss bending [J]. *Mechanical engineering and automation*, 2021(04): 123–125.

Study on influencing factors of tunnel ventilation

Mingzhu Zhang*
Yunnan Province Dianzhong Water Diversion Project Construction Management Bureau, Yunnan, China

Guoquan Xu
China Railway First Bureau Group Co., Ltd, Xi'an, China

ABSTRACT: In this study, the forced ventilation system of the tunnel under construction is studied by a computational fluid dynamics model. The influence factors such as wind speed of air duct, construction equipment, and cross-sectional area of the tunnel are investigated, and the flow field and temperature distribution in tunnel space are determined. The results show that the area near the working face can be divided into a jet area, reflux area, and vortex area. By quickly improving the working area environment and allowing the construction workers to enter the tunnel within the calculated entry period, the blasting period can be significantly shortened, and the necessary construction procedures can be reasonably implemented. The flow field and temperature distribution deduced in this study can be applied to other similar projects.

1 INTRODUCTION

In the actual tunnel construction ventilation, the ventilation effect often fails to meet the design requirements, and there are various reasons. Other factors affecting the ventilation efficiency are not considered in the ventilation calculation design, which leads to the design value failing to meet the actual ventilation requirements. (Gao et al. 2019; Gao et al. 2019; Huang et al. 2020; Lin et al. 2017; Wang et al. 2008). Fluent finite element analysis software is used for numerical simulation, and tunnel construction ventilation is simulated by finite element software (Luo et al. 2020; Liu 2020; Zhu et al. 2020). From the point of view of numerical analysis, according to the actual construction conditions, the airflow distribution law and temperature change in the process of construction ventilation are simulated and compared with the actual monitoring data of the construction site, and the influence of construction equipment on ventilation efficiency is studied. Considering the influence factors of heat generated by construction equipment and harmful gas on ventilation, the distribution law of the flow field is simulated, and the influence laws of various influencing factors on temperature reduction and dust removal are studied.

In order to ensure the physical and mental health of tunnel constructors and provide a good construction environment, it is especially important to ventilate and reduce dust, cool down, and remove harmful gases in the tunnel work area. The theoretical research of tunnel ventilation mainly uses the basic theories of conservation of mass, conservation of momentum, and conservation of energy under reasonable assumptions to calculate the velocity field and temperature field in the tunnel, study the solutions and optimize the ventilation scheme (Cao 2017; Fang et al. 2014). Considering the influence of construction equipment such as internal combustion engines and second lining trolleys on ventilation efficiency, the models of construction equipment are added to the simulation for simulation calculation.

According to the engineering example of the Shanchongqing Tunnel of Changsha-Shijiazhuang Expressway, the ventilation characteristics of the Shanchongqing Highway Tunnel are studied, the

---

*Corresponding Author: 27943055@qq.com

field ventilation monitoring data are collected, and the construction ventilation is simulated by ANSYS fluent.

2 PROJECT OVERVIEW

Shanchongqing tunnel is a super long tunnel on the expressway from Yiliang County to Shilin Yi Autonomous County, Kunming. The elevation of the end area of the tunnel is between 1650.45 ~ 1959.172m, and the relative elevation difference is 308.722m. It belongs to the cutting low and middle mountain landform area. According to the results of geological survey, drilling, and geophysical exploration, the main bottom layer in the tunnel area is quaternary eluvial diluvium. The construction conditions are poor and the buried depth is large. The construction ventilation mainly adopts the pressure ventilation mode. Press in ventilation is adopted for construction ventilation, and the layout of construction ventilation is shown in Figure 1 below.

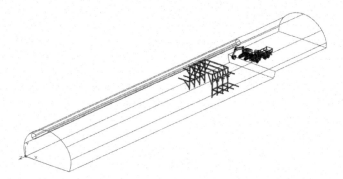

Figure 1. Schematic diagram of ventilation layout in Shanchongqing tunnel construction.

3 COMPUTATIONAL MODEL

The wind speed, air temperature, humidity, and tunnel wall temperature at different distances from the tunnel face are monitored on-site. Three measuring points are arranged on each section, and the human respiratory belt height is 1.5m for continuous monitoring. The average value of the monitoring value is taken, and the secondary lining temperature is measured with an infrared temperature measuring gun, so as to provide parameters for simulation and verify the accuracy of the simulation.

The overall model is continuity equation, momentum conservation equation, energy conservation equation and component transfer equation. Compared with the standard $k - \varepsilon$ model, RNG$k - \varepsilon$ model can respond better to the influence of transient flow and streamline bending. The ε equations and coefficients come from analytical solutions, which improves the ability of high strain flow of the model. Includes options to predict vortex and low Reynolds number flow. It can simulate medium complex flows such as jet impingement, separated flow, swirling flow, etc., and is limited by the assumption of isotropic vortex viscosity. Turbulent kinetic energy k equation and turbulent kinetic energy dissipation rate ε equation.

3.1 Theoretical equation

Continuity equation:

$$\frac{\partial \rho}{\partial t} + \frac{\partial}{\partial x_i}(\rho u_i) = 0 \qquad (1)$$

Where: ρ is the gas density; u_i is the x_i speed in the direction; t is ventilation time.

Momentum conservation equation:

$$\frac{\partial}{\partial t}(\rho u_i) + \frac{\partial}{\partial x_j}(\rho u_i u_j) = -\frac{\partial p}{\partial x_i} + \rho g_i + \frac{\partial \tau_{ij}}{\partial x_j} + F_i \qquad (2)$$

Where: u_i and u_j are the velocity tensors; x_i and x_j are the coordinate tensors; ρg_i is gravity volume force; p is static pressure; F_i it is gravity volume force and other volume forces, τ_{ij} is the viscous stress component.

Energy conservation equation:

$$\frac{\partial}{\partial t}(\rho T) + \frac{\partial}{\partial x_i}(\rho u_i T) = \sum \frac{\partial}{\partial x_i}\left(\frac{K}{c_p}\frac{\partial T}{\partial x_i}\right) + S_T \qquad (3)$$

Where: T is the temperature; c_p is the specific heat capacity; K is the heat transfer coefficient of the fluid; S_T is viscous dissipation rate.

Component transfer equation:

$$\frac{\partial}{\partial t}(\rho c_s) + \frac{\partial}{\partial x_i}(\rho c_s u_i) = \frac{\partial}{\partial x_i}\left[D_s \frac{\partial}{\partial x_i}(\rho c_s)\right] \qquad (4)$$

Where: c_s is the concentration of component S; ρ is the bulk density of component s; D_s is the diffusion coefficient of component s

RNG-equation:
Turbulent kinetic energy equation:

$$\frac{\partial}{\partial t}(\rho k) + \frac{\partial}{\partial x_i}(\rho k u_i) = \frac{\partial}{\partial x_j}\left(\alpha_k \mu_{eff} \frac{\partial k}{\partial x_j}\right) + G_k + G_b - \rho\varepsilon - Y_m + S_k \qquad (5)$$

Dissipation rate equation:

$$\frac{\partial}{\partial t}(\rho\varepsilon) + \frac{\partial}{\partial x_i}(\rho\varepsilon u_i) = \frac{\partial}{\partial x_j}\left(\alpha_\varepsilon \mu_{eff} \frac{\partial \varepsilon}{\partial x_j}\right) + C_{1\varepsilon}\frac{\varepsilon}{k}(G_k + C_{3\varepsilon}G_b) - C_{2\varepsilon}\rho\frac{\varepsilon^2}{k} - R_\varepsilon + S_\varepsilon \qquad (6)$$

G_k is the turbulence kinetic energy produced by the average velocity gradient, G_b is the turbulence kinetic energy produced by buoyancy; Y_m Fluctuation due to excessive diffusion during recompression; α_k and α_ε are the reciprocal of the effective Trump numbers of k and ε, respectively; S_k and S_ε are defined as source terms.

Model constants: $C_{1\varepsilon} = 1.42$, $C_{2\varepsilon} = 1.68$, $C_\mu = 0.09$, $\alpha_k = 1.0$, $\alpha_\varepsilon = 1.3$

3.2 Grid division

The 100m-long tunnel is meshed, and the proximity and curvature control is used to mesh. Figure 2 shows the results of mesh size and mesh quality, with the minimum size of 2.5e-002m, the maximum surface size of 1.0m, the maximum size of 2.0m and the growth rate of 1.2. There are 5,238,654 grids, and the grid quality is evaluated by the Aspect Ratio. The minimum aspect ratio is 1.0567, the maximum aspect ratio is 14.187, and the average aspect ratio is 1.8489. The restriction requirement of a fluent solver is less than 100, and the grid division meets the requirements. Figure 3 shows the results of grid division.

3.3 Parameter setting

The inlet wind speed is set according to the actual detected wind speed. The boundary of the inlet is the outlet of the duct in the tunnel, V=20m/s, the compressed gas is the external natural atmosphere, and the measured temperature is 26°C.

Smoothing	Medium
Transition	Slow
Span Angle Center	Fine
Curvature Normal Angle	Default (18.0 °)
Num Cells Across Gap	Default (3)
Proximity Size Function Sources	Faces and Edges
Min Size	2.5e-002 m
Proximity Min Size	2.5e-002 m
Max Face Size	1.0 m
Max Size	2.0 m
Growth Rate	Default (1.20)
Minimum Edge Length	2.0430 m
⊞ Inflation	
⊞ Assembly Meshing	
⊞ Patch Conforming Options	
⊞ Patch Independent Options	
⊞ Advanced	
⊞ Defeaturing	
⊟ Statistics	
Nodes	139881
Elements	722540
Mesh Metric	Aspect Ratio
Min	1.1576
Max	12.245
Average	1.8381
Standard Deviation	0.45245

Figure 2. Grid size and quality.

Figure 3. Grid division results.

Uniform pressure at the exit:

$$\frac{\partial v_i}{\partial x_i} = 0, \quad P = P_{out} = 0$$

Both the tunnel side wall and the working face are non-slip walls, and all nodes located in the walls use the non-slip condition: v = 0; Considering the hydration heat of concrete, the temperature of the primary support and secondary lining is 38°C, and the initial wall temperature is 38°C.

4 RESULTS AND ANALYSIS

4.1 Model validation

The model verification is based on the Shanchongqing Tunnel of Yishi Expressway, and the model is established according to the actual size. The field monitoring of the flow field, temperature, and humidity at different distances from the tunnel face are carried out, and the variation rules of temperature, wind speed, and humidity in the construction environment are obtained. The simulated value is very close to the measured actual value. Figure 4 shows the temperature cloud picture, wind speed cloud picture, and volume drawing of the outlet wind speed of the ventilation pipe of 20m/s.

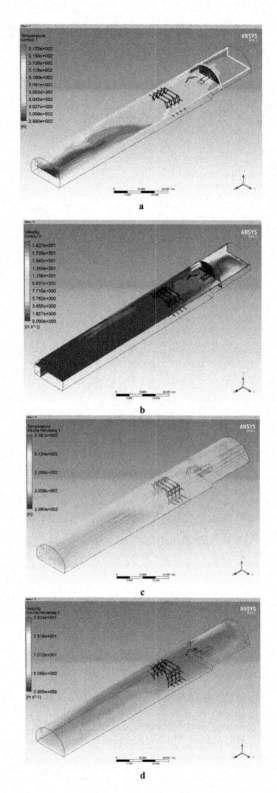

Figure 4. Wind speed cloud chart and volume chart.

From the temperature cloud chart, it can be seen that the heat generated by the internal combustion engine has exchanged heat with the air, and the temperature in the tunnel is obviously higher from the inverted arch, and the average temperature at the inverted arch exceeds 30°C. It can be seen from the wind speed cloud chart and volume rendering that there is an obvious speed reduction after passing through the construction equipment and the trolley in the second village.

4.2 *Comparison of results*

Figure 5 is the vector diagram of simulated wind speed under four different conditions and parameters. The wind speed changes smoothly without the obstruction of construction equipment. In the case of obstruction, there is more turbulence and the wind speed drops rapidly. With the increase of the wind speed at the outlet of the ventilation pipe, the resistance becomes larger, and there is no obvious difference in the wind speed after passing through the second lining trolley.

According to the actual monitoring and simulation under four different conditions and parameters, the flow field distribution is obtained. The simulation results calculate the average wind speed flowing to the tunnel exit with a section of 2m, and the actual monitoring results calculate the average wind speed flowing to the tunnel exit with a section of 5m.

From the simulation results, it can be seen that the wind speed decreases obviously after the airflow passes through the construction equipment and the second lining trolley, and the wind speed changes faster than that without obstacles such as construction equipment.

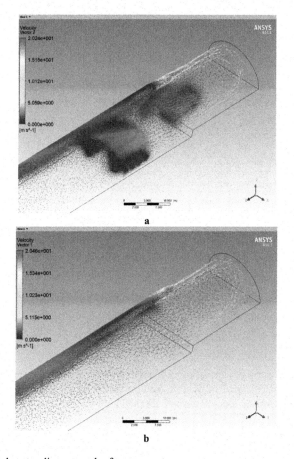

Figure 5. Wind speed vector diagram under four parameters.

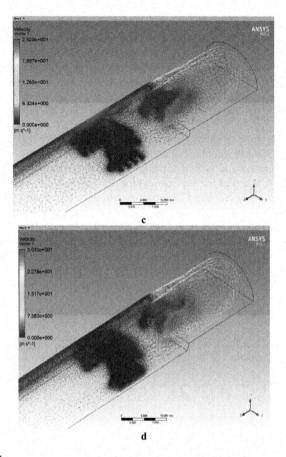

Figure 5. Continued.

According to the actual test and the simulation comparison of temperature changes under four different conditions and parameters, it can be seen from the simulation results that the temperature in the workshop of construction equipment and the second lining platform has obviously increased. Compared with the internal combustion engine, there is no obvious change in temperature.

From the temperature change curve, it can be seen that the pressed gas is blocked to form a vortex when passing through the construction equipment, which makes the temperature rise due to the failure to remove the working area in time after the heat exchange between the gas and the equipment.

5 CONCLUSION

Through the monitoring of the ventilation environment in the construction of the Shanchongqing Highway Tunnel in Yishi Expressway, and the simulation of the construction ventilation with ANSYS fluent, the following conclusions are obtained.

Because of the influence of the heat generated by the internal combustion engine of construction equipment and the high-temperature harmful tail gas discharged on the construction environment, if the temperature can't be lowered and discharged from the work area in a short time, a vicious circle will be formed, making it difficult to improve the temperature and air quality in the work area.

The excessive temperature in the work area will also affect the service life of internal combustion engine equipment, so it is necessary to exhaust the work area.

Under the condition that the tunnel model, grid division, wall parameters, and calculation model are unchanged, different wind speeds at the outlet of the air duct are adopted to study the degree of influence of construction equipment under different wind speeds. The calculation results show that the increase in wind speed has no obvious improvement on the cooling effect of the work area.

In practical engineering, not only the inverted arch excavation has an impact on ventilation, but also the operations such as slag tapping, uniting, and grouting will affect the temperature of the work area. From the simulation results of this paper, it is reasonable to arrange the jet fan at the second lining trolley to exhaust air, which can quickly exhaust the gas trapped between the second lining trolley and the inverted arch, and ensure a good working environment.

REFERENCES

Cao Weiyang. *Ventilation optimization and risk management of large section gas tunnel construction* [D]. Chongqing University, 2017.

Fang Yong, Peng Pei, Zhao Zicheng, Zhou Chaoyue. Study on the influence of outlet position of an air duct on ventilation effect of tunnel construction [J]. *Chinese Journal of Underground Space and Engineering*, 2014,10(02):468–473.

Gao Feng, Zhang Jie, Lian Xiaofei, Tang Yuchen, Qi Huaiyuan, Huang Lei. Study on parameters of forced ventilation in single-head driving of spiral tunnel [J]. *Journal of Chongqing Jiaotong University* (Natural Science Edition), 2019,38(04):41–46.

Gao Junru, Zhang Bo, Wang Yao, Qu Haobo, Yao Zhijun. Research on key technologies of improving working environment in high altitude extra long highway tunnel construction. [J]. *Modern Tunnel Technology*, 2019,56(06):11–18.

Huang xianzhou, Chen Shi, Wei Zhiguo, Li junde, Guo chun. Study on ventilation technology in mixed construction of lancang river extra long tunnel. [J]. *Chinese Journal of Underground Space and Engineering*, 2020,16(S1):353–359+382.

Lin Yan Qing, Chang Jun, Li Yan, Li Xianting. Numerical simulation of air distribution and analysis of purification effect of highway bypass purification station [J]. *Tunnel Construction*, 2017,37(06):684–690.

Liu Zhaochun. Numerical simulation of ventilation in single head tunneling [D]. Xi'an University of Technology, 2010.

Luo Zhenmin, Wang Zijin, Su Bin, Ni Xing. Numerical simulation of gas migration in goaf based on FLUENT [J]. *Mining Safety and Environmental Protection*, 2020,47(03):17–21.

Wang Dongdong, Liu Mao, Li Jianfeng. Application of FLUENT in research on leakage and diffusion of toxic gas accidents in highway tunnels [J]. *Journal of Safety and Environment*, 2008(02):140–143.

Zhu Yingwei, Zhang Guang, Hu Shaohua, Luo Yi, Pu Qingsong. Simulation of the diffusion process of explosive gas in drilling and blasting construction of a single tunnel [J]. *Blasting*, 2020,37(01):126–133.

Research on the reinforcement measures of the existing wind turbine foundation

Guohua Li*
CCCC Fourth Highway Engineering Co., Ltd.; Beijing, China

Hanke Sheng*
School of Civil Engineering, Shandong Jianzhu University, Jinan, China

Lifen Li*
CITIC CONSTRUCTION, Beijing, China

Wenming Wang*
School of Civil Engineering, Shandong Jianzhu University, Jinan, China

ABSTRACT: The wind turbine foundation is one of the most important parts of the wind turbine structure. The safety and stability of the wind turbine foundation must be guaranteed under extreme loads during operation. Based on an actual project, this paper establishes the overall finite element model of wind turbine foundation and foundation ring in ABAQUS. Corresponding to the actual engineering situation, the reinforcement and transformation measures of the adding stiffening beam and expanded outer ring beam are proposed for the updating wind turbine. The finite element analysis results show that the proposed reinforcement measures are feasible and effective. The proposed reinforcement measures can effectively ensure the safety and stability of large wind turbine operations and provide important theoretical basis and engineering experience for similar projects.

1 INTRODUCTION

In recent years, with the rapid development of China's economy, energy consumption is also increasing. As the energy structure dominated by coal needs to be adjusted, vigorously developing new energy has become the strategic choice to promote sustainable development of the economy (Wu 2011; Zhang et al. 2009). Wind power energy has the fastest speed among developing new energy sources. From onshore wind power to offshore wind power, China's wind power industry and technology have made leapfrog development. As the wind turbine foundation is the bottom force-bearing system of the whole wind turbine structure, its safety is the key factor to ensure stable power generation. Therefore, scholars have carried out a serious of in-depth studies on the mechanical characteristics and safety of the wind turbine foundation. Wang Hongwei discussed the feasibility of reinforcing the wind turbine foundation with the concrete ring beam and calculated the stress of the wind turbine foundation under different heights of the ring beam (Wang 2016). On the basis of basic safety testing, Zhang Feng put forward a series of treatment methods, such as repairing concrete cracks, repairing the damages, correcting the horizontal deviation of the

---

*Corresponding Authors: liguohua@ccccltd.cn, 877675536@qq.com, lilf26@citic.com and wangwenmingmr@sdjzu.edu.cn

foundation ring, and grouting to reinforce the structure (Zhang et al. 2020). Hu Liangming et al. analyzed the stress and damage of the wind turbine foundation under extreme load through ABAQUS large finite element software, and put forward planting vertical and radial bars as well as increasing the cross-section of the column to reinforce the structure (Hu et al. 2021). Based on the research work of many scholars, China has issued special design specifications for fan foundations (China Architecture & Building Press 2007). However, the current research mainly studies the safety performance of the existing wind turbine foundations and reinforcement of their common defects, but it is seldom on the research of the transformation of existing foundations with a replaced higher power wind turbine.

In 2021, the Ningxia Autonomous Region's Development and Reform Commission issued the Notice on the Pilot Update of "replacing big with small" (Ningxia Energy (Development) No.601,2021), proposing to carry out the pilot work of updating old wind farms in accordance with the basic principle of "replacing big with small". It is suggested that the mainstream models with large single turbine capacity and advanced technology should be selected to replace the original small-capacity wind turbines when updating the old wind farms, and strive to maximize the utilization of land and wind energy resources in the old wind farms. Retrofitting old wind farms is a low-carbon construction model that can help the country achieve its goal of "peaking co2 emissions by 2030 and achieving carbon neutrality by 2060" (Wang 2020). However, in the renovation of the old wind farm, it is the core issue how to reasonably solve the connection between the new wind turbine and the existing foundation. The main difficulty is how to ensure that the existing foundation has enough carrying capacity. Therefore, a new method of enlarging the outer ring beam combined with the bottom plate to add a stiffening beam was proposed.

In this paper, combined with the actual project, aiming at the stressed and vulnerable parts of the wind turbine foundation, the method of enlarging the outer ring beam combined with the bottom plate to add a stiffening beam is proposed. The overall finite element model is established by using the finite element software ABAQUS to analyze the deformation and stress distribution of the wind turbine foundation and foundation ring. Combined with the engineering practice, the validity and reliability of the modified foundation ring are verified. The research in this paper can effectively guarantee the overall structure's safety of the existing wind turbine foundation transformation, and provide an important theoretical basis and engineering experience for the following engineering.

2 INTRODUCTION FOR THE FINITE ELEMENT MODEL OF WIND TURBINE FOUNDATION

In this paper, we established a refined reinforced-concrete finite element model in ABAQUS (a universal finite element software), used concrete plastic damage constitutive (CDP), and considered isotropic compression and pulling causing damage and cracking of the material. The model could also show the inelastic cracking and destructive behavior of various strength concrete materials. Relying on an actual wind power project in China, the refined overall three-dimensional finite element model of the reinforced-concrete wind turbine foundation is established. The specific dimensions are as follows: the bottom circular radius is 9.4m; the top circular radius is 3.35m; the foundation is 3.4m high. Then we established a refined reinforcement mesh model and confirmed the spacing of bars according to the engineering drawings. The specific dimensions of the wind turbine foundation ring are: an outer diameter of 2.15m, an inner diameter of 2.07m, a thickness of 80mm, and a height of 1.8m. The wind turbine foundation uses an embedded wind turbine foundation and the foundation section, and the local reinforcement diagram is shown in Figure 1.

The soil size is 50 m×50 m×30 m, which has a structural horizontal size being three times the length size. It has a height direction dimension of 1.5 times the horizontal dimension of the structure and 6 times the vertical dimension of the structure. The size meets the static calculation requirements. Rebars are embedded into concrete foundations using Embedded contact. The

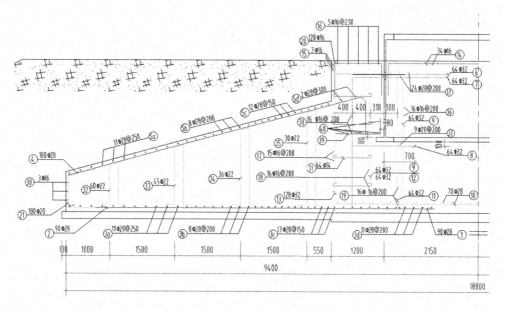

Figure 1. Schematic diagram of wind turbine foundation section and reinforcement (partial).

wind turbine foundation-ring FEM model is shown in Figure 2. The constitutive relationship and parameters of materials are shown in Table 1.

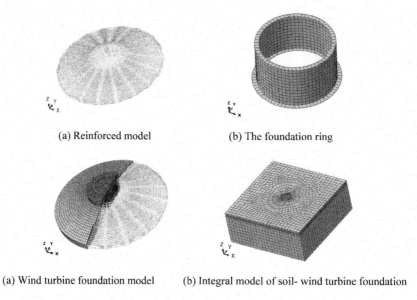

(a) Reinforced model   (b) The foundation ring

(a) Wind turbine foundation model   (b) Integral model of soil- wind turbine foundation

Figure 2. Finite element model of wind turbine foundation-inserted ring.

The mechanical characteristics of the overall wind turbine foundation are more complex due to the unorientation and circulation recurrence of the wind load. We give the simplified design load acting state of external force according to the load conditions in practical engineering. The specific loads are shown in Table 2.

Table 1. Constitutive and parameters of various materials.

Material	Constitutive structure	Parameter	Numerical value
(a) Wind turbine foundation	CDP	Density ρ_{c1} (kg/m^3)	2400
		Elastic moduli E_1 (GPa)	32.5
		Poisson ratio	0.20
		The tensile yield stress σ_{t1} (MPa)	3
		Compressive yield stress σ_{c1} (MPa)	30
(b) Reinforced	Elastic-plastic	Density ρ_r (kg/m^3)	7800
		Elastic moduli E_r (GPa)	200
		Yield stress σ_r (MPa)	458
(c) The soil	Drucker-Prager	Density ρ (kg/m^3)	1800
		Elastic moduli E (MPa)	335
		Poisson ratio	0.3
		Friction angle	20

Table 2. Design load of wind turbine foundation.

Fx (kN)	Fy (kN)	Fz (kN)	Mx (kN*m)	My (kN*m)	Mz (kN*m)
609.8	609.8	−2932.3	46706	46706	1024

3 REINFORCEMENT OF THE EXISTING WIND TURBINE FOUNDATION

3.1 The reinforcement scheme of the existing wind turbine foundation

Under the action of horizontal load and bending moment, the wind turbine foundation is susceptible to uneven displacement, deformation, and overturning. In addition, after the reform of the existing wind turbine to be a higher-power one, the wind turbine foundation is bound to bear the greater loads. Therefore, a new reinforcement scheme for the existing wind turbine foundation is proposed, and the schematic diagram of the reinforcement scheme is shown in Figure 3. The expanding outer ring beam is used to increase the stiffness of the foundation plate, which is universal in engineering measures. The multiple anchor bolts are added to the wind turbine foundation plate to strengthen the wind turbine foundation structure. The measures can not only reduce the adverse effects of the upper wind turbine's self-weight and vertical load but also reduce the risk of wind turbine foundation overturning. The width of the expansion outer ring beam is 2 m, and the thickness is the same as the thickness of the wind turbine bottom plate, which is marked in red in Figure 3. In addition, according to responses of the wind turbine foundation under the design load, a multi-channel stiffening girder is provided on the wind turbine foundation bottom plate aiming at the junction between the neck and the bottom of the wind turbine foundation, where is one of the most vulnerable positions. The section size of the stiffening girder is 0.4 m×0.8 m (width×height), which is marked in blue in Figure 3. Both the expansion outer ring beam and stiffening girder are reinforced concrete materials.

3.2 Comparison of the responses of the wind turbine foundation before and after the reinforcement

The response of the wind turbine foundation and foundation ring after the reinforcement is shown in Figure 4. It can be seen that the vulnerable position of the wind turbine foundation has not changed after the reinforcement, but the maximum displacement is only 0.5 mm. The displacement of the wind turbine foundation is greatly controlled compared to that before the reinforcement. The

Figure 3. Schematic diagram of the existing wind turbine reinforcement scheme.

maximum tensile stress of the wind turbine foundation is only 0.85 MPa, which appears in the neck position of the wind turbine foundation. The maximum compressive stress is only 1.23 MPa. The maximum deformation of the fan base ring is only 0.37 mm, which occurs on the top side of the fan base ring, which corresponds to the load application direction and the maximum deformation position of the fan base. The maximum Mise stress of the foundation ring is only 3.42 MPa, which also appears at the top of the foundation ring. The results show that the wind turbine foundation reinforcement measures combined with the expanded diameter outer ring beam and the bottom plate stiffening beam can enhance the overall bearing capacity of the wind turbine foundation to a certain extent, and reduce the damage degree of the vulnerable parts of the fan foundation neck under extreme loads, so as to avoid dumping the platform.

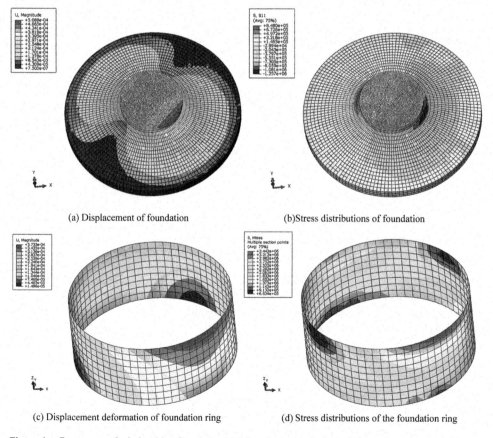

(a) Displacement of foundation   (b) Stress distributions of foundation

(c) Displacement deformation of foundation ring   (d) Stress distributions of the foundation ring

Figure 4. Responses of wind turbine foundation and foundation ring after reinforcement.

The responses of the foundation and the foundation ring before and after the reinforcement are shown in Table 3. The control rate of the displacement of the foundation is 8%, and the control rate of the tensile stress of the foundation is 11%. The control rate of the displacement of the rebars is 8%, and the control rate of the tensile stress of the rebars is 25%. The control rate of the displacement of the foundation ring is 6%, and the control rate of the tensile stress of the foundation ring is 28%. In the reinforcement scheme, the expansion of the foundation can increase the foundation bottom area, reduce the load uniform distribution pressure of the vertical wind turbine, and increase the horizontal anti-overturning ability. The anchor bolts applied at the bottom of the foundation can penetrate into the surrounding soil to provide a better constraint on the wind turbine foundation. The adoption of the multi-channel stiffening girders on the junction of the neck and the bottom of the wind turbine can effectively reduce the deformation and stress of the wind turbine foundation.

Table 3. The responses of the exiting wind turbine foundation before and after the reinforcement.

	Foundation displacement deformation (mm)	Foundation tensile stress (MPa)	Rebars displacement deformation (mm)	Rebars stress (MPa)	Foundation ring displacement deformation (mm)	Foundation ring stress (MPa)
Before reinforcement	6.4	1.59	6.4	106.3	6.4	111.8
After reinforcement	5.9	1.43	5.9	80.7	6.0	80.4
Control rate	8%	11%	8%	25%	6%	28%

According to the results, the adoption of the expansion of the outer ring beam and the bottom plate stiffener beam would enhance the bearing capacity of the wind turbine foundation to a certain extent. The reinforcement measures can reduce the damage to the vulnerable positions of the wind turbine foundation, and provide an effective transformation reinforcement control reference for the transformation of the existing wind turbine to a larger wind turbine.

4 CONCLUSION

In this paper, corresponding to the actual engineering situation, the reinforcement and transformation measures of the adding stiffening beam and expanded outer ring beam are proposed for the updating wind turbine. The investigation of the insufficient bearing capacity of the foundation ring after the transformation of the existing wind turbine to a high-power wind turbine is carried on thoroughly. Through the finite element analysis, the revealing conclusions can be obtained:

(1) Focusing on the damage mechanism and the dangerous positions, an innovative reinforcement measure is proposed for the wind turbine foundation. The expanding outer ring beam is used to increase the stiffness of the foundation plate. The multiple anchor bolts are added to the wind turbine foundation plate to strengthen the wind turbine foundation structure. In addition, a multi-channel stiffening girder is provided on the wind turbine foundation bottom plate.
(2) The results of finite element analysis show that the addition of the fan foundation reinforcement measures of the enlarged diameter outer ring beam and the bottom plate stiffening beam can effectively improve the overall bearing capacity of the fan foundation and reduce the bearing capacity of the fan under extreme loads. The damage degree of the foundation neck wearing parts can prevent the platform from falling, at the same time effectively prevent the development of foundation punching damage, and increase the safety and stability of the fan structure.
(3) After the reinforcement measure, the control rate of the displacement of the foundation is 8%, and the control rate of the tensile stress of the foundation is 11%; the control rate of

the displacement of the rebars is 8%, and the control rate of the tensile stress of the rebars is 25%; the control rate of the displacement of the foundation ring is 6%, and the control rate of the tensile stress of the foundation ring is 28%. Based on the control rate, the reinforcement measure has been proved to have significant control effects on the entire wind turbine system. It can effectively enhance the bearing capacity of the wind turbine foundation and reduce the damage to the vulnerable positions under extreme loads.

(4) After ensuring the existing foundation bearing capacity, the follow-up can be aimed at the existing foundation and the connecting way of the new fan for research.

REFERENCES

Design regulations on subgrade and foundation for WTGS of the wind power station (FD003-2007)[S]. Beijing. China Architecture & Building Press, 2007.

Hu Liangming, Liu Zhipeng, Zeng Yu, et al. Stress and damage analysis of wind turbine foundation reinforcement based on ABAQUS[J]. *Water Resources and Hydropower Engineering*, 2021, 52(5): 223-233.

Wang Fan. Carbon neutralization, blowing the "14th five-year-plan" wind power charge[J]. *Wind Energy*. 2020(12): 20–27.

Wang Hongwei. Finite element analysis of the wind turbine foundation reinforced with ring beam[J]. *Renewable Energy Resources*. 2016.34(4): 558–562.

Wu Guihui. The energy situation and the ways of development in China[J]. *Strategic Study of CAE*. 2011,13(04):4–8.

Zhang Feng, Li, Qingshi, Hu, Hui. Analysis on reinforcement for defects of wind turbine foundation using foundation ring[J]. *Technology Wind*. 2020. 12: 174–178.

Zhang Wenliang, Liu Zhizhuang, Wang Mingjun, et al. Research status and development trend of smart grid[J]. *Power System Technology*. 2009. 33(13):1–11.

Study on deterioration law of concrete in corrosive environment

Yujie Jiang, Guanglun Jiang & Kunlin Wang
Shandong Highspeed Yunnan Development Co., Ltd., Kunming, China

Lei Yu*
Beijing Xinqiao Technology Development Co., Ltd., Beijing, China

Xiuqiang Song
Shandong Highspeed Yunnan Development Co., Ltd., Kunming, China

Xiaoyu Yang
Beijing Xinqiao Technology Development Co., Ltd., Beijing, China

ABSTRACT: It is important to design an accelerated corrosion test to simulate the strong acid corrosion environment. In this work, the corrosion and deterioration laws of ordinary concrete under different pH values and different chloride ion concentrations were compared and investigated. The results show that the acid corrosion effect in the solution increases with the decrease of pH value, and the strength of concrete is more easily damaged, but it is not conducive to the penetration of chloride ions. After the corrosion of pH=2, Cl%=6%, the porosity of concrete increases, but the average pore size is almost unchanged.

1 INTRODUCTION

The damage mechanism of concrete materials shows that harmful particles enter concrete from initial micro-cracks or internal pores of the concrete, corrode the internal structure of concrete through physical penetration and chemical action, and finally cause damage to the structure of concrete materials, especially in the chemical neutralization, which is more serious under acidic conditions.

A bridge named Laohu-shanchong locates on the Mengzi highway in the Yunnan province in China. The pile foundation of the bridge will be constructed through the acid soil in this place where was a waste iron mill before. The soil was acidic and there was chloride in the soil. Studying the impact of the corrosive environment on the designed concrete is very important to decide whether to change the concrete proportion or not.

This paper mainly investigates the deterioration mechanism of hydrogen ions and chloride ions on concrete. Based on the investigation, analysis, and evaluation of the corrosive environment, the laboratory conditions are used to simulate the typical corrosive environment of acid chloride ions in the engineering site. The accelerated test method was used to study the influence of corrosion conditions on the corrosion and deterioration of concrete.

2 MATERIAL AND EXPERIMENTS

2.1 Materials

The cement is P.O 42.5 ordinary Portland cement. The fine aggregate is river sand with a fineness modulus of 2.8. The coarse aggregate is 5mm-31.5mm continuous graded crushed stone, the mixing

---

*Corresponding Author: yuleimabel@163.com

water is drinking water, and the water reducing agent is polycarboxylic acid. Water reducing agent, water reducing rate is 20%.

2.2 Mix proportion designed

The mix ratios of the designed concrete are designed, as shown in Table 1. When mixing with concrete, the concrete slump is 200 ± 20 mm.

Table 1. The proportion of ordinary concrete (kg/m^3).

cement	water	sand	stone	Water reducing agent
360	170	817	1083	3.6

2.3 Experimental section

2.3.1 Design of simulated test

By detecting the soil of the Laohu-shanchong bridge site, the chloride ion concentration is about 6%, and the pH=2. Therefore, the test solution in the lab was a NaCl solution with pH=2 and a concentration of 6%. At the same time, to compare the accelerated test effects of different corrosion parameters, other corrosion solutions were designed, as shown in Table 2.

Table 2. Acid corrosion test solution information.

Number	Solution type	NaCl concentration (NaCl Dissolved solids)	pH (Concentrated HNO$_3$ titration)
F	Accelerated corrosion solution	6%	2
D1	Contrast etch solution 1	1%	4
D2	Contrast etch solution 2	3.5%	4
D3	Contrast etch solution 3	6%	4
D4	Contrast etch solution 4	1%	3
D5	Contrast etch solution 5	3.5%	3
D6	Contrast etch solution 6	6%	3
D7	Contrast etch solution 7	1%	2
D8	Contrast etch solution 8	3.5%	2

2.3.2 Test method

The cube blocks of 100mm×100mm×100mm were made and cured to 28d age under standard curing conditions, then separate the specimens into two parts. One is the test group and the other is the control group Put the test group specimens into the corrosion solution. The control group specimens were put into the tap water.

The compressive strength was tested at 28 d, 56 d, and 90 d age according to ISO 4012-1978. The property of the chloride penetration resistance was by comparing the depth of the chloride Penetration.

When the age of soaking age was 90 d, take out the specimens and split them into two parts from the middle of the ones. Drip the silver nitrate on the surface of the plane of cleavage. Then measure and record the depth of the grey parts.

The pore structure parameters were tested by the Mercury Injection Test method. The amount of the different diameter pores was calculated and the pore distribution curve was plotted.

3 ANALYSIS OF TEST RESULTS

3.1 Strength variation

Test the compressive strength of concrete blocks in different ages of corrosion environment, and compare the strength changes. The compressive strength loss rate is used to represent the strength change of concrete after sulfate erosion, and the calculation method is as follows:

$$\Delta CS = \frac{CS - CS_0}{CS_0} \times 100\%$$

ΔCS – Loss rate of compressive strength;
CS – Compressive strength after immersion in a corrosive solution
CS0 – Compressive strength from water curing to age.

Strength changes of ordinary concrete in a corrosive environment are shown in Figure 1.

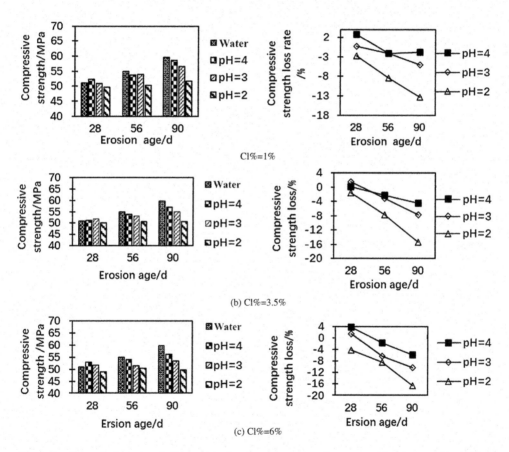

Figure 1. Strength changes of the concrete in the corrosive environment with constant chloride ion concentration and different pH values.

As can be seen from Figure 1, when the chloride ion concentration is constant, the lower the pH value is, the stronger the corrosion effect on concrete is, and this trend becomes more obvious with the extension of erosion age. Under various chloride concentration conditions, the strength of concrete increased after 28 days of erosion by the corrosive solution of pH=4 and pH=3.

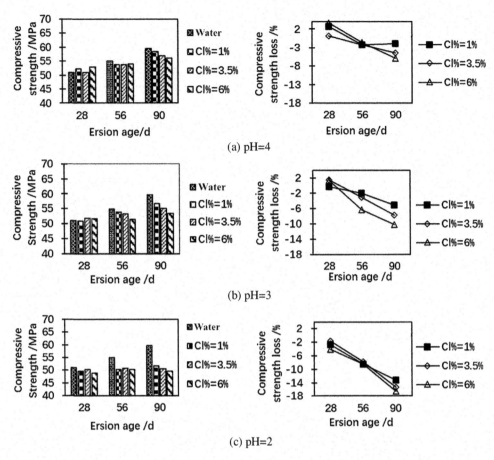

Figure 2. Strength change of the concrete in the corrosive environment with constant pH value and different chloride ion concentrations.

It can be seen from Figure 2 that at the initial stage of erosion, when pH=4 and pH=3, the strength of concrete in corrosion solutions with different chloride ion concentrations increases. In the middle stage of erosion, the strength of concrete begins to decline due to the erosion of corrosive solution, but the regularity shows no obvious changes. At the late erosion stage, when the pH value is constant, the higher the chloride ion concentration is, the stronger the corrosion effect on concrete is.

3.2 *Change of chloride penetration depth*

The penetration depth of free chloride ion in concrete was measured by silver nitrate colorimetry. The change of penetration depth of chloride ions in the corrosive environment in ordinary concrete is shown in Figure 3.

It can be seen from Figure 3 that the depth of chloride penetration increased by the increase of chloride ion concentration and the pH value. The depth of chloride penetration was almost the same between the pH=2 and pH=3 when the chloride ion concentration was 6%.

3.3 *Porosity change*

The porosity changes of ordinary concrete in a corrosive environment are shown in Figure 4 below.

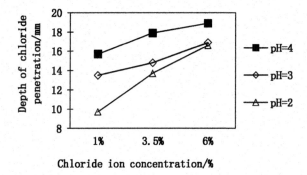

Figure 3. Change of chloride penetration depth of ordinary concrete in the corrosive environment.

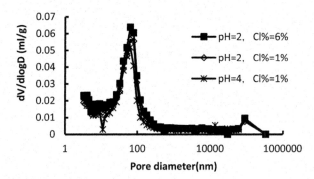

Figure 4. Porosity change of ordinary concrete.

As can be seen from Figure 4, with the decrease in pH value, the acid corrosion in the solution increases. After the corrosion of pH=2, Cl%=6%, the porosity of concrete increases, but the average pore size is almost unchanged.

4 CONCLUSIONS

This paper mainly investigated the influence of corrosion conditions on the law of corrosion and deterioration of concrete, and the main conclusions are as follows:

(1) With the decrease of pH value, the acid corrosion in the solution is enhanced.
(2) The designed mix proportion of the concrete is not very good at resisting the acid. The compressive strength decreased from about 60MPa to under 50MPa after soaking in pH=2, Cl%=6% solution for 90d.
(3) The more easily the concrete is damaged, the more unfavorable it is to the penetration of chloride ions. In the late stage of erosion, the higher the chloride ion concentration is, the stronger the corrosion of concrete will be.

ACKNOWLEDGMENTS

This work has been supported by the grant of the Yunnan Branch Company of Shandong Highspeed Incorporated Company, China. The Technology Plan Item was set up by the Transportation Department of Yunnan Province, China. The name of the Item is 'Study on key technology of durability of pile foundation structure in strong acid soil environment'.

REFERENCES

Wang Chao, Liu Zhao -Lei, Yu Lei. Relationship between anti-frozen durability and pore structure on concrete in freeze and thaw cycle environment[J]. *Matec Web of Conferences*, 2018, 238: 64–68.

Wang Qiannan, Gu Chunping, Sun Wei. Evolution law of microstructure in hydration process of cement-fly ash-silica fume high-performance concrete [J]. *Material Guide*, 2017, 31 (12), 85–89.

Xing, Jie; Yu, L. Selection and applicability analysis of filling materials for concrete hole structure [J]. *New Construction Materials*.2020(6), 51–55.

Yu, L. *Durability of concrete material and its optimization method* [M]. China Building Industry press. 2018.

Yu, L.; Lv, S.; Zhao, Z.; Liu, Z. Effect of slurry coating modified methods on water absorption of recycled coarse aggregate[J]. *Coatings* 2022, 12, 363.

Yu, L.; Zhang, S.X.; Chen, L. Anti-acid corrosion property of concrete improved by microstructure optimizing[C]. International conference on novel functional materials, ICNFM 2018. *EDP Sciences*. 2018, (238), 56–59.

Author index

Bai, J. 302
Bian, Y. 406
Bing, Z. 196
Bu, S. 562

Chai, J. 28
Chang, J. 452
Chen, B. 269
Chen, C. 554
Chen, H. 302, 406
Chen, L. 249, 406
Chen, M. 249
Chen, S. 363
Cheng, L. 236, 342
Chu, H. 295
Chuanyao, G. 212
Ciren, N. 139
Cui, S. 432

Dalin, Q. 90
Daolin, S. 90
Ding, G. 20
Ding, H. 189, 236
Dingxu, W. 423
Duan, B. 537
Duoji, Y. 139

Fan, J. 432
Fan, X. 377
Fang, D. 295
Fang, X. 123
Feng, C. 510
Feng, X. 363
Feng, X.-D. 160
Feng, Y. 47
Fu, J. 205
Fu, M. 123
Fu, Y. 47
Fuxi, N. 196

Gan, Y. 510
Gao, M. 249
Gu, C.-Y. 53

Gu, J. 229
Gu, Z. 20
Guan, D. 11
Guo, H. 139
Guo, Y. 406

Han, D. 249
Han, J.-H. 53
He, C. 302
He, T. 236
He, X. 406
Hou, Y. 286
Hu, K. 249
Hu, M. 123, 205
Huang, R.-Y. 160
Huang, T. 60
Huang, X. 349
Hui, J. 255
Huiling, W. 90
Huo, H. 286
Huo, Y.-J. 160

Jian, H. 82
Jianbo, X. 370
Jiang, G. 581
Jiang, K. 286
Jiang, X. 236
Jiang, Y. 581
Jianjing, L. 438
Jiao, L. 326
Jiao, W. 510
Jin, S. 38
Ju, H. 123
Jun, Y. 423

Lei, Y. 274
Li, B. 394
Li, C. 76, 255, 280
Li, G. 349, 574
Li, K. 302
Li, L. 574
Li, M. 406, 516
Li, S. 20

Li, X. 545, 562
Li, Y. 562
Li, Z. 82, 363
Lianding, W. 523
Liang, Z.-W. 60
Lin, H.-B. 332
Lin, J. 545
Lin, Q. 510
Liu, C. 221
Liu, D. 229
Liu, J. 452
Liu, K. 363
Liu, L. 47
Liu, W. 205
Liu, X. 123, 130
Liu, Y. 123
Liu, Z. 229, 400

Ma, J.L. 179
Ma, X. 481
Mao, D. 263
Min, W.K. 145

Pan, W. 302
Peng, Y. 196
Peng, Z. 236

Qi, Q. 554
Qi, W. 168
Qi, X. 423
Qiang, R. 82, 145
Qianqian, C. 415
Qiao, H. 152
Qiu, Y. 70

Rao, H. 263
Rui, W. 377
Ruiqing, L. 196
Ruiqing, X. 415

Shang, D. 302
Shang, L. 179
Sheng, H. 574
Song, A. 503

Song, X. 581
Sun, C. 342
Sun, G. 205
Sun, L. 493
Sun, Q. 562
Sun, Z. 537

Tang, H. 406
Tang, Z. 229
Tao, D. 249
Tao, F. 503
Tao, L. 377
Tao, R. 160
Tao, S. 311
Tenzin, S. 139
Tian, Z. 394
Tianliang, Y. 377
Tong, L. 189

Wang, A. 286
Wang, G. 139
Wang, H. 263
Wang, J. 400
Wang, K. 471, 581
Wang, M.-G. 60
Wang, Q. 47
Wang, R. 545
Wang, W. 574
Wang, Y. 255
Wang, Z. 432

Wei, M. 523
Weihong, H. 370
Wen, Z. 152
Wu, Z. 152, 189

Xian, N. 318
Xianzhe, T. 104
Xiao, F. 545
Xiao, W. 432
Xiaomin, Y. 196
Xie, E. 460, 481
Xie, M. 20
Xie, Y. 116
Xinghua, Y. 445
Xu, C. 189
Xu, G. 532, 566
Xu, S. 189
Xu, Y. 545
Xue, B. 481
Xue, L. 400

Yan, L. 212
Yan, W. 3
Yang, C. 123
Yang, H. 221
Yang, L. 394
Yang, X. 255, 516, 581
Yang, Y. 221, 406
Yang, Z. 168
Youzhi, W. 212

Yu, L. 581
Yu, Y. 286
Yu, Z. 537
Yuan, J. 510
Yuhang, F. 370

Zeng, Q.-F. 332
Zeyun, W. 104
Zhang, C. 20, 516, 537
Zhang, D. 249
Zhang, H. 493
Zhang, J. 95, 255
Zhang, K. 516
Zhang, L. 11, 47, 384
Zhang, L.X. 179
Zhang, M. 532, 566
Zhang, R. 110
Zhang, S. 152
Zhang, X. 70, 295
Zhang, Y. 28, 249, 510
Zhang, Y.-X. 53
Zhang, Z. 152
Zhao, J. 139
Zhao, N. 356
Zhao, Y. 318, 554
Zhu, B. 76, 280
Zhu, L. 139
Zhu, R. 236
Zou, H. 400